Production Operations Management

Thomas E. Morton
Carnegie Mellon University

South-Western College Publishing
an International Thomson Publishing company I(T)P®

Cincinnati · Albany · Boston · Detroit · Johannesburg · London · Madrid · Melbourne · Mexico City
New York · Pacific Grove · San Francisco · Scottsdale · Singapore · Tokyo · Toronto

Acquisitions Editor: Charles McCormick
Developmental Editor: Jamie Gleich Bryant
Production Editor: Kelly Keeler
Production House: DPS Associates, Inc.
Cover Design: Ann Small
Marketing Manager: Joe Sabatino

1 2 3 4 5 WST 1 0 9 8 7

Printed in the United States of America

ISBN: 0-877-09524-8

Library of Congress Cataloging-in-Publication Data

Morton, Thomas E.,
        Production and operations management / Thomas E. Morton.
            p.   cm.
        Includes bibliographical references.
        ISBN 0-87709-524-8
            1. Production managment.   II. Title.
        TS155.M7632 1999
        658.5--dc21   98-47966
                                                              CIP

I(T)P®

International Thomson Publishing

South-Western College Publishing is an ITP Company. The ITP trademark is used under license.

BRIEF CONTENTS

MODULE 7
Appendices

C O N T E N T S

MODULE 2
Forecasting

MODULE 3
Scheduling

MODULE 4
Project Management

MODULE 5
Planning

MODULE 65
Total Quality Management

MODULE 7
Appendices

Historically, the operations and engineering functions of the firm have been relegated somewhat to sit with Cinderella in the ashes. Production people have been viewed as glorified bean counters, shaving a nickel off production costs, while marketing and finance types held the fast track to top management. Yet engineers and operations managers are well represented as CEOs of Japanese firms. Enter the fairy godmother, sending Cinderella to the ball! Intense global competition has brought wide recognition that production is strategic. Early on, the Japanese showed that cost reduction in mature industries could provide a major competitive edge in world markets. Next, they pioneered drastic reduction in inventories (Just-In-Time) to improve quality, reduce lead-times, and promote communication and innovation within the firm. These massive reductions in inventory, in turn, have reduced shop buffers, and made better scheduling a must. Still later, they led the way to shift quality ideas away from counting defects, toward changing the production process to drastically reduce defects and capture new markets. But the fact that operations management is finally being seen as strategic is not enough. We must master the innovative production techniques being implemented around the world, and then push on into the forefront. This text is intended to provide a foundation for those willing to make that effort.

The book and the complementary POMQuest software are designed to be modular. The text is completely self-contained without the software, although POMQuest modules are designed to fit the corresponding book module fully, and to give the student power to attain a deeper understanding of the material with much less effort than long, tedious hand exercises. Each of the book modules: Forecasting, Inventory, Scheduling, Project Management, Planning, and Total Quality Management, can be used independently of the others; within a module later chapters often represent materials which can be omitted if time constraints require. Thus a wide variety of courses can be designed effectively.

A module usually opens with a broad introductory chapter, which gives a strategic view of the topic, followed by basic standard material, followed by advanced material, followed by implementation and newer ideas. Almost every chapter presents a major case, to illustrate the practical use of the ideas being presented. There are also many examples, "micro-cases," to illustrate techniques as they are developed.

Now we sketch just a few of the unique features of each of the modules, and of the associated POMQuest software. A broad mix of qualitative and quantitative forecasting techniques provides a complete coverage of techniques in broad use for long range, medium range, and short range forecasting. In particular, mixed man/machine methods for strategic forecasting are emphasized, including the scenario and Delphi methods. The last chapter forecasts about the future of forecasting! POMQuest offers full support for the scenario method, regression analysis, and various smoothing methods. A popular feature is the "cloaked" forecasting game, where the student and the machine see one new demand at a time, and compete for the best forecast.

There are currently about $1 trillion in inventory in the United States, representing a cost of perhaps $200 billion a year. Japanese rhetoric about the importance of zero inventories is only a start. We need to know the effect of cutting setup costs in half, or of shortening lead-times by two-thirds. An innovative intuitive approach to probabilistic inventory models, together with the power of POMQuest, allows the student to understand the results of these models, many not even attempted in POM books, without much mathematics. The last chapter provides a novel approach to inventory systems.

It used to be felt that shop scheduling was not all that important, since buffer inventories could compensate for poor scheduling. But now with the Just-In-Time (JIT) philosophy, the pressure is to eliminate buffers, and scheduling becomes much more important. Here both classical and modern heuristic methods are developed first for the one-machine case, and then for the job shop. These methods include dispatch heuristics, neighborhood search, tabu search, and simulated annealing, as well as the author's bottleneck dynamics approach. All are presented intuitively; POMQuest software makes it easy to compare different methods.

A new frontier in world competition is to complete new product development and new facilities with much shorter lead-times. Better project management techniques are important here. A number of classic and modern heuristics are developed for models ranging from the standard critical path problem, through scheduling multiple projects with different importance and urgencies. A full chapter is devoted to design and control. POMQuest gives unprecedented power to solve complex project management problems.

The planning module covers a large number of topics. At the strategic level, topics include capacity expansion, make versus buy, facility layout, facility location, learning and experience curves, and product and process life cycles. At the aggregate planning level, a number of approaches to production smoothing are developed intuitively, as well as logistics and machine replacement. At the tactical planning level, MRP, MRP II, order planning, and assembly line balancing are developed. A brief introduction to such investment topics as risk and decision methods is also given.

TQM perceives the entire organization as a vehicle for delivering complete customer satisfaction. The emphasis is shifting away from finding the defects in products already manufactured, and upstream to improving the production process and lowering the defect rate. Shoji Shiba and co-authors have written an outstanding book explaining the Japanese approach to TQM, *A New American TQM—Four Practical Revolutions in Management*, Productivity Press, 1993. They have graciously allowed their book to be condensed as a chapter in this module. In addition, a good treatment of conventional statistical quality control is given in the final chapter.

Forecasting

1

Introduction to Forecasting

1.1 WHAT IS FORECASTING?

A common opening statement in a book on forecasting is: "Forecasting is the process of predicting the future." While this is true, it is not much help since *all* human inference and reasoning is, in a very deep way, about predicting the future!

> *"If I stand in the safety zone, the fork-lift will not run over me."*
> *"If I heat the same mixture of metals as yesterday, it will again melt at 8050 degrees."*
> *"Workers respond to a courageous line supervisor."*

Thus, in order to try to define forecasting, let's back off a little bit and look at the broader idea of inference. A fundamental universal fact of human existence is that we cannot *know* anything with *certainty*:

*   Will the sun come up tomorrow?
*   Are there any electrons at the bottom of the sea?
*   Will I die in my sleep tonight?

All of the known "principles" (not theorems!) of inference may be classified into four laws:

1. Law of inertia—**repetition**
2. Law of continuity—**interpolation**
3. Law of the mean—**aggregation**
4. Law of decomposition—**focus**

Let us give an example of each to help clarify the ideas.

1. "Fit a line to past data and use this to extrapolate to the future." This is the **repetition** law; we are assuming the past will repeat into the future. (This is sometimes called the **induction** law.)
2. "Vary a drug level slightly and expect no strange effects." This is the **interpolation** law; we are assuming minor changes in input do not produce large changes in the output.
3. "Look at summary sales data for a group of products to get the 'big picture.'" This is the **aggregation** law; we are assuming averages are in some way more reliable than individual values.
4. "Model the machine cell of interest carefully; consider the rest of the shop in summary fashion." This is the **focus** law; we are assuming situations far away from the machine cell have less effect on it.

We can all think of situations where these "laws" don't work; yet we use them every day. Essentially we have no other choice, and the laws do work well for so many things. Caution is always in order, however. For a number of years in the 1980s, housing prices in Boston went up 10 percent a year as regularly as clockwork. People who really couldn't afford to buy a house reasoned: "If the payments get to be too much, I can always sell the house in three years and take my 30 percent profit." Since many people believed this, it helped prices to continue to go up. However, eventually the bubble burst, prices fell, and these naive forecasters got hurt.

Two very helpful terms here are inductive versus deductive reasoning. **Induction** is a hypothesis, forecast, or belief based on observations on the world and similar experience. **Deduction** is theorem proving. Given that we *accept* A and B as true, we also can show C is true. Any good business/scientific/living procedure needs both induction and deduction, but induction is much more important, since if the beliefs that A and/or B are true are weak, deduction can show little useful about C.

Herbert Simon, one of the fathers of both cognitive psychology and artificial intelligence, speaks of "well-structured problems" and "ill-structured problems." Well-structured problems are those for which we can be reasonably confident that some solution procedure will be adequate, and ill-structured problems are those for which we cannot. Since we can always be confident about the deductive part, we may say that "well-structured" means that in the given problem the induction part is fairly accurate, and the opposite is true for "ill-structured."

We started out by asking "What is forecasting?" **Forecasting**, as we shall use it, is a method for guessing the future by the law of repetition; that is, by extrapolating from the past. Forecasting is often classified into subjective, objective, or mixed types. A **subjective** forecasting method is based strictly on human judgment. An **objective** method is based strictly on the formal evaluation of data according to a given procedure. A **mixed** method, such as a decision support system (DSS), is based on both. We shall see that some mixed methods are closer to purely subjective methods, while others are closer to purely objective methods.

Human judgment tends to be superior for ill-structured problems (although the artificial intelligence field is trying to change this), while formal data evaluation methods tend to be superior for well-structured problems. As we shall discuss in the next section, long-horizon strategic problems tend to be ill-structured, while short-horizon tactical problems tend to be fairly well-structured. This implies that long-horizon problems tend to use judgmental methods, middle-horizon problems tend to use mixed methods, and short-horizon problems tend to use objective methods.

1.2 FORECASTING IN BUSINESS

Business forecasting can be classified by the time horizon of the problems the forecasts are intended to solve. Most such classifications have either four or five levels. We present one with five levels in Table 1-1.

The area of business forecasting which is probably the best known is demand forecasting for marketing and production at levels 2 to 5 of Table 1-1. Marketing forecasts sales for new product lines to give strategic information about their sales later at maturity. It forecasts sales for existing product lines to give feedback on whether the current sales techniques are working well or not. Either marketing or production will also produce individual item forecasts.

Production needs both product line and individual SKU (stock-keeping units) forecasts to order raw materials properly and to plan/schedule the shop floor.

Many texts look only at demand forecasting and only at the shorter horizons, Levels 3, 4, and 5. This approach is somewhat limited for two reasons. First of all, the table shows that there are a broad variety of things to be forecast besides demand. But even more

Table 1-1

Classification of Forecasting
Problems by Time Horizon

Level	Examples	Horizon
1. Long Strategic	Sell mainframes or PCs China's economic growth rate Budget deficit Chip speeds/costs	2–10 years
2. Short Strategic	Production smoothing Next labor contract New product popularity Product costs Supplier contracts	1–2 years
3. Tactical	Timing and size of orders Current vendor lead times Net manpower levels New equipment lead time Seasonal factors	3–12 months
4. Requirements	Monthly product line sales Monthly item sales Current vendor lead times Overall shop load Individual machine loads	1–12 weeks
5. Dispatch	Shift schedules Processing speeds Likely floor jams Good current routings Day/week sales	1–6 days

importantly, it is actually strategic forecasting which tends to make and break companies. Throughout the 1980s IBM downplayed the PC market and worked to hold the mainframe market, only to eventually realize the permanency of the shift away from mainframes to desk computing. IBM lost a large part of its total demand in this process, before it managed to turn the situation around.

In the 1960s and '70s Detroit underestimated the competition inherent in imported cars, which were smaller, more fuel efficient, highly reliable, and inexpensive, and lost market share dramatically. Detroit has finally developed a number of cars which are competitive on all counts, and they have won their market share back.

In general, American companies were slow to understand the importance of improving the way of making a product (process) rather than improving the product itself. The Japanese therefore perfected the technique of "reverse engineering," allowing them in many cases to reproduce the new U.S. product and then improve the process to make it with higher quality and less expense. This problem has not been solved.

Perhaps the reason strategic forecasting is not usually discussed to any extent is that objective forecasting methods are not very useful for these ill-structured problems. However, we will discuss some techniques for strategic forecasting, especially scenario forecasting and the Delphi method.

Learning about forecasting is in itself a fairly ill-structured process, and so it may be worthwhile, before going on, to make some important points.

1. **Even in well-structured situations, forecasts are usually somewhat in error; in ill-structured situations forecasts are often very much in error.** A single-number forecast is often treated in formulas and procedures as if it were exact and correct. The system and/or the user should expect errors and have ways to deal with them.

2. **A good forecast says something about its likely error size.** This can have a number of forms.

   a. In scenario forecasting, we actually make a group of possible forecasts. This group itself reflects our thoughts about error.
   b. In smoothing, we may smooth past errors in addition to smoothing past demands, and thus forecast our average error.
   c. In situations where we model the underlying demand process, we may actually be able to calculate the variance of the distribution of the forecast error.

3. **The percentage error for product groups will usually be lower than for each individual product.** Most texts would suggest that this goes down by the square root of the number of products, due to the way independent errors cancel each other out. However, the errors are, in fact, not independent. Much of the error is in the popularity of the line; this part of the error is the same for every item and does not cancel out. Thus, in practice the effect is positive but much less than the formula suggests.

4. **Forecasts should mix subjective and objective information when available, since different kinds of information are being captured.** This leads to the idea of decision support systems, or man/machine interactive systems.

5. **Forecasting accuracy drops rapidly as the horizon increases.** This is essentially because unforeseeable changes in the world (limitations in our understanding) accumulate as we look further into the future. (This even happens looking back in the far past to some extent.)

1.3 APPROACHES TO FORECASTING IN BUSINESS

1.3.1 Overview

Remember that we have classified forecast approaches as subjective, objective, or mixed. Subjective forecasts are based entirely on human judgment; objective forecasts use formulas to manipulate historical data; mixed forecasts involve combining human judgment and formulas. We further classify objective methods into time-series models and causal models. Time-series models use no other data but the historical values of the variable being forecast, while causal models try to explain the future by using additional information.

Each of these approaches can, in turn, be sub-classified into several individual methods, as shown in Table 1-2. We next describe each of these methods very briefly.

Forecast Approaches	Individual Methods
Subjective	Hierarchical Surveys Expert panels The Delphi method
Objective—Time Series Models	Moving averages Exponential smoothing Discounted regression
Objective—Causal Models	Econometric Structural
Mixed	Scenario forecasting Interactive hierarchical Decision support systems (DSS)

Table 1-2

A Classification of Forecasting Approaches

1.3.2 Subjective Methods

Hierarchical Method. The law of "focus" implies that people with the most knowledge about a particular set of customers will be able to make the best forecast. Thus, in forecasting overall demand for a product, it might make sense to ask each salesperson for a forecast of demand for his or her particular customers. Then the sales manager of a region could take all these individual forecasts for the region and produce an aggregate regional forecast. This aggregate forecast could, in the simplest case, be simply the sum of the individual forecasts; or the sales manager could try to correct likely biases of some of the individual forecasts before summing; or sometimes other more complex corrections could be made (such as for individual forecast overlaps).

For obvious reasons this is called a **bottom-up** forecasting method. In other situations the forecast (goal) is, instead, set at the top by the national sales manager. He or she allocates the goal among the regional sales managers, who in turn allocate among the sales force to produce sales forecasts (goals) for each person in the sales force. This is called a **top-down** approach.

These same sort of issues arise in large R&D projects over several years. Estimates of costs and resources may be formed bottom-up or top-down or by mixed approaches which try to reconcile the two methods.

Surveys. Surveys carry the idea of focus one step further. If you want to know about customer demand, ask the customers directly about their plans. (Surveys are just as important in learning about the unknown present or the unknown past as the unknown future. For example, a survey of how many companies actually use MRP computer systems may help researchers design better systems.) Customer surveys can be quite effective in:

    a. Forecasting market share
    b. Product redesign
    c. Product repackaging
    d. Setting prices
    e. Modifying advertising

However, surveys are extremely difficult to carry out effectively. It is important to design the questionnaire so that the responder will really understand what the survey taker wants to know and will have incentives to fill it out and answer truthfully. Often the response rate is only about 30 percent, and those who answer and say they like the product are unlikely to be exactly representative of those who don't answer. Finally, the survey cannot practically be sent to everyone, and it is difficult to ensure a representative sample. (An important kind of survey is a test market where a new product is actually tried out. This is an important type of forecast, but outside our scope.) Ways of addressing these problems may be found in any good book on market research.

Expert Panels. Almost every meeting of a company's management may be thought of as trying to combine the opinions of "experts" to derive a forecast and/or a related plan.

Sometimes the managers meet as a group and come to a consensus. For example, at a nuclear fuel tube plant that the author knows about, every Tuesday morning the senior scheduler, the scheduling assistant, two floor engineers, one or more machine operators, and the production manager would meet for several hours to plan for the next week. This meeting would include forecasting which items would be needed, where the bottlenecks would be, where breakdowns or material shortages might be critical, and so on. The meeting was quite sophisticated and complicated, using as inputs the results of running their OPT scheduling package (which they didn't trust much), tentative bar chart schedules (Gantt charts), and so on.

Sometimes the expert panel will itself simply be used as input to the final decision-makers. For example, people from all over the company may suggest company sales goals, but the CEO will probably insist on making the final decision. Again, a large amount of technical input may be involved.

The Delphi Method. The Delphi method is a special kind of expert panel which tries to arrive at a consensus, without having individual experts cave in too easily to group pressure. (The oracle at Delphi in ancient Greece was famous for predicting the future.)

The members of the group work essentially in isolation. Each receives controlled data input, such as normal time series data and opinions/surveys (statistically analyzed). In the first round the members are given questionnaires to respond to anonymously to give their forecasts and supporting material. The responses are analyzed statistically, for example, giving the mean and the spread of the forecast. This summary of the first round is given back to the group. People can anonymously feel the group pressure from this, but also feel free to "stick to their guns." Then a second round is taken, then a third round, and so on. Usually at most three or four rounds are performed, since the method is intensive both of management and technical support time.

In Section 2.2 we will present a case in which a company used both the scenario method and the Delphi method.

1.3.3 Objective Methods—Time Series Models

Remember that all forecasting involves the (often false) assumption that the future will be like the past. Time series models do this in the most straightforward way possible. A time series is just the regularly spaced past recorded values of the item we wish to forecast over some time interval. For example, if we wish to forecast monthly sales, the time series might be monthly sales for the item over the past 36 months. Time series models use only these past values of sales to predict future sales. For this reason it is often called a **naive** method.

Moving Averages. Perhaps the oldest time series method of all is to simply let the sales forecast for next period equal the actual sales this period. A slightly less naive method is to take the total sales for last year, divide by 12, and assume this figure as the sales for each month of the next year. The point here is that the data tends to be noisy or random. Averaging can **smooth** or **de-randomize** the data. One problem with this method is that as next year progresses we are not averaging in the new months, which are probably more up to date. We are also keeping the oldest data, which is getting more and more out of date. This problem led to the **moving average**, which averages in the newest month each month and deletes the oldest month, so that the most recent 12 months are always in the average.

This method will also not work well if there is a strong **trend**, or tendency towards growth or decline. We will see later how to adapt the method to estimate this trend and thus correct the simple moving average. Similarly, the product may sell very well in summer and poorly in winter, so that we must correct for **seasonality**. Finally, the product may exhibit cyclical (secular) variations, which are longer term than seasonal fluctuations and more irregular. Time series models cannot really cope with cyclical variation, and hence must be enriched into causal models by adding business cycle corrections, for example.

Examples of time series exhibiting some of these patterns are given in Figure 1-1.

Exponential Smoothing. Note that the moving average must make a tradeoff. If it includes a great many prior months in the average, it will handle randomness very effectively; however, it will be using a lot of data which is not very current and hence rather obsolete. A ten-month moving average basically puts a 10 percent weight on each of the last ten months of data and zero weight before that. Perhaps it might make sense to let the weights drop off more smoothly, for example: 10 percent, 9 percent, 8.1 percent, 7.3 percent, and so forth. This is exactly what the technique of exponential smoothing does.

Figure 1-1

Some Types of Time
Series

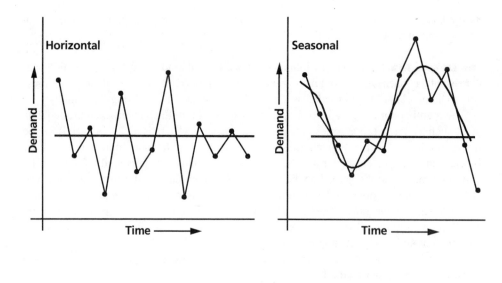

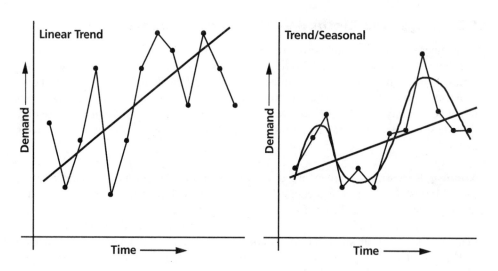

Exponential smoothing has become very popular, primarily because it doesn't require a great deal of data storage or manipulation to use. Moving averages and exponential smoothing are really fairly similar in accuracy and in how their formulas are redesigned for more complicated situations. We will discuss these issues at length in Forecasting Chapter 3.

Discounted Regression.   Regression is a rather general causal objective method which will be discussed in Section 1.3.4. Basically, a curve (usually a straight line) is fit to the past data in such a way as to minimize some measure of the errors of the data from the curve. Then the line or curve is extrapolated into the future to produce the forecast.

Here we want to limit our discussion of regression to fitting the line to the time series data only in such a way as to minimize the squared errors of the data points around the line, as shown in Figure 1-2.

The idea of discounted regression seems superficially different from moving averages or exponential smoothing, but it is actually a more general approach which contains the others as special cases. To include the idea that older data is worth less than newer, we weight the observations with geometrically decreasing weights looking back: 0.100,

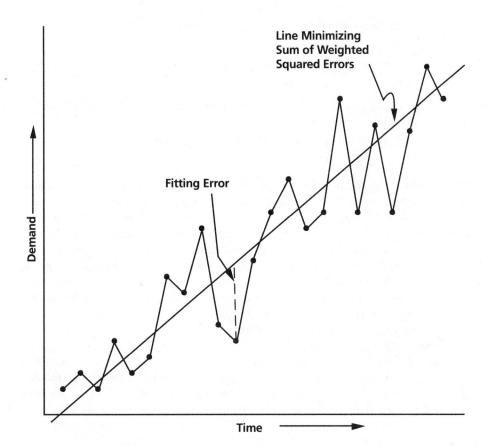

Figure 1-2

Fitting a Weighted
Regression Line to Time
Series Data

0.090, 0.081, . . . (here the weights decrease by 10 percent each period). We can show that moving averages and exponential smoothing may be obtained as special cases. Why use all three methods? Discounted regression is not quite as efficient computationally as the others, since a whole new regression must be computed each time period. On the other hand, regression is more general since causal variables are easily incorporated. Again, we will look at these issues more carefully in Forecasting Chapter 3.

1.3.4 Objective Methods—Causal Models

Remember that a method in which the forecast is derived in a straightforward way simply from historical data is called an objective forecasting method. We have already discussed time series methods in which only the past values of the variable being forecasted are needed. Causal models also use data from other sources in the prediction, and are usually predicted on the belief that there is some theory or understanding as to how the other variables influence the situation. Procedures which simply try different formulas or formula variations until something fits pretty well are really just glorified time series models.

Econometric Models. A very important class of causal models are the **econometric** models. These are very popular because:

1. The forecast (dependent variable) is just a weighted sum (usually linear) of the predicting variables (independent variables).
2. The weights are usually selected to minimize the squared errors in fitting the model to the data.
3. Regression is a powerful, well-developed, fast method for solving such problems.

As an example, suppose we have three causal variables:

T for the year
P for our product price
Q for our competitor's price

which we wish to use to forecast the variable I for our income from the product. E is an estimate we are going to make for future income from the product.

We wish to select weights a, b, c to form a forecasting equation

$$E = a + bT + cP + dQ$$

At each time T in the past time series, we observed particular values of the causal (independent) variables T, P, and Q and the dependent variable to be forecast I. For each past observation, and any particular choice of weights (forecasting equation) we can compare the retrospective forecast for that past observation with the actual value. We now square the errors and sum them. A technical procedure embedded in all regression software then chooses the set of weights to minimize this sum of squared errors. We hope that the line which fits the past well will forecast the future well. (This is not always true, however.) To make a forecast, we then go to a future year T, and for any choice of our price P and competitor's price Q, we can make an estimate of our resulting income, E, which we hope will be reasonably close to the true resulting income I.

It is sometimes said that econometric forecasting is rarely used for planning operations. This is not really so. An example or two may be helpful. Helmer [*Interfaces* 1980] discusses, for example, helping hospital management to predict nursing-hour requirements by ward, shift, day of the week, and month of the year. These variables are often represented by 0-1 variables called **dummy variables**. After fitting all the past data, management can tell how much extra service Ward 7 takes, how much extra service is needed on Thursdays, and so on.

Similarly, Chen and Winters [1966] discuss forecasting demand for an electrical utility. Besides using time series data, the model can estimate how much electricity usage changes on cloudy or rainy days, hot days, very cold days, holidays, or specific days of the week. In addition, econometric models are useful at higher levels, when long-term sales forecasts need to include forecasts of GNP, housing starts, Japanese tariffs, and so forth.

Structural Models. Structural models are causal models which are usually non-linear and pay much more attention to modeling exactly how the variables are interrelated. Structural models are extremely widespread but are often not recognized as forecasting.

For example, in the nuclear fuel tube shop scheduling problem mentioned previously, once management predicts the load on the system, due dates, and importances, the automatic scheduling module may be run, giving forecasts of which jobs will be done in what order on which machines and what the lead time through the shop will be for each item. Thus, the raw forecasts plus the scheduling module in effect represent a structural forecasting model.

Frank Bass [1969] first developed a diffusion model (taken from the biological sciences) for forecasting the pattern of sales growth for a brand new product. There are assumed to be two classes of purchasers, innovators and imitators, for a product, such as refrigerators, that a purchaser will usually buy only once. Innovators decide to purchase pretty much at a constant rate, independent of everything else, whereas imitators buy more as others buy more of the item. Thus, early growth of the product is at a constant rate, and then it explodes as the imitators catch on; finally, a saturation point is reached. This is an excellent example of a powerful structural model.

A structural example of forecasting for ordering raw materials is as follows: A shop makes assembled products. A panel of experts forecasts the amounts and timing of customer orders, which is the basis for what is called a "master production schedule." An MRP (material requirements planning) system determines all the components needed and their timing by "exploding" the inherent requirements to build the master production schedule. These in turn give a forecast of the timing and quantities of raw materials needed, finally resulting in a forecast of raw material inventory levels, and thus finally a forecast of timing and quantities of orders that will be necessary from suppliers. Thus the panel of experts plus the MRP system are, in effect, a structural forecasting model for raw material ordering.

1.3.5 Mixed Models

We have already discussed a number of models which use both judgment and objective methods to derive a forecast. It should be clear, perhaps, that the boundary between a structural model and a mixed model is a little vague. Nevertheless, there are several types of mixed models that are of particular interest.

Scenario Forecasting. Suppose a company must decide whether or not to make a large strategic but very risky investment. Suppose there are just too many varied opinions about the future to expect something like Delphi to reach a good consensus. The possibility of large errors must be considered. In this case, the CEO may ask the staff to construct 15 or 20 possible complete views of the world, called **scenarios**. Each possible scenario is evaluated financially and given a measure such as net present value, or payback. The bad scenarios and very good scenarios are considered, along with the firm's attitude toward risk, in making a final judgmental decision. Note that although probabilistic models are not being considered, the spread of the scenarios acts in a way like a distribution of good and bad outcomes.

Interactive Hierarchical. Remember that in the hierarchical method, we either put together individual forecasts by a number of people (bottom up) or split an overall goal (judgmental forecast) down into individual goals at the bottom (top down). An interactive hierarchical system can operate in either of these two modes, as well as a number of others. For example, it might initially act bottom up, but if the resulting forecast disagrees with a previously stated goal, some sort of average may be struck between these, to represent a new overall goal. The new goal can then be distributed downward in a top-down procedure, or perhaps all the original bottom-up forecasts may be directly reduced or increased by the same percentage to make the new goals

Forecasting Decision Support Systems. A decision support system for forecasting (forecasting DSS) is just a computerized mixed forecasting system, which allows the user flexibility in how to solve forecasting problems. The interactive hierarchical system just described is one example of a forecasting DSS. Some of the software in the supporting software module also has this interactive quality, and can be classified as a simple DSS.

1.3.6 Big Picture Exercises

1. Explain intuitively each of the following time series terms:

    a. Random
    b. Stationary
    c. Linear trend
    d. Curvilinear trend
    e. Seasonality
    f. Cycle

2. Compare and contrast a pure time series procedure with a similar procedure which uses additional causal factors.

3. One drawback that is often cited for the Delphi method is that it takes a long time to carry out. Suppose the head of your MIS department comes up with a scheme to computerize the Delphi method so that each expert will sit at a separate computer. Since the results of a previous round will be instantaneously available, the next round can be completed right away. What is wrong with this scheme?

4. How is the Delphi method similar to typical expert panel methods? How is it different? What is the advantage of the Delphi method?

5. Why does the scenario approach not attempt to estimate forecast errors? What does it use instead?

6. What is wrong, or at least dangerous, about the statement: "The average real rate of return of all bonds for the last 50 years has been –1.1 percent. Therefore bonds are not a good investment."?

7. Discuss the role of forecasting in each of the following areas of a company:

   a. Marketing
   b. R&D
   c. Finance
   d. Manufacturing
   e. Distribution

8. Consider the problem of choosing an appropriate person to marry from a given number of suitors. What forecasting concerns might one have in such a situation? In particular, list the short-term, intermediate-term, and long-term forecasts you might have considered. What sorts of data might be useful in attempting to make better forecasts in each area? What methods mentioned here would be closest to those you might use in making those forecasts?

9. Discuss the following statement from the CEO: "It's not my fault we built a warehouse twice as big as we needed. Our long-term forecast was not accurate."

1.4 SUMMARY AND PREVIEW OF THE FORECASTING MODULE

Forecasting Chapter 2 considers strategic forecasting approaches, both long term and short term. In Sections 2.2, 2.5, and 2.7 a company application scenario is given with a five-to-ten year horizon. In Sections 2.3 and 2.4 two methods, the scenario approach and the Delphi approach, are developed and compared. In Section 2.6 regression forecasting is developed briefly.

Forecasting Chapter 3 considers tactical/requirements forecasting, also called smoothing. Section 3.2 develops smoothing basics. The Clifton Wards scenario is presented in Sections 3.3 and 3.5 to illustrate the ideas. Finally, Section 3.4 discusses adding trends and seasonality to the model. More advanced topics are presented in Appendices A to E.

Forecasting Chapter 4 discusses the coming information explosion and the so-called "information superhighway." Section 4.2 discusses three major examples of new directions in forecasting, and Section 4.3 provides cautions as to the difficulty of this kind of extrapolation. The Appendices contain a number of additional forecasting topics. Appendix A gives a brief review of the normal distribution, including probability foundations. Appendix B sketches the extension of regression to many variables. Appendix C discusses a number of types of special regression variables useful in business. Appendix D develops several methods for estimating seasonal factors, while Appendix E discusses group forecasting of similar products. Appendix F discusses several methods for estimating future forecast errors. Appendix G gives a complete table of the unit normal distribution for reference.

CHAPTER 2

Strategic Forecasting Approaches

2.1 INTRODUCTION

Many production and operations management teachers do not consider long-term strategic forecasting an important topic. This is unfortunate, for manufacturing strategy is now considered by many experts to be critical for the survival of American industry. Which emerging technology will win out over the next five years so that it must be invested in *today*? What is the emerging direction of consumer tastes in automobile safety? What is the cost learning curve on a process which is unprofitable today? How will the fast emerging fiber optics field affect AT&T's entry into the home entertainment business?

The defining characteristics of long-term strategic forecasting are:

1. **Very long time horizon**—The basis for choosing a time horizon in a decision problem is roughly how long it takes to recover from a mistake. An inventory under-order may be corrected in a month; over-capacity may not be corrected for five to ten years. A typical long-term strategic plan is for a five-year period (with at least some intuitive feeling about further events). This is a long enough time for an unexpected Gulf War to come and go, for the compact disc to grow to dominate the recorded music market, and for downsizing to become a household word.

2. **Extreme difficulty of forecasting**—Time series and objective causal models are notoriously ineffective for long-term strategic forecasting. Even the best subjective methods have a very spotty record. The big historical winners and losers in this high stakes game are the stuff of legend. This is closely related to the fact that large unpredictable events can occur.

3. **Huge financial stakes are involved**—The very term "strategic" has become a synonym for "life and death issue." A company whose existence is at stake will be willing to spend large amounts of time and effort to forecast by every method possible, to pay huge sums to consulting experts, and to replace the current CEO by someone it feels has a better intuition about the future.

Perhaps it is not surprising that operations management texts often do not venture into these waters—most methods which are in practical use are not deeply quantitative, and in any event are difficult to describe and to justify. Nevertheless, the manufacturing executive does not have the luxury of ignoring strategic forecasting and must be a careful consumer of the best available methods.

The first company application scenario in this chapter, presented in Section 2.2, is Crawly Caterpillars (CC), a well known manufacturer of construction equipment. Crawly Caterpillars wants to make a decision about the timing and amount of capacity expansion, and thus needs five-year forecasts of sales, costs, and profits, and a rough salvage value of the company at the end of that five years. In Section 2.3 the scenario approach is explained and applied to CC. In Section 2.4 the Delphi method is developed and its application to CC is given.

In Section 2.5 Crawly Caterpillars is recalled to develop a short strategic company forecasting problem. Short-term strategic problems with a two- or three-year horizon are most often solved by econometric (regression) forecasting. In Section 2.6 regression forecasting is explained rather informally. Appendices A and G discuss the normal distribution and give tables of the unit normal distribution. Appendix B discusses regression with more than one variable, while Appendix C discusses special types of regression variables useful in business. Section 2.7 finishes the Crawly Caterpillar problem.

2.2 COMPANY APPLICATION SCENARIO—CRAWLY CATERPILLARS

(***Note:*** *Based in part on an article about American Hoist & Derrick, by Basu and Schroeder [1977]*).

Crawly Caterpillars, Inc., is a well-known manufacturer of earthmoving construction equipment with current annual sales of about $330 million a year. The CEO of CC wants to develop a long range plan for capacity expansion and thus needs five-year forecasts of sales, costs, and profits, and a rough salvage value of the company at the end of five years, all at different levels of capacity. This is considered largely an operations problem, since sales are expected to depend critically on costs and tightening reliability and delivery times. Since these forecasts represent actual valuations of the company, rather than simply goals, top CC management is extremely concerned with forecasting as accurately as possible. In the past, Crawly Caterpillars sold everything it could make. Sales forecasts relied principally on subjective judgment, and the errors have been a source of concern to top management. With the desire to expand capacity, these errors have become much more important. Management felt that time series estimates were not completely adequate, since historical sales did not reflect true demand, but only previous capacity constraints. Additionally, rapidly changing economic conditions made simple time series estimates even less reliable. Due to this concern, the CEO and her staff are reluctant to rely upon any single forecasting approach and decide to try and compare two rather different methods: the scenario approach and the Delphi method.

2.3 THE SCENARIO APPROACH

2.3.1 Overview

The Scenario approach involves:

1. Choosing decision alternatives to evaluate
2. Creating a small number of alternate complete forecasts (scenarios) of the future (probably no fewer than 3, rarely more than 25)
3. Evaluating, for each scenario, the cost or profit of each decision alternative (by some carefully stated methodology)
4. Weighing carefully the good, medium, and bad outcomes
5. Making the final decision

These steps may be carried out in a number of different ways. However, the following methods are common:

1. Decision alternatives are selected independently of the formal scenario process.
2. Scenarios may be selected by a single group, choosing a central scenario, then varying demand, for example, up or down 20 percent, timing economic

recovery in year 1 or 3 or 4, factoring inflation at 3 or 5 percent, and using other various combinations.

3. A number of different groups of executives may be appointed, each charged with coming up with their most realistic scenario. If necessary, a few pessimistic scenarios may be added.

4. In some cases the evaluation methodology has been agreed on in advance, and there is no question of opinion at this point.

5. Using the evaluated scenarios to make the decision is easily the hardest part. This is really a pure judgment call. Should a single bad scenario kill an otherwise good decision, for example?

2.3.2 Creating Scenarios

Crawly Caterpillar decided to create eight two-person scenario teams, each consisting of an expert of known strong opinions, and a staff assistant. These individuals were selected on the following criteria:

• They had been doing the judgmental forecasts
• They had been responsible for using the forecasts
• They were affected by the forecasts
• They were experienced in marketing/sales

Each group was asked to estimate a five-year time series for each of the following:

• GNP
• Industry sales
• CC sales

Each group was given the time series history for the last seven years for each of these three items.

2.3.3 Evaluating and Using Scenarios

After the scenarios were created, they were collected and formally evaluated by the CEO's staff. The CEO did not wish to contaminate the second Delphi method study to come, and so she designated four experts who were not to participate in the Delphi study. One of the eight scenarios indicated that capacity expansion was not called for at all, two of the eight indicated an aggressive program of expansion. The remaining five were quite mixed. The pessimistic scenario was finally discarded because it seemed somewhat unrealistic to all four experts. However, no conclusion could be agreed on with respect to the aggressive expansion scenarios. Because she knew that if the Delphi study were not coming she would have to make an immediate decision, the CEO terminated the scenario work at this point, swore the four to secrecy, and turned to the Delphi study.

2.3.4 Scenario Exercises

1. What are the advantages and disadvantages if only one or two scenarios are evaluated in doing a scenario approach study? If 50 or 100 are evaluated?

2. What are the advantages and disadvantages if only two decision alternatives are evaluated in doing a scenario approach study? If ten are evaluated?

3. Suppose a certain decision looks good under some scenarios, but bad under others. Discuss the strengths and weaknesses of some possible formal procedures for giving an overall evaluation of the decision.

   a. Average of the scenarios
   b. Weighted average of the scenarios

    c. Best of the scenarios

    d. Worst of the scenarios

    e. Second best of the scenarios

    f. Second worst of the scenarios

    g. CEO judgment

4. Explain: "A manager can always control the outcome of a scenario study by adding a scenario known to make the decision look good or bad." How could the CEO protect against such manipulation of the process?

5. One approach to scenarios is the "break-even" scenario. Suppose the decision is whether or not to build a certain capacity warehouse, and that depends almost entirely on whether the rate of demand increase over the next ten years will be 2, 4, 6, 8, or 10 percent. The scenario group under this approach would find the rate of increase such that the warehouse would just be worthwhile. Management could then decide whether the break-even was likely to be achieved. Evaluate the strengths and weaknesses of this approach.

6. Create a detailed problem to flesh out problem 5, and determine the break-even scenario.

7. A drug company has the opportunity to license a fantastic new Alzheimer's medication for a $10,000,000 one-time payment. The product will earn a profit of $1,300,000 a year, for an unknown number of years N, $1 < N < 15$. To keep the problem simple, ignore interest. Let each scenario be an integer value of N. Evaluate the profit or loss from each possible scenario. What is the break-even scenario? What investment criterion in cost accounting is the break-even scenario a duplicate of?

8. In problem 7 suppose the profit in each year may be 90, 95, 100, 105, or 110 percent of the nominal profit given (same in every year). Evaluate a tradeoff between the profit rate and the break-even N. How might this be useful in applying the scenario method?

2.4 THE DELPHI APPROACH

2.4.1 Overview

The Delphi method involves the following activities:

1. A panel of experts is selected to make judgmental decisions.
2. Common background data is supplied to the panel.
3. Each member of the panel makes the desired forecast every round.
4. A summary of the responses from one round is given to everyone in the next round.

The basic idea here is that each expert makes his/her judgment in secret to avoid undue peer pressure. At the same time, the summary of the responses of his/her peers in the previous round provides feedback about the opinion of the rest of the group.

2.4.2 Using the Approach

At Crawly Caterpillars, the Delphi study involved selecting 20 key individuals from the expertise pool described previously. Just as before, the primary five-year forecasts were wanted for GNP, industry sales, and CC sales. Time series history was made available on these three items to each member of the panel at the start. The histories were given graphically and in absolute tabular and percentage increase tabular form.

After the first round was run, an analysis of the forecasts was performed. For each forecast, the responses were summarized by maximum, mean, minimum, and standard deviation. A complete, anonymous table of all twenty responses was also provided. This material was given to all the panelists, and they were allowed to make a revised set of choices. Then a third round was run. At this point, the forecasts were all fairly similar, and the Delphi method was terminated. Using the current year's sales as 100, the mean forecasts for the next five years from the method were 109.3, 116.3, 125.0, 135.2 and 146.0. Using these forecasts, management did a decision analysis and concluded that a corresponding design with a 40 percent capacity increase coming on line in year 2 would be consistent with this forecast.

Since the scenario forecasts had given capacity expansion decisions ranging from 0 percent expansion by year 5, to 80 percent by year 1, with most scenarios yielding 40 to 55 percent expansion in years 2 or 3, management was quite satisfied that the scenario results and the Delphi results were consistent with each other. Management finally implemented the 40 percent expansion in year 2 design suggested by the Delphi method.

In retrospect, five years later the actual sales figures were 111.3, 119.2, 124.0, 140.1, and 150.6. Management was satisfied at this point with the forecast and the resulting decision, partly because this accuracy was better than had historically been achieved, and partly because actual demand growth was somewhat greater than predicted.

2.4.3 Comparing Subjective Forecasting Methods

Expert panel, scenario, and Delphi subjective forecasting methods have different strengths and weaknesses:

1. The scenario method encourages management to think in terms of a "distribution" of possible outcomes, and to consider both good and bad cases. The panel approach tends to push for a quick consensus, and is vulnerable to grandstanding, political considerations, bandwagon effects, and so on. The Delphi method allows much more independence due to the anonymity, but there is still great anonymous group pressure to produce a single output. Explicit recognition of a range of possible outcomes is an advantage of the scenario approach.

2. On the other side of the coin, an important advantage of the Delphi approach is that it tends to provide a final reasonably uniform estimate of sales among the different managers. This helps induce cooperation among management in implementing the resulting decisions. While the panel method also provides a common estimate as an output, many times managers are pushed quickly into supporting something they may not really believe and are less cooperative later. The scenario approach makes no direct attempt to build consensus.

3. The panel approach is often low effort, while the scenario and Delphi approaches are high effort. The Delphi approach is also a high calendar time approach, since time must be left between rounds to allow experts to digest the results of the last round.

2.4.4 Delphi Exercises

1. It is sometimes argued that the anonymity in the Delphi method can be a disadvantage when each expert has different expertise to contribute which the others would recognize. Suppose a husband and wife are remodeling their house. A number of major decisions must be worked out by the man, the wife, the architect, the interior designer, and the kitchen designer. List some examples where anonymity would help, and some where it would hurt.

2. Would it be helpful for a group of five friends to use the Delphi method to predict the exact scores of the next football game? What useful idea does this illustrate?

3. What are the advantages of larger size versus smaller size panels of experts in the Delphi method?

4. Enlist four students as a panel of experts using the Delphi method to try to come to a consensus about how long a popular movie currently playing will last as a first-run movie. Hold a post-evaluation meeting later to see how good the forecast was.

5. Try the same exercise with a new movie, and eight students. What observations do you have about the difficulty of the method and the accuracy of the method with varying panel sizes?

6. Read up on the results of four or five Delphi studies reported in the journals, and write up a cross-evaluation.

2.5 COMPANY APPLICATION SCENARIO—CRAWLY CATERPILLARS (REPRISE)

The management of the Crawly Caterpillars company were quite enthusiastic about the success of the Delphi method study for their capacity expansion problem and the generally confirming results of their separate-scenario study. They went ahead and implemented the resulting recommendation to add 40 percent to capacity in the second year.

It is now the beginning of the sixth year since that study. As a result of adding capacity, management now has three years of quarterly sales data not contaminated by capacity constraints. Their production planning people would like to utilize this data to do a two-year forecast for the purpose of making an aggregate plan for production and work force levels. Thus, their second problem qualifies as short-term strategic forecasting, rather than long-term. Although, with the advent of the capacity expansion, total year 6 capacity can meet total year 6 demand, demand for construction equipment is quite seasonal, with the peak in the summer. It is not possible to produce enough in the summer quarter for the summer needs, so some combination of the following strategies is required:

1. Produce excess in the winter, and carry inventories to the next summer.
2. Produce part of the needs as overtime in the spring and the summer.
3. Hire in the spring and lay off in the fall.
4. Subcontract peak demand to other manufacturers.

Although this planning has been done on a rather intuitive basis in the past, the company now feels it is time to find a good consultant to help provide a better two-year forecast and do a more formal aggregate plan. They hire an "expert" from Toomuch Tech. The expert studies their situation thoroughly and then recommends the following:

1. Use linear regression to estimate future sales, using trend, seasonal factors, and housing starts.
2. Estimate the average size of the forecast errors for each of the twelve quarterly forecasts.
3. Compute a safety stock for each quarter, based on the expected forecast errors.
4. Produce twelve corrected (deterministic) forecasts, taking these safety stocks into account.
5. Use a linear programming aggregate planning model to set decisions on production, work force, hiring, firing, etc. for the next two years.
6. Review the reasonableness of the results, and make any necessary corrections.

In starting to implement this plan, the staff went to the company database, and pulled out total company sales and housing starts for the past three years; that is, years 3, 4, and 5.

Year	Spring	Summer	Fall	Winter
3	123	136	111	42
4	163	170	34?	58
5	163	164	121	72

Table 2-1

Company Sales (1,000s)

Year	Spring	Summer	Fall	Winter
3	50	30	10	5
4	60	50	15	10
5	40	40	25	0

Table 2-2

Housing Starts (10,000s)

The staff also realized that, while Tables 2-1 and 2-2 would be enough to allow fitting a regression to the past three years, in order to use the regression they would need to have an estimate of housing starts for the next two years. They subscribed to an economic forecasting service, which provided them with the estimates shown in Table 2-3.

The staff thought the consultant could supply the forecast errors from the results of the regression. However, the consultant explained that these were errors in fitting the past, and hence were really not good estimates of the errors in forecasting the future. The staff hadn't saved past forecast errors, but finally made a judgment to treat average forecast errors as something like 10–15 percent of the forecast. They decided to make one set of runs assuming 10 percent, and another assuming 15 percent, and check the sensitivity.

We will come back to the Crawly Caterpillar case in Section 2.7, after we learn the necessary regression tools.

2.6 ECONOMETRIC MODELS AND REGRESSION TOOLS

2.6.1 Overview

In short-term strategic forecasting, it is not often appropriate to forecast future sales simply based on the past sales time series. For problems with a time horizon up to a year, **smoothing** or time series methods can work quite well, as we shall see in Forecasting Chapter 3. However, for problems with a horizon of at least two or three years, it is important to include outside variables such as Gross National Product, housing starts, the interest rate, and so on. Remember that we call such a model a causal model.

Ideally, one would like a complete theoretical model which incorporates these outside variables in the actual manner they affect sales. Such causal models we have termed **structural** models. Very often, however, we do not understand the "true" relationship between past sales, outside variables, and future variables well enough to build a trustworthy structural model. It is practical, then, to simply settle for a simple linear model with the right variables in it, with each variable having an unknown weight. Then the weights are varied systematically to best fit the past relationship between sales and the other variables. Usually the "best fit" is taken so as to minimize the sum of the squared errors of these past "forecasts" (hindcasts?). This is typically done with a software package.

Year	Spring	Summer	Fall	Winter
6	30	25	12	6
7	50	40	18	12

Table 2-3

Estimated Housing Starts (10,000s)

There are many excellent texts that discuss the theory of regression. Thus we present just the basics here in order to provide some understanding of the use of regression software, such as POMQuest. See also Pindyck, R. and D. Rubinfeld [1991]. Our order of development will be to first give an intuitive example showing briefly how econometric forecasting is used. In Section 2.6.2 we develop the basic ideas of linear regression. In Section 2.6.3 we briefly discuss the actual application of econometric forecasting more carefully again for the Crawly Caterpillar case, and discuss the strengths and weaknesses of regression as a forecast procedure. Appendices A to F give more information on several forecasting topics.

A Small Example. Every six months the production manager of the Instant Microwave Company determines an aggregate sales forecast for the next two years in six-month intervals. The forecast is used to plan inventory and work force levels for these future periods. As an aid in this forecasting problem, he long ago discovered that a forecasted increase in disposable income will usually be followed by an increase in oven sales, and that an increase in housing starts will be followed two quarters later by an increase in refrigerator sales. Also, sales seem to be affected by the price in the previous year. There does not appear to be a clear trend; that is, sales do not seem to strongly increase or decrease over time.

The manager begins to construct a causal model. In general this is rather difficult, for he must select only those variables which are the most relevant, and must understand the appropriate time lags in the way the variables affect price.

2.6.2 Linear Regression

General Discussion. In the simplest case, at time t there is one variable we would like to predict (called the **dependent** variable) for some number of periods k into the future. (For k negative the equation would predict a fit to a particular past sales period.) For ease of discussion, we first consider the case where there is just one explanatory or causal variable (called the **independent** variable).

If we stick with linear relationships, our model becomes

$$P_{t,k} = P_t + B_t X_{t,k}$$

This is the equation for a straight line where P_t is the intercept and B_t is the slope. The subscript t means the model was fit by using the data available at time t; a new equation will typically be fit at time $t + 1$ and so on. $P_{t,k}$ means the "prediction for sales in period $t + k$ as seen from period t." $X_{t,k}$ means the "estimated value of the causal variable in period $t + k$ as seen from period t." (Note that for $k <= 0$ this will not be an estimate, but the actual known value.)

Since this is a linear model, subtracting a constant from $X_{t,k}$ will not change the model if we add an equal amount to the constant P_t to compensate. Thus, we may assume $X_{t,0} = 0$, that is, $X_{t,k}$ really represents the change in this variable from time t. In that case $P_t = P_{t,0}$. That is, the intercept has a natural interpretation as the value of sales, as predicted by the regression, in the current period, and the equation may be rewritten as:

$$P_{t,k} = P_{t,0} + B_t X_{t,k}$$

Note: It is customary in learning regression to write the regression equation more like $Y = A + BX$. However, we assume the student has run into regression before, and thus we have taken the liberty of using symbols which show the connections between regression and moving averages/exponential smoothing in the next chapter.

Consider the relationship as shown in Figure 2-1. The straight line intersects the Y axis at point A and has a slope which can be expressed as a change in Y for a given change in X, or $\Delta Y / \Delta X$. The slope of the line is constant, and is given by $B = \Delta Y / \Delta X$.

Figure 2-1
Slope of a Line

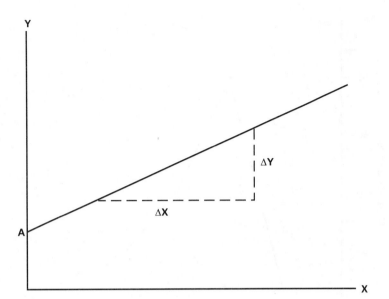

Consider the following example:

Microwave Sales Y (million $)	Relative Time k	Relative Housing Starts (thousand houses)
20	0	0
30	−1	50
50	−2	150
10	−3	−50

A good start in analyzing data such as this is to plot the variable to be forecast versus each single causal variable. As can be seen from Figure 2-2, plotting sales versus time does seem to indicate that sales are decreasing over time but the fit is not very good. In particular $k = -3$ is sufficiently out of line with the rest of the points to cause concern. One might guess, perhaps, that sales are cyclical with time.

On the other hand, Figure 2-3 also shows that plotting sales versus relative housing starts has a perfect fit! Since relative housing starts are correlated with time, we now might interpret relative housing starts as the driving variable, which may have a cyclical behavior. Thus, we settle for a single variable model. (In an exercise you will be asked to investigate putting both independent variables in the model.) It can be seen from Figure 2-3 that the equation of the line minimizing the fitting errors (with zero error) for the housing start version of the model is

$$P_{t,k} = 20 + 0.2X_{t,k}$$

Our purpose, of course, is to use this equation to predict future sales. If we decide to do this, and if relative housing starts for next period are estimated at 120, the forecast equation would estimate sales as

$$P_{t,1} = 20 + 0.2X_{t,1} = 20 + 0.2(120) = 44$$

Some would rhapsodize that because this was a perfect fit to the data, we can be very confident of this result. Unfortunately, this is simply not the case. If relative housing starts for next period are estimated at −120, then the equation would estimate sales as $P_{t,1} = 20 + 0.2(-120) = -4$! Certainly a perfect equation would not predict negative sales. Also, if relative housing starts were 800, would we be sure sales would make it all the way to 180?

Figure 2-2

Microwave Sales versus
Relative Time in Example

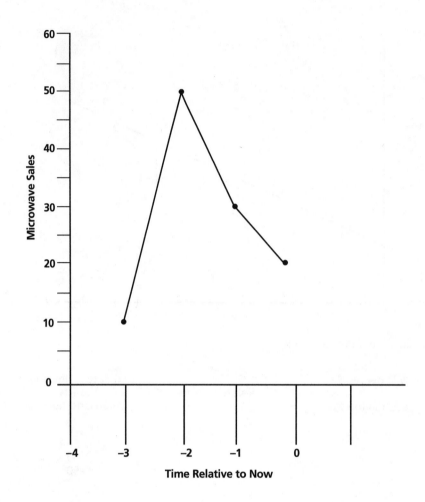

Figure 2-3

Microwave Sales versus
Housing Starts for Example

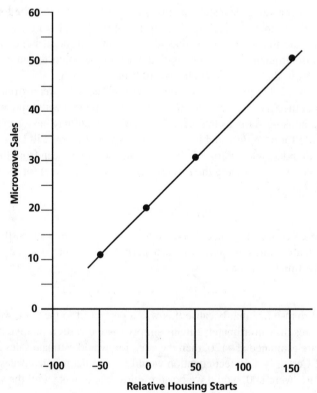

One point here is that we have data for only housing starts between –50 and 150. There is no guarantee that points outside this range would have a linear relationship. Finally, we must always remember that using the past to forecast the future is never guaranteed. It works well sometimes, but not always. Consider now, the following set of somewhat similar data. When this data is plotted in Figure 2-4, it can be seen that a linear model still seems reasonable, but that the fit is less perfect.

Microwave Sales (million $)	Relative Starts (thousand houses)
24	0
28	50
53	150
8	–50

In a technical sense, we say that the *degree* of the relationship is not as strong as in the first case, but that the *direction* of the relationship is the same. It will be shown that the equation $P_{t,k} = 20 + 0.20X_{t,k}$ no longer exactly minimizes the fitting error, but it remains very close.

Best Linear Fit. (See also Pindyck and Rubinfeld [1991].) Assume now that a sample of n observations has been taken on oven sales $Y_{t,k}$ and housing starts $X_{t,k}$, for a number of past years indexed by $t + k$ (k negative). We wish to choose values of the constants $\hat{P}_t$ and $\hat{B}_t$ (estimates of P_t and B_t) to minimize errors of the type

$$E = \left[Y_{t,k} - \hat{B}X_{t,k} \right]$$

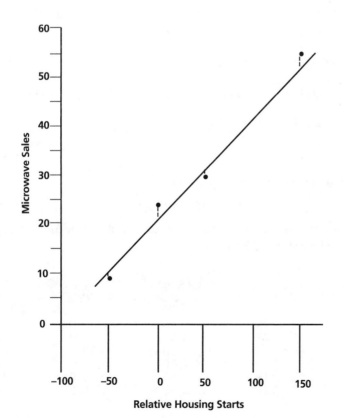

Figure 2-4

Revised Example—
Microwave Sales versus
Housing Starts

or more precisely to minimize the sum of these errors squared. We simplify notation by calling the average of the $Y_{t,k}$ values $\overline{Y}$, of the $X_{t,k}$ values $\overline{X}$, of the products of $X_{t,k}$ and $Y_{t,k}$ to be $(\overline{XY})$ and of the squares of $X_{t,k}$ to be $(\overline{X^2})$.

We wish to choose values for $\hat{P}_t$ and $\hat{B}_t$ to minimize the equation

$$E = \sum_{k=0,n-1}\left(Y_{t,-k} - \hat{P}_t - \hat{B}_t\, X_{t,-k}\right)^2$$

Now use calculus and find values $\hat{P}_t$ and $\hat{B}_t$ to minimize E. The derivative of E with respect to and $\hat{P}_t$ gives the first of the normal equations, and the derivative with respect to $\hat{B}_t$ gives the second of the normal equations

Normal Equations.

$$\overline{Y} = \hat{P}_t + \overline{X}\hat{B}_t$$

$$(\overline{XY}) = X\hat{P}_t + \left(\overline{X^2}\right)\hat{B}_t$$

This is simply two linear equations in the two unknowns $\hat{P}_t$ and $\hat{B}_t$. If we multiply the first equation by $(\overline{X})$ and subtract to eliminate $\hat{P}_t$ we easily obtain

Least Squares Estimators for One Variable.

$$\hat{B}_t = \left[\left(\overline{XY}\right) - \overline{XY}\right]/\left[\left(\overline{X^2}\right) - \left(\overline{X}\right)^2\right]$$

$$\hat{P} = \overline{Y} - \left(\overline{X}\right)\hat{B}_t$$

To give an example of calculating a least squares regression equation in one variable, consider again the data corresponding to Figure 2-4. Remember that this data was somewhat changed from but similar to the data for Figure 2-3, which gave a perfect fit for the regression equation

$$P_{t,k} = 20 + 0.2X_{t,k}$$

We first compute $\overline{Y}$, $\overline{X}$, $(\overline{XY})$, and $\left(\overline{X^2}\right)$.

$$\hat{B}_t = \left[2237.5 - (37.50)(28.25)\right]/\left[6875 - (37.50)^2\right] = 0.215$$

$$\hat{P}_t = 28.25 - (37.5)(0.215)$$

$$\hat{P}_t = 20.17$$

The optimally fitting regression equation is

$$P_{t,k} = 20.17 + 0.215X_{t,k}$$

Thus a fair-sized change in the data only changed the intercept by 1 percent, and increased the optimal slope by 7.5 percent.

Table 2-4

Foundation Equations for Fitting the Data in Figure 2-4

Relative Time k	Sales Y	Rel Starts X	XY	X²
0	24	0	0	0
−1	28	50	1400	2500
−2	53	150	7950	22500
−3	8	−50	−400	2500
Sum:	113	150	8950	27500
Average:	28.25	37.50	2237.5	6875

Coefficient of Determination. There are a number of issues about trying to decide:

    a.   Whether or not a regression has the appropriate variables
    b.   Whether or not a linear model is fairly appropriate
    c.   What the errors to be expected from using the regression might be
    d.   Whether putting in a variable improves the forecast much or not

In this subsection, we discuss only the latter issue.

Considering again our example of oven sales based on housing starts, a reasonable question is: How much improvement does adding housing starts make over the simpler time series model of simply basing oven sales on the average of past sales, that is

$$P_{t,k} = \overline{Y}$$

The sum of the squares of error for that simpler model is usually called SST for "sum of squares total" so that

$$SST = \sum_{k=0,n-1}\left(Y_{t,-k} - \overline{Y}\right)^2$$

This is the magnitude of the error when the mean of the $Y_{t,i}$ values is used to represent the average of sales (analogous to a moving average forecast).

Now we introduce the causal variable $X_{t,-k}$ and analyze the effect it has on this "sum of squares total." In Figure 2-5 the average value for the independent variable Y_{av} is shown. If we look at point B, we can see that before the linear relationship was introduced, the error of estimation was AB; once the linear relationship was introduced the error was reduced to BC. Therefore AC represents the amount that was explained by introducing the linear relationship. Measuring the *total* amount of error that has been explained by the introduction of the regression line, we have

$$SSR = \sum_{k=0,n-1}\left(P_{t,-k} - \overline{Y}\right)^2$$

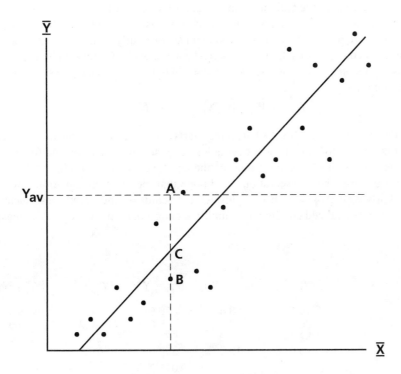

Figure 2-5

Reduction of Errors Due to Regression

where $P_{t,-k} = \hat{P}_t + \hat{B}_t X_{t,-k}$ is the value predicted by the regression equation. (This pictorial argument could be supplemented by a more careful mathematical argument, but we choose not to muddy the waters.)

A popular measure of the improvement caused by introducing the causal variable X is the ratio SSR/SST, which is the proportion of the Y variation explained by the differences in the X. This ratio is called the *coefficient of determination R^2*, or often simply "R^2" for short. Therefore an R^2 of 0.9 indicates that 90 percent of the variability *in the data* (no guarantee that this will hold for future forecasts) has been eliminated by the introduction of the causal variable. To illustrate the computations of R^2, we return to the same example. The computations are shown in Table 2-5. We see that for this problem the original sum of squares was 1041.5, and that 1016.2 was eliminated by adding X to the regression.

$$R^2 = SSR/SST = 1016.2/1041.5 = 0.976$$

We might, therefore, say that 97.6 percent of the variability in oven sales has been explained by the introduction of the variable housing starts. However, we must repeat once again, that although a 98 percent fit has been achieved on past data, this does *not* show how well the model will forecast the future.

Regression with No Constant Term. In some situations it is appropriate to consider regressions where the constant term is forced to be zero; that is, where the regression line is forced to go through the origin or (0,0) point. It turns out that the same regression formulas hold, except that we treat the terms X and Y as if they were zero. Thus the appropriate modified equation is simply

$$\hat{P} = 0; \quad \hat{B} = \left(\overline{XY}\right)/\left(\overline{X^2}\right)$$

We shall have occasion to use this idea when we discuss dummy variables in Appendix C.

Regression with Many Variables—Overview. We will treat the more realistic case where variations in the variable being forecast are related to more than one causal variable in Appendix B. However, we will discuss this case enough here to be able to use regression software packages and understand them at least fairly well. In our example, we might expect that the level of sales for ovens can be better explained by both housing starts and disposable income. If we assume the relationship to be linear, the regression equation can be written as:

$$Y_{t,k} = \hat{P}_t + \hat{B}_{1,t} X_{1,t,k} + \hat{B}_{2,t} X_{2,t,k}$$

where Y is sales, X_1 is the level of housing starts, and X_2 is the level of disposable income. If there are more independent variables, we just add more terms. As for the one variable case, we wish to find the values of the coefficients which minimize the mean square error in fitting past observations, and hope that the resulting equation forecasts the future fairly well. Appendix B goes through the details of finding this best linear fit, and finding the generalized coefficient of multiple determination which gives a measure

Table 2-5

Computation of the Coefficient of Determination

Sales $Y_{t,k}$	$X_{t,k}$	$P_{t,k}$	$(P_{t,k} - \overline{Y})$	$(P_{t,k} - \overline{Y})^2$	$(Y_{t,k} - \overline{Y})$	$(Y_{t,k} - \overline{Y})^2$
24	0	19.8	8.4	70.6	−4.2	18.5
28	50	30.6	2.4	5.8	−0.2	0.0
53	150	52.1	23.9	571.2	24.8	615.0
8	−50	9.0	−19.2	368.6	−20.2	408.0
				1016.2		1041.5

of how well the linear forecasting model fits the data. It also generalizes the idea of a regression with no constant terms (if all independent variables are zero, then the forecast is zero) and discusses statistical significance for the multivariate case. However, we can best get some idea of what multiple regression is about by returning to the Crawly Caterpillar example, after the exercises.

2.6.3 Regression Exercises

1. It is sometimes argued that the best straight line forecast fitting data would minimize the average absolute size of the errors (MAD) rather than minimizing the average squared errors as in ordinary regression.

    a. Give a number of examples where the cost of forecast errors would indeed seem to be linear in their size.
    b. Give a number of examples where the cost of forecast errors would go up faster than linear in their size. (***Hint:*** Inventory control is one.)

2. The usual regression forecasting model assumes the trend is constant, while a more realistic model might assume a random walk on the trend. Quantitatively compare errors to be expected five or ten periods out under both types of assumptions.

3. A manufacturer of fine women's jewelry is interested in identifying the underlying causes of a salesperson's success or failure. Suppose that you accepted the project. What kinds of causal factors would you consider? How would you obtain the data?

4. What sorts of factors would you consider important in building a model to predict:

    a. The value of used computers
    b. The demand for insurance
    c. The demand for color TV sets
    d. The running time of a computer program
    e. The demand for jogging weights

5. The Sportscraft Company has been experiencing increasing demand for the last six quarters for a newly introduced jogging shoe.

    a. Draw a graph of these six pieces of data. Using a ruler, determine an approximate solution, and estimate the slope and the intercept.
    b. Compare with the exact solution. (Manually, or using the software.)
    c. Use this result to forecast demand for the next eight quarters.
    d. Do you trust the accuracy of these results?

Quarter	Demand	Quarter	Demand
1	152	4	722
2	226	5	1522
3	417	6	1837

6. A computer firm feels that sales of their PC-9.6 are sensitive both to the price and the amount of advertising (not lagged). The past data is shown in the table on the following page.

    a. Try to obtain an approximate solution by "hunt-and-peck."
    b. Solve the problem exactly, either manually or with software.
    c. What is the forecast for next year for a price of 21 and a budget of 30?

Sales	Price	Advertising Budget
17	18	28
15	20	30
14	16	27
18	24	32
15	18	27
22	29	34
15	21	30
18	22	33
17	23	35
17	20	29

2.7 Company Application Scenario— Crawly Caterpillars (Finish)

Overview. To see regression in practice, we return to Crawly Caterpillars' problem concerning forecasting for aggregate production planning. Forecasting with a horizon of one or two years is rather commonplace to make use of linear regression with causal variables such as housing starts. Much longer horizons are more likely to require major judgmental input, whereas shorter horizon problems do not typically bother with the exogenous causal variables.

In the next subsection we will carry out and discuss the forecasting process for Crawly Caterpillars' aggregate planning problem. In the final section we shall say something about the strengths and weaknesses of linear modeling in general.

Crawly Caterpillars—Regression Procedure and Results. The staff labeled the current and previous quarters as 1, 2, 3, 4, 5, 6, 7, 8, 9, 10, 11, 12 and the future quarters to be forecasted as 13, 14, 15, 16, 17, 18, 19, and 20. The independent variables included in the regression were k, the quarter past or future; H, the housing starts; and Q1, Q2, Q3, and Q4, variables indicating the quarter. The latter are called "dummy variables" and are explained in Appendix C. Here it is enough to understand that the equations Q1 = 1 and Q2 = Q3 = Q4 = 0 say nothing else but that the data is for a first quarter. The dependent variable was sales.

It is very useful to do some pre-analysis of the data. One purpose is to look for "outliers." These are individual bits of data which are so far from our expectations that we may expect a data entering error, a data gathering error, or perhaps some very unusual real event, such as a snowstorm.

If it can be shown that the outlier was caused by a mistake and the mistake can be fixed, we simply correct the mistake before running the regression. If there is an unusual

Table 2-6

Input for the Crawly Caterpillars Regression

Time k	Starts H	Q1	Q2	Q3	Q4	Actual Sales
1	50	1	0	0	0	123
2	30	0	1	0	0	136
3	10	0	0	1	0	111
4	5	0	0	0	1	42
5	60	1	0	0	0	163
6	50	0	1	0	0	170
7	15	0	0	1	0	34?
8	10	0	0	0	1	58
9	40	1	0	0	0	163
10	40	0	1	0	0	164
11	25	0	0	1	0	121
12	0	0	0	0	1	72

Number of obs.	=	12
F(6,6)	=	212.7
Prob > F	=	0.0000
R-Square	=	0.995
Adj R-square	=	0.991
Root MSE	=	12.4

Table 2-7

Regression Output for
Crawly Caterpillars

Variable	Coefficient	Std. Error	t	Prob >t
k	3.27	1.11	2.9	0.026
Starts	0.32	0.53	0.6	0.561
Q1	117.1	27.1	4.3	0.005
Q2	124.0	22.3	5.6	0.001
Q3	93.7	13.0	7.2	0.000
Q4	29.5	11.4	2.6	0.041

event (such as a snowstorm), and we don't know how large its effect is, we may decide to simply remove the point from the regression. However, there is also a danger in being too quick to remove an offending observation. For example, in the current situation we could plot the data against time. Sales of 34 at time = 7 shows up as a very bad outlier. Checking the data, sales personnel find that the number has been misentered (it should have been 134) so the value can be corrected in the data set. (Actually, even if we had not recognized this problem before the regression, plotting the errors, or residuals, afterward would still reveal the problem.) It is also clear from the pre-plot that there should be a significant trend and seasonal pattern. Because we have dummy variables, we regress, forcing the regression not to have a constant term.

The first line says the number of observations was 12. The next two lines say that the program checked whether it was possible that the overall improvement from the regression could have been at random. An F ratio with 6 and six degrees of freedom was calculated, and the ratio was 212.7, which is extremely unlikely at random within four degrees of accuracy (p value = 0.0000). R-Square = 0.995 means 99.5 percent of the variation in sales were "explained" by doing the regression. The next line calculates the adjusted R-Square which is a correction for small sample size.

Either R-Square (regular or adjusted) is almost too good, and would make one worry whether the data were phonied (which it was!). The Root Mean Square Error gives a type of average error (square root of the sum of the squares of the errors divided by the degrees of freedom for SSE) of points from the fitted regression, which was about 12, or about 10 percent of the average value of demand.

The next part of the output shows, for each independent variable, the size of its effect in the regression and how much error there likely was in estimating it. The effect (coefficient value) divided by its standard error is called the t value and measures how safe it is to say that variable is helping the regression. Roughly speaking, a t value of 2.0 or more is quite safe, those of 1.0 or below are not very safe, and those in between are in between. The final column simply gives the probability that the t value could be that large if the variable in reality added nothing to the regression.

For example, the time variable k has a coefficient of 3.3 which means the trend is estimated at 3.3 per quarter. With a t value of 2.9, it is safe to assume it belongs in the regression. The housing starts variable has a coefficient of 0.32, which means that one additional unit of 10,000 starts causes extra sales of 0.32 times one unit of 1000 sales, or 320 extra sales. However, the standard error of this coefficient is larger than the coefficient itself (t = 0.6), so there is no guarantee that it should be in the regression. All four seasonal coefficients are quite significant, and the seasonal factors behave properly quarter by quarter.

Figure 2-6

Pre-Plot of the Data Against Time

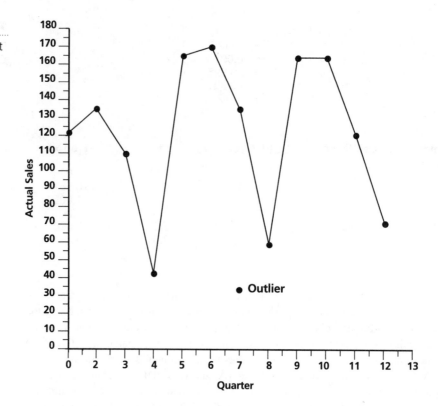

Since we have regressed without a constant, the seasonal factors will not add to zero. We can get an equivalent regression by subtracting the average value of their coefficients from each, calling this same number the constant. That is, define

$$A = (117.1 + 124.0 + 93.7 + 29.5)/4 = 91.1$$

Making these adjustments, the forecasting equation we finally get is:

$$S_{0,k} = 91.1 + 3.27k + 0.32H + 26.0Q_1 + 32.9Q_2 + 2.6Q_3 - 61.6Q_4$$

The only variable which is uncertain in this forecast equation is housing starts. All the other variables have small standard errors compared to the size of their coefficients, and hence we are very comfortable with them. But housing starts has a standard error about twice the coefficient size; we are not even sure whether, running with new data, it would have a positive or negative coefficient.

Certain experts would argue that management expected that housing starts would be important and expected a positive coefficient, which we found. The adjusted R^2 is higher with it left in, so leave it in! Other experts would counter that housing starts are really confounded with trend and seasonal factors. The latter are the important variables, so leave housing starts out.

The author tends to side with following the intuition of management and leaving it in. But it probably doesn't matter too much one way or the other. In this case, management decided to leave housing starts in the analysis, but to keep a close eye on its actual performance. Then they used the regression equation to make the forecasts for the next two years, as shown in Table 2-8. Finally, Figure 2-7 plots the errors from the regression fit for the first three years. These errors seem quite random, which they should if the regression is to be meaningful.

Crawly Caterpillars—Next Steps. At this point, the CC staff had completed step 1 of the consultant's recommendation, that is, to estimate the next eight quarters' sales by

Table 2-8

Crawly Caterpillar's
Aggregate Planning Forecast

Time k	Starts H	Q1	Q2	Q3	Q4	Forecast Sales
13	30	1	0	0	0	169
14	25	0	1	0	0	178
15	12	0	0	1	0	147
16	6	0	0	0	1	84
17	50	1	0	0	0	189
18	40	0	1	0	0	196
19	18	0	0	1	0	162
20	12	0	0	0	1	99

Figure 2-7

A Plot of the Regression
Errors

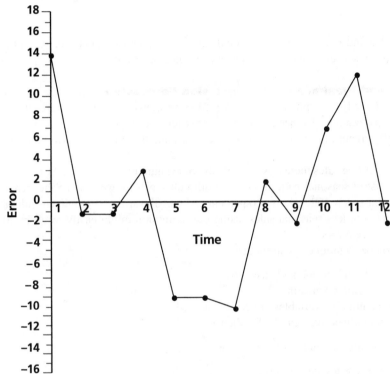

regression. step 2 seemed much more difficult: Estimate the expected forecast error on average for each of these eight forecasts.

They were aware that the mean squared error of the regression measured only retrospective fit of past data and did not accurately estimate forecasting problems. But they had no previous forecast experience to use for estimating future forecasting experience from past forecasting experience.

They did, however, have previous experience in choosing safety stocks. After some discussion they agreed that having extra stock on hand equal to 25 percent of the forecast reflected past choices quite well. The consultant agreed that this would do until the company accumulated more forecasting experience. This completed the company's make-do solution for steps 2 and 3.

Step 4 was then quite easy. The safety-adjusted demand estimates in a quarter are just the actual forecast plus (or minus) the amounts by which safety stock increased or decreased from the previous quarter. (This is the extra amount needed to adjust the safety stock.) The method also needs the entering safety stock from the last quarter previous to the forecast, which happened to be 25.

The safety-adjusted demand estimates as calculated in Table 2-9 are the actual production needed for a month if CC desires to avoid miscalculations and stockouts. Note that

Table 2-9

Adjusted Forecasts for
Planning

Time k	Forecast	Safety Stock	SS Increase	Adjusted
		25		
13	169	42	17	186
14	178	45	3	181
15	147	37	–8	139
16	84	21	–16	68
17	189	47	26	215
18	196	49	2	198
19	162	41	–8	154
20	99	25	–16	83

the adjusted demand exaggerates the seasonal pattern considerably, and hence is an important correction. These are important issues in aggregate planning.

Strengths and Weaknesses of Regression Forecasting. Over the past three years, sales at Crawly Caterpillars have increased a very consistent 10 to 12 percent a year. The seasonal pattern has also been extremely consistent. Average fitting errors have been only about 10 percent of the forecast. Is it safe to assume that the future will behave this nicely?

Not really. Strong sales increases have a habit of eventually leveling off. Also, extreme weather can distort seasonal patterns. If, as a difficult scenario, we assume the trend for the next two years were to level off at 6 percent and global warming brought considerably milder winters with less seasonal sales, using our regression might easily result in 20 to 30 percent average errors.

Regression has a number of strengths:

1. It is well understood and easy to use.
2. It is extremely versatile.
3. Nonquantitative variables are easily handled.
4. Many nonlinearities can be handled.

But there are also a number of weaknesses:

1. It is perhaps too easy to use.
2. Linearity and independence are strong and unrealistic assumptions.
3. Fitting the past gets confused with forecasting the future.

With all these caveats, econometric regression remains a very powerful tool for middle range horizon problems.

Tactical Forecasting—Smoothing

3.1 INTRODUCTION

The tactical and requirements forecasting issues we will explore here in Chapter 3 are characterized by:

- a. Very short to short horizons of one week to twelve months, with a typical horizon of six to twelve weeks
- b. Low dollar value and multiple item forecasts
- c. Relatively routine forecasting

Thus, the focus here will be on low to middle effort, very standardized mechanized time series forecasting, with little input from outside causal factors, and only occasional human interaction to correct special situations.

Forecasting Chapter 3 develops tactical/requirements forecasting from both a theoretical and a practical point of view. First, in Section 3.2 a general introduction to smoothing is given and three different time series methods are presented. In Section 3.3 a company application scenario is presented, representing a firm which must control a large number of individual items. In Section 3.4 trend and seasonal corrections are developed; while in Section 3.5 the company scenario is re-introduced, and a tentative solution is presented.

Appendix D discusses estimating seasonal factors, Appendix E discusses models which treat multiple products simultaneously, and Appendix F gives smoothing methods for estimating forecast errors. The associated POMQuest software supports this material.

3.2 SMOOTHING BASICS

3.2.1 Introduction

Overview. In this chapter we are concentrating on short-term demand forecasting. A typical situation is the following: Inventory levels for a number of individual products are reviewed weekly, bi-weekly, or monthly by computer, and demand forecasts are updated. Enough of a product must be ordered to both cover demand and avoid possible stockouts before the next order arrives. If we are about to place an order, the next order won't be placed for two weeks. The lead time for that next order to arrive is five weeks, so our current forecast must make a good estimate of "average" and "near maximum" demand over the next 7 (2 + 5) weeks until the next order can arrive. It is characteristic of the inventory control problem that repeated estimates are needed of the *distribution* (in order to estimate the maximum "reasonable" demand) of demand over a period of weeks longer than the interval between updating the forecast. Actually, it suffices typically to make a "point" estimate (average demand) and a "range" for that forecast. (We might estimate sales of 300, but feel 90 percent sure that sales will be between 250 and 350, for example.)

Regression.   Recall that in the last chapter we made forecasts, similar to those needed here, by regression, basically by fitting to the data a straight line which minimizes the average squared error. The slope of the regression line estimates the trend, or rate of growth of the demand mean. The height of the regression at the current time estimates the de-randomized current demand level. The residual variance about the line gives us a good idea of the fitting errors in using this line to interpolate (forecast) demand for other times in the past. Remember that we have said that because there is no guarantee that the future will be like the past, this residual variance should not usually be used directly to estimate our future forecasting errors.

Curvilinear Fits.   Sometimes forecasters fit more complicated curves, such as a parabola, to the data. However, if your knowledge of the underlying process generating the demand is scanty, this can actually give much worse forecasts than a simpler model.

Moving averages and exponential smoothing are widely used for the short-range forecasting problem; conventional linear regression is typically not used. This is true for several reasons:

Figure 3-1

The Regression Approach to Forecasting

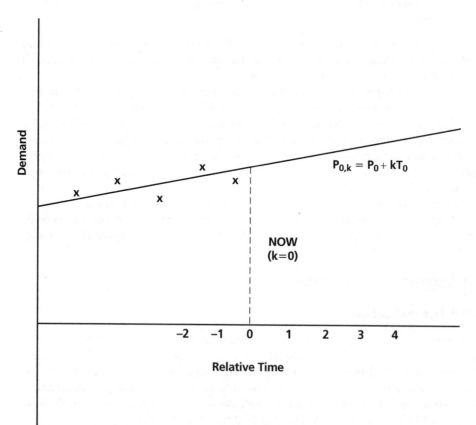

$$P_{0,k} = P_0 + kT_0$$

NOW (k=0)

Relative Time

Figure 3-2

Danger of Curvilinear Fits

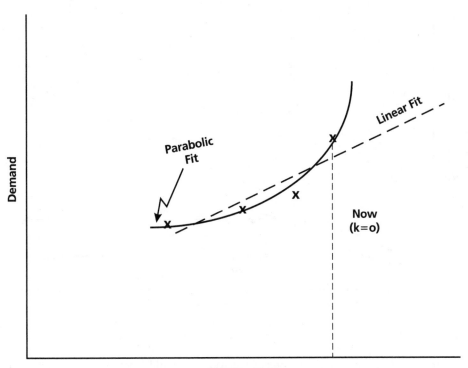

a. Conventional regression treats all of the demand history as equally important in making the forecast, while in practice old information is often of relatively little value, due to changes in competitive position, product obsolescence, and so forth. Thus, a technique is needed which weights recent history more heavily.

b. Just as one may prefer a simple linear regression to a fancier parabolic regression when the process is poorly understood, so one may even prefer to act as if the trend is zero when the trend is small by comparison with the randomness or if the trend is quite unstable and rapidly changing.

c. Since large numbers of products (perhaps as many as 100,000) are being forecast once or twice a month, the procedure should be relatively simple in terms of computer storage and computational cost. Both moving averages and exponential smoothing have much lower computational costs than does regression. In addition, exponential smoothing has very low storage requirements.

Actually, in today's environment, when a single personal computer may easily have a several gigabyte disk storage drive, with plug-in additional drives, and computational speeds are measured in megaflops, issues of computation time and speeds for regression are probably much less relevant. The other issues can be attended to also. For instance, regression can easily be modified so that the importance to the regression (weights) decreases smoothly going back in time. If the weights are decreased geometrically, this is called **discounted regression**. Discounted regression actually behaves quite similarly to exponential smoothing and is also very flexible since it allows all sorts of econometric variables and adjustments to be made if desired.

3.2.2 Level Demand

Moving Averages. The idea of the moving average is very simple: the effect of randomness is reduced by averaging together a number of observations. The problem of old data is dealt with by averaging only over a recent interval of periods, such as six months or a year. If the averaging is done weekly, then each week one newly experienced demand will

Figure 3-3

Dangers of Extrapolating a Trend

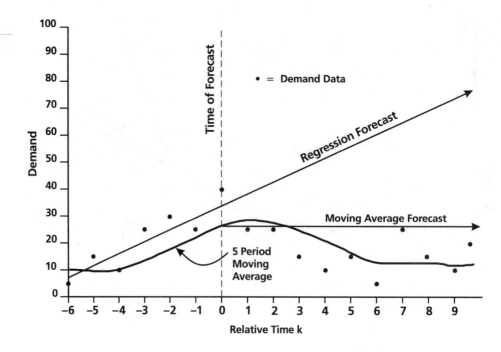

be averaged in and one at the beginning of the averaging will be dropped. Hence the term "moving average."

In formal terms, let

$$\ldots, D_{t-4}, D_{t-3}, D_{t-2}, D_{t-1}, D_t$$

be the record (time series) of past demand, where D_t has just been experienced, D_{t-1} is last period's demand, and so forth. Suppose N is chosen as the number of periods to average. Let $P_{t,j}$ (P for prediction) mean "the forecast, made at the end of time t, for expected demand in period $t + j$." For convenience, we write $P_{t,0} = P_t$, the prediction for period t. It is very important to notice that P_t is *not* the definition of the forecast for period $t + 1$; that is written $P_{t,1}$. P_t is the forecast for period t, which has already experienced the demand D_t! It may seem strange to talk about forecasting a period already finished. But P_t is our estimate of **de-randomized** demand; it is our "hindcast" of what demand "should" have been without the random component.

In general, we distinguish between the forecast P_t, and the moving average F_t. P_t may be corrected for seasonality or trend, or any of a number of other things, while the moving average is simply that:

$$F_t = (1/N)(D_{t-N+1} + \ldots + D_{t-1} + D_t) = (1/N)\sum_{i=1,N} D_{t-i+1} \tag{1}$$

or

$$F_t = F_{t-1} + (1/N)(D_t - D_{t-N}) \tag{2}$$

[(2) is obtained from (1) by replacing t by $t - 1$ in (1) and then subtracting the second equation from the first.] The forecasts for the various periods are given by:

$$P_t = F_t \tag{3a}$$
$$P_{t,j} = F_t \tag{3b}$$

If we forecast weekly and a moving average of six months is used, then $N = 26$. Equation (1) says that the current moving average is produced by averaging the last 26 demands. Equation (2) is produced from equation (1) by subtracting equation (1) for $t - 1$ from equation (1) for t. This produces an equivalent but simpler looking expression which tells how the average changes from week to week. In words, "the new average is equal to the previous average plus a fraction of the amount by which current demand per week has increased from the demand of six months ago." Note that, in engineering terms, $(D_t - D_{t-N})$ may be considered an error signal, and that we add a portion of the error signal to the previous moving average to obtain the new one. Equation (3) says that the forecast for this or any future week is simply equal to the moving average; no trend corrections or seasonal factors are involved here.

What size N should we use? There is no simple answer because there is a tradeoff between two objectives. A large value of N will average out randomness better, but will also cause the moving average to respond more slowly to permanent changes in demand. In practice, one might choose N by one of several procedures. One would be to simply choose N similar to that used for similar items in the industry; that is, by experience. Another would be to simulate the effect of using different Ns on a large amount of past data on the computer, choosing the one giving the lowest mean square error or perhaps the one giving the best performance in helping to manage an inventory system. (A third would be to specify formally a mathematical process generating the demand and solve the problem theoretically.) We cannot definitely solve the problem of how to set N here; however, it is very instructive to see how the forecasting system would respond with various N's to several different kinds of simple pure demand input situations, which are illustrated in Figure 3-4.

(a) Horizontal — demand remains constant indefinitely

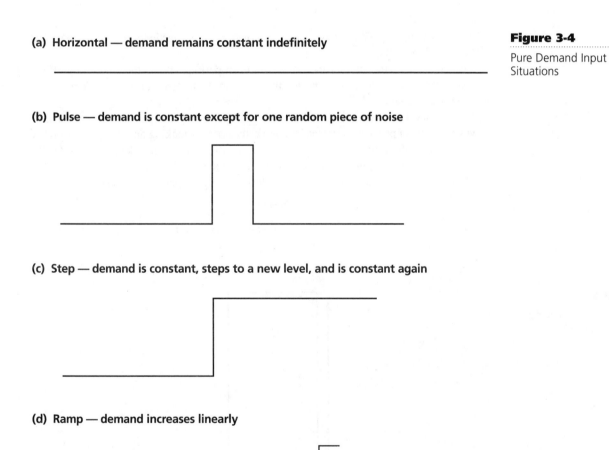

Figure 3-4

Pure Demand Input Situations

(b) Pulse — demand is constant except for one random piece of noise

(c) Step — demand is constant, steps to a new level, and is constant again

(d) Ramp — demand increases linearly

In case (a), where demand is horizontal, we have

$$D_j \text{ identically} = D \text{ for all } j \tag{4a}$$

and, hence,

$$F_t = (1/N)\Sigma_{i=1,N}(D) = D \tag{4b}$$

Thus, independent of N, the moving average gets the "right" answer, as we would certainly insist. We say the moving average is "unbiased."

In case (b), where there is a pulse of amount E in period t, we would have:

$$D_j \text{ identically} = D \text{ all } j \text{ except } j = t$$

$$D_t = D + E$$

Then it is easily seen that

$$\ldots F_{t-3} = F_{t-2} = F_{t-1} \qquad = D \tag{5a}$$

$$F_t = F_{t+1} = \ldots = F_{t+N-1} = D + (1/N)E \tag{5b}$$

$$F_{t+N} = F_{t+N+1} \cdots \qquad = D \tag{5c}$$

That is, an error of E/N persists for a total of N periods, starting with the pulse period as shown in Figure 3-5.

The larger N is, the smaller the error is in each period. This is the smoothing effect. However, the smaller N is, the shorter the time until the error disappears. This is the responsiveness effect.

Notice that the *total* error for all periods is $N(E/N) = E$ and is not influenced by N! However, for most purposes, such as inventory, the costs of making an error go up roughly as the square of the error, so that for a pulse, the cost is something like $N(E/N)^2$ or E^2/N. Thus for a pure pulse, (pure noise) the larger the value of N the better.

In case (c), where there is a permanent step of size E in period t we have

$$D_j = D \qquad \text{for } j < t$$

$$D_j = D + E \quad \text{for } j >= t$$

Figure 3-5

Moving Average Response
to a Random Pulse

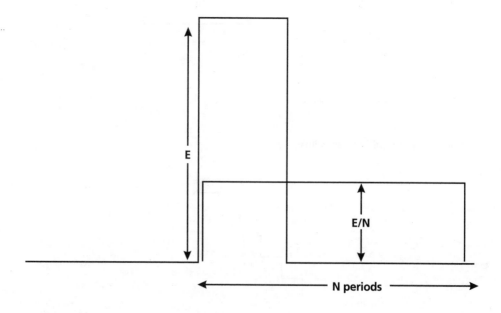

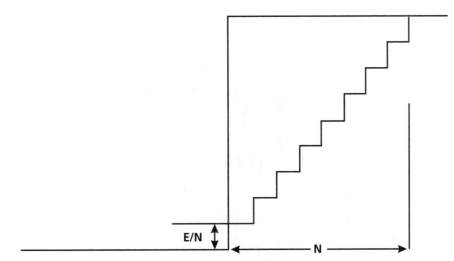

Figure 3-6

Moving Average Response
to a Step

Here a little algebra shows that

$$\ldots = F_{t-2} = F_{t-1} = D \tag{6a}$$

$$F_t = D + (1/N)E, \ F_{t+1} = D + (2/N)E, \ \ldots \ F_{t+N-2} = D + [(N-1)/N]E \tag{6b}$$

$$F_{t+N-1} = F_{t+N} = \ldots = D + E \tag{6c}$$

In this case it is clear that the *smaller* the value of N the better. (Given a mean square error criterion, an exercise asks you to quantify this statement.)

Finally, in case (d), suppose demand is increasing by an amount T (for trend) in each period; that is:

$$D_{t+j} = D_t + jT$$

Then we have

$$Ft = (1/N)\sum_{i=1,N}[D_t - (i-1)T]$$

$$= D_t - [1/N][\sum_{i=0,N-1}i]T$$

$$= D_t - [(N-1)/2]T$$

That is, the forecast lags demand permanently by an amount $(N-1)T/2$, as shown in Figure 3-7. Another way of putting it is that for a six-month moving average and a linear trend, the moving average is always lagging current demand by about three months. (This is certainly reasonable, since the average age of the data being used is three months.) Here too, the smaller the value of N the better, for a perfect constant trend. It would seem important if there is a consistent trend, to correct the moving average for this lag.

As we have stated before, the moving average has the disadvantage that N demands must be kept in active storage for each product. Using (2) does not avoid the problem; we still will have had to have D_{t-N} stored for the last N periods to be able to use it in period t. Given today's computer capabilities, this storage problem is not as serious as it was 30 years ago. Thus we will want to compare the advantages and disadvantages of moving averages with other methods along other dimensions as well.

A different kind of reason moving averages seem a bit clumsy is that we weight the last N demands at a constant weight $1/N$ and suddenly drop the weight to zero for demands further back. Perhaps it seems intuitive that smoothly decreasing weights on the demands would be better.

Figure 3-7

Moving Average Response
to a Trend

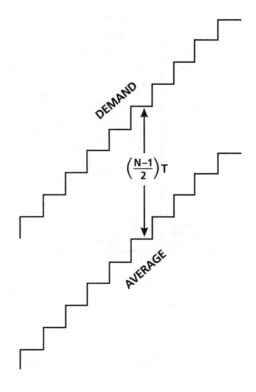

Trying to implement this intuitive idea leads to the concept of a general weighted average. Consider a set of weights which add to 1.0, such as: 0.5, 0.3, 0.2, 0.1, 0.05, 0.0, 0.0, . . . The general weighted (moving) average rule associated with these weights would be:

$$F_t = 0.5D_t + 0.3D_{t-1} + 0.2D_{t-2} + 0.1D_{t-3} + 0.05D_{t-4} \cdots \qquad (7)$$

Symbolically, a general weighted average can be defined as follows:

$$F_t = \Sigma_{i=1,\inf} w_i D_{t+1-i} \qquad (8a)$$

where

$$\Sigma_{i=1,\inf} w_i = 1.0 \qquad (8b)$$

(Note that we will never have demands going all the way back to time t equal to minus infinity. However, if we truncate a number of terms whose coefficients add only 0.0001, for example, little harm is done.)

Exponential Smoothing. Exponential smoothing is a second major forecasting method which has become very popular in the last 35 years or so. It doesn't require much computer storage per item being forecast and weights past information in a smoothly decreasing way further into the past. (Nevertheless, the simple moving average has some advantages, such as the ease of understanding of top management.)

With exponential smoothing, the only two pieces of data needed are the previous period's forecast and the latest demand. We simply average together the last moving average and the latest demand using weights adding to 1.0 as shown in equation (9):

$$F_t = (1 - \alpha)F_{t-1} + \alpha D_t \qquad (9)$$

or

$$F_t = F_{t-1} + \alpha(D_t - F_{t-1}) \qquad (10)$$

As with the simple moving average, the forecasts are given by:

$$P_t = F_t \tag{11a}$$

$$P_{t,j} = F_t \tag{11b}$$

The smoothing constant α must be chosen by those using the forecasting system, and allows a tradeoff between quick response and smooth response, much as N did for the moving average.

Equation (10) is just a slight rearrangement of equation (9), and shows that exponential smoothing may be considered to add a fraction of an error signal to the old forecast, exactly as equation (2) showed was the case for the moving average. In fact comparing the two equations shows that α and $1/N$ play very similar roles. (We shall actually show that two such systems setting α about at $2/N$ behave very similarly to each other.) Equations (11a) and (11b) are identical to (3a) and (3b) for moving averages.

Equation (1) shows that moving averages are a special type of a general weighted average. It is not at first obvious from equation (9) that exponential smoothing is also a kind of general weighted average, but with smoothly decreasing weights. We show this next. We work with equation (9) repeatedly, substituting it into itself for earlier values of t:

$$F_t = \alpha D_t + (1 - \alpha)F_{t-1}$$

$$= \alpha D_t + (1 - \alpha)[\alpha D_{t-1} + (1 - \alpha)F_{t-2}]$$

$$= \alpha D_t + (1 - \alpha)\alpha D_{t-1} + (1 - \alpha)^2[\alpha D_{t-2} + (1 - \alpha)F_{t-3}]$$

$$\cdots$$

$$F_t = \alpha D_t + \alpha\beta D_{t-1} + \alpha\beta^2 D_{t-2} + \alpha\beta^3 D_{t-3} \cdots \tag{12}$$

where $\beta = 1 - \alpha$

Thus the weights decrease in a decreasing geometric fashion going back in time. In the limit, with many very short periods, the weights would decay in an exponential fashion, which is the continuous analog to geometric decay. Hence the name "exponential smoothing." (It is left as an exercise to show that the weights α, $\alpha\beta$, $\alpha\beta^2$, . . . add to 1.0.) Thus equation (9) is equivalent to equation (12), so that both the moving average in (1) and exponential smoothing in (9) are seen as special cases of general weighted averages.

How does one choose a good α in practice? Some authors would say "$\alpha = 0.1$ is reasonable." However, this is quite *unreasonable*, since the appropriate α depends on the length of the period (forecasting frequency) chosen. That would be like saying "set N equal 26" without knowing whether the period length was a day, a week, or a month! Yet moving averages of 26 days and 26 months are very different indeed. As before, one can utilize experience, simulation, or theoretical methods to set α. Or if N is known reasonably well, α can accurately be approximated (as shown below) by $\alpha = 2/N$. For example, a rather typical N of six months translates to an α of about 0.08 on a weekly basis, or about 0.01 on a daily basis.

We turn now to studying the response of exponential smoothing to various simple demand input situations, as we did for moving averages. In the horizontal case we have:

$$F_t = [\Sigma_{i=1,\inf}\alpha(1 - \alpha)^{i-1}]D = D \tag{13}$$

Hence exponential smoothing is also unbiased, irrespective of the α chosen.

In the second case, where there is a "noise" pulse of amount E in period t, it can be seen that:

$$\ldots = F_{t-2} = F_{t-1} = D \tag{14a}$$

$$F_t = D + \alpha E, \quad F_{t+1} = D + \alpha(1 - \alpha)E, \ldots, F_{t+j} = D + \alpha(1 - \alpha)^j E \tag{14b}$$

Note that the maximum error is in period t and is of size αE; the error dies geometrically by fraction $(1 - \alpha)$ each period thereafter. It is left to the exercises to show that the total error over all periods due to the pulse is E, as for the moving average (as in Figure 3.8). Thus,

Figure 3-8

Exponential Smoothing
Response to a Pulse

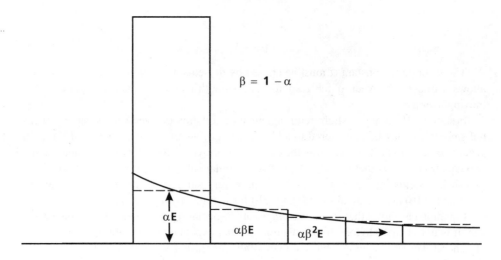

clearly, the smaller α the better in the case of pure random noise. (It is also left to the exercises to evaluate the total error cost as a function of a when costs are proportional to the square of the error.)

In the third case, where demand increases permanently in a step fashion (as in Figure 3.9) from D to $D + E$ at period t (notice at the end of period t we don't know whether E is noise or step!) we can see that:

$$\ldots = F_{t-2} = F_{t-1} = D \tag{15a}$$

$$F_t = (D + E) - (1 - \alpha)E, \, F_{t+1} = (D + E) - (1 - \alpha)^2 E, \ldots \tag{15b}$$

That is, the errors are $\beta E, \beta^2 E, \beta^3 E, \ldots$ where, as before, $\beta = 1 - \alpha$. It is easily seen that the total errors are $[(1 - \alpha)/\alpha]E$. Thus, for a permanent change of size E we want α as large as possible, for the quickest possible response.

Figure 3-9

Exponential Smoothing
Response to a Step

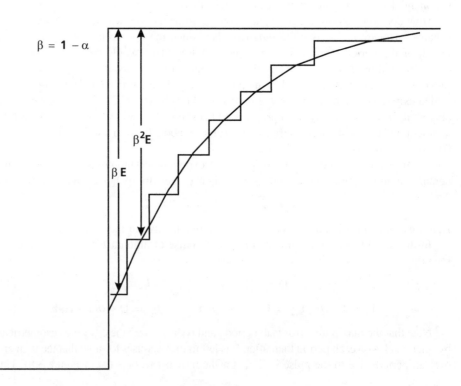

Finally, in the fourth case, where demand increases by a perfect trend of size T (as in Figure 3-10), so that $D_{t+j} = D + (j - t + 1)T$, we have:

$$F_t = \sum_{i=1,\inf} \alpha(1 - \alpha)^{i-1}[D - (i - 1)T]$$

$$= D - \alpha \sum_{i=1,\inf} i(1 - \alpha)^i T$$

$$= D - \alpha \left[\sum_{i=1,\inf} i(1 - \alpha)^i \right] T$$

It is left to an exercise to show the term in the brackets sums to $(1 - \alpha)/\alpha^2$. Hence finally we have:

$$F_t = D - [(1 - \alpha)/\alpha]T \tag{16}$$

So, while for the moving average case the lag was $(N - 1)/2$ periods in equilibrium, for exponential smoothing the lag is $(1 - \alpha)/\alpha$ periods. If we equate the two lags, we get a rather good way to get an equivalent N for a given α, or an equivalent α for a given N:

$$(N - 1)/2 = (1 - \alpha)/\alpha$$

yielding

$$N = (2 - \alpha)/\alpha \text{ or equivalently } \alpha = 2/(N + 1) \tag{17}$$

or approximately (say, if $\alpha < 0.1$)

$$N = 2/\alpha \text{ or } \alpha = 2/N \tag{18}$$

The student will have the opportunity, using the software, to compare the results of exponential smoothing and simple moving averages using "equivalent" smoothing factors.

Discounted Regression. There is an intimate connection between regression forecasting, which we studied in Forecasting Chapter 2, and moving averages and exponential smoothing. Suppose we wish to fit the last N periods of demand using regression. That is, we wish to find constants P_t and T_t to make an appropriate forecasting equation $P_{t,k} = P_t + T_t k$. Thus we want to choose P_t and T_t to:

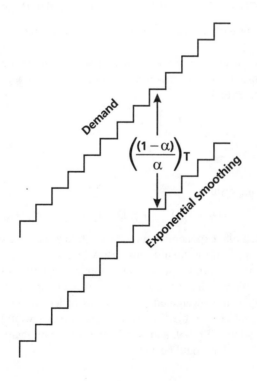

$$\min \Sigma_{k=0,N-1}[(P_t - T_t k) - D_{t-k}]^2 \qquad (19)$$

In the moving average and exponential smoothing models of this section we have been looking at the stationary demand situation where the trend is small and/or unstable, so that we wish to suppress it; that is, treat it as zero. Suppressing it in the regression minimization equation leads to:

$$\min \Sigma_{k=0,N-1}[(P_t - D_{t-k}]^2 \qquad (20)$$

Taking the derivative of this expression with respect to P_t and setting it equal to zero leads directly to the equation:

$$P_t = (1/N)(D_t + D_{t-1} + \ldots + D_{t-N+1})$$

This is just equation (1). Regression over N periods with suppressed trend is identical to a simple moving average over N periods.

Of course, simply averaging the last N periods of demand is less complicated than running a regression each period with suppressed trend. This is, in fact, the main reason regression is less often used in short term forecasting. On the other hand, regression is extremely flexible and can easily incorporate all sorts of other effects. For example, a week with a holiday in it can be coded with a dummy variable to handle the holiday effect. This, and the fact that computational speeds have increased so greatly, makes regression a viable choice in practice.

As an example of the flexibility of regression, suppose that we feel the demand data is of decreasing relevance to our current decision as we look back into the past. Suppose that $N = 6$, and that we consider the relative importances of the last six demands to be 0.37, 0.25, 0.15, 0.10, 0.08, 0.05. Then the equation to minimize the squared errors weighted by their importance would be:

$$\min[0.37(P_t - D_t)^2 + 0.25(P_t - D_{t-1})^2 + \ldots + 0.05(P_t - D_{t-5})^2]$$

Taking the derivative with respect to P_t and setting it equal to zero leads us to the result:

$$P_t = 0.37D_t + 0.25D_{t-1} + 0.15D_{t-2} + 0.10D_{t-3} + 0.08D_{t-4} + 0.05D_{t-5}$$

This is identical to our earlier idea of a general weighted average, now limited to a fixed number of terms.

As an important special case, suppose we assume the appropriate weights on past data go down in importance by a geometrical factor. In particular, suppose the weights for the N demand points are given by:

$$\alpha, \alpha\beta, \alpha\beta^2, \ldots, \alpha\beta^{N-1}$$

where

$$\beta = (1 - \alpha)$$

This would give us the result:

$$P_t = \alpha D_t + \alpha\beta D_{t-1} + \alpha\beta^2 D_{t-2} + \ldots + \alpha\beta^{N-1}D_{t-N+1} \qquad (21)$$

This looks very much like exponential smoothing. In fact we have exactly equation (12) except we have chopped off the small terms past N in that series.

We must be a little careful, because of the chopped off terms. Our weights no longer quite add up to 1.0. We would have to scale these weights up by the factor $1/(1 - \beta^N)$ in the regression. The resulting weighted regression is called **discounted regression**. The larger N and/or α is, of course, the less the correction factor would differ from 1.0. For example, if $\alpha = 0.1$ so that $\beta = 0.9$, and $N = 25$ the correction factor would be 1.077; for $N = 50$ the correction factor would be 1.005.

If we idealized the regression with geometrically declining weights to have an infinite number of terms, then the result obtained would be identical to exponential smoothing. We call such an idealized regression **infinite discounted regression**. (If it seems likely to cause no confusion we will simply call it discounted regression also.) We see that discounted regression with only a constant term and no trend term is identical to exponential smoothing. The smoothing factor α corresponds to the geometrically declining importance, [with factor $(1 - \alpha)$] of demands as one looks back into the past.

In practice we would likely limit ourselves to perhaps 25 terms for $\alpha = 0.1$, and make the correction to make weights add to 1.0. The results obtained from such a finite discounted regression and from exponential smoothing are nearly indistinguishable. We study this issue in the exercises.

One of the advantages of discounted regression is the very fact that all the old demand data is saved and available. The user may wish to inspect old data for outliers, or increase demand by 20 percent for periods in the third quarter, due to suspected under-reporting or the like. Or the data may span the end of one customer catalog and the start of the next. In this case, the user may, in retrospect, desire to discount data more heavily in the previous catalog than the formulas suggest and to give weight to the buyer's initial forecast for the new catalog. Or the user may desire to use dummy variables to add a day of the week effect, a weather effect, or a temperature effect. Thus, it would seem that the great flexibility of discounted regression makes it a very viable alternative. The actual choice between moving average, exponential smoothing, and regression is a matter of judgment and skill of the human forecaster in an individual situation.

3.2.3 Level Demand Exercises

1. A kitchen appliance company forecasts coffeemaker sales by using a weighted average of the last four periods of data (decreasing going further into the past): .5, .3, .1, .1. Time series data for coffeemakers are:

Time:	1	2	3	4	5	6	7	8
Sales:	23	30	39	32	28	40	30	25

   a. At the end of period 8 what is the forecast for the next period?
   b. What was the previous period's forecast for period 6?

2. Using simple moving average techniques, determine a forecast for periods 1 to 20. Graphically compare your forecast with the actual. Let $N = 10$, and assume

$$D_0 = D_{-1} = \ldots = D_{-9} = 140$$

Period	Demand	Period	Demand
1	140	11	39
2	130	12	142
3	145	13	132
4	41	14	161
5	131	15	112
6	140	16	142
7	137	17	151
8	162	18	157
9	143	19	153
10	131	20	138

3. Repeat problem 2 with $N = 4$.
4. Repeat problem 2 for exponential smoothing with

$$F_0 = 140 \text{ and } \alpha = 0.2$$

5.   Repeat problem 4 for exponential smoothing with $\alpha = 0.5$.
6.   Compute the mean square error for each solution in problems 2 through 5. Which pairs of methods are the most similar? Which one performs the best?
7.   Consider a weighted moving average system where the weights decrease linearly to zero N periods in the past.

   a.   Prove it to be unbiased.
   b.   Derive the reaction to a pulse.
   c.   Derive the reaction to a step.
   d.   Derive the reaction to a perfect trend.

8.   If $\beta = 1 - \alpha$, show the exponential weights α, $\alpha\beta$, $\alpha\beta^2$, . . . add to 1.0.

3.3 COMPANY APPLICATION SCENARIO—CLIFTON WARDS

Clifton Wards is a large chain of wholesale outlets and warehouses which resupplies almost every aspect of retail stores. It is famous for carrying "everything under the sun." It is equally famous for rarity of stockouts and for aggressive expediting and resupply when stockouts do occur.

At the heart of Clifton Wards' operations management system is a large scale monthly-review forecasting and inventory control system with over 130,000 individual items. Each item must be forecast, reordered, expedited (if necessary), and so on, on a repetitive monthly basis. There is also an emergency reactive system which protects against major forecasting errors showing up between regular forecasts.

Wards carries 36 months of demand history for each item, giving a demand file of 4,680,000 individual demands. In addition, the file contains demand histories by families and by lines (groups of families). Forecast errors are also saved by individual item and month, as well as a fair amount of lesser storage, leading to the full forecast file of about 11,000,000 entries. This is not a large problem as fairly common disk sizes for personal computers are measured in gigabytes. (It is also possible to dedicate each disk to one line by using a plug-in disk system as well.) It does impose considerable requirements in terms of backup procedures and in cross-checking the integrity of the database.

The company as a whole does not have one single forecasting system, but several for different purposes. These are not well integrated. For example, marketing needs to make aggregate forecasts for each of 346 lines. It makes these forecasts using simple moving averages, sometimes corrected for trend and/or seasonality. It has been found that the marketing VP understands moving averages the best; in fact, he insists on this approach.

Middle volume items, and/or reasonably high volume items, of which there are about 50,000, are forecasted using exponential smoothing on an item by item basis. Getting decent seasonal patterns for these items is very difficult, since seasons shift somewhat from year to year, and adjusting this many patterns manually does not seem feasible.

The remaining 80,000 items do not contribute much directly to total profits, but must be maintained to keep the full service image which Wards prizes. Individual forecasts have not typically been kept for this type of item. Aggregate forecasts are made for the 20 to 100 types of items forming a "group" (for example wing tip shoes of all sizes and colors), and demand and inventory records are kept item by item. The aggregate forecast allows setting a stocking level for the **group**. Comparing the overall inventory for the group with the desired level gives a group order. Then the computer roughly distributes that order to individual items by their relative need.

Clifton Wards is not very satisfied with the current forecasting and inventory control system. The different parts of the system are not very compatible with each other, and there seems to be far too much overstock and simultaneously too much stockout on the low value items. The CEO decides to hire some outstanding person with an MBA and a good background to redesign the system.

The CEO hires Sammita Spade, a bright young recent graduate with a good background in operations management and systems design, and tells her to take two or three months and come up with a good comprehensive proposal. She spends a few weeks talking to everyone in the plant, reviewing her forecasting and inventory notes, and formulating an initial plan. She talks this initial impression over privately with the CEO, so as not to arouse any opposition prematurely. The CEO asks her to develop the ideas more completely and to devise some sort of preliminary testing. They agree to give Sammita six months, after which she is to make a really strong presentation to the others.

3.4 TRENDS AND SEASONALITY

3.4.1 Overview

In tactical or short term forecasting, simpler models are often better, which is one reason we have given a great deal of emphasis to stationary smoothing models. For example, in demand series with a small- to medium-sized trend, but with large amounts of random noise, we may fit noise and mistake it for a trend, as shown in Figure 3-3 on page F–36. At the same time, if we do stationary exponential smoothing with no trend, we know the forecast lags by about $[(1 - \alpha)/\alpha]T$. With $\alpha = 0.1$ and weekly periods, this is a lag of about nine weeks. In a typical inventory system, nine weeks of growth may represent 1 or 2 percent error in the forecast, which is easily absorbed in the inventory safety stock.

Similarly, if we desire to build a fancier model which corrects for the fact that demand has peaks and valleys during the year, that is, seasonality, it may not be worthwhile to correct for items which have no peaks and valleys that are more than, say, 30 percent above and below the yearly average. This is especially true if there is a great deal of noise in the demand and/or if the size and timing of the peaks shifts rather dramatically from year to year.

With all these caveats, models that correct for trend and seasonality can be extremely useful. One way to get around the problem of too much noise is to make a grouped forecast of a number of similar products, which tends to average out the noise. These ideas are discussed in Appendix E. Another idea is to present both corrected and uncorrected forecasts to the user, who can compromise between the two views using a simple user interface (DSS).

Summary and Preview. In Section 3.4.2 we present and discuss trend-corrected exponential smoothing models, and point out briefly that trend correction models are also easily constructed for moving averages, and discounted regression. A development of these models is left to the exercises. In Section 3.4.3 we develop and analyze the basic seasonal factor models for exponential smoothing, again leaving details of the extension of moving averages and discounted regression to the exercises. Next we discuss methods for estimating seasonal factors. Section 3.4.4 gives trend and seasonal exercises.

3.4.2 Trend Correction

Let us develop our trend method rather intuitively. Suppose the trend has been relatively constant for some length of time, and we have been doing simple exponential smoothing, that is:

$$F_t = F_{t-1} + \alpha(D_t - F_{t-1}) \tag{22}$$

Then by the analysis of Section 3.2, this moving average is lagging the trend-corrected moving average by $[(1 - \alpha)/\alpha]T_t$ where T_t is the trend. Thus, if we knew the true trend, and that it was stable, we could make a trend corrected version P_t of the moving average by

$$P_t = F_t + [(1 - \alpha)/\alpha]T_t \tag{23}$$

Unfortunately, we do not know the trend. But why can we not update an estimate of the trend every period, just as for the moving average? If the trend has persisted for some while, the *moving average difference* $\Delta F_t = (F_t - F_{t-1})$ should be a good "new observation" estimate of the trend. Thus the complete trend-corrected system we obtain is:

$$F_t = F_{t-1} + \alpha(D_t - F_{t-1}) \tag{24a}$$

$$T_t = T_{t-1} + \beta(\Delta F_t - T_{t-1}) \tag{24b}$$

$$P_t = F_t + [(1 - \alpha)/\alpha]T_t \tag{24c}$$

$$P_{t,j} = P_t + jT_t \tag{24d}$$

Table 3-1 illustrates the calculation of the forecasting model in practice. It is also designed to show the danger of model overshoot if the trend is not stable. Note that P_t is well behaved while the trend is well-behaved, but overshoots (or undershoots) markedly when the trend changes sharply. Note also that the overshoot is much stronger when the apparent trend is extrapolated into the future, as for $P_{t,10}$.

We turn now very briefly to trend correction for moving averages. Trend-corrected versions of simple moving averages bear a very close relationship to the comparable equations for exponential smoothing. This can be seen for the stationary case by comparing equations (2) and (10) in Section 3.2.2. Basically, α and $1/N$ correspond. Also $(D_t - F_{t-1})$ and $(D_t - D_{t-N})$ correspond. Here we have N_1 corresponding to α and N_2 to β. Given these direct correspondences, you will be asked to create the equation system equivalent to (24) in the exercises.

Note that discounted regression is automatically already corrected for trend.

3.4.3 Seasonal Correction

For many items, sales peak predictably at certain times of the year. For example, children's clothes sell heavily at Easter, at back-to-school time, and at Christmas. If these peaks for a given item yield rather predictable additional sales (additive seasonal factors) or rather predictable multiples of usual sales (multiplicative seasonal factors), then the corresponding seasonal factors may be calculated externally and simply inserted into the forecasting model. When these peaks are somewhat less predictable, we may wish to forecast them by smoothing along with the basic model, in much the same way that we forecast trend. Forecasting is somewhat more difficult, however, since, if we wish to forecast the "November" effect, we have only three observations in the last three years to go on, and the effect of data aging will become extreme before we can smooth out the unwanted noise in the past November sales.

We first assume that the seasonal factors are known, for simplicity (that is, they were estimated by someone else first). Again we concentrate on exponential smoothing. The assumption that November sales have a seasonal amount (factor) *added* to normal sales is called the additive model. If it is assumed that the factor *multiplies* normal sales, it is called the multiplicative model. We will work with additive factors first, and then show that modifications to produce multiplicative factors are very minor.

Table 3-1

Example of Trend Overshoot

				$\alpha = \beta = 0.1$				
t	1	2	3	4	5	6	7	8
D_t	14	15	16	15	14	13	12	11
F_t	5.0	6.0	7.0	7.8	8.4	8.9	9.2	9.4
T_t	1.0	1.0	1.0	0.98	0.94	0.90	0.84	0.77
P_t	14.0	15.0	16.0	16.6	16.9	16.9	16.7	16.3
$P_{t,10}$	24.0	25.0	26.0	26.4	26.4	25.9	25.1	24.0

In the additive model we assume we have available additive corrective factors a_j, which give the amount extra which is expected to be sold in period j beyond that in a "normal" or average period. It is clear that these factors should sum to zero over a year's time. We define F_t as the current smoothed estimate of the amount to be sold in a normal period; that is, we smooth a "normalized" series of demand. Each demand is first deseasonalized by subtracting the a_t appropriate for that period. Then the deseasonalized series is smoothed to obtain the new deseasonalized moving average. We get a reseasonalized prediction for any future period by adding back the additive factor for that period to our current best estimate of normalized demand. This gives the following set of equations:

$$F_t = F_{t-1} + \alpha[(D_t - a_t) - F_{t-1}] \tag{25a}$$

$$P = F_t + a_t \tag{25b}$$

$$P_{t,k} = F_t + a_{t+k} \tag{25c}$$

Note that, due to inaccuracies in this model and demand data input, forecasts could be produced which the decision maker knows are unreasonably small for a period. A typical way this might happen is that the demand level has a negative trend, and so the value of F_t decreases considerably, while the a_{t+k} have not been adjusted. Then, if the a_{t+k} is large and negative, $P_{t,k}$ in (25) could easily even become negative, for example. For this reason, the decision maker might set reasonable minimum values x_{t+k} in advance for the forecasts and replace (25) by

$$P_{t,k} = \max [F_t + a_{t+k}, x_{t+k}] \tag{25d}$$

A commonly taken value is $x_{t+k} = 0$, so that no forecast can be negative.

Suppose, as a simple illustration, that there are four periods in a year, $\alpha = 0.5$, and the additive demands and factors are as shown in Table 3-2.

Note that in this particular model the additive seasonal correction works very well, as evidenced by the small evenly balanced errors shown in the last row. Here there is little change in F_t over time, which tends to make the additive model stable.

In the foregoing model, if the overall demand level doubles, the differences from peaks to trough do not change. If, however, the new customers have the same seasonal buying pattern as the old ones, it may be more appropriate to assume that the peaks vary by a constant *percentage*. Thus for the multiplicative model we assume m periods in a seasonal cycle with factors a_j. These factors (averaging 1.0) specify the ratio of expected demand in the period to the demand in a normal or average period. Thus, these multiplicative factors sum to m over a full seasonal cycle, such as a year.

The deseasonalizing and reseasonalizing work in exactly the same way as before, except that multiplying and dividing replace subtracting and adding:

$$F_t = F_{t-1} + \alpha[(D_t/a_t) - F_{t-1}] \tag{26a}$$

$$P_t = a_t F_t \tag{26b}$$

$$P_{t,k} = a_{t+k} F_t \tag{26c}$$

The multiplicative system is popular in practice, because the sizes of the seasonal adjustments automatically adjust in proportion to F_t, and thus in some sense may be

t	0	1	2	3	4	5	6
a_t		50	−150	100	0	50	−150
D_t		210	90	280	195	295	40
F_t	200	180	210	195	195	220	205
P_t		230	60	295	195	270	55
$D_t - P_t$		−20	30	−15	0	25	−15

Table 3-2
....

Additive Seasonal Factors
with Exponential Smoothing

considered somewhat self-correcting. However, the multiplicative approach has a different yet somewhat similar problem as the additive. This is that, if a_t in (26a) is very small, we are essentially dividing by zero, so that any stray demand which is realized but is not in the model will have a very large effect on the average.

As an example, suppose $F_{t-1} = 3$, $\alpha = 0.1$, and $a_t = 0.1$, so that our expected demand for this period, as of last period was $P_{t-1,1} = (0.1)(3) = 0.3$. That is, we roughly expected to sell one unit every three periods. Now, suppose some other wholesaler runs out of stock in this item and comes over and buys $D_t = 5$ from us on the sly to keep his customers happy. Then our adjusted normalized moving average becomes $F_t = 3 + 0.1[(5/0.1) - 3] = 7.7$. Thus, our smoothed forecast has tripled from one stray random experience. It will gradually smooth down to about 3 again, but in the meantime tremendous amounts of over-ordering of this item will occur. We can verify, more extremely, that in a part of the season for which $a_t = 0$, any arriving random order of any size would produce an overwhelming problem! For this reason (26a) is usually modified to something like this:

$$F_t = F_{t-1} + \alpha[D_t/(\max(a_t, x_t)) - F_{t-1}] \quad (26a')$$

The appropriate value for x_t to use is a matter of experience in a situation, but a very common choice is $x_t = 0.5$.

In Table 3-3 we rework the previous example to employ multiplicative factors, with the same data to show the difference between additive and multiplicative factors.

Note here, especially in period 2, that a high demand combined with a very low seasonal factor can cause the deseasonalized demand to be unstable. This in turn causes the forecast demand for period 3 to be very high (by 64), which will, in turn, cause a typical inventory system, which might be planning for six weeks ahead, to order $384(64 \times 6)$ units of excess inventory. We repeat that the comparison for this example is biased in favor of the additive model, since there is no change in the overall level of demand, which would have been the situation that multiplicative factors are designed for.

You will be asked in the exercises to see how much the situation in Table 3-3 would be alleviated if seasonal factors had been limited in the formula by $x_t = 0.5$.

Correction of the moving average formulas for seasonality follows exactly the same principle as for exponential smoothing:

1. Deseasonalize the actual demands.
2. Smooth the normalized model.
3. Reseasonalize the resulting forecasts.

Creating this model for additive and/or multiplicative factors is addressed in the exercises.

Adding additive seasonal factors to discounted regression with suppressed trend is just the very simple matter of adding appropriate dummy variables and not including trend as a variable. This is also left as an exercise.

3.4.4 Trend/Seasonal Smoothing Exercises

1. Using the trend-corrected exponential smoothing model, compute a trend-corrected moving average for quarters 1 through 24. Assume that the model has

Table 3-3

Multiplicative Seasonal Factors with Exponential Smoothing

t	0	1	2	3	4	5	6
a_t		1.25	0.25	1.50	1.00	1.25	0.25
D_t		210	90	280	195	295	40
F_t	200	184	272	229	212	224	192
P_t		230	68	344	212	280	48
$D_t - F_t$		−20	22	−64	−27	15	−8

been in operation for some time, and that last period's smoothed demand is $F_0 = 15$ and its smoothed trend is $T_0 = 5$. Let $\alpha = 0.1$ and $\beta = 0.2$. Graph the forecast one period ahead versus actual.

Period	Actual	Period	Actual
1	22	13	77
2	30	14	106
3	28	15	85
4	26	16	72
5	40	17	98
6	55	18	128
7	49	19	111
8	40	20	95
9	55	21	122
10	79	22	151
11	68	23	133
12	61	24	113

Do you see any pattern in the forecast errors?

2. Solve problem 1 by discounted regression, with a discount factor of 0.1. How does this method compare? (Do the regression either manually, or with the software.)

3. "One danger of correcting for trend in a seasonal factor model is that the estimation of the trend will be very sensitive to time shift errors in the season."

   a. Discuss this statement intuitively.
   b. Can you discuss it quantitatively?

4. Suppose seasonal factors for a class of customers are indeed multiplicative, but that demand is actually a mixture of three classes of customers, each with different factors. Discuss forecasting problems which might occur if the fractions of each class are changing over time.

5. Discuss problems which might occur in seasonal factor forecasting by one-time demand "outliers." What could be done to help the forecaster?

6. How could one decide which products to group as having similar seasonal patterns?

   a. Judgmentally?
   b. Quantitatively?

7. What kinds of difficulties might there be, in problem 6, with purely quantitative methods?

8. A product which is forecast monthly has multiplicative seasonal factors (periods 1 through 12): 0.5, 0.5, 0.5, 0.5, 0.5, 0.5, 2.0, 2.0, 2.0, 1.0, 1.0, 1.0. Using $F_0 = 10$, $\alpha = 0.1$, and actual demands 5, 5, 6, 4, 5, 7, 22, 18, 20, 14, 12, 14:

   a. Derive the series F_t and P_t.
   b. Derive the series $P_{t,2}$.

9. Create and solve a problem analogous to problem 8 for additive seasonal factors.

10. Re-solve problem 1 by adding multiplicative seasonal factors to that analysis. Let these factors be 1.0, 1.2, 1.0, and 0.8.

11. Derive a trend-corrected model for moving averages.

12. Discuss trend-corrected models for discounted regression.

13. Derive additive and multiplicative seasonal models for moving averages.

14. Discuss additive seasonal models for discounted regression.

3.5 CLIFTON WARDS—REPRISE

After six months Sammita makes a full presentation to the top managers of the company. She suggests that each of the 346 lines of interest to marketing be considered as a separate aggregate forecast with trend and multiplicative seasonal factors built in wherever these are strongly significant (in about 36 of the lines). A good user interface should be built to allow adjusting line seasonal factor patterns to fit time shifts in a given year, and so forth. A moving average will be used rather than exponential smoothing, since this seems desirable to the marketing VP, and in preliminary testing Sammita does not find that choice to make all that much difference. Almost all items will be forecast by applying percentage-of-line multipliers to the overall line forecast. In a few cases, fairly large volume items with unusual trends/seasonal factors will be pulled out from the line and forecast separately. Interval forecast errors are to be estimated directly as a function of the interval forecast. Until the necessary study can be carried out to confirm this, errors will be treated as a simple fixed fraction of the forecast for large volume items and to be Poisson for small volume items. Another study needs to be carried out to initialize the system. Industry experience seems to indicate that a six-period moving average should be tested for basic smoothing and for trend, while a two-period moving average seems like a good starting place for seasonal factors.

Sammita feels she needs more study to decide whether very small volume full service items should be ordered by group or simply allocated on the basis of a group total requirement as at present. She is also interested in studying further how to reduce the volume of reports that the current system generates. She is inclined to think that no reports should be generated automatically, but that a manager should be able to query any part of the forecasting process easily on the computer. The manager should also be able to selectively print out desired reports under immediate control. The finance VP and the data processing VP express some concern about the software development costs of all this, and Sammita promises to do a preliminary cost analysis.

C H A P T E R 4

Forecasting the Forecasting of the Future

4.1 INTRODUCTION

If "forecasting is the process of forecasting the future," then clearly forecasting "forecasting" must be the process of forecasting how the science and the art of forecasting will change in the future. This is, on the face of it, a very difficult topic. It is certainly a subjective and strategic problem with horizons of 5 to 20 years; we have already argued at length that we must be humble about any guesses that we choose to call "forecasts" in such an environment.

Yet there are some important things that we can see and say about this question. How we forecast depends on how much information we have and how well it is organized. If a tank were coming at me in the field, I might forecast its progress as a steady straight line, and so dodge to one side. However, if I could intercept the communications between the tank and the field commander, I might find it is about to turn in the direction I was going to jump and so stay put.

Forecasting is the Poor Man's Information. Forecasting based simply on the fact that the past will repeat itself is often accurate, but just as often it is not. If the repetition from the past is all that is available, it should, of course, be used. But it is always superior to use more information if it is available. For example, suppose a man came to the same Cadillac dealer and bought a new yellow Cadillac Seville with every possible option on May 1 of every year for the last 20 years. This year his mother's obituary appears March 17. The dealer confidently purchases the yellow Cadillac Seville and has it waiting. But the man never shows. It turns out he bought the car only to please his mother, and therefore the situation had changed drastically for him.

As another example, when hula hoops first came out in the 1950s, they enjoyed a brief explosive exponential growth. An alien knowing nothing else might project sales of billions within ten years! However, novelty makers understand the nature of a fad, and so look at the growth pattern of similar objects to make sort of a "seasonal" or **fad growth pattern** to get a better idea of the maximum likely market size and the topping out point. Here sophisticated information is not as important as understanding "similar" product situations, which is a difficult judgmental issue.

(The next two subsections use material from *The New Forecasting Challenge: Networked Manufacturing*, Lefrancois, Davidson, and Morton, Carnegie-Mellon University [1993]; by permission.)

The Information Explosion. The current manufacturing and distribution environment is quietly but surely giving way to a new form of business: high-tech networked organizations. *Business Week*, in June 1993, reported the story of the networked Frank's

Nursery in Detroit Michigan: scanners and satellites reduce paperwork and make for shorter checkout lines. Workers who used to spend hours recording the status of thousands of items now use hand held scanners to read product code labels on items, and, if an item is out of stock, directly feed through their information network a request for replenishments to headquarters. Long checkout lines caused by credit card authorizations? No big deal! A $4 million satellite system networking its stores with VISA USA Inc. reduces the 45-second authorization waiting time down to a mere seven seconds.

Perhaps the best example of networking is that used by Wal-Mart. Using information technology, including satellites to link each point of sale to distribution centers, headquarters, and suppliers, Wal-Mart can now track every sale and see what is selling and what is sitting. By linking themselves to the Wal-Mart network, suppliers like Polaroid can now analyze in detail the retail sales of their products, evaluate their rising and falling stars, and, finally, use these figures to plan their production schedules.

Rocketing Down the Information Highway. Recently, the national news magazines and the halls of government have been speculating about the information superhighway, which is a glossy term for the coming fiber optics, satellite, electronics, TV, and phone conglomerate which seems to be coming within ten years to give us all thousands of channels, unlimited movies on demand, full access to libraries, and other massive data.

What is perhaps not as widely realized is that the same revolution is coming to provide massive information availability to industry, which will be perhaps just as important an "information superhighway."

A report by the Iacocca Institute in 1991 states that within 15 years, the foundations of the globally competitive firm will be continuous change, quick response, and improvement. These in turn will be based on a revolution in information availability based on powerful desktop computing, massive data transfer by satellites and fiber optics, customer/supplier interactive systems, distributed databases, and global information networking with suppliers and customers.

Overall, in the forthcoming information economy that will characterize the next 15 years, *knowledge* will become the key to the competitiveness of the networked firm, and *high knowledge forecasting* will be necessary to make that knowledge accessible.

In the next section, we will look in some detail at what the information superhighway will mean to the types and sophistication of forecasting that companies will use.

4.2 EXAMPLES OF TRENDS IN FORECASTING

4.2.1 Overview

In this section we will give several major examples of how the information explosion may be expected to affect forecasting. In Section 4.2.2 we discuss forecasting input needs for assembly. In Section 4.2.3 we give an introduction to forecasting high tech spare parts requirements. In Section 4.2.4 we introduce the topic of needed research in retail forecasting, and how it will be affected by mega-information.

4.2.2 Ordering Inputs for Assembly

Overview. In the 1960s and 70s, operations researchers dealt with an information-poor manufacturing environment. Modeling was, of necessity, very localized, as in the Stage 1 example below. As more computational power and outside information became available, operations researchers and forecasters tended not to broaden the scope of their models and integrate them so as to capture the newly available information. Rather, they focused on making the already existing models more complex and finding ways to solve them more exactly. In the meanwhile, information researchers independently developed systems to capture all that new information. However, most of them neglected to use the full power of modeling and forecasting in their richer information models. Operations researchers and forecasters eventually moved in to strengthen these new systems, but the process has usually been quite inefficient.

To illustrate this point, we show the development of forecasting procedures over several decades for the problem of forecasting demand and ordering raw material inputs for an assembly shop.

Stage 1. Independent Demands. In the 1960s and '70s operations researchers and forecasters solved this ordering problem in the following fashion:

1. Use independent floor-usage time series for each raw material to forecast it as a separate problem.
2. Use delivery time series to forecast the distribution of each lead time.
3. Model each item as a separate inventory problem, and develop order quantities and safety stock levels for each item separately.

Even if the time series methods used were very precise and the inventory problem was solved exactly optimally for each item, an obvious major weakness in this approach is that the inputs are used in fixed proportions in each unit of output, thus making the input demands very highly correlated rather than independent.

Floor managers often intuitively understood this problem and sometimes (explicitly) set aside kits or groups of raw materials needed to make given outputs. If these needed kits were subtracted from the inventories before using the inventory models, better results would, in fact, occur. In effect, managers found a way to add fixed-proportion information to the problem.

Stage 2. Material Requirements Planning (MRP). Through the implementation of material requirements planning (MRP) systems, the process was modified in the following ways:

1. The demand forecasts were made for the final products instead of forecasting the inputs directly.
2. The final demand forecasting process involved a mixture of known future orders, likely future orders, and time series data, combined manually.
3. Demands, called timed demands, were estimated for each future time period, not just a single period.
4. Timed demands for the original inputs could be estimated, allowing ordering as before by:

   a. Using the final timed demands thus created
   b. Exploding these demands into assemblies, subassemblies and original inputs
   c. Allowing historical assembly stage lead times for each assembly and subassembly.

Still pretty much the industry standard today, the MRP approach brought into the field numerous improvements over the previous approach. However, the MRP approach is still far from using all the information available. Important information areas still not fully implemented, or still in the future, include:

- Current material lead times and customer orders
- Current local shop assembly stage lead times
- Better merging of known orders and time series information

Stage 3. Networking Vendors and Suppliers (DRP). The third step is in process: the implementation of distribution requirements planning (DRP). This is part of a larger electronic interconnection trend called electronic data interchange (EDI). For the firm, the basic promise of DRP is:

1. The ability, with the cooperation of vendors, to peek electronically into a vendor's MRP system to estimate a current order's actual lead time
2. With the cooperation of the industrial customer, to peek electronically into the customer's MRP system to estimate timing and quantity of future orders

This whole process is now becoming much more common and the forecasting issues now become much more subtle: How should the firm integrate this information with its estimates of their other suppliers and customer figures and how worthwhile is it?

Stage 4. Future Assembly Input Issues. There are still other weaknesses in the MRP process which need to be dealt with.

1. **Assumption of constant lead-times within the shop.** Actually, lead times will be much longer in a busy shop, and very short in a lightly loaded shop. This can be addressed with simple models which fit a historical function to lead time as a function of shop load. Or it can be addressed in more sophisticated ways by simulating the actual shop scheduling in the current situation.
2. **Estimating final demand by manually mixing known, DRP, and time series methods.** Here it is necessary to find simple ways to combine these data, either by developing formulas, or by developing DSS (decision support systems).

4.2.3 High Tech Spare Parts Requirements

Consider the difficulties faced by a major player in the high quality computer printer market. The company must perform its R&D aggressively and imaginatively to stay ahead, or at least abreast, in a rapidly evolving technology. But the company must also maintain a reputation for extremely high quality and reliability for the existing printers in use by customers. In days gone by, the company had seen the production, logistics, and inventory control of spare parts as a rather minor tactical problem. But top management now see customer service as strategic. The CEO has mandated that reliability of the printers be improved by a factor of 8, and that maintainability (reliability plus quick repair) be improved by a factor of 20. This high standard of service is to be maintained for printers up to 15 years old!

Good forecasting of the need for spare parts becomes critical. Such forecasting requires knowing:

1. How many units of what kind and age are currently out in "the field" (in use by customers)
2. What the failure rate is (and will be in the future) by type of printer, type of component, age of the printer, and use history
3. When (now and in the future) the customer will repair, or choose to scrap, the unit

These questions are difficult enough for a stable technology product like a toaster or a refrigerator. An improved toaster can often be assumed to have similar reliability characteristics to the one it replaces. However, a new printer with some new technology may have very different failure rates, even for the same component.

Why is forecasting so important? Why not just produce enough extra parts to be safe? There are at least three main reasons that good forecasting for spare parts is essential:

1. Economical production runs
2. Reduced logistics inventories
3. Centralized logistics stocking

The manufacturing department desires large production runs to achieve economies of scale, which must be traded off with excessive inventory costs. For a not-so-common spare part this economic batch size might be as much as two years. But if the part or the printer may be obsolete in less than two years, it may be that a large part of the current run may eventually be discarded as worthless. While models have been developed to deal with this situation, improved forecasting is critical in producing the largest economical lots consistent with usefulness of the entire lot.

The need for logistics inventories has two components:

1. The truly random failure component even if the overall forecast is excellent
2. Technological forecast errors in estimating failure rates and obsolescence

Forecasting of the random component is difficult to improve, but for technologically changing products, it is not the largest component. Poor technological forecasting may result in doubling or tripling the inventories, or worse, in bad understocking and resulting poor service.

Centralized part stocking can reduce inventories by combining offsetting random component failures. It also reduces the number of small inventory centers and increases the quality of inventory control. At the same time, however, when failures occur the central stocking point must express the parts to the point of need to avoid serious degradation of customer service. If the technological forecasts are bad, this will be a frequent occurrence and customer good will suffer. So centralized stocking is practical only with good forecasting.

Just as we found for ordering raw materials for assembly, there are at least three stages forecasting has gone through for spare parts forecasting in high tech situations:

- Independent demands
- Stable failure rate functions
- Changing failure rate functions.

We discuss each of these briefly in Appendix A.

4.2.4 Example of Research in Retail Forecasting

Up to this point we have given two large examples to show how forecasting must progress from what we might call simple time series forecasting to **structural forecasting**, where the forecasting procedure may be dramatically improved by building more information into the procedure.

By contrast, here we pick just one forecasting area, retail forecasting, and illustrate a number of unresolved problems that forecasters in this area face:

- Forecasting very small demands
- Forecasting new products based on sales of old products
- Forecasting how new products steal demand from other products.

4.3 LIMITATIONS ON FORECASTING FORECASTING

Finally, it must be pointed out again that we are trying to predict the direction of forecasting years into the future, which is notoriously difficult. If, in 1960, we had tried to pick the state of forecasting today:

a. We might have guessed the progress of computational speeds fairly accurately.
b. We probably would have guessed storage capabilities tolerably well.
c. We would have not seen the ease of large scale transfer of data over long distances.
d. We would have probably missed entirely the demise of the mainframe computer and the dominance of desktop computing and networking.
e. We would have missed the overriding importance of standardized software packages.

Thus, while it is worthwhile for us to peek into the future, we must always remember that in 30 years people will look back with some amusement at our efforts!

BIBLIOGRAPHY

General/Books

Armstrong, J. (1978). *Long-Range Forecasting: From Crystal Ball to Computer.* New York: Wiley.

Armstrong, J. S. (1984). "Forecasting by Extrapolation: Conclusions from Twenty-five Years of Research," *Interfaces* 14, 52–66.

Bass, F. (1969). "A New Product Growth Model for Consumer Durables," *Management Science* 15, 215–227.

Chambers, J., S. Mullick and D. Smith (1974). *An Executive's Guide to Forecasting.* New York: Wiley.

Chen, G. and P. Winters (1966). "Forecasting Peak Demand for an Electric Utility with a Hybrid Exponential Model," *Management Science* 12, B531–B537.

Helmer, F., E. Opperman and J. Suver (1980). "Forecasting Nursing Staffing Requirements by Intensity-Of-Care Level," *Interfaces* 10, 50–55.

Magee, J. (1958). *Production Planning and Inventory Control.* New York: McGraw-Hill.

Morrison, N. (1970). *Introduction to Sequential Smoothing and Prediction.* Hightstown, NJ: McGraw-Hill.

Nelson, C. (1973). *Applied Time Series Analysis for Managerial Forecasting.* San Francisco: Holden-Day.

Pindyck, R. and D. Rubenfeld (1991). *Econometric Models and Economic Forecasts.* New York: McGraw-Hill.

Steiner, G. (1979). *Strategic Planning.* New York: The Free Press.

Wilson, J. and B. Keating (1990). *Business Forecasting.* Homewood, IL: Richard D. Irwin.

Judgment/Technological

Ahlburg, D. A. (1992). "Predicting the Job Performance of Managers: What Do the Experts Know?," *International Journal of Forecasting*, 7 (4), 467–472.

Ang, S. and M. O'Connor (1991). "The Effect of Group Interaction Processes on Performance in Time Series Extrapolation," *International Journal of Forecasting* 7 (2), 141–149.

Basu, S. and R. Schroeder (1977). "Incorporating Judgments in Sales Forecasts: Application of the Delphi Method at American Hoist and Derrick," *Interfaces* 7 (3), 18–27.

Brauers, J. and M. Weber (1988). "A New Method of Scenario Analysis for Strategic Planning," *Journal of Forecasting*, 7 (1), 31–47.

Brown, R. (1959). *Statistical Forecasting for Inventory Control.* New York: McGraw-Hill.

Brown, R. (1962). *Smoothing, Forecasting and Prediction of Discrete Time Series.* Englewood Cliffs, NJ: Prentice-Hall.

Bunn, D. and G. Wright (1991). "Interaction of Judgemental and Statistical Forecasting Methods: Issues and Analysis," *Management Science* 37 (5), 501–518.

Conroy, R. and R. Harris (1987). "Consensus Forecasts of Corporate Earnings: Analysts' Forecasts and Time Series Methods," *Management Science* 33 (6), 725–738.

Dakin, Stephen and J. Scott Armstrong (1989). "Predicting Job Performance: A Comparison of Expert Opinion and Research Findings," *International Journal of Forecasting* 5 (2), 187–194.

Fildes, R. (1991). "Efficient Use of Information in the Formation of Subjective Industry Forecasts," *Journal of Forecasting*, 10 (6), 597–617.

Finon, D. and B. Lapillonne (1983). "Long Term Forecasting of Energy Demand in the Developing Countries," *European Journal of Operational Research* 13 (1), 12–28.

Fischoff, B. (1988). "Judgmental Aspects of Forecasting," *International Journal of Forecasting*, 4 (3), 331–339.

Huss, W. R. (1988). "A Move Toward Scenario Analysis," *International Journal of Forecasting*, 4 (3), 377–388.

Lefrancois, Davidson, and Morton (1993). "The New Forecasting Challenge: Networked Manufacturing," Pittsburgh, PA: Carnegie-Mellon University.

Linstone, H. and M. Turoff (1975). *The Delphi Method: Techniques and Applications*. Reading, MA: Addison-Wesley.

Lobo, G. J. and R. D. Nair (1990). "Combining Judgmental and Statistical Forecasts: An Application to Earnings Forecasts," *Decision Sciences,* 21 (2), 446–460.

Lootsma, F. A., P. G. M. Boonekamp, R. M. Cooke and F. Van Oostvoorn (1990). "Choice of a Long-Term Strategy for the National Electricity Supply Via Scenario Analysis and Multi-Criteria Analysis," *European Journal of Operational Research,* 48 (2), 189–203.

Parenté, F. J., J. K. Anderson, P. Myers and T. O'Brien (1984). "An Examination of Factors Contributing to Delphi Accuracy," *Journal of Forecasting*, 3 (2), 173–182.

Schoemaker, P. J. H. (1991). "When and How to Use Scenario Planning: A Heuristic Approach with Illustration," *Journal of Forecasting*, 10 (6), 549–564.

Simon, H.A. (1990). "Prediction and Prescription in Systems Modeling," *Operations Research,* 38 (1), 7–14.

Wright, G. and P. Ayton (1989). "Judgmental Probability Forecasts for Personal and Impersonal Events," *International Journal of Forecasting,* 5 (1), 117–125.

Regression/Econometrics

Berkowitz, M. K. and G. H. Haines, Jr. (1984). "Forecasting Future Canadian Residential Heating Demand: An Illustration of Forecasting with Aggregated and Disaggregated Data," *Journal of Forecasting*, 3 (2), 217–227.

Bopp, A. E. (1985). "On Combining Forecasts: Some Extensions and Results," *Management Science,* 31 (12), 1492–1498.

Gardner, E. S., Jr. and E. McKenzie (1985). "Forecasting Trends in Time Series," *Management Science,* 31 (10), 1237–1246.

Pindyck, R. and D. Rubenfeld (1991). *Econometric Models and Economic Forecasts*. New York: McGraw-Hill.

Smoothing Articles

Chambers, M. L. and R. W. Eglese (1988). "Forecasting Demand for Mail Order Catalogue Lines During the Season," *European Journal of Operational Research* 34 (2), 131–138.

Chen, G. and P. Winters (1966). "Forecasting Peak Demand for an Electric Utility with a Hybrid Exponential Model," *Management Science* 12, B531–B537.

Lev, B. (1970). "A Note on the Analysis of Peak-Demand Forecasts of an Electrical Utility," *Operations Research* 18, 174–179.

Muralidhar, K. and M. J. Tretter (1991). "The Impact of Special Requirements on the Estimation of Electrical Demand," *Management Science* 37 (3), 368–373.

Muth, J. (1960). "Optimal Properties of Exponentially Weighted Forecasts," *Journal of the American Statistical Association* 55, 297–306.

Ritzman, L. P. and B. E. King (1993). "The Relative Significance of Forecast Errors in Multistage Manufacturing," *Journal of Operations Management* 11 (1), 51–65.

Sarin, R. (1979). "An Approach for Long Term Forecasting with an Application to Solar Electric Energy," *Management Science* 25, 543–554.

Sharp, J. A. and D. H. R. Price (1990). "Experience Curve Models in the Electricity Supply Industry," *International Journal of Forecasting* 6 (4), 531–540.

Winters, P. (1960). "Forecasting Sales by Exponentially Weighted Moving Averages," *Management Science* 4, 324–342.

Inventory

2

MODULE

Introduction to Inventory

1.1 LET'S TAKE STOCK!

1.1.1 Overview

There has been so much emphasis in the last few years on drastically reducing inventories (think of such buzzwords as "zero inventories," "Just-In-Time [JIT]," and "time-based competition" to name a few) that one might get the impression that conventional inventory control is no longer very important.

Nothing could be further from the truth. Despite very real major reductions in inventories by a few companies, the annual investment in inventories in the United States in just manufacturing, wholesale, and retail operations is on the order of $825 billion! If we estimate the cost of carrying inventory at around 20 percent per year, we see the total cost of inventories at $160 billion a year. (For strategic reasons, the Japanese would say this figure is much too low.)

We may distinguish three levels of inventory control: a. short-term, b. tactical, and c. strategic. In short-term control, we take the overall system as given, including demand, lead times, setup costs, and so on, and try to optimize only two variables:

1. When to order?
2. How much to order?

The horizon for short-term inventory control is typically one week to three months. Most of the topics in Inventory Chapters 2 and 3 involve short-term control.

In tactical situations, we control various other production variables as well, including work force, overtime, scheduling, and so on. Here the horizons are three months to a year. Topics include material requirements planning, aggregate planning, and logistics, which are covered in the Planning module.

In strategic situations, we alter the nature of the process itself to drastically change the inventory problem. Methods for doing this include:

1. Just-In-Time (JIT)
2. Major setup time reduction
3. Lead time reduction

Some of the strategic inventory issues are discussed in Inventory Chapter 4.

In general, the models that we work with can be used to describe either ordering from an outside vendor or from a different internal department. This means that, from the point of view of the model, conventional inventory control and production planning are often quite similar. This similarity should not be overemphasized, however, since the inventory control model may have to be changed to some degree before it is suitable for production planning.

1.1.2 Types of Manufacturing Inventories

There is a rather reasonable classification scheme for manufacturing and distribution inventories depending on how much value added has been incorporated by the firm:

1. Raw materials
2. Components/Subassemblies/Unfinished items
3. Work-in-process
4. End items/Finished goods

Raw materials are any inventories maintained by a company which the company has not yet processed in any way. This would include such obvious raw materials as iron ore, sand, or glass. However, by our definition, it could include computer chips or other expensive items which have not yet been processed.

Components/Subassemblies/Unfinished items have been processed to some extent by the company, but are not yet finished. They may leave the production area and be stored off the line, but will still not revert to being called raw material. *They already have value added*.

Work-in-process is similar to components, et al. It is actually a mixture of raw materials and components that are currently a part of the production process. So some raw materials may be part of work-in-process, and some components may not be.

Finished goods are simply goods which are finished and ready for sale. They are almost never left in the work area, but are moved out into final storage or packaging.

There is often some ambiguity about classification, since a company may sell some unpainted furniture but paint some for final sale. Is a given unpainted piece to be considered finished goods or not? Perhaps we need a new term for such goods.

1.2 WHAT ARE INVENTORIES FOR?

1.2.1 Overview

In a very fundamental sense, inventories arise because it is not convenient to have an item be supplied (by being produced or arriving from elsewhere) precisely at the time it is needed. If it is supplied three weeks before being needed, it adds 1.0 to the appropriate inventory for those three weeks. The whole point of Just-In-Time is that the unit should arrive precisely when needed, creating neither inventories nor stockouts. Reasons for holding inventories are reasons *not* to do Just-In-Time. Reasons to keep inventory low are reasons *for* Just-In-Time.

1.2.2 Reasons for Holding Inventories

There are a number of reasons for holding inventories. These reasons encompass several factors, which are discussed in the following paragraphs.

Setup Costs/Times. Some machines/resources are dedicated to a single product, but most will make a variety of products from time to time. The process of changing a machine over from making product A to product B involves one or more types of out-of-pocket expenses called, in aggregate, the **direct setup cost**, and typically some amount of lost productive time on the machine itself, called the **setup time**. If an opportunity cost per hour of the down machine time is assigned then a **total setup cost** can be assigned as the sum of the direct and indirect costs. The problem then is to produce a lot of the proper size, trading off the setup cost against the extra inventory costs in an appropriate manner.

Some common direct setup costs include:

a. Worker/engineer labor
b. Test equipment
c. Wasted product in evaluating new machine settings
d. Wasted product in flushing a continuous process

The most common practice for evaluating lost machine time is to cost out the total value added of product which could have been made in this time. Unfortunately, this may be far too high or far too low. If a uniform product is being made and the plant is at full capacity, it makes sense to value the machine at the loss of capacity. However, more commonly the shop is at less than full capacity; the price should then vary with how significant a bottleneck the lost machine time produces. (See the Scheduling module and/or Morton and Pentico [1993].)

Other Large Lot Efficiencies. There are many other reasons besides setup costs that cause large lots to be subject to "economies of scale." For example, as the lot proceeds, workers may be able to gradually make it faster/better. (That is, overall there is a learning process, with some loss of knowledge since the last time the lot was made.) The "lot" may actually be an order placed by a retailer to a wholesaler (or manufacturer) with stated quantity discounts. There may be more than one way to manufacture the product, if one has a lower per unit cost involving a larger setup cost, that would tend to encourage larger lots. The process parameters of the machine may get fine tuned even more accurately the longer the lot runs.

Uncertainties in Demand. Perhaps uncertainties in external customer demand are considered most often in determining the amount of inventory. For example, a retailer such as Sears stocks a great number of different items in order to find favor with the customer. If the customer nevertheless requests one or more items which are not on hand, it is likely he or she will go elsewhere, either immediately or after some number of such bad experiences. For this reason, the retailer has a motive to carry a large number of different items with a goodly stock in any that might run out. Thus inventories provide a "buffer" against displeasing the customer.

With industrial customers the situation gets considerably more complicated. The customer may sign contracts, specifying in general what sorts of things he will buy and how often. But the "in general" still leaves a great deal of uncertainty. The customer may accept a lead time for an order of five weeks, for example, when placing an order, rather than expect instantaneous delivery. However, if the five weeks turns into seven weeks (once too often) a strong, long-standing customer may still be lost. The manufacturer may protect against this situation by keeping a number of possible types of inventory:

a. Finished product inventory
b. Emergency excess productive capacity "inventory"
c. Work-in-process inventories
d. Raw material inventories

Determining what kinds of inventories to carry, and how much, is a very challenging problem.

Uncertainties in Supply/Production. We have looked at why a supplier may wish to carry final inventories to protect the lead time to the retail/industrial customer. The customer may wish to carry precisely the same type of inventory of that product so that if the lead time is longer than expected, his/her own use will not be adversely affected. Of course, if both are carrying inventories of the same thing for the same reason, this may not be very efficient overall.

Another source of supply uncertainty is major disruptions. American auto firms may claim to be using Just-In-Time production, and yet carry two months supply of an auto chassis manufactured in Brazil. This is necessary due to the uncertain rate of production in the Brazilian plant and to the large uncertainties in ocean shipping times.

Supply Capacity. In an industry which has capacity only marginally greater than overall year-round needs, a customer always faces the risk that an order may not be completely supplied, and the supplier faces the risk that in some months there will be too much demand and supply will have to be rationed. In these situations, if there is at least some excess supply on average, the industry may carry rather large inventories to alleviate this situation.

Production Smoothing. Production smoothing (aggregate planning) is an important special case of supply capacity problems for firms whose demand is subject to heavy seasonal variation. The firm can typically produce enough on average, but not during peak periods. It must choose some mixture of:

a. Producing in off periods, and carrying "seasonal" inventories into the peak periods
b. Working overtime in the peak periods
c. Hiring and laying off workers for peak and down periods
d. Subcontracting

This topic is treated in the Planning module.

Scheduling. In a shop with many different versatile machines, where all sorts of things are being manufactured, it will inevitably be the case that the load on a given machine will be "lumpy." Sometimes far more raw material will arrive than can be processed in a short time, and there will be a long line or "inventory" at the machine. Conversely, at other times the machine will be empty.

Many times books tend to say that these inventories are due to "randomness." However, even with perfect knowledge six weeks ahead, there would still be unevenness of need for each machine. Thus, the true culprit is "lumpiness." Lumpiness is the price paid for the flexibility. A high speed transfer line producing one product needs very little inventory; it is not flexible and therefore not lumpy.

Information Costs. Many times inventories are kept simply because the item is too unimportant to control in a full scale inventory system. Inventories can hide the effects of poor information. It can be less costly to the manufacturer to maintain large inventories of small volume items than to provide the data processing support to keep detailed records for them. Even though these types of costs can be very important, they are rarely treated formally in inventory models. The manager is expected to keep these factors in mind on an informal basis.

Transportation/Logistics. Pipeline inventories are those which occur because goods are actually in transit. Transportation inventories depend heavily on the mode of transport. Airline pipelines will be measured in hours in the air and up to days in storage between flights. Railroad and truck pipelines will be measured in days to weeks. Ocean shipping pipeline inventories can easily be measured in months. Investment in shipping pipelines can thus be very substantial and tends to counter the inherent saving from the very cheap unit cost of shipping. Such factors can make multinational production to take advantage of cheap labor less effective.

Speculation. If the value of a natural resource, or a product of any kind, is expected to increase noticeably at some point in the future, it may be profitable to buy or produce a large quantity of the item now and store it for use or sale in that future time. As an example, paper mills often stockpile excess paper rolls during business downturns when the price is low, hoping to sell them in the next business upturn. Wheat farmers may build large granaries on their land and hold wheat for a higher price.

1.2.3 Motives for Not Holding Inventory

There are also many motives for reducing inventories, which must be compared with the advantages of inventories listed previously. These are often separated into motives which can be assigned reasonable **costs**, at least very roughly (termed **Cost Motives**), and those for which it is difficult to assign numerical costs at all (**Subjective Motives**). Some of these are discussed in the following paragraphs.

Cost Motive—Opportunity Cost of Capital. The opportunity cost of alternative investment of the funds tied up in the value of the inventory itself is by far the most important inventory cost in most applications. At first, you might think the interest rate that the company should use as an opportunity cost would be something like the 5 percent you might get in a money market account, or maybe the 6 percent you might get in bonds.

However, companies are usually involved in risky ventures, are highly leveraged, and banks will not always lend them as much as they would like. Thus, they must earn higher rates of return to stay in business. Numbers like 20 or 30 percent are common (even higher where the company is not well understood by the finance community).

Cost Motive—Variable Cost of Storage Space. By "variable" physical storage space, we mean that costs are rather explicit and vary directly with the number of units stored. If we are renting space, this will usually be quite accurate. Also, for long-range planning purposes for our own warehouses, this will also be true, since we may always build more warehouses or rent some out.

If we are renting the space from an external party, the cost is simply the actual rental cost per unit per month, or perhaps per volume per month (which can be converted to a unit charge). For long-range planning purposes, if we are using our own space almost to capacity, we would determine an internal rental charge based on the cost to build the space, prorated yearly, times the cost of capital discussed just above.

Cost Motive—Fixed Cost of Storage Space. For short to middle run purposes, things are often a little more complicated for fixed storage costs. We may have rental contracts which are somewhat fixed, for which our costs do not vary directly with the number of units stored. If we are committed to more units than we have actually stored, the out-of-pocket costs for storing a few more units will then be close to zero. Similarly, if we own our own space and the warehouse is under-used, the warehouse is a sunk cost and the out-of-pocket cost will then be close to zero. However, if the warehouse is full or nearly full, and we cannot build or rent outside space in the short run, the "price" of the warehouse will really be a price (transfer price) charged to those wanting to store goods in the warehouse, a price which will just balance the demand and supply for the space. Determining this "price" has much the same character as "pricing" a shop machine, and will be discussed in the Scheduling module. In general, this "shadow price" will fluctuate up and down depending on how much competition there is currently for the fixed warehouse space.

Cost Motive—Costs for Taxes, Insurance, and Guards. The cost for taxes, insurance, guards, and other needed personnel may be treated similarly to the costs of the physical space discussed previously. These costs are usually somewhat smaller. If they vary fairly directly with the amount of inventory, they may be treated as a direct cost. If they are more or less fixed with the warehouse, then they would not be covered by the "price" of the warehouse as we discussed.

Cost Motive—Costs for Breakage, Spoilage, and Deterioration. The relative importance of breakage, spoilage, or deterioration varies greatly by the type of item. Breakage tends to be high for furniture and mirrors, while spoilage and deterioration in a goods warehouse will be minimal. Spoilage is of overwhelming concern for fresh produce. Although deterioration and spoilage are very similar, deterioration often indicates a longer time period for which inventory models work better, and might include chemical changes such as paint weathering, paper yellowing, circuits drifting, and so on.

Cost Motive—Cost of Obsolescence. Obsolescence of a product is a gradual or sudden decrease in value due to the release of superior competing products. It may be planned and deterministic. For example, Sears plans to introduce an improved can opener at Christmas, and plans to lower the price on the old one by 20 percent to sell out remaining inventory. Since effects here are large and known, obsolescence of this type should not be simply added into the costs of inventory. A newsboy-type model is more appropriate; see Inventory Chapter 3, Periodic Review Models. Another common situation is that obsolescence is probabilistic, representing the unknown introduction of competing products, but even so quite regular and predictable over groups of products.

Cost Motive—Cost of Loss of Flexibility for Finished Goods. Suppose that a mainframe computer manufacturer makes the basic RX-5000 machine in three varieties: vanilla (80 percent of sales), strawberry (10 percent), and chocolate (10 percent). These varieties differ only in some final modifications made to one basic chassis. One strategy to provide quick lead times much of the time would be to carry large inventories of the finished vanilla machines, none of the basic chassis, and none of the other flavors. Thus 80 percent of the time costs are low and delivery is quick. However, 20 percent of the time vanilla computers must be "cannibalized," that is, stripped back to the basic chassis and re-manufactured to another flavor. This causes the lead times to be quite long, and the computer to be totally more expensive. If we compare this with the strategy of carrying only the chassis and producing flavors to order, we see lower overall costs, but higher lead times. This higher cost we may call the cost of loss of flexibility involved in carrying finished goods.

Subjective Motive—Confusion on the Shop Floor. If work-in-process inventory tends to be stored right on the shop floor, high inventories will cause a number of problems: difficulty in finding desired WIP, damage to the inventory, difficulty in maneuvering personnel and materials, and so forth. If the WIP is carried directly by fork-lift from the machine to a bulk storage area and back again, the situation is a little better. The trucks themselves will tend to crowd the floor excessively and cause similar types of confusion, however lost and damaged material problems will typically be somewhat reduced.

Subjective Motive—Poorer Process Control. Suppose a machine operator produces a damaged piece of WIP. If he is honest about it and reports it, he gets into a lot of hassles: perhaps a dressing down from his boss, certainly lots of paperwork to fill out, arranging for the unit to be disposed of, and black marks for costs on his machine. Therefore, if he has an inventory of these units which were produced before and meant to buffer the needs of downstream machines, he will be tempted to say nothing, add the defective unit to the inventory, and send a good unit downstream instead. Eventually bad units will accumulate and cause a lot of trouble, but perhaps this worker will be working elsewhere, or the problem may be blamed on another shift, and so on.

At the other extreme, if no such inventories are being carried, there will be no good spare unit to send downstream when a damaged unit is produced. Then the operator will have no recourse but to report the damage to his boss, who will initiate an investigation into the problem and quickly fix the process. While this issue is subjective, the Japanese consider it to be very important strategically.

Subjective Motive—Poorer Communication and Coordination. If the same machine operator is not carrying an output buffer unit, then the downstream need must be forecast more carefully by the supervisor, so that the machine operator can produce it exactly when needed. The supervisor must also think ahead to make sure that no one else will be requesting the production of a unit in conflict. This leads ultimately to the strong need for better communication, coordination, and overall shop scheduling to avoid lumpy use of the operators and machines. This might actually have been considered a disadvantage in the old days. However, the improved communication and coordination can provide strategic advantages in producing a lean, responsive shop.

Subjective Motive—Inadequate Pressure to Streamline Process. This is closely related to the two previous motives. Higher inventories mean it is difficult to pin down where or when bad units were produced, and also make it difficult to see which parts of the process are working well and which are not. This final motive is much more inconclusive, however, and has to do with seeing the process completely and in detail, in order to make continual improvements quickly and easily. Again, the Japanese have emphasized this point very strongly.

1.2.4 Overall Objectives and Categories of Inventory Costs

Most quantitative inventory models consider revenue as fixed (or hidden in a penalty cost) and hence use cost minimization as the optimization criterion. However, occasionally revenue effects are important, so that profit maximization will be considered explicitly. In this Inventory module we will look primarily at cost minimization models.

Objectives. In minimizing costs, the technically correct method is Net Present Value, that is, to multiply future period t costs by $(1 + r)^{-t}$, add them up, and find a decision which minimizes these discounted costs. One way to simplify the mathematics of the model is to use models which minimize average costs per period. In these models one simply treats interest as an expense. We will discuss and compare both types of models.

Average cost per period formulations turn out to be excellent approximations to the NPV equivalent whenever decisions are really being made only on how much to purchase or produce in the near future. We designate such problems as "short-horizon problems." Recognizing short-horizon problems in management science is very important in general, precisely because simpler and more intuitive models are adequate.

Categories of Inventory Costs. While all the advantages and disadvantages to holding inventory that we have discussed previously are extremely important, in practice we mostly simplify them into four categories: holding cost, order cost, stockout cost, and salvage value.

Holding Cost. The holding cost, also known as the carrying cost or the inventory cost, is the sum of all costs which increase with the amount of inventory being carried. This may be defined as "on hand," meaning physically present at a specified time, or as "in system," meaning all inventory on hand or in the process of being delivered from former orders (also known as "book" inventory). Often the yearly holding cost is approximated as simply a percentage of the value of the merchandise.

For example:

22 %	=	cost of capital
5 %	=	storage, taxes, and insurance
3 %	=	obsolescence
1 %	=	spoilage
31 %	=	"hard" cost of holding
10 %	=	subjective factors
41 %	=	"total" cost of holding

By breaking the cost of holding into a conservative and a liberal estimate in this fashion, the manager gives his/her superiors more flexibility in their thinking.

Suppose now that management accepts the 31 percent figure and would like an interpretation of what it means. An item valued at $250 would have an annual holding cost of $h = (0.31)(\$250) = \$77.50$. If we held 500 of these items for three years, the total holding cost over the three years would be $(\$77.50)(500)(3) = \$116,250$.

Order Cost. Usually the ordering (or purchase) cost is approximated as being comprised of two components: $K + cx$. K is referred to as the setup cost, while c is referred to as the unit production or purchase cost. The order cost function is shown in Figure 1-1.

It is often stated in textbooks that the setup cost K should include only the actual explicit costs incurred when the order is made. For example, in a purchase order one would include the paperwork costs of making the order, the fixed costs independent of the size of the order that might be charged by the vendor, costs of order generation, handling costs, and costs of receiving the order. Authors of these books would say that the costs of maintaining the purchasing department should not be allocated or prorated into the setup costs, since they are sunk costs and do not vary with the decision to order.

This is true if the purchasing department has a low utilization. However, if it is congested, adding a new purchase order will increase the waiting time of the other orders, and thus increase effective lead times on ordering stock. Hence some price should actually be charged for purchasing department usage to reflect implicit costs being added to all the other orders being processed. This issue will be discussed more completely in the Scheduling module.

Production costs are a little more complicated than purchasing costs. Setup of an order on a machine will typically involve both an explicit setup cost and a setup *time*. The time used should be multiplied by the appropriate congestion price for the machine to obtain an implicit setup cost. The explicit and implicit setup costs would then be added together to get an overall setup cost on the machine.

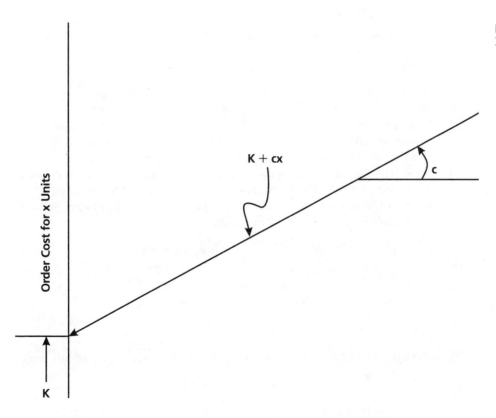

Figure 1-1

The Order Cost Function

Similarly, the variable cost of production of the item on a machine would consist of direct variable costs such as materials, variable labor, power, and so forth, as well as the implicit variable cost, due to delaying other jobs, of the processing time on the machine.

Stockout Cost. The stockout cost is also known as the **shortage cost**, or sometimes simply as the **penalty cost**. Suppose at a given point there is an inventory I_s (called the starting inventory) and a demand D occurs, leaving an ending inventory I_e, that is: $I_e = I_s - D$. If the ending inventory is negative, that number of units is called the stockout or shortage. At one extreme, called the lost sales case, these unmet sales are simply lost (or are met in some different manner such as an emergency shipment, at higher cost). The company incurs a stockout cost P per unit for each item lost, and then inventory is reset to zero. In the lost sales case the penalty per unit includes both the explicit lost revenue for the item and the implicit customer dissatisfaction. The latter is difficult to measure, but it is important to make at least some crude estimate.

At the other extreme, called the backlogging case, these unmet sales are patient and will be served when inventory becomes available again. The penalty here is usually taken as proportional to the time the customer waits; that is, the penalty is pt. (Many texts use p for both types of stockout, but we prefer the clarity.)

Salvage Value/Cost. Sooner or later any item will be discontinued. After the last order has arrived and that customer has been served, the ending inventory I_e at that point must be disposed of. Usually this is assumed to bring a salvage value of v times the ending inventory (if positive), where v is less than or equal to the variable ordering cost c. The difference is called the salvage cost per unit s, where $s = c - v$. In an important special case where the item is still actively sold elsewhere, the salvage value may be as much as c, so that $s = 0$, simplifying the model.

1.2.5 Inventory Purposes Exercises

1. Discuss briefly:

   a. Three levels of inventory control
   b. The two basic questions of short-term inventory control
   c. Three strategic questions in inventory control

2. Discuss from your personal experience two motives for holding inventory and two motives for not holding inventory. (These motives should not be listed in the text.)
3. Pretend you are a new manufacturer. Choose a specific product to manufacture. Discuss specifically the four types of manufacturing inventories (see Types of Manufacturing Inventories) that would arise for this particular product.
4. Shove It rents earth moving equipment. Each basic Wildcat tractor costs the company about $120,000. The inventory of tractors varies monthly depending on the number of rentals that month. During the last five months of last year, Shove It had the following ending inventories of tractors:

Month	# of Wildcats
August	17
September	12
October	20
November	52
December	117

The company uses a 22 percent cost of capital. Storage is 6 percent and liability insurance is 3 percent.

    a. Determine the total handling cost over the five-month period, based on ending inventories.

    b. Assuming you can extrapolate these five months, estimate the average annual cost of the tractor inventory.

    c. Do you see any problems with your assumption in problem 4b?

5. Universal Computers is a discount computer store in Raleigh, North Carolina. It carries 650 different inventory items and has gross annual sales of $4,500,000. It is trying to decide how much it can afford to invest in a new inventory system with operating expenses of $53,000 a year. Savings are estimated at 2 percent of gross sales. How much can it afford to pay and still get a five-year payback?

6. Discuss special motives for holding/not-holding inventory for Universal Computers in problem 5.

7. Universal Computers orders a high-end notebook computer from Itashi, Japan. It takes seven weeks to receive each order. Universal's records reveal that on the average, over the last two years, it has ordered 52 notebooks every three months. Assume for sake of discussion that demand is very regular, so that orders and shipments repeat regularly.

    a. What is the annual demand for notebooks?

    b. Plot pipeline inventory (ordered but not received) as a function of time over a one-year period. What is the average pipeline inventory?

    c. Multiply the annual demand by the replenishment time as a fraction of a year. What do you notice?

8. Consider the following inventory history.

Month	Units Received	Demand
Start Inventory	380	—
January	220	530
February	155	620
March	610	415
April	195	455
May	550	225
June	1135	655

    a. Determine ending inventory for each month if excess demands are backlogged.

    b. What is the total cost in this case at $2 per backlogged unit per month? (Assume demand occurs at the beginning each month, while ending inventories and costs are evaluated at the end of the month.)

    c. Determine ending inventory for each month if excess demand is lost.

    d. What is the total cost in this case at $10 per lost sale?

1.3 TYPES OF INVENTORY PROBLEMS AND METHODS

1.3.1 Overview

There is a rather large variety of different types of inventory problems and systems, and many approaches for solving them. We provide just a brief overview of these models in this section.

1.3.2 Classification of Inventory Problems

It is useful to give a relatively simple classification of the types of inventory problems. In actually demonstrating procedures to solve these various kinds of problems, we shall start with the most basic cases and gradually build up to more advanced scenarios. Our classification is given in Table 1-1.

Demand Type. Demand type refers to the underlying behavior of demand after smoothing out "noise." The simplest and most important case is when the underlying process is **level**. That is, demand is basically constant or stationary, with the possible exception of noise and similar exceptions.

The next important case is when the underlying process is **lumpy**. It may indeed be rather constant over the long run, but in the short run, big orders may alternate with small ones or periods of no demand. Demand into an MRP (material requirements planning) system is often like this.

For the *seasonal* case, demand may be quite smooth in a given month, but will have large peaks at certain times of the year (other seasonal lengths occur occasionally, such as weeks or quarters) and valleys at other times of the year.

The *general* case is essentially a combination of the seasonal case and the lumpy case, except that in addition the pattern may not really repeat very well from year to year due to trends and cyclical and competitive factors.

Forecast Quality. Inventory control is always based on some sort of a demand forecast over a relevant period. (Six to ten weeks is typical for retail and wholesale forecasting; 13 to 26 weeks is more common for MRP forecasting.) In some cases this forecast may be accurate within 10 to 20 percent, especially if there are a few large customers who place orders in advance. In this case we say the forecast is **good** (alternative terms are **known** or **deterministic**); we simply model demand as being given.

In retail and wholesale inventory, the uncertainty is more likely to be 25 to 50 percent, and we will model demand as probabilistic (typically normal with a certain mean and standard deviation). This is called the **probabilistic** case (or the **stochastic** case).

In strategic situations, or new product introductions and so forth, it may be somewhat foolhardy to pretend we know the mean and standard deviation of demand. We say our forecast is very **poor**. Modeling techniques such as scenario forecasting or the Delphi method may be more appropriate. Other terms used for this situation are **risk** and **uncertainty**. (Unfortunately, these terms are often confused with the probabilistic case.)

Table 1-1

Classification of Inventory Problems

Type	Cases
1. Demand Type	Level Lumpy Seasonal General
2. Forecast Quality	Good (Known) Probabilistic Poor
3. Inventory Motive	Economies of Scale (Setups) Limited Capacity Probabilistic/Uncertainty
4. Review Method	Continuous Periodic
5. Stockout Type	Backlogging Lost Sales Mixed
6. Lead Time	Zero Fixed Variable

Inventory Motive. From the list of motives for maintaining inventories considered previously, we shall consider only two here: the setup cost motive for either the deterministic or probabilistic cases, and the stockout avoidance motive in the probabilistic case.

Review Method. The review method refers to the way one decides when to make a new order. In a **continuous review** system, one updates the inventory and forecasts each time an order is disbursed (this is also called a **transaction** system). An order may be triggered when the inventory is seen to fall below a given level. Thus review and ordering can occur at any point in time.

In a **periodic review** system, one does not keep track and consider ordering transaction by transaction, but simply accumulates the transactions, corrects the forecasts, and makes a new order on a regular basis. (Typically this is once a month, but sometimes once every two weeks or every week.) The upkeep on such a system is lower, although the inventories required are therefore somewhat higher. A periodic review system is also useful in coordinating multiple-item orders to the same vendor.

Stockout Type. We have already discussed the stockout types somewhat, but we repeat them for clarity. Under the **backlogging** assumption, customers facing a stockout are assumed to wait indefinitely for their order, and the inventory is shown as negative to show the debt. Under the **lost sales** assumption, customers will not wait at all, and inventory is reset to zero. There are a number of possible **mixed** cases, which unfortunately typically complicate the model.

Lead Time. The lead time is the time between the moment an order is placed and when the merchandise arrives in inventory. Lead times may vary greatly depending on the number of resources required and how congested these resources are currently. If the order is placed to a wholesaler across the street who carries adequate inventory, then few resources are involved and the lead time will be quite short. In such a case, it is convenient to model the lead time as *zero*.

If long transportation times are involved, or if the vendor typically produces after receiving the order, then it may be convenient to model the lead time as a *constant*. However, if either transportation or the shop floor have variable loads over time, the lead time will vary significantly and may be treated as *probabilistic*.

1.3.3 Types of Problems—Exercises

1. Give three examples in each case of products/industries where

   a. Demand is fairly constant and fairly deterministic
   b. Demand is seasonal and fairly deterministic
   c. Demand is level but lumpy/variable
   d. Demand is both seasonal and highly variable

2. Give three examples in each case of products/industries where the main motive for holding inventory is

   a. Economies of scale
   b. Limited capacity
   c. Probabilistic/uncertainty

3. Give three examples in each case of products/industries where the review method is likely to be

   a. Continuous
   b. Periodic

4. Give three examples in each case of products/industries where stockouts are likely to be primarily handled by

   a. Backlogging
   b. Lost sales
   c. Mixed

5. Give three examples in each case of ordering situations in which lead time may likely be modeled as

   a. Zero
   b. Fixed
   c. Variables

1.4 SUMMARY AND PREVIEW OF THE INVENTORY MODULE

Inventory Chapter 2 considers known demand inventory models of a number of types. The general rolling horizon approach is discussed first. Section 2.2 uses a company application scenario to illustrate the basic inventory problem. Section 2.3 considers the simplest case—lot sizing models with level demand. Models analyzed include the basic EOQ model and extensions. Section 2.4 again considers lot sizing models with deterministic demand, but now allows the demand to vary arbitrarily over time. Section 2.5 reconsiders the application problem in light of our newly acquired tools.

Inventory Chapter 3 considers the case of uncertain demand. Section 3.2 presents Uncle Sam's Seafood once more, focusing on safety stock issues. Section 3.3 develops periodic review models; here, ordering is done on a regular cycle. Section 3.4 gives a brief introduction to continuous review models, and shows that the myopic solution procedure is still an excellent approach. Section 3.5 visits Uncle Sam's Seafood a final time, to incorporate safety stocks into our earlier work.

Inventory Chapter 4 puts together much of what has been learned in the Forecasting module and the Inventory module into a discussion of practical forecasting/inventory systems. It also explores a number of recent developments in inventory modeling. Many of these developments have been spearheaded by Japanese manufacturers, although they have been adopted and further refined by most major firms around the world.

Inventory Models with Known Demands

2.1 INTRODUCTION

In Inventory Chapter 1 we discussed a number of important (and often subtle) motives for carrying or not carrying inventory. We also presented a number of variations in assumptions in inventory models that we need to consider. These issues tend to complicate our consideration of inventory problems, and to make our life a little more interesting. A different difficulty is that inventory models tend to be complicated mathematically and to contain a number of variables. To gain insight into what is really going on, it is important whenever possible to use approximate models that have fewer variables and are easy to analyze. Often such simple models turn out to approximate more complicated situations very nicely. Learning how to tell when this is so is a skill that is profoundly important, and not typically easily learned in the business world. We emphasize learning this "approximate simplicity" skill.

One way to simplify models is to assume that demand occurs at a known fixed rate over time. This is a good approximation to many real situations. We study such models first, and through sensitivity analysis show that the results are not very sensitive to medium-sized errors in demands or estimates of the cost parameters. As a bonus, the simple EOQ result that we obtain turns out to be a useful part of the solution to many more complicated models.

Another way to simplify models is to use formulations that minimize average cost per period, rather than a technically correct discounted net present value (NPV) formulation. The errors in using the average cost per period method are approximately corrected for by treating interest as an expense. A useful insight here is that this approximation is excellent whenever the effects of wrong decisions are correctable in a short period of time; that is, so called "short-horizon problems." We will see that this is true because interest compounding doesn't have much effect in under a year.

Another justification for using oversimplified models is that they may be fairly accurate for the near future, where forecasts are good. The near-horizon simplification can then be used repeatedly in a rolling horizon approach. We explain this rolling horizon idea next.

The Rolling Horizon Approach. The decisions a businessperson makes in the current time period will affect the kinds of decisions he or she can make in the next time period, which in turn will affect the profitability of decisions in the following time period, and so on. Thus, the model maker who understands how all the decisions are interrelated would really prefer to solve a very large model stretching very far in the future (often glorified by the name **infinite horizon model**). Such a model is extremely difficult to solve computationally. What's worse, the quality of forecast information about demands, costs, and other needed information drops off very rapidly after about three to six months into the future, so that what is being solved further out would be of such low quality that it would be of little use.

For this reason, a rolling horizon procedure is usually employed in real applications. Two parameters are chosen by experience or by intuition, namely C, the **planning cycle**, and T, the **forecast horizon**. The planning cycle, or frequency of replanning, will often coincide with the order cycle in periodic review inventory models. This is most often taken as one week, two weeks, or one month at the tactical or requirements level.

Suppose at time t the last planning cycle is complete and it is time to initiate a new plan. The decision maker uses estimated data from the time interval $(t, t + T)$ to plan decisions using some optimization model that is based on the same T period interval. The early part of this solution is relatively reliable, since it mostly uses the forecasts in the early part of the interval. The latter part of this solution is relatively unreliable, but gives us some help in determining the long-range effects of the early decisions. We use only the more reliable decisions from time t until time $t + C$, and then make a new plan, using updated forecasts from $t + C$ to $t + C + T$. We then use the first part of this solution, from $t + C$ to $t + 2C$, and use the improved forecast at $t + 2C$, to solve the problem from $t + 2C$ to $t + 2C + T$, and so on.

One great advantage of the rolling horizon approach is that we may be able to use a simpler model over just T periods than over a long horizon. For example, even though demand is really not deterministic, it may be known rather well for three months into the future. Also, even though demand is really not all that level, it may be fairly level for three months into the future. Then we may be able to use $C = 1$ week, $T = 13$ weeks, and solve successive 13-week horizon models, using the first week of the new solution each time. We will discuss these ideas more thoroughly after we develop the level deterministic lot size model in Section 2.3.

2.2 COMPANY APPLICATION SCENARIO—UNCLE SAM'S SEAFOOD

Uncle Sam's Seafood (USS) is a gigantic wholesale and retail fresh fish outlet located in the heart of Pittsburgh's Strip District. (The Strip District is an area two blocks wide and fifteen blocks long just outside downtown Pittsburgh, between the railroad tracks and the Allegheny river. It is the center of wholesale distribution of produce, meat, and fish for the greater metropolitan area of 2.5 million people.) USS was one of the first in the area to fly in live lobsters, fresh shrimp, other shellfish and fish at a premium price some fifty years ago. It has expanded in a number of ways, and now does a very large business in frozen lobsters, shellfish, and fish as well. It also sells related gourmet meats and foods, and recently has added a limited broader selection of groceries for the customers' convenience. It has a large restaurant on the premises that is very popular. USS earns about $3.4 million a year on revenues of $24.6 million.

Uncle Sam has a variety of different but important stocking problems to sort out. For example, if a special grade of extra large gulf shrimp becomes available, Uncle Sam knows that once these shrimp arrive, any not sold within three or four days must be marked down and sold quickly at a loss (or frozen and sold at a loss). Thus, he must order a quantity that balances the lost revenue of lost sales through not having enough with the holding cost and salvage losses of ordering too much. (We have simplified the problem here for the sake of the example. Practically, there would be competition from other types of shrimp and several markdowns in price might be possible. These complications become more important for lobsters, which can be kept somewhat longer in the tank.)

At the other extreme, finding a good solution for the same grade of frozen shrimp poses a fairly different problem. It has a shelf life of perhaps six months in a carefully controlled freezer. Here the tradeoffs are between holding costs associated with ordering a large amount at one time and the ordering setup costs associated with the mechanics of ordering.

USS has some frozen products, such as turkey, that are highly seasonal in nature. Here the EOQ-type principles would seem to apply, except that it would appear to make sense to order larger quantities in periods of high demands and lower quantities during the rest of the year.

Interactions between product inventories can also cause problems. At times Uncle Sam finds that while individual lot sizes seem reasonable, the overall storage needs are sometimes greater than total freezer capacity. Could the lot sizes be adjusted downward to accommodate this? Should more freezers be bought? How many? What if orders cover a number of different products at once? How should the ordering costs be shared among the orders? How low should stocks of the previous order get before he places another? When should price break choices be taken?

2.3 LOT SIZING—STEADY DEMAND

2.3.1 Overview

Models for which demand is relatively well known for a reasonable time into the future and for which the primary tradeoffs are holding costs versus economies of scale are called **lot sizing** models. The most fundamental and best known of such models assumes that demand is also relatively constant and that economies of scale are simply embodied in a setup cost. This model is generally called the **EOQ** model (for economic order quantity). The very simplest version of this model gives rise to many children models (variations), hence we term it the **Granddaddy EOQ** model.

2.3.2 Granddaddy EOQ Model

The Basic Model. We make the following assumptions:

1.   The demand rate is a known D units per unit time.
2.   The setup cost is K per order placed.
3.   There is a proportional ordering cost of c per unit.
4.   There is a holding cost of h per unit per unit time.
5.   The objective is to minimize average total cost per unit time.
6.   No shortages are allowed.
7.   The entire order is received immediately.

(The last assumption may be changed to a fixed lead time, as we shall see.)

In this model units are arbitrary, as long as they are consistent. The default unit of time is assumed to be a year. Similarly, product units could be units, dozens, tons, or dollars. We notice that:

1.   There is no point in producing or ordering except when inventory is zero.
2.   Each order should be of the same size Q.

To see exactly why these facts are true, study Figure 2-1. Note that the area under the sawtooth is proportional to the total holding cost. If we could produce a policy with the same number of setups, but smaller area, it would obviously be a better policy.

Now look at the first ordering point, where we have assumed that inventory for some reason is not zero. If we had simply waited until inventory was zero before ordering, we would have saved a cost of the amount ordered early, times the amount of time ordered early, times the holding cost. This shows point (1) above.

There is also no loss of generality to assume that time zero is set at an ordering point. Now if we ordered say, Q, at time zero, then at the next time inventory drops to zero, the situation looks exactly the same as at time $t = 0$: same inventory, same pattern of expected demand, and same costs. Thus we certainly may as well order Q again. This shows (2), giving the picture shown in Figure 2-2.

Figure 2-1

EOQ Model–Inventory
Levels from Arbitrary
Ordering Policy

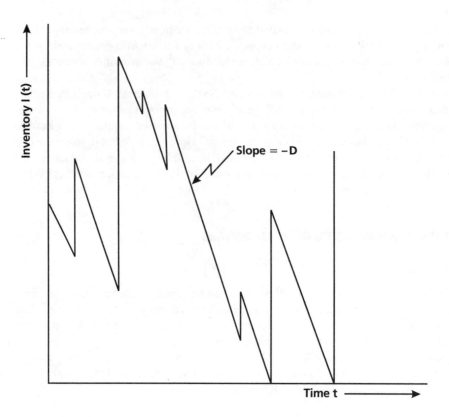

Figure 2-2

EOQ Model—Inventory
Levels from Reasonable
Policy

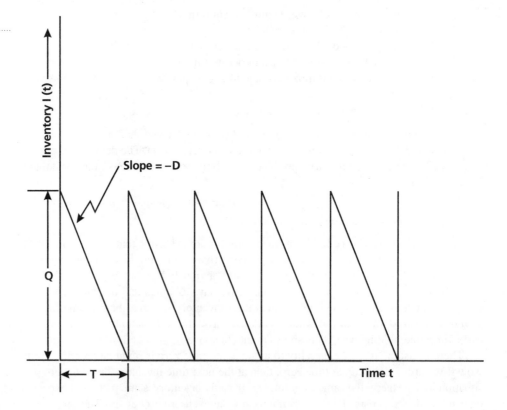

The time between orderings is given by $T = Q/D$. At first blush one might think that we would want to minimize the total cost per ordering cycle. However, the ordering cycle is shorter for smaller Q, and hence the average cost per time unit may go up even as the cost per cycle continues to go down. Another way of saying this is that T is really $T(Q)$ and we must consider this in the minimization.

Next, we derive an expression for the average (annual) cost as a function of the lot size Q. Looking at Figure 2-2, the average inventory level is $Q/2$; thus the annual inventory cost is $hQ/2$. The average number of setups (annually) is $N = D/Q$, so that the average annual setup cost is $K(D/Q)$.) The average annual purchase cost is cD, however it is not relevant to the decision, since it is independent of Q. Thus the total annual incremental cost C_I is

$$C_I(Q) = (KD)(1/Q) + (h/2)Q \qquad (1)$$

Now we wish to find Q^{**} to minimize $C_I(Q)$. (We use ** to represent the Granddaddy result, and * to represent any model variation or child we create later.) We assume that the function is defined and has a derivative everywhere on an interval. In this case, the minimum must occur either at some place where the derivative is zero or at one of the two endpoints.

A type of function called **convex** is especially easy to deal with. Convex functions are U-shaped (essentially they have a positive second derivative). Facts about convex functions include:

1. Any power such as AQ^a for any a, and $A > 0$ is convex.
2. Sums of convex functions are convex.
3. A convex function can have a zero derivative in the interval in at most one place.
4. If such a place exists, it is the minimum.
5. Otherwise, the minimum occurs at an endpoint.

We see by inspection that (1) is a convex function. Taking the derivative of (1) and setting it equal to zero yields

$$-KD/(Q^{**})^2 + h/2 = 0 \qquad (2)$$

This yields a square root formula for Q^{**} with both positive and negative roots. However, only the positive root is in our interval. Note that we have managed to avoid taking the second derivative, which is not a big deal here, but can be extremely painful for more complicated functions.

We can then write down rather easily formulas for Q^{**} the Granddaddy EOQ, C_I^{**} the optimal incremental cost, and T^{**} the cycle time between orders.

$$Q^{**} = [2KD/h]^{0.5} \qquad (3a)$$

$$C_I^{**} = hQ^{**} = 2\,KD\,/Q^{**} = [2KDh]^{0.5} \qquad (3b)$$

$$T^{**} = Q^{**}/D \qquad (3c)$$

Formula (3a) occurs many times in this Inventory module, and you will probably find it useful to memorize it. If you remember that holding costs at optimal are obviously $(h/2)Q^{**}$ and that holding costs and setup costs are equal at the optimal, you will remember that total costs are hQ^{**}. Thus the formula for C_I^{**} is the same as for Q^{**}, except that h gets moved upstairs.

Example 2-1. Eaton water bond typing paper at the local stationery store is sold at a rather steady rate of 80 reams per week. The paper has a wholesale value of $5.00 a ream and sells for $12.00 a ream. It costs the store $30.00 to place an order; holding costs are based on an annual rate of 20 percent. Determine the optimal number of reams of paper for the stationery store to buy per order, and the number of orders to place per year. What is the optimal yearly holding cost and the optimal yearly setup cost for this item?

Solution. First we must convert all inputs to standard units. We choose to convert interest to a weekly rate, to be consistent with sales. The weekly holding cost is (1/52) times the holding rate times the variable cost, so that $h = (1/52)(0.20)(5) = 0.0192$. Substituting into the EOQ formula, we obtain

$$Q^{**} = [2KD/h]^{0.5} = [(2)(30)(80)/(0.0192)]^{0.5} = 499.6, \text{ rounded to } 500$$

The number of times to order per week is $N = D/Q^{**} = 80/500 = 0.16$. Thus the cycle time is 6.25 weeks. The average annual holding cost is $(h/2)Q^{**} = (0.50)(500.) = \$250$. The average annual setup cost is also $250.

Example 2-1 illustrates some of the problems that may arise using simple models. Ordering every 6.25 weeks may be inconvenient; the store might wish to order every month or every two months, or perhaps every six weeks. What would the cost penalty be? We could simply calculate the costs from (1) of these alternatives, but we will learn an easier method using sensitivity analysis, discussed in the following paragraphs. Another issue is that the store might actually buy several items from the vendor simultaneously. How could we calculate a compromise order frequency for several items? Also, if the store has very limited shelf space, 500 reams of paper could conceivably be inconvenient. We will consider these issues next.

Consideration of the Order Lead Time. We assumed, in deriving the EOQ formula, that the order would be produced/delivered immediately, with zero lead time. Of course, that is never exactly true. However, this causes no problems when demands are known, and the lead time is relatively fixed and known. Suppose in Example 2-1 that the typing paper had to be ordered two weeks in advance. If we simply place the order for 500 reams of paper two weeks before our inventory will run out (before the end of the cycle), the order would arrive exactly at the right time, as if there were no lead time. The optimal placement of the order is shown in Figure 2-3.

In practice we would not want to specify that the order should be placed exactly two weeks before the end of the cycle, because the estimated end of the cycle might be somewhat in error. It is thus better to specify the reorder to occur when there are exactly

Figure 2-3

EOQ Model—Deriving the Reorder Point for the Example

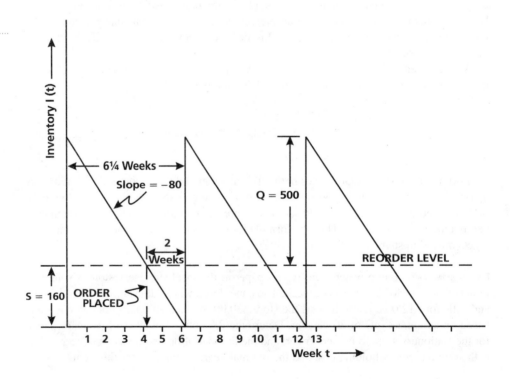

two weeks of expected needs on hand. This amount of inventory is called the **reorder-point.** ("When your stock gets down to 160, that's the time to buy some more.") From Figure 2-3, we can see that s, the reorder point, is the product of the lead time L and the demand rate (time for both in the same units), that is, $s = DL$. (Here it is easier to convert both to weeks.) For the example, using weeks, $s = (2)(80) = 160$.

2.3.3 Sensitivity Analysis

In this section we examine the question of how important it is to follow the EOQ formula exactly. We want to learn how to estimate how sensitive costs are to changing Q for practical reasons some amount from the "optimal"; or how much does it cost us to make typical errors in estimating D, K, h, and so forth?

What would it cost in Example 2-1, for instance, to order every month; that is, to take $Q = D/N = 4160/12 = 346.7$ rather than $Q^{**} = 499.6$? The simple brute force way to solve this would be to calculate $C_I(Q) = KD/Q + hQ/2 = (30)(4160)/(346.7) + (1)(346.7)/2 = 533.40$ whereas $C_I(Q^{**}) = \$499.60$. The penalty is about $\$33.80$ or 6.8 percent, even though our percentage error in Q was $(Q - Q^{**})/Q^{**} = (499.6 - 346.7)/(499.6) = 30.6$ percent.

We could find this cost penalty in this straightforward way for any particular problem. However, we can gain considerable insight into the way the cost error varies with the percentage error in Q by developing a general formula for this relationship. It is possible to look at a problem and estimate the approximate cost of changing the Q in our head! We do this, more specifically, by deriving an expression for the ratio of the non-optimal cost to the optimal cost as a function of the ratio of the non-optimal to the optimal order quantities.

Let Q^{**} be the optimal order quantity, and C_I^{**} the optimal incremental cost. Because setup and holding costs are equal at the optimum, we know that

$$C_I^{**} = 2[hQ^{**}/2] = 2[KD/Q^{**}] \tag{4a}$$

and that

$$[C_I/C_I^{**}] = [KD/Q]/C_I^{**} + [hQ/2]/C_I^{**} \tag{4b}$$

Substituting (4a) twice into (4b):

$$[C_I/C_I^{**}] = [KD/Q]/[2KD/Q^{**}] + [[hQ/2]/[2hQ^{**}/2]$$

or, finally:

$$[C_I/C_I^{**}] = 0.5[\ Q^{**}/Q + Q/Q^{**}\ ] \tag{5}$$

Equation (5) is the central formula for sensitivity analysis on the Granddaddy EOQ formula. For example, if the actual Q chosen were 2.0 times the optimal Q^{**} then the cost penalty ratio would be $0.5(2 + 1/2) = 1.25$, so that we would pay exactly a 25 percent cost penalty.

For small percentage errors, the result of (5) may be estimated easily. Define $Q/Q^{**} = (1 + x)$ where x is close to zero, then

$$[C_I/C_I^{**}] = 0.5[\ (1 + x) + 1/(1 + x)\ ]$$

but we know

$$1/(1 + x) = 1 - x + x^2 \ldots$$

so that

$$[C_I/C_I^{**}] = 1 + x^2/2 \ldots$$

or

$$[C_I/C_I^{**}] = 1 + x^2/2 \text{ approximately} \tag{6}$$

That is, the fraction error in cost goes up as the square of the fraction error in the order quantity. Thus a 10 percent error in Q produces about $(0.1)^2/2$ or $(1/2)$ percent error in cost. A 5 percent quantity error produces a (1/8) percent cost error; and a 20 percent quantity error produces about a 2 percent cost error. (The actual answer by plugging into (5) is 1.7 percent but for *estimating* sizes of *errors* this is probably accurate enough.) Notice that, since the cost error goes up as the *square* of the order error, a 20 percent order error is about 16 times as serious as a 5 percent error. Notice that changes in the quantity of 10 to 20 percent are not cause for serious concern. Notice also from (5) that the cost error is multiplicatively symmetric; the same cost error will occur if we order 30 percent more than optimal or if optimal is 30 percent more than our order. (Note that this is not quite the same thing as saying the cost is symmetric whether the order is 30 percent too large or 30 percent too small. If the order is 30 percent too small, then the optimal quantity is $(1.0/0.7 - 1.0)$ or 43 percent larger than the order. Thus, a high error of an amount D is less important than a low error of an equal amount.)

We have talked thus far only about the effects of errors or changes in Q from "optimal." But how do errors in estimating such cost/demand parameters as h, K, and D affect cost? Our solution to this question is to translate errors in the parameters into an error in Q, and then use (5) or (6) to translate this error in Q into an error in cost.

Let us start by investigating how Q^{**} would be affected if K were in error by a percentage, so that we measured the setup as $K(1 + \Delta K)$, where Δ represents the relative error in estimating K. Using equation (3a) we would have

$$[Q/Q^{**}] = [2K(1 + \Delta K)D/h]^{0.5}/[2KD/h]^{0.5} = (1 + \Delta K)^{0.5} \tag{7}$$

Thus the ratio change in Q is just the square root of the ratio change in the setup cost, and in the same direction. By exactly the same arguments we may determine that

$$[Q/Q^{**}] = (1 + \Delta D)^{0.5} \text{ and } [Q/Q^{**}] = (1 + \Delta h)^{-0.5} \tag{8}$$

Formulas (7) and (8) are quite easy to use, and give exact results. However, for percentage errors in costs/demands of only about 10 to 20 percent there is an excellent approximation which is even easier.

Recall from your calculus that there are easy and effective approximations for taking the square root of a number which is close to 1.0. Let the number for which the square root is desired be $(1 + a)$ where a may be positive or negative. Then:

$$(1+a)^{0.5} = 1 + 0.5a + \ldots \tag{9}$$

That is, $(1 + a)^{0.5}$ can be approximated by $(1 + 0.5a)$. The error involved in this approximation is proportionate in size to a^2. If a is 0.1, for example, a^2 is 0.01, so the error will be very small.

Thus for a percentage error of ΔK in the setup cost K, by (8) and (9) the error in Q will be about $(1/2)\Delta K$, and by (6) the percentage cost error will be about $(1/8)(\Delta K)^2$. The same will hold for percentage errors in D or h.

Example 2-2. Powersave, a supermarket wholesaler, sells about 6000 cases of Oh-So-Slim diet cola a year. Fixed charges from the factory are about $400 per order. The wholesaler uses a 2.5 percent holding cost rate per month. A case of cola from the factory costs $3.20 and is sold to retailers for $4.50. Because Oh-So-Slim is sweetened with aspartame, which has a limited shelf life, Powersave has a policy of discarding any inventory not sold within two months of purchase. What standing order size should they use? If this standing order size is less than the EOQ, what cost penalty is incurred? What cautions might be given about the solution?

Solution. First we compute the EOQ. The monthly demand for cola is $6000/12 = 500$. The monthly holding cost per case is $(.025)(3.20) = 0.08$. From the Granddaddy EOQ formula the optimal lot size is $Q^{**} = [(2)(400)(500)/(0.08)]^{0.5} = 2236$. This represents $T^{**} = Q^{**}/D$ months supply, so that $T^{**} = 2236/500 = 4.45$ months' supply.

Since Powersave's policy means it cannot buy more than a two months' supply, the standing order should actually be a two-month supply, or 1000 cases. To see the cost of the shelf life restriction, we can employ sensitivity analysis. Since $Q^{**}/Q = 2236/1000 = 2.236$ is not close to 1.0, we cannot employ our approximations. Using (5) directly, we have that $C_I/C_I^{**} = 0.5(2.236 + 1/2.236) = 1.342$ so that the cost penalty on setups and holding combined is 34.2 percent. Now with no shelf life restriction $C_I^{**} = hQ^{**} = (0.08)(2236) = \$178.88$ a month. The shelf life restriction costs us an extra $(0.342)(178.88) = \$61.18$ or $\$0.12$ a case, which is 9 percent of the gross markup on the item, and hence quite significant to Powersave.

2.3.4 Critiques of the Granddaddy EOQ

The basic EOQ model is very widely used in practice. However, there are a number of criticisms made of it. We will consider three types of them here:

1. Minimizing net present value is superior to minimizing average cost per time.
2. It is not important to exactly optimize an existing poor system (call this the process improvement issue).
3. The model should be more complicated and realistic.

Net Present Value (NPV) versus Average Cost. Here we sketch the NPV version of the EOQ model, and show that, although this model is technically superior, it really leads to essentially the same answer. Let r now be the interest rate, and g be the holding cost per unit time net of the cost of capital (since that is now taken into account by discounting future cash flows). That is, $g < h$, where h included an interest charge. That is, if c is the cost per unit of the item then

$$h = g + rc$$

We keep the symbols K for the ordering cost, D for the demand forecast per unit time, t for a point in time, and $T = Q/D$ as the cycle time for a particular order size.

It is still clear for this revised model that we should order only when inventory is zero and that time between batches T should always be the same. Finally, without loss of generality, we may assume that inventory is zero at time $t = 0$. Thus, for any T we might pick, we could determine the corresponding cost $C(T)$ (no longer incremental) by the following recursive relationship:

$$C(T) = (K + cDT) + D \int_{t=0,T} [(g)(T-t) - c]e^{-rt}dt + e^{-rT}C(T) \qquad (10)$$

$C(T)$ on the left says that the sum of the terms on the right gives the total discounted cost for a particular T. The first term on the right says that our current ordering cost is the setup plus the unit cost c times Q which is DT. The second term adds up our total inventory cost from now until the end of the first cycle. At time t, the inventory level will be $D(T-t)$ with a holding cost rate of g, and at the same moment we will be obtaining revenue of c at the same rate, all discounted back to the present by e^{-rt}. (Additional revenue is being obtained in addition to c, but it does not depend on T and so is sunk.) The integral adds up this cost over the time interval $[0,T]$. The third term says that we can take advantage of symmetry rather than computing the cost of the second cycle, then the third cycle, and so on. By symmetry, at the start of the second cycle we will face total discounted future costs of $C(T)$ all over again. But they are of somewhat less concern, since we may discount them back to the present again.

Although we shall not do it in detail here, it can be shown that we can solve (10) as closely as we want by using the Taylor series expansion for e^{-rt}:

$$e^{-rt} = \sum_{j=0,\inf} (-1)^j [(rt)^j/(j!)] \qquad (11)$$

After substituting (11) into (10) and collecting terms we would find that

$$C(T) = (1/r)[K/T + (1/2)(g + rc)DT + (1/12)r^2KT + \ldots]$$

And substituting $Q = DT$ gives

$$C(Q/D) = (1/r)[KD/Q + (g + rc + (1/6)r^2K/D)(Q/2) + \ldots] \quad (12)$$

Now suppose the units are annual. Since r is about 0.1 so that many terms are small,

$$C(Q/D) \text{ is approx. } (1/r)[KD/Q + (h + error)(Q/2)] \quad (13)$$

Thus, inside the brackets we just have the Granddaddy expression for average cost per unit time, with a small correction on h to reflect compound interest effects! And all the $1/r$ multiplier does is to capitalize the cost flow per unit time into a total equivalent discounted cost, so that, indeed, the two models give the same answers up to a very good first order approximation!

As an example, suppose that $c = \$100$, $g = \$10$ per year, $r = 0.15$ per year, $K = \$100$, and $D = 1000$ units per year. This will give $h = 10 + 0.15(100) = 25$, (correction to h) = $(1/6)(0.15)(2)(100)/(1000) = 0.005$, or 0.02 percent, a very small correction indeed, since we already have an idea that the cost error would be about the square of this error divided by 8!

Process Improvement Issues/JIT. There is a popular new school of thought in competitive companies around the world to the effect that improving the manufacturing and/or distribution of a product (process improvement) is strategic for the company, while such issues as optimal setting of the ordering and other parameters for the existing procedures (current process) are tactical only. Thus, it is often argued that inventory models such as EOQ are somewhat a waste of time, and may even be harmful.

One such strategic process idea which came about as the result of the Kanban system at Toyota is called **Just-In-Time** (JIT.) This philosophy says that for a number of reasons discussed in Inventory Chapter 1 (for example, identification of quality problems before inventories of defective parts accumulate), inventories are *evil* and should be held to zero! This is typical Japanese hyperbole (remember zero defects); what is meant is that inventories should be reduced to the absolute bare essentials. Then we should keep on striving to reduce them further!

Consider the case of Powersave again. The JIT strategic group would probably ask questions like:

1. It seems excessive to spend $100 six times a year or $600 for orders on a product which sells in total only 6000 cases a year. There must be a clever redesign of the process to reduce the setup cost drastically. For one example, why not coordinate ten orders at a time on the same order form? Maybe the order cost goes up to $120, but the effective demand for the aggregate product will be 60,000 cases a year. The EOQ will go up by a factor of $[(120/100)(60,000/10,000)]^{0.5} = 2.683$. Thus the new EOQ will be $(2236)(2.683) = 5999$. However, in months' supply for the aggregated product this is only $(12)(5999)/(60,000) = 1.20$. Thus, this one process change, aggregating ten orders together and coordinating them, has reduced optimal inventories from 4.45 months to 1.20 months, very much a JIT-type move. The general issue of multiple products in a common batch with a common setup and order cycle will be treated in Section 2.3.6, Multiple Products in a Cycle.

2. Considering all the strategic reasons for keeping inventories low discussed in Inventory Chapter 1, 2.5 percent inventory cost per month seems very low. Suppose the true holding cost should be 6 percent for strategic total reasons. By equation (8) this would reduce the EOQ in question 1 by the factor $(2.5/6.5)^{0.5} = 0.620$, so that the optimal EOQ for the aggregated product group would drop to $(0.620)(1.20) = 0.744$ months. Further, the strategic group might argue that since

it would be very difficult to get the accounting group to accept a 6 percent per month figure, and since these strategic motives are hard to quantify and even to understand in some cases, why not drop the EOQ idea entirely, and simply push harder for managers to drastically reduce inventories; that is, to simply adopt JIT as the dominant force?

This argument between EOQ and JIT is complex. Certainly Toyota can justifiably claim much success with JIT, and now a large number of manufacturers around the world have done likewise. However, it is important that the baby not be thrown out with the bath water. Every new approach must be evaluated carefully and adopted with common sense. If political issues do not get involved, and if it were easy to get everyone to agree on the solution to strategic issues, then the following combined EOQ/JIT approach would probably be valid.

EOQ/JIT Synthesis.

1. If holding costs and setup costs can be agreed on and are not under consideration for change, the EOQ approach is basically valid.
2. Every effort must be made to reduce setup costs by a number of means, and to strategically estimate the true holding costs.
3. Political considerations may make the relative usefulness of the EOQ and JIT paradigms vary considerably among firms and situations.

More Complex and Realistic Models. Other criticisms of the EOQ model have to do with it being too simple and needing more sophistication. Much of the rest of Inventory Chapter 2 and Chapter 3 address these complications. However, many times using the more complex models causes difficulties and confusion which can outweigh the theoretical savings involved.

2.3.5 Finite Production Rate

If we review Figure 2-2, we see that the sawtooth shape of the inventory level over time presented there implies that the batch comes into inventory all at once, and then is depleted at a constant finite rate D as demand occurs. This is appropriate if:

1. The goods are being ordered and arrive all at once. (The delivery lag does not matter here.)
2. The goods are being ordered and are paid for all at once.
3. The goods are being ordered, and any split payment is over an interval of time much shorter than the order cycle.
4. The goods are being produced, but the time taken to produce them is much smaller than the order cycle.

On the other hand, if the time over which goods arrive or are produced is a substantial part of the order cycle, we can make a correction. (The meaning of substantial will be quantified as part of the solution.) We will develop the model for a production run, but the split order case is really covered as well.

Let D be the demand rate for the product as before, and $P > D$ be the constant production rate. Then we may define $\rho = D/P$ as the fraction of the order cycle for which we produce. (During the rest of the cycle the machine may be busy on other products not in the model.) Exactly at the time when production finishes, we will have produced our order quantity Q, but ρQ will have already flowed out as demand, so that at this point inventory will be $(1 - \rho)Q$, and this will be the maximum inventory. The new inventory situation is shown in Figure 2-4.

Now the area of a triangle is just half the base times the height. The base is T, as in the Granddaddy model, but the height has been reduced from Q to $(1 - \rho)Q$. Now recall that

Figure 2-4

Inventory Sawtooth for the
Finite Production Rate Case

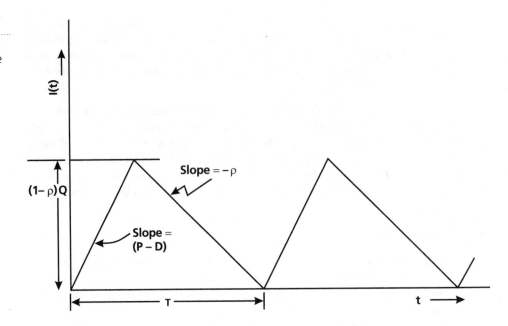

the holding cost in Granddaddy was $0.5hQ$; the new ordering cost will be $0.5h[(1 - \rho)Q]$. But this may be re-written as $0.5[(1 - \rho)h]Q$. Thus, we may simply use the Granddaddy model, with the only change being that the holding cost h has been decreased to $(1 - \rho)h$. (Intuitively, a fraction ρ of free units, which are never held, are being mixed with a fraction $(1 - \rho)$ at full cost.) We can stress this unity with the Granddaddy model by expressing our new answers in terms of the original. Remember ** represents the original Granddaddy result, and * our modified finite production rate result. The complete finite production rate solution is then:

$$h \rightarrow \quad (1 - \rho)h \tag{14a}$$

$$Q^* = (1 - \rho)^{-0.5}Q^{**} \tag{14b}$$

$$C_I^* = (1 - \rho)^{0.5}C^{**} \tag{14c}$$

$$T^* = (1 - \rho)^{-0.5}T^{**} \tag{14d}$$

Notice that as the demand rate D increases to P, so that the product occupies all of the machine, and ρ approaches 1.0, the order quantity goes to infinity and the average inventory level goes to zero. This just represents the case of a dedicated machine which produces its product continually. As expected, this is an efficient situation when it can be found, since there are no setup costs and no cycle inventory costs.

Example 2-3. A silicon valley software firm manufactures the software disc for the "Killer John" computer game. Demand is a fairly constant 2000 units per year, but the unit can be produced on the corresponding flexible manufacturing cell at 5000 per year. Cost accountants have certified that it costs $75 on average to initiate a production run. Each unit costs $2 to manufacture and is sold for $5 to the company which assembles the game. The cost of holding is estimated at 25 percent. Determine the best size for the production run, the time of the production run, the time length of the order cycle, and the annual incremental cost of holding and setup for the item, as well as the maximum inventory level for the item.

Solution. We modify h appropriately, and then solve the Granddaddy model. We see that $\rho = 2000/5000 = 0.4$. Thus the revised holding cost is $h' = (1 - 0.4)(0.25)(2.00) = 0.30$, and $Q^* = [2(75)(2000)/(.30)]^{0.5} = 1000.0$. The time length of the order cycle is simply $1000/2000 = 0.50$ years. The machine is 2.5 times as fast as needed, so that the time length of the production run is $0.5/2.5 = 0.2$ years. The annual cost is $h'Q^* = (0.30)(1000) = \$300.00$. Half of this is for setups, and half is for inventory cost as usual. The maximum inventory level is $(1 - \rho)Q^* = 0.6(1000) = 600.0$.

2.3.6 Multiple Products in a Cycle

In this section, we consider a multiple product extension of the EOQ model, in which we order several products as a group with a common cycle, or produce several products in the same rotation each cycle, to reduce total ordering/setup costs. (Review the process improvement discussion for the Powersave example in Example 2-2.) This larger model at first sight seems rather complicated, but is actually easily solved by aggregating the products and simply utilizing the Granddaddy EOQ model directly. For definiteness, we solve the ordering problem first, and then show the modifications necessary for the production floor version.

Ordering Multiple Products from a Vendor. It is very common for wholesalers/retailers to order a number of small or medium volume items from a common vendor at the same time, using a common order sheet with one line to each item order; thus, the items have a common order cycle.

In particular, distributors usually estimate a major setup cost K per order form called the **header cost** and a minor setup cost K_j called the **line cost** for each item j ordered. We consider only the simplest case, where a cycle time T is to be determined, such that all items will be ordered at the beginning of each cycle.

We analyze the problem by aggregating setup costs and holding costs, treating the resulting aggregate product by the Granddaddy EOQ methodology. The aggregate setup cost is the sum of the major and minor setup costs; the aggregate demand is just the sum of the demands; the aggregate holding cost is just the weighted average of the individual holding costs:

$$K' = K + \Sigma K_j \qquad (15a)$$

$$D' = \Sigma D_j \qquad (15b)$$

$$h' = [\Sigma h_j D_j]/[\Sigma D_j] \qquad (15c)$$

There are a number of special cases, when K, K_j and h_j are simply related, where the aggregated solution is even simpler. This will be investigated in the exercises.

Example 2-4. Reconsider Example 2-1. Actually, the stationery store sells six types of paper obtained from Hammermill Paper Co. and can choose to order all items in a common cycle, or all individually. The $30.00 setup cost per order given in that example was actually a sum of the header and line setups; that is, $K = \$28.00$ and $K_j = \$2.00$ for all items. All the paper wholesales for $5 a ream and retails for $12. The holding cost is still 20 percent per annum. However, demands for the six types of paper have a large range:

Paper #	Reams per Week
1	10
2	20
3	40
4	80
5	160
6	320

Note that paper #4 formed our example in 2-1, so that we already know if it was ordered separately the optimal cost would be $499.60. We also know from the Granddaddy formulas that the optimal cost when all other parameters are held constant goes up with the square root of demand. We have conveniently arranged the demands to go up by powers of two, just to save a little calculation. Thus the costs go up from product to product by $2^{0.5} = 1.41$, so that we quickly obtain the optimal costs if each is ordered separately as 176.49, 249.60, 352.99, 499.60, 706.54, 999.20; the total yearly cost if each item is ordered separately is $2984.42.

What would be the cost if we ordered them all together at a common frequency? Now $K' = 28 + 6(2) = 40$; $P' = 10 + 20 + 40 + 80 + 160 + 320 = 630$; $h' = h = (1/52)(0.2)(5) = 0.0192$. Thus $Q^* = [2(40)(630)/(.0192)]^{0.5} = 1620.2$ and $C_I' = h'Q^* = \$1620.20$. Thus group ordering is superior to individual ordering.

Multiple Product Production Cycles. In a similar fashion, items produced on a certain machine in a shop can very often be classified into groups of similar products. There is a major setup cost K for configuring the machine for the group and a minor setup cost K_j for fine tuning that adjustment for each product. As an example, the machine might extrude pipe into a smaller diameter. The major setup might involve setting the diameter incoming and outgoing and the metallurgical properties of the pipe. This might take, perhaps, 12 hours. The minor setup might be to set the machine further to a given pipe length, with a given finish on the ends; this might take half an hour. Notice that the whole repeated cycle for several products may take only a part of the machine's capacity, so that several of these aggregate products may be handled on the same machine. The finite production rate modification is easily handled by defining $\rho_j = D_j/T$, and decreasing each holding cost by $h_j \rightarrow (1 - \rho_j)h_j$.

In this simplest formulation of the production cycle problem, the analysis given above for the multiple product ordering from a vendor may be utilized directly. There is a complication directly in determining the setup costs K and K_j. Actually, in doing a major setup, there are two types of costs, an actual explicit cost E and a setup time S, which represents lost time on the machine. Even if the machine is not completely saturated, adding more setup time will increase lines throughout the shop and cause other work to be delayed. For this reason, management may assign a congestion price R per unit time for using the machine to cover the additional congestion. (If not, take $R = 0$.)

Thus the setup costs to be used in the EOQ formula would be:

$$K = E + SR; \quad K_j = E_j + SR_j \tag{16}$$

2.3.7 Planned Backlogging

There are many ordering and/or production situations in which the inventory manager will deliberately make a few customers wait at the end of a cycle until the new EOQ is produced; this is the planned backlogging case.

As an example, a supermarket may replenish the pop in the warehouse once every two months in an EOQ fashion. Toward the end of the period, if some brands are out of stock, the consumer will not know the policy was deliberate, and will usually substitute from other brands that are still in stock, or be promised by the manager that "the new shipment will be in next week."

The Model. The simplest assumption is that the backlogging cost p is like a holding cost in that the cost is proportional to the time waited. Clearly the ratio of p/h is likely to be much larger than 1.0. In the Granddaddy case, p was effectively infinite. The inventory diagram for this case is a little more complicated; it is shown in Figure 2-5. We now have two decisions to make:

Figure 2-5

Inventory Levels for the
Backlogging Case

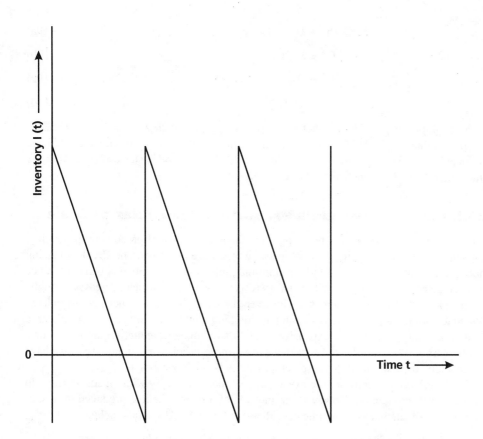

1. Choosing the order cycle T
2. Choosing what fraction of the cycle λ to be in stock

Our strategy is to first hold T fixed, and solve for the best λ. What Q' should be the maximum positive stocking level? If we are in stock λ percent of the time, consider the last unit we decide to stock. The extra inventory cost for stocking it is $h(\lambda T)$, while the stockout cost we saved by stocking it was $p(1 - \lambda)T$. If we were at the optimum λ, then the net marginal cost will be zero: $h(\lambda T) - p(1 - \lambda)T = 0$. Canceling T and solving for λ we obtain

$$\lambda = p/(p + h) \tag{17}$$

Now for a given T, allowing stockouts hasn't changed the setup cost in a cycle; however, our overall inventory costs are certainly lower. Let's see if we can "fudge" this into a decrease in h so that we can make use of the Granddaddy model to finish the job.

If we are in stock only the fraction of time λ, then also our maximum inventory level has been reduced by a factor λ. Since inventory costs are proportional to the area of a triangle λ times as high and λ times as wide, the inventory costs proper have gone down by a factor λ^2. However, we must not neglect the added stockout costs triangle. It has an area of $(1 - \lambda)^2$ times the Granddaddy inventory area, and in addition stockouts cost p/h times as much as holding costs. Thus, total inventory costs and stockout costs as a fraction of old inventory costs are exactly $\lambda^2 + (1 - \lambda)^2(p/h)$. But from (17) we see that $\lambda = (p/h)/[(p/h) + 1]$ so that $(p/h) = \lambda/(1 - \lambda)$; substituting in, the fraction of old inventory costs are exactly

$$\lambda^2 + (1 - \lambda)^2 \, [1/(1 - \lambda)] = \lambda \tag{18}$$

Thus, we may derive all the results we want from the Granddaddy results just by assuming that h has decreased by factor λ:

$$h \rightarrow \lambda h \qquad (19a)$$

$$Q^* = \lambda^{-0.5}Q^{**} \qquad (19b)$$

$$C^* = (\lambda h)(1^{-0.5}Q^{**}) = \lambda^{0.5}C^{**} \qquad (19c)$$

$$T^* = \lambda^{-0.5}T^{**} \qquad (19d)$$

As an example, if $p = 2h$, a rather low stockout penalty, then $\lambda = 2/(2 + 1) = 2/3$, $= 1 - 1/3$, so that $\lambda^{0.5}$ is 0.816. (By our simpler square root approximation, we could have estimated $(1 - 1/3)^{0.5} = 1 - 1/6 = 0.833$.) We would choose to be in stock 67 percent of the time, and Q^* would be increased about 22 percent.

2.3.8 Quantity Discounts/Production Economies of Scale

For a production system that is not congested, the average cost of processing, producing, and shipping an order usually goes down as the order size increases. The simple lot sizing model itself, with setup cost K and constant marginal cost c exhibits this behavior, since the average cost of an order O will be $(K + c(O))/O = c + (K/O)$ which decreases strongly, and then less strongly, as O increases. However, there are all sorts of other savings to large lots which are not a part of K. For example, shipping a large amount can use a rail car, a smaller amount needs a more expensive truck, a still smaller amount requires UPS or a similar carrier. Or, consider the fact that larger, more efficient machines typically have larger setup costs, so that they can be employed only for larger orders.

Producers need to consider the exact way that their costs vary with lot size in order to precisely plan production. However, the motives of a price schedule produced by a supplier for customers is more complicated. Reasons for giving discounts include:

a. If the supplier has strong competition, then most production savings must be passed on to stay in business.
b. Even with little competition, lower prices based on the lot savings may induce more total buying from the customer and thus produce larger profits.
c. Lower prices may encourage the buyer to find more uses for the goods.

Since the lot size situation for the producer and for the supplier are somewhat different, we will consider them separately.

Quantity Discounts from the Supplier. Quantity discounts are very common for goods of all types, whether retail, wholesale, or industrial. Although there are many different types of quantity discount procedures employed, there are two that are the most important: **all-units** and **incremental**. In both cases there are one or more quantity breakpoints, defining changes in the unit cost. The all-units case simply applies the discount effective in an interval to all units of the order; the incremental method applies the discount only to the units past the breakpoint. In either case, we wish to minimize an average cost function which is smooth on an individual interval but changes for the next interval. Thus, we may simply minimize costs on each interval, and choose the minimum of these. In turn, on each segment, the minimum occurs either at the EOQ point, if there is one on the interval (**realizable**), or at an end point of the interval.

Definition. The **critical set** is all the realizable EOQs plus the discount breakpoints. In Figure 2-6 there are three critical points: a realizable EOQ and two breakpoints. We can always solve the problem by evaluating the cost function at each critical point and choosing the minimum. Sometimes we can find shortcuts.

Example 2-5. The Prybar Can Opener Company issues the following price schedule to wholesalers for its top model opener. For orders of fewer than 50 openers, the company charges $60 per opener; for more than 50 but fewer than 150, it charges $55; for orders of

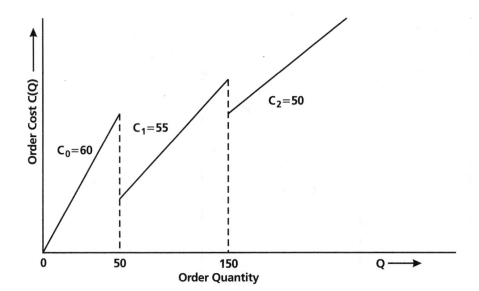

Figure 2-6

All-Units Discount Ordering
Function

150 or more, it charges $50 per opener. Note that this schedule is all-units. Mathematically we may define the ordering cost $C(Q)$ by:

$$C(Q) = 60Q \text{ for } 0 <= Q < 50$$

$$55Q \text{ for } 50 <= Q < 150$$

$$50Q \text{ for } 150 <= Q$$

The function $C(Q)$ is pictured in Figure 2-6. In Figure 2-7 we show the corresponding graph for the same example, but assume incremental application of the discount. Note that for the same example, the incremental method will always have higher average costs than the all-units method. (Of course, the manufacturer might compensate by giving smaller price breaks for the all-units method.)

The all-units method as it stands seems somewhat irrational. In the example above 49 units would cost $2990 while 50 units would cost only $2750. Why would Prybar be willing to charge less for a larger order? A different way to look at it is: why would the customer ever buy between 46 to 49 when 50 is cheaper?

The reason for the rather odd all-units method is that it is extremely easy to use and for the customer to understand. It probably goes back a thousand years. In the author's experience, the salesperson will refuse to sell 46–49 because "you'd be better off at 50." The salesperson will even try to avoid selling 40, because "10 more units will only cost you $35 each."

All-Units Case. Let us work through the analysis of the all-units case using Example 2-5.

Example 2-6. Assume Wallmat is a large discount chain which expects to use the can opener model at a fairly constant rate of 8000 per year. Its staff estimates the fixed cost of an order at $15 and holding costs at 25 percent of the variable cost. From Example 2-5, c_1 = 60, c_2 = 55, c_3 = 50 are the appropriate costs on the three intervals. The corresponding holding costs will be $h_1 = (.25)(60) = 15.00$, $h_2 = (.25)(55) = 13.75$, $h_3 = (.25)(.50) = 12.50$.

We first calculate the EOQs for each of these holding costs:

$$Q_1{}^{**} = [2(15)(8000)/(15.00)]^{0.5} = 126.5$$
$$Q_2{}^{**} = [2(15)(8000)/(13.75)]^{0.5} = 132.1$$
$$Q_3{}^{**} = [2(15)(8000)/(12.50)]^{0.5} = 138.6$$

Figure 2-7

Incremental Cost Ordering
Function

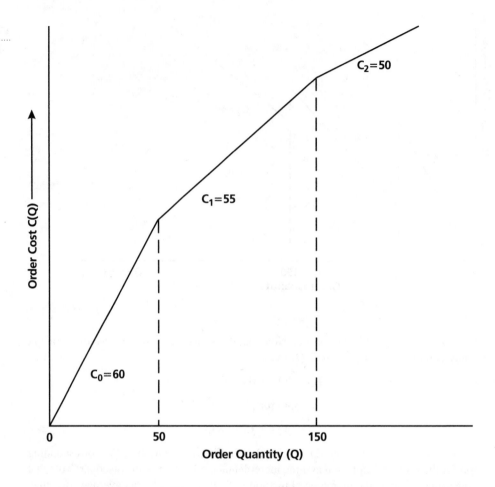

Remember that one of these EOQs is *realizable* if that quantity can be ordered at the unit price used in determining it. Note that these quantities are all for the intermediate price break, so that only Q_1^{**} is realizable in our example.

Look at Figure 2-8, which depicts the three curves (one for each possible unit price) of annual cost as a function of the order quantity and marks the realizable portions with the heavy lines. It is clear that the curve with the next price break always lies entirely below the previous one. That is, since Q_1^{**} is realizable, we will take at least this quantity, which is the cheapest for the first two curves. The only way we could achieve a lower cost would be to try the next breakpoint, since the cost can go down only here. There are thus two candidates for the optimal solution, 132.1 or 150. We choose between these two by the brute force method of simply calculating the annual cost for each choice.

The average annual cost for each curve is given by

$$T_{Ij}(Q) = DC_j + DK/Q + 0.25c_jQ/2$$

for feasible choices $j = 2$ or 3. Substituting $Q_j = 132.1$ and 150, and using c_j of 55 or 50, respectively, we have

$$T_{I2}\ (132.1)\ = (8000)(55) + (8000)(15)/(132.1) + (0.25)(55)(132.1)/2\ = \$441,800$$
$$T_{I3}\ \ (150) = (8000)(50) + (8000)(15)/(150)\ + (0.25)(50)(150)/2\ \ \ \ = \$401,900$$

Thus, we take the final price break and order 150 at a time.

Incremental Case. A consultant analyzing the Wallmat Company ordering rules in Example 2-6 used their data but erroneously assumed the price schedule was for incremental quantity discounts. That is, (s)he assumed that can openers cost \$60 each for orders of less than 50; the first 50 cost \$60 each and the remainder \$55 each for units after the

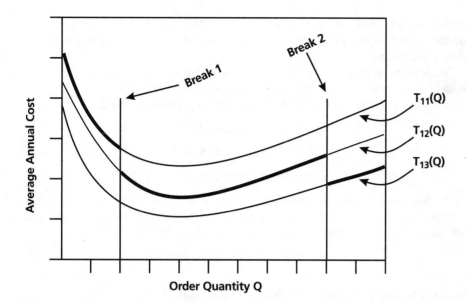

Figure 2-8

All-Units Average Cost
Function

first 50 but less than 150; the first 50 cost $60 each, the next 100 cost $55 each, and the remainder cost $50 each for units after the first 150. How can we mathematically express the incremental ordering cost function shown in Figure 2-7? With a small bit of figuring we see that

$$60Q = 60Q \text{ for } 0 <= Q < 50 \qquad (20a)$$

$$C(Q) = 3000 + 55(Q - 50) = 250 + 55Q \text{ for } 50 <= Q < 150$$

$$8500 + 50(Q - 150) = 1000 + 50Q \text{ for } 150 <= Q$$

Thus we see that

$$60 \text{ for } 0 <= Q < 50 \qquad (20b)$$

$$C(Q)/Q = 55 + 250/Q \text{ for } 50 <= Q < 150$$

$$50 + 1000/Q \text{ for } 150 <= Q$$

There are three average annual cost curves, depending on which of the three ordering intervals is involved. We can write the three generally as

$$C_{1j}(Q) = DC(Q)/Q + KD/Q + I\,[C(Q)/Q]Q/2 \qquad (21)$$

(I is the yearly holding cost rate as a fraction of the unit value. For our example $I = 0.25$.) If we substitute numerically and write them out these equations become:

$$C_{I1}(Q) = (8000)(60) + (15)(8000)/Q + 0.25(60)Q/2$$

$$C_{I2}(Q) = (8000)(55 + 250/Q) + (15)(8000)/Q + 0.25(55 + 250/Q)Q/2$$

$$C_{I3}(Q) = (8000)(50 + 1000/Q) + (15)(8000)/Q + .25(50 + 1000/Q)Q/2$$

Or after simplification:

$$C_{I1}(Q) = 480,000.00 + (15)(8000)/Q + 0.25(60)Q/2 \qquad (22)$$

$$C_{I2}(Q) = 440,031.25 + (265)(8000)/Q + 0.25(55)Q/2$$

$$C_{I3}(Q) = 400,125.00 + (1015)(8000)/Q + 0.25(50)Q/2$$

Each of these three functions is a standard Granddaddy EOQ formula, with a constant amount added for the purchase cost, an effective total setup cost increasing from 15 to 265 to 1015 and a holding cost decreasing from 15 to 13.75 to 12.50. We could plot each of the three curves as before, and mark with a heavier line the curve which applies in each of the three intervals.

We leave as an exercise for the reader to show that in the incremental case, the minimum of the composite cost curve cannot occur at a price breakpoint.

But we can find the EOQs using (22) and the Granddaddy formula:

$$Q_1^* = [2(15)(8000)/(0.25)(60)]^{0.5} = 126.5$$

$$Q_2^* = [2(265)(8000)/(0.25)(55)]^{0.5} = 555.3$$

$$Q_3^* = [2(1015)(8000)/(0.25)(50)]^{0.5} = 1139.8$$

Of the three, only Q_3^* is realizable, hence the optimal order quantity is 1139.8. We may compute the average cost in two ways, either using formula (21) directly, or recognizing that the cost will be the purchase cost plus the standard EOQ cost of hQ^*.

$$T_I^* = 407,019. + (.25)(50)(1139.8) = \$421,266$$

Other Discount Pricing Methods. Some methods try to modify the all-units method to avoid the possibility of paying more for less. In our all units Example 2-6, for example, 50 units cost 50($55) = $2750, while 40 cost 46($60) = $2760. In one method, called the boxcar method (because the price break comes for a full carload), buying 46, 47, 48 or 49 would cost $2750 also, and the user would be encouraged to take 50.

Note also, however, that ordering 44 units costs $2640, so that the next 5 units only really cost $16 each. Thus, the salesperson might discourage the buyer from buying just below the irrational area also.

Figure 2-9

Modifications of the Simple All-Units Method

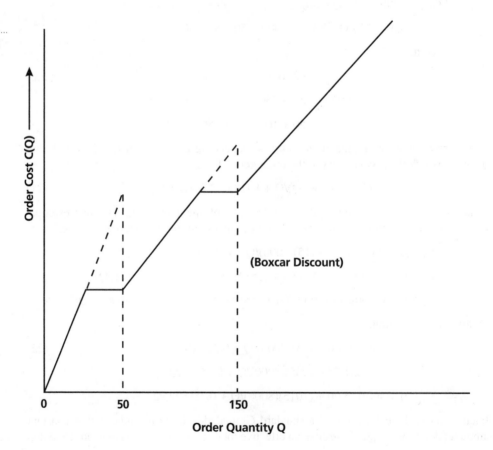

In a different kind of ordering method, the seller tries to impose some kind of a setup cost directly. In buying or selling bonds the cost might be "$10 plus 1/4 percent of value." Or there might be a minimum of 100 units in a sale, which is an indirect way of charging a setup cost. Or there might be a stated shipping charge independent of order size, or a cover charge, and so forth. In general, consumers don't like setup charges, which is why they are often hidden. Sometimes there is a rounding type charge, such as "$10,000 for each carload, plus $0.10 a pound for the remaining part carload."

Production Economies of Scale. Production shops also have situations which are similar to incremental quantity discounts. Suppose there is a choice of whether to machine a product by three different means. The simplest method is to have a worker produce it manually on a lathe. Suppose this method has a cost of $100 setup and $60 for each item in the lot. An intermediate method is to produce it in a flexible manufacturing cell. Suppose this method has a $1000 setup charge and $50 cost for each item in the lot. Finally, the lot can be produced on a modern flexible transfer line for a $5000 setup charge and $40 for each item in the lot.

It is clear that lots between 0 and 900 should be done manually, those between 900 and 4000 should be done in the cell, and lots above 4000 should be done on the transfer line. It should also be clear that the composite cost curve is exactly an incremental cost curve of the type we have just discussed, and can be solved in an identical fashion. We illustrate this cost curve in Figure 2-10.

As a different example, if the machine makes a number of types of products, the workers may "forget" to some extent how to make the product efficiently on the start of the next lot, and so may gradually get more and more efficient for a larger lot. This would lead to the inventory curve shown in Figure 2-11.

There are many types of situations where there are production lot sizes on the production floor, but many of these are too complicated to discuss here.

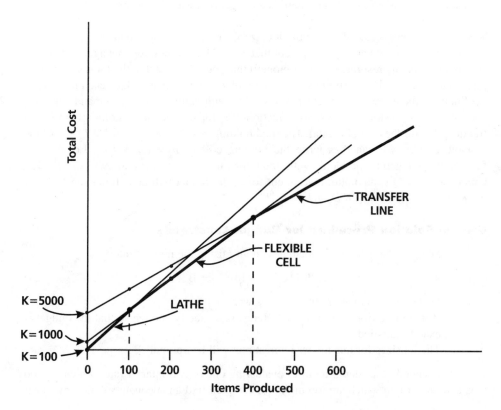

Figure 2-10

Choosing Between Three Production Methods

Figure 2-11

Production/Inventory Curve
with Learning & Forgetting

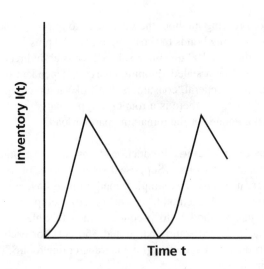

2.3.9 Multiple Products with Resource Constraints

Most of the EOQ models we have investigated so far have looked at single product models with tradeoffs essentially between setup costs and holding costs. In practice, whether it is on a production floor, or at a wholesale or retailer location, we will be lot sizing for many different items simultaneously. Although it is very simple to solve for each lot size separately and independently, this may not be accurate, for any of the following reasons:

    a. An overall budget constraint on maximum dollar inventories
    b. An overall warehouse constraint on the maximum inventory volumes
    c. An overall one-machine constraint on production times plus setup times
    d. A job shop constraint on total work-in-process inventory
    e. A job shop constraint on each machine's capacity for multiple machine jobs

    Here we consider cases where there is a budget or a warehouse constraint.

Budget Constraints. If use of the lot size formula in a shop produces total lot sizes which require more inventory investment than the budget allows, top management should simply raise the interest rate (price of money) that should be used in the lot size formulas just enough so that the constraint will not be violated, rather than reduce each lot size.

    Suppose there are N products $j = 1, \ldots N$, with setup costs K_j, demand rates D_j, variable costs c_j, a storage rate I_{js} as a fraction of c_j for storage, and a holding rate I_r as a fraction of c_j for the cost of capital. The total holding cost h_j is a fraction $I_j = I_{js} + I_r$ of the variable cost c_j. We can thus write the holding cost as $h_j = (I_{js} + I_r)c_j$. Let us look first at the budgeting problem, with total maximum investment allowed of B. The Granddaddy EOQ's maximum investment for each product will be c_j times the Q^{**}_j, or $c_j[2K_jD_j/(I_{js} + I_r)c_j]^{0.5} = [2K_jD_jc_j/(I_{js} + I_r)]^{0.5}$.

General Solution Procedure for Budget Constraints.

    1. See if the constraint is violated without raising the interest rate:

$$\Sigma[2K_jD_jc_j/(I_{js} + I_r)]^{0.5} <= B?? \tag{23}$$

    2. If there is no violation, the lot sizes were optimal.
    3. If there is a violation, raise the interest rate exactly enough so that the budget is exactly satisfied.
    4. The lot sizes for this higher interest rate will be optimal.

    In the general case, step 3 requires evaluating one or two interest rates which are too low, and one or two which are too high. We can then find an adequate solution by linear interpolation, or by graphing dollars used as a function of the interest rate, as shown in Figure 2-12. Note by looking at equation (23) that there is an important special case which is easy to solve without multiple solutions and interpolation. If the storage percentage costs are identical across products, that is $I_{js} = I_s$, then the total percentage cost $I = I_s + I_r$ will be identical across all products. So then, if I_r is increased by a certain amount, all holding costs h_j will go up by some common percentage, and thus all quantities Q_j will be reduced by the same percentage. Thus we need simply only reduce all Q_j^{**} by the common percentage necessary to achieve the budget! We state this more formally, as shown below.

Special Case for Budget Constraint.

1. Suppose that there is a budget constraint, and a constant storage percentage cost I_s across products.
2. Suppose that unconstrained lot sizes add up in dollars to $B^\# > B$.
3. Compute $f = B/B^\#$.
4. The corrected lot sizes are simply $Q_j^* = f Q_j^{**}$.
5. The corresponding interest rate is easily found.

Example 2-7, Budget Constraint. A retailer, Montgomery Roebucks, sells three "big-ticket" items (refrigerators, stoves, air-conditioners.) Management considers the cost of storage to be 10 percent per year for all items, and the cost of capital to be 15 percent per year. Management has budgeted a maximum dollar investment in these big-ticket items at $40,000. The other relevant costs and demand figures are given in Table 2.1. The items are ordered from separate vendors. What are the optimal order quantities which do not exceed the budget?

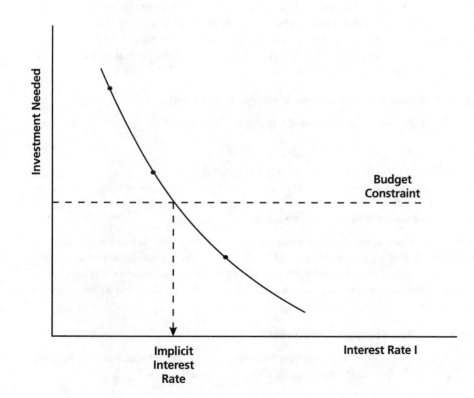

Figure 2-12

Determining the Budget Constrained Interest Rate

Table 2-1

	1	2	3
Demand	2000	800	950
Variable cost	300	450	240
Ordering setup	200	150	125

Solution. We first determine unconstrained EOQ solutions for each product:

$$Q_1{}^{**} = [2(200)(2000)/(0.1 + 0.15)(300)]^{0.5} = 103.3$$

$$Q_2{}^{**} = [2(150)(800)/(0.1 + 0.15)(450)]^{0.5} = 46.2$$

$$Q_3{}^{**} = [2(125)(950)/(0.1 + 0.15)(240)]^{0.5} = 62.9$$

We next determine the maximum dollar investment $B^{\#}$:

$$B^{\#} = c_1 Q_1{}^{**} + c_2 Q_2{}^{**} + c_3 Q_3{}^{**} = (300)(103.3) + (450)(46.2) + (240)(62.9)$$

$$B^{\#} = 66938 > 40000 = B; \quad f = 40000/66938 = 0.598$$

Thus the budget-adjusted order quantities are

$$Q_1{}^{*} = (.598)(103.3) = 62; \quad Q_2{}^{*} = (.598)(46.2) = 27.6; \quad Q_3{}^{*} = (.598)(62.9) = 38$$

To determine the effective interest rate to produce this result, notice that if quantities go down by the ratio of 0.598, then the holding cost must go up by $(1.0/0.598)^2 = 2.796$. Thus, I changes to $I^{\#} = (.25)(2.796) = 0.699$. But the rate for storage is 0.1, so the effective interest rate is $I_r{}^{\#} = 59.9$ percent. Top management should, perhaps, be advised that the restrictive budget has produced opportunities in raising lot sizes that return 60 percent; they may reconsider the budget restriction somewhat.

Storage Constraints. We now turn to considering storage constraints. The same general procedure works, except that we must vary an implied storage cost to restrict the lot sizes to the storage constraints, which is slightly more complicated. We now define the storage rate as $I_{js} = w(v_j/c_j)$ where w is the common storage cost per square foot, v_j is the square foot per unit for item j, and c_j, as before, is the unit cost of j. Thus, the storage cost per unit for j is $I_{js}c_j = w(v_j/c_j)c_j = wv_j$. Thus, in this case, we increase w to force smaller lot sizes to fit the storage constraint. We first give the modified general procedure, and then the one for the special proportional case.

General Solution Procedure for Storage Constraint.

1. See if the constraint is violated without raising the storage rate per square foot:

$$\sum v_j [2k_j D_j/(wv_j/c_j + I_r)c_j]^{0.5} <= V \; ?? \tag{24}$$

2. If there is no violation, the lot sizes are optimal.
3. If there is a violation, raise the storage rate w just enough so that the storage constraint is exactly satisfied.
4. The lot sizes for this higher storage rate will be optimal.

In general, step 3 again requires a search solution with a final linear interpolation or by graphing, similar to that in Figure 2-12. There is again a special proportional case which is easy to solve. The condition for a simple proportional reduction in all lot sizes to be optimal is that the cost per unit volume of all products be the same. (Watches and popcorn do not work.)

Special Case for Storage Constraint.

1. Suppose that there is a storage constraint, and a constant variable cost per unit per square foot of storage; that is, all c_j/v_j are equal.

2. Suppose that the unconstrained lot sizes add up in storage volume to $\Sigma v_j Q_j^{**} = V^{\#} > V$
3. Compute $f = V/V^{\#}$
4. The corrected lot sizes are simply $Q_j^* = fQ_j^{**}$
5. The corresponding effective storage cost is easily solved for.

Example 2-8, Storage Constraints. Montgomery Roebucks' top management has decided that the 60 percent interest rate implied by their big-ticket budget is too high. They decide to compromise by giving the big-ticket department an explicit cost of capital of 35 percent and removing the budget constraint. The 10 percent storage figure was actually fictitious, however, so they wish to assign a storage cost per square foot which will just use up the available space of 1800 square feet. Assume that the three big-ticket items consume 8, 15, and 12 square feet per unit, respectively. What are the order quantities resulting from the 35 percent charge, and from adding the storage constraint of V = 1800 square feet? What should management charge the department per square foot to induce it to find these optimal quantities on its own?

Solution. First we find the EOQs which result from the 35 percent cost of capital, and no storage cost:

$$Q_1^{**} = [2(200)(2000)/(0.35)(300)]^{0.5} = 87.3$$

$$Q_2^{**} = [2(150)(800)/(0.35)(450)]^{0.5} = 39.0$$

$$Q_3^{**} = [2(125)(950)/(0.35)(240)]^{0.5} = 53.2$$

Next determine if these quantities violate the storage constraint:

$$V^{\#} = (8)(87.3) + (15)(39.0) + (12)(53.2) = 1921.8 > 1800 = V$$

Yes, it does violate the constraint. Next we check to see if the simplifying proportionality assumption is satisfied:

$$c_1/v_1 = 300/8 = 37.5; \quad c_2/v_2 = 450/15 = 30.0; \quad c_3/v_3 = 240/12 = 20.0$$

Since these ratios are unequal, we cannot use the simple solution procedure. Rather we find $V^{\#}$ as a function of the storage cost rate w, and find the w for which $V^{\#}(w) = 1800$. We already know that $V^{\#}(0) = 1921.8$, so $w > 0$. Now,

$$V^{\#}(w^*) = \Sigma v_j [2K_j P_j/((w^*(c_j/v_j) + I_r)c_j)]^{0.5} = 1800 \qquad (25)$$

A good first guess is to approximate the c_i/v_i as being equal at their average value of $(1/3)(37.5 + 30.0 + 20.0) = 29.2$. If they were equal, we could use the special procedure to reduce all lot sizes by the same percentage, that is, by the ratio 1800/1921.8. This is equivalent to raising the holding cost rate from 35 percent to 35 percent of $(1921.3/1800)^2$ = 39.88 percent. We can find the implied w^* by solving $(w^*)(29.2) = (.3988 - .3500) = 0.0488$. Thus $w^* = 0.00167$. This is of course not the answer exactly. However, it suggests that we try $w^* = 0.00167$ as a solution to (25), to see how close it is, and whether it is too low or too high. Substituting in we have $V^*(.00167) =$

$$(8)[2(200)(2000)/((.00167)(37.5) + .35)(300)]^{0.5}$$

$$+ (15)[2(150)(800)/((.00167)(30.0) + .35)(450)]^{0.5}$$

$$+ (12)[2(125)(950)/((.00167)(20.0) + .35)(240)]^{0.5}$$

$$= 8(80.39) + 15(36.07) + 12(50.80) = 643.1 + 541.1 + 609.6 = 1793.8$$

Since, in this approximate solution, we are not using quite all of the storage space, our w^* must be too high. Notice, however, that 1793.8 only differs from 1800 by about 3/10 of 1 percent, so that this solution is really very accurate.

Since our starting solution was quite accurate, we might use it as a heuristic.

Heuristic for Storage Constraints.

1. Take an (weighted?) average of the variable costs per square foot of the various items.
2. Treat all items as having this value, and solve the proportional storage problem.
3. Obtain the implied storage cost per square foot.
4. Solve for the EOQs which would result from this storage cost.

Although these computations are somewhat tedious to do by hand, they can be carried out quite quickly and easily using spreadsheets or other computer software.

2.3.10 Lot Sizing Exercises

Granddaddy EOQ Model. Read the following problems, and write the answers on a separate sheet of paper.

1. An electronics outlet sells a particular type of compact disc player at a reasonably constant rate of 135 annually. The players are purchased from the parent company at a transfer price of $75.00 each, provided annual purchases exceed 100. The outlet figures that it costs $50 per order in terms of telephone calls, paperwork, and labor to place an order for the players. The parent company sets a cost of capital at 20 percent per year; the outlet estimates other holding costs at 8 percent per year.

   a. How many compact disc players should be ordered at a time?
   b. At what time interval will orders be placed?
   c. What is the annual cost of holding for this item?
   d. What is the annual cost of setup for this item?
   e. The current policy is to order twice a year. How much extra holding cost is involved? How much setup cost is saved?

2. Suppose in problem 1 that the replenishment time is four weeks.

   a. At what on-hand inventory should the outlet reorder?
   b. What is the average amount of inventory on order? (**Hint**: plotting the amount on order versus time may be helpful).
   c. How much demand occurs while waiting for an order?
   d. Relate (b) and (c).

3. The finance officer in a large firm needs about $10,000 in cash every day to pay everyday bills. He has $10,000,000 in bonds. Bonds pay 0.03 percent interest per day, the checking account pays nothing. Selling bonds to put in the checking account incurs a $50 transaction cost plus 1/4 percent of the value of the bonds.

   a. How much in bonds should be cashed at one time and added to the checking account?
   b. How often must the officer cash bonds?
   c. What is the yearly cost of fixed transaction costs and lost interest?
   d. How does the variable transaction cost rate affect your decisions?

4. A large appliance store sells about 450 refrigerators a year, 45 percent of which come from GE, at a wholesale cost of $380 each. The shop considers itself to have a cost of capital of 15 percent, storage costs of 8 percent, and miscellaneous holding costs of 4 percent. Each order has labor costs of $20, telephone costs of $4, and other paperwork and miscellaneous costs of $7.

   a. Determine the optimal timing and order quantity for the GE refrigerator orders.

b. If the replenishment time is five weeks, what is the reorder point based on inventory on hand?

c. The store currently buys refrigerators from GE once a quarter. What percentage extra cost does this entail?

5. Rita works for Nanosoft Corporation as a supervisor of software programmers. She earns about $35 an hour. She supervises Tim, who makes $20 an hour. Nanosoft costs their time at 1.8 times the direct labor cost. Rita knows from past experience that a formal review of Tim's progress takes four hours of preparation in advance, about one-half hour each for the review itself, and about one-half hour plus 0.05 hour for every eight-hour day since the last review. She also estimates (somewhat crudely) that, if T is the number of hours since the last review, then Tim's total production over the T periods will be $(\$60)(1.0 - 0.005T)T$. Rita would like to know exactly how often she should give Tim a formal review. (**Hint**: you can choose units so that $T = Q$ and $D = 1$.)

a. Solve the problem from first principles.

b. Carefully formulate by the Granddaddy model, and solve that way.

c. Rita has only had time to review once a month. What is the extra cost involved in terms of (review costs + Tim).

d. Since Rita is overworked, what is dangerous about accepting this solution?

Sensitivity Analysis.

6. In looking back at the solution to a Granddaddy EOQ problem, a manager discovers that the holding cost used turned out to be 20 percent too high, the setup cost was 45 percent too high, and the demand was 30 percent too low.

a. Using sensitivity approximations, estimate the percentage error induced in the order quantity, and in the total average incremental cost.

b. Repeat (a) using exact figures, and compare results.

7. Many managers say that if errors are made in lot-sizing it's better to be on the high side. Does your knowledge of sensitivity analysis justify this statement?

8. Reconsider the compact disc player lot sizing problem in problem 1.

a. Re-solve part (e) using approximate sensitivity analysis. Compare the approximate and the exact answers.

b. Suppose the setup cost were actually $70 rather than the $50 used in the example. What would be the exact and approximate error in the order quantity? In the total incremental cost?

c. What are the exact and approximate errors in the total incremental cost if the true setup cost was $70 and the true cost of capital was 30 percent rather than 20 percent?

9. In the Nanosoft Corporation example, suppose the 0.005 coefficient in Tim's total production over T periods formula is known so crudely that it could be anything from 0.002 to 0.010.

a. What is the range for the true optimal T^{**}?

b. What is the largest percentage cost error that could result by using 0.005 as the coefficient?

Critiques of the Granddaddy EOQ Model.

10. Suppose in a discounted lot size model that $c = \$400$, $r = 0.15$, $g = \$40$ per year, $K = \$1000$, and $D = 2000$ units per year. What is the approximate correction to h in converting the discounted cost model to the average cost model?

11. Reconsider problem 1 for the discounted cost case that is discounted by $e^{-0.20t}$ with no linear interest expense.
   a. Use equation (12) and the approximate sensitivity analysis to estimate the percentage difference in order quantity which would result by comparison with problem 1.
   b. What would be the approximate percentage improvement in cost by using the NPV model rather than the average cost model?

12. It is sometimes argued that JIT and Kanban work quite well for a very stable assembly line system with maximum production rate such as at Toyota in the 1980s but are more difficult to enforce when demand is highly variable or when it is necessary to produce in a job shop situation. Critique this argument.

13. One way the Japanese brought about drastic reductions in setup times is by developing ways to set up the next job in parallel while running the current job on the same machine. While this clearly reduces setup *times* for the job, explain situations for which it might or might not reduce setup *costs*, where we define the setup cost as direct setup costs plus lost time on the main machine times its congestion price plus lost time on the auxiliary machine times its congestion price.

Finite Production Rate.

14. The Meltit Company produces a chemical compound that is supposed to be superior to rock salt in de-icing roads and sidewalks. One of the main products, Meltkwik, can be produced at the rate of 8000 pounds per day. Annual demand for the compound is 1.2 million pounds per year. The fixed cost for a production run of Meltkwik is $210 and the variable cost of production is $0.38 a pound. The company uses 24 percent as its cost of capital and 12 percent for storage and handling. There are 300 days in a year.

   a. What is the optimal production run for Meltkwik?
   b. What portion of the time during the Meltkwik cycle time is it being produced, and what percent is it not?
   c. What is the total incremental cost annually for this product? How is that divided between holding and setup costs?
   d. If the compound sells for $0.70 a pound, what is the gross profit realized (before other expenses such as administration, marketing, and overhead)?

15. Now suppose the production rate in problem 14 was incorrectly treated as infinite.

   a. Find the optimal batch size under this erroneous assumption.
   b. Find the exact percentage increase in cost caused by this error.
   c. Approximate this increase in cost by sensitivity approximations.

16. Suppose that several products each are produced on the same machine, and that the total annual demand of these products is less than the total capacity of this machine. Suppose the production cycle for each product is calculated separately using a one-product finite production rate EOQ model.

   a. Show by example that there is no reason to believe that there is any feasible solution for which these different production cycles can coexist on the machine without interference.
   b. Suggest one or more ad-hoc procedures to fudge the system into feasibility in practice.
   c. Can you estimate how much cost these fudges may add?

Multiple Products in a Cycle.

17. A sheet metal job shop has a single all purpose NC machine. Currently there are four parts that are run in a common production cycle on the machine with a joint setup

cost of $200. Ignore the interaction of this machine with other machines needed for these parts. Holding costs are considered to be 25 percent per year; setup *times* are small. The other relevant information is presented in the following table.

Part Number	Annual Contract	Setup Cost	Unit Cost	Yearly Production Rate
1	3000	$85	$25	50,000
2	4500	130	65	20,000
3	1500	70	35	35,000
4	1200	100	50	45,000

    a. What part of the machine's capacity do these four parts use?
    b. What is the optimal cycle time T?
    c. What are the optimal cycle quantities for each product?
    d. What is the annual incremental cost for this solution?

18. Rita, at Nanosoft, (problem 5) finds that if she reviews all four programmers in a cycle, then she can reduce her advance preparation from four hours for each, to eight hours for the group plus one additional advance hour for each. Re-solve problem 5 using this cyclical policy.

19. Suppose in problem 17 you had made the approximation that production times were infinite.

    a. Solve the problem under this assumption.
    b. What difference in quantities would result? Cost error?
    c. Which would you suggest in practice, considering the importance of using very simple models for communication where possible?

Planned Backlogging.

20. Give four different products for which one might produce part of the demand after it occurs (that is, there is a production lead time) rather than in advance, where the motive would be to save costs toward the end of a lot size cycle.

21. Explain each of the following other motives for which one might produce a product after the demand, and give two or three concrete product examples for each.

    a. Custom product
    b. Deteriorating product
    c. Service product

22. Re-solve problem 1 if the backlogging cost is 2.5 times the holding cost; 5 times the holding cost, or 10 times the holding cost. In each case, how much would be the cost of using the problem 1 answers as an approximation?

23. Reconsider problem 3 with backlogging.

    a. Suppose the backlogging charge is 0.15 percent per day. Give the modified solution and compare it by sensitivity with the original in cost.
    b. What does deliberate backlogging represent here?
    c. Do you think any individuals or firms employ this strategy?

Quantity Discounts/Production Economies of Scale.

24. A computer manufacturer has an annual requirement of 24,000 fancy memory chips which are used in three different models of Pentiac personal computers. It can out-source them from another manufacturer at $3 per chip, as long as it will contract to buy 24,000 during the next year. It can produce them in a given flexible machine cell at $2.80 a chip with a setup cost of $500, or on a flexible transfer line

at $2.60 a chip with a setup cost of $1000. Assume a 30 percent cost of holding. Assume that a typical cyclic solution will be used.

a. What method should be used, and what is the optimal lot size?
b. What is the optimal incremental cost on an annual basis?
c. Other than the cost, what might be tricky about using the outsourcing solution?

25. A kitchen appliance wholesaler sells an aluminum frying pan by the following all-units schedule: minimum order 25 frying pans; for fewer than 50 frying pans $3.00 per pan, for 50 to 100 pans $2.75 per pan, for 100 or more pans, $2.50 a pan. Monty's department store sells 95 pans per year. The accounting department stipulates that the fixed cost of placing an order is $10, and holding costs are based on a 20 percent cost of capital, with 8 percent other holding costs.

a. What are the realizable EOQs?
b. What is the critical set?
c. What is the optimal order quantity?
d. What is the total cost per year?

26. In the calculation of an optimal policy for either the all-units or the incremental cost schedules, you first determine the value for which the derivative is zero for each of the three curves. Suppose you do this when there are three such curves, and obtain the values 850, 880, and 910 for curves 1, 2, and 3 respectively. The two breakpoints are 700 and 900 respectively.

a. What are the possible choices for the optimal quantity for the all-units case? Explain.
b. What are the possible choices for the optimal quantity for the incremental units case? Explain.

27. Classy Chassis sells frames for personal computers to computer manufacturers. For quantities ordered up to 50 of frame A, the firm charges $400.00 per frame, $360 each for 50 up to 200 frames, and $340 for each frame of quantities 200 or over. A small computer manufacturer expects to use about 180 per year. Order setup costs are $75.00 and holding costs are based on a 20 percent annual interest rate. What should the size of the standing order be?

Multiple Products with Resource Constraints.

28. A prefabricated home builder sells three popular styles of homes. Management considers the capital cost on unsold homes to be 20 percent and the cost of protecting the vacant homes to be 8 percent. (All dollar figures are in thousands.) Management has budgeted maximum dollar investment in unsold homes at 25,000. Homes sell at a rather regular rate. There is an economy to building a group of homes at once, which is modeled as a fixed cost. Variable cost of a home includes labor, machinery, and materials. The following table lists the demand, direct cost, and group setup costs for three years.

Item	1	2	3
Yearly Demand	800	950	1800
Direct Cost	90	150	80
Group Setup	125	175	200

Different style homes cannot be grouped together.

a. What are the optimal order quantities which do not exceed budget?
b. What would this unconstrained solution cost?

c. What are the optimal order quantities which fit the budget?

d. What is the effective interest rate due to the constraint?

29. Consider the Montgomery Roebucks Example 2-7 in the text again.

a. Solve the problem again for $V = 1500$.

b. Solve the problem again for $V = 1000$.

2.4 LOT SIZING—VARYING DEMANDS

2.4.1 Overview

The economic order quantity model which we have been studying assumes that demand is relatively known and relatively constant over time. There are many situations where demand is relatively known, but quite bumpy/erratic over time. These situations might be categorized as:

1. **Highly seasonal demand**—back to school period, Christmas, Easter, large planned sale period or periods, interference from new product

2. **Permanent demand change**—product being discontinued, new product market being added, new product competitor

3. **Erratic known demand**—large orders from industrial customers into MRP system, small volume retail luxury product, financial instruments, real estate

We illustrate these three demand situations in Figure 2-13.

(1) Highly Seasonal Demand

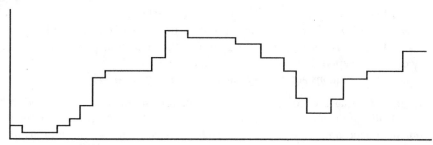

(2) Permanent Demand Change

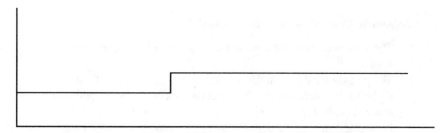

(3) Erratic Known Demand

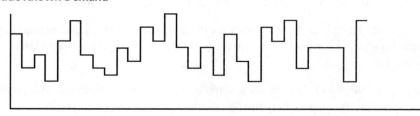

Figure 2-13

Types of Variable Known Demand

The only difference between the Granddaddy model and the varying demand case is in the complexity of the demand pattern, but it is quite a difference. In the steady demand case a single number D is sufficient to describe demand indefinitely. By looking at the sample varying demand patterns in Figure 2-13 we can see that fully describing future varying demand might get very complicated.

Fortunately, our sensitivity analysis results of Section 2.3.3 suggests that lot sizing models are not very sensitive to errors. We found that an error in Q^{**} of 10 percent involved only about a 1/2 percent error in cost. Although we will not prove it here, a similar result holds for a 10 percent error in the exact time a given demand occurs. Thus we simplify our description of the demand pattern without losing much accuracy. We divide the future into equal time intervals (buckets); usually one- or two-week buckets are chosen. We sum up all the demand that will occur in each bucket. All demand is assumed to occur at the beginning of the time period.

With this simplification, which is a very good approximation, any demand profile no matter how complicated can be represented simply as a sequence of one-period demand numbers. Because of the insensitivity of lot sizing models to small errors, it doesn't matter very much how complicated demand really is inside each "bucket":

Example Demand Pattern									
Time	1	2	3	4	5	6	7	8	9	10
Demand	0	17	19	40	18	6	0	0	15	0

2.4.2 Model; Heuristics

Introduction. We make the following simplifying assumptions:

a. Future time is divided into equal periods or "buckets."
b. Ordering or production happens only at the beginning of a period.
c. Demand is assumed to occur uniformly throughout the period.
d. An N-period finite horizon problem is to be solved.
e. Such solutions are used repeatedly on a rolling horizon basis.

The first lot sizing decision turns out to be not very sensitive to the demand in the far future. Utilizing this fact, we use a rolling horizon procedure: solve the current N period problem, produce/order the first lot size recommended, wait until this lot runs out, solve the current N period problem at that point (with improved forecasting information then available), produce/order the first lot size recommended, and so forth.

The Dynamic (Variable) Lot Size Model.

1. The objective is to minimize the sum of holding and penalty costs over an N-period horizon.
2. The periods have known demands $D_1, D_2, \ldots, D_t, \ldots, D_N$.
3. Ordering/production occurs at the beginning of a period t, with setup cost K, variable cost c, and quantity Q_t.
4. Ending inventories are denoted by I_t; successive inventories are related by $I_{t+1} = I_t + Q_t - D_t$; no backlogging is permitted.
5. A holding cost h per period is charged on ending inventory in the period.

Proposition. There is an optimal policy for the dynamic lot sizing problem requiring producing/ordering only when ending inventory from a previous period is zero (and demand is not zero).

Proof. The diagram below shows a supposed optimal production plan with production when inventory is not zero. In particular, suppose at some time k we produced with some

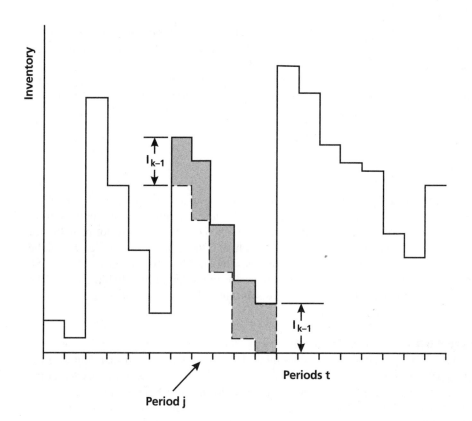

Figure 2-14

Proof that Production Is
Preceded by a Regeneration
Point

ending inventory I_{k-1} remaining in stock. Find the first previous production period j. An alternate plan producing I_{k-1} less in period j and I_{k-1} more in period t would produce the shaded inventory savings shown without any other cost changes. This contradicts the fact that the plan was supposed to be optimal.

A period where inventory is zero is called a **regeneration point**. Such points have a number of nice properties. We have proved here that production must come immediately after a regeneration point. The reverse is also true. Any regeneration point followed by a period of non-zero demand must be immediately followed by production. Call such a regeneration point an **active regeneration point**.

Proposition. In at least one optimal schedule:

a. Active regeneration points and production points alternate.
b. Each production is equal in amount to total demand for the block of periods between two successive active regeneration points.

Example 2-9. Pre-Fab Suppliers make a number of prefabricated products for home builders. Their demand for their Model 9 prefabricated kitchen is quite erratic. They produce the item for a setup cost of $40, and variable cost of $2000. They estimate their holding cost per unit at $10 per week (26 percent per year.) Their orders are booked almost completely for the next four weeks, and they have a fairly good idea of orders for the following five weeks. They estimate coming demands as:

Week	1	2	3	4	5	6	7	8	9
Demand	5	7	2	0	1	4	7	7	1

There is currently a starting inventory, due to inexact prior forecasts, of two kitchens. What production plan should Pre-Fab implement? When should they re-solve the problem to correct for new errors?

We will solve this problem by a number of different heuristics, and also by the optimal procedure, to illustrate and compare the different methods. (Some heuristics value by ending inventory, this does not affect their answers.)

The first thing we note is that opening inventory is not zero, as would be required by our model. This is easily handled by assigning the inventory to immediate demands in order, and producing the revised problem:

Week	1	2	3	4	5	6	7	8	9
Demand	3	7	2	0	1	4	7	7	1
Starting Inventory	0								

Lot-for-Lot Heuristic. The lot-for-lot heuristic assumes that the period length has been chosen to roughly approximate a good cycle time and thus simply produces every period without worrying about setup costs. Thus, the cost of the lot-for-lot heuristic for this problem will include nine setups at $40 each, or $360. Ending inventories will all be zero, so that total inventory cost is zero for this solution. Thus the total cost is $360 + $0 = $360. Notice that setup costs are much more for this solution than holding costs. The Granddaddy EOQ model had these two costs as equal. Thus, we might suspect this solution is far from optimal.

Simple EOQ Heuristic. In this heuristic we take advantage of the known robustness of the Granddaddy model, simply smoothing demand to be level and then applying the EOQ model, rounding to even periods as necessary. A small correction is needed at the end of the problem, since the leftover demand after the last EOQ may be too small to support a setup well. We make the simple change that if the leftover demand at the end is less than half of its suggested EOQ, then the final setup will be deleted and the needed amount added to the previous lot size.

In our example, the average period demand is $32/9 = 3.56$. Plugging this directly into the Granddaddy EOQ formula gives:

$$Q^{**} = [2(40)(3.56)/(10)]^{0.5} = [28.44]^{0.5} = 5.3$$

Thus we should try to set-up for every 5.3 units of demand. In our example, this suggests we produce for 3 in period 1, and 2.3 units of the 7 demanded in period 2. Rounding down, we produce 3 in period 1, and then produce again in period 2.

Starting over in period 2, we want to produce only 5.3 of the 7, but must produce for at least one period, so produce 7 for period 2 itself.

Starting over in period 3, if we produce 5.3, we produce for periods 3, 4, 5, and 2.3 of the 4 units in period 6. Rounding up, we produce 7 units in period 3, for 3, 4, 5, and 6.

Starting over in period 7, we produce just for 7.

Starting over in period 8, we produce just for period 8.

Starting over in period 9, we have only 1 unit of demand available for a desired amount of 5.3. So, by our ending correction procedure, we add it to the production in period 8. A simple way to show our production plan is (1)(2)(3 4 5 6)(7)(8 9).

The cost of this plan is five times $40 or $200 for setups. Computed inventories are shown below.

Period	1	2	3	4	5	6	7	8	9
Production	3	7	7	0	0	0	7	8	0
Demand	3	7	2	0	1	4	7	7	1
Ending Inv.	0	0	5	5	4	0	0	1	0

Thus, the total holding cost is $10(15) = $150 and the total cost of this solution is $200 + $150 = $350, which is less than for the lot-for-lot solution of $360. (With narrower buckets lot-for-lot would look much worse. Thus bucket size is an important issue.)

Rolling EOQ Heuristic. As before, we first calculate a Q^{**} over the whole nine periods as 5.3, but then convert this to a cycle time of $(5.3/32)(9) = 1.5$ periods. We set 1.5 periods as our shorter horizon, and calculate an EOQ based on demand in the first 1.5 periods. Average demand $= (3 + 0.5(7))/1.5 = 6.5/1.5 = 4.3$; corresponding EOQ is $[2(40)(4.3)/10]^{0.5} = 5.9$. So we try to produce 5.9 which rounds as before to 3 for this period.

In period 2, average demand $= (7 + 0.5(2))/1.5 = 5.3$; corresponding EOQ is $[2(40)(5.3)/10]^{0.5} = 6.5$. So we produce 7 for period 2 as before. Continuing in this manner, our rolling horizon EOQ solution is (1)(2)(345)(6)(7)(89). The setup cost is $240 and the inventory cost is $30, for a total of $270, the best solution so far.

The Silver-Meal Heuristic. The Silver-Meal heuristic tries various cycle lengths for the first period, and chooses the cycle length with minimum cost. This procedure is then repeated.

We define $C(j,k)$ as the total holding and setup cost per period if a production lot covers periods $j + 1$ to k, that is, periods j and k are neighboring regeneration points (0 inventory) and $A(j,k) = C(j,k)/(k - j)$ as the average cost per period over this lot. We try one period as the cycle, then two periods, then three periods, and so on, stopping when the cost first increases, and take the minimum to date.

We have
$$A(j - 1, j) = C(j - 1, j) = K$$
$$A(j - 1, j + 1) = C(j - 1, j + 1)/2 = [K + hD_{j+1}]/2$$
$$A(j - 1, j + 2) = C(j - 1, j + 2)/3 = [K + h(D_{j+1} + 2D_{j+2})]/3$$

or more generally,

$$C(j - 1, j + m) = [K + h(D_{j+1} + 2D_{j+2} + \ldots + mD_{j+m})]/(m + 1)$$

In doing the examples we will do the brute force calculations a few times, but then resort to the tabulation of all useful $C(j,k)$ as shown in Table 2-2.

(*Note:* Table 2-2 will be used a number of times in the rest of this section. You may find it useful to copy it to have it available in making and checking computations.)

For convenience we reproduce our example again:

Week	1	2	3	4	5	6	7	8	9
Demand	3	7	2	0	1	4	7	7	1

Now $A(0, 1) = 40$
$A(0, 2) = [40 + 10(7)]/2 = 110/2 = 55$

We produce for period 1 alone, since a two-period cycle is more expensive per period.

Table 2-2

Tabulation of $C(j,k)$

Cost of Lots Produced in Period $j + 1$ to Last Through k

Start $= j + 1$

j	k = 1	2	3	4	5	6	7	8	9
0	40	110	150	150	190				
1		40	60	60	90	250			
2			40	40	60	180			
3				40	50	130			
4					40	80	220		
5						40	110	250	280
6							40	110	130
7								40	50
8									40

Now we roll the horizon to period 2, and number from it.

$$A(1, 2) = 40$$

$$A(1, 3) = [40 + 10(2)]/2 = 60/2 = 30$$

$$A(1, 4) = [40 + 10((2) + 2(0))]/3 = 60/3 = 20$$

(From now on we use the table)

$$A(1, 5) = 90/4 = 22.5$$

Thus we produce in period 2 for periods 2, 3, and 4. Now repeat the process.

Our total plan is given by (1)(2 3 4)(5 6)(7)(8 9). From the table, the cost of this solution is $270, of which setup costs are $200, tied with rolling the EOQ for best solution.

The Least Unit Cost Heuristic. The Least Unit Cost heuristic (LUC) is identical to the Silver-Meal heuristic, except that we choose the cycle time which minimizes the average cost per unit of demand, instead of the average cost per unit of time. For convenience, define D_{jk} as the aggregated demand between periods j and k. Then the LUC heuristic involves calculating

$$U(0, 1) = C(0,1)/D_{11}$$

$$U(0, 2) = C(0,2)/D_{12}$$

$$U(0, j) = C(0,j)/D_{13}$$

As before, stop when the average increases; also use the same correction at the end of the horizon in case of a remainder small lot size. Hence the solution of the least unit cost heuristic is (1 2)(3 4 5)(6 7)(8 9). We see from the table that the cost of this solution is $380. This is much worse than any of the other heuristics.

Part-Period Balancing. The Granddaddy EOQ formula splits costs exactly equally between setup costs and inventory costs. We have seen previously that the heuristics which perform the best also split these costs nearly evenly. In the Part-Period Balancing method (PPB) we try more and more periods in the lot size, watching total inventory costs until they equal the setup costs. This may occur in the middle of a period (hence the name), in which case we round to the nearest period. Our final solution for this problem for PPB is (1 2)(3 4 5)(6 7)(8 9). This solution is identical to the result for the Silver-Meal heuristic and is the same cost as the rolling EOQ solution, or $270.

2.4.3 The Wagner-Whitin Algorithm

Introduction. The Wagner-Whitin [1958] algorithm (WW) solves the basic dynamic lot sizing model exactly rather than heuristically. We present a new version of the algorithm, whose computation is linear in the number of periods, rather than quadratic as for the usual algorithm. Thus, it is reasonable to say that except for very large system problems, or research work, computation time for the improved WW is not an issue. However, the heuristics we have learned are often understood and incorporated into more complex heuristics more easily; they are user friendly.

The Algorithm. Consider again the Pre-Fab Suppliers problem in Example 2-9. We reproduce for convenience the nine demands, recalling that we have a setup cost of $40, and a holding cost of $10 per unit per period. We also reproduce the $C(j,n)$ table.

Week	1	2	3	4	5	6	7	8	9
Demand	3	7	2	0	1	4	7	7	1

Table 2-2
Tabulation of $C(j,k)$

| **Cost of Lots Produced in Period $j + 1$ to Last Through k** |

Start = j +1

j	k								
	1	2	3	4	5	6	7	8	9
0	40	110	150	150	190				
1		40	60	60	90	250			
2			40	40	60	180			
3				40	50	130			
4					40	80	220		
5						40	110	250	280
6							40	110	130
7								40	50
8									40

Remember that we found it useful to tabulate $C(j,k)$, which is the total setup and holding cost for producing in period j for the entire interval (j,k) which is shown in Table 2-2. (We have taken the liberty to not show any $C(j,k)$ which could not be in the optimal solution because they individually are larger than some known solution to the entire problem! They grow monotonically as k is increased for the same j.)

One laborious way to get the optimum is to enumerate all the different ways the lots could break up the periods. For example, suppose we wanted the optimum solution just to the four-period problem. (That is, force ending inventory after four periods to zero.) There are just eight ways the periods can be broken up:

$$(1)(2)(3)(4) \text{ Cost} = 40 + 40 + 40 + 40 = 160$$
$$(1)(2)(3\ 4) \text{ Cost} = 40 + 40 + 40 = 120$$
$$(1)(2\ 3\ 4) \text{ Cost} = 40 + 60 = 100 \text{ (Min)}$$
$$(1\ 2)(3)(4) \text{ Cost} = 110 + 40 + 40 = 190$$
$$(1\ 2)(3\ 4) \text{ Cost} = 110 + 40 = 150$$
$$(1\ 2\ 3)(4) \text{ Cost} = 150 + 40 = 190$$
$$(1\ 2\ 3\ 4) \text{ Cost} >= 150 = 150+$$

This is quite practical for four jobs. However, for general N, the number of such possible partitions is $2^N - 1$. Thus, for our nine-period Pre-Fab Suppliers example, we would not evaluate $2^4 - 1 = 8$ costs, but $2^9 - 1 = 256$ costs. And for a 30-period problem, we would evaluate 2^{29} costs, or about 1 billion! There must be a better way.

There is. Note that we evaluated both $(1)(2)(3\ 4)$ and $(1\ 2)(3\ 4)$ in our solution. But this depends on which is better: $(1)(2)$ or $(1\ 2)$. This question will need to be answered over and over in longer problems. Why not determine that the best solution to the two-period problem is $(1)(2)$ with a cost of 80, save it in a table, and insert it in the solution to save time whenever needed? In particular, why not optimize the one-period problem, then the two-period problem, using our table for the one-period problem, then the three-period problem, and so on. Let us write $[[1,3]]$ as the optimal partitioning for the three-period problem, let $C(3)$ be its (optimal) cost, and save all these in a table.

Now we can reduce our brute force search to costing four choices rather than eight:

$$[[1,3]](4)$$
$$[[1,2]](3\ 4)$$
$$[[1,1]](2\ 3\ 4)$$
$$[[1,0]](1\ 2\ 3\ 4)$$

That is, we look at all possible choices for the last breakpoint. The cost of the part to the left has been saved as the optimum solution to a shorter problem, and is just looked up.

The part to the right is looked up in our $C(j,k)$. We start with the zero-period problem (which has cost = 0) and work up. The worksheet for our Example 2-8 problem is shown in Table 2-3 (n represents current problem length; $C(n)$ the optimal cost for that problem, and $j^*(n)$ the regeneration period which is one less than the optimal last time to produce). In case of ties, we pick the smallest j^* for n having the minimum cost. It can be shown that j^* increases in n, which means we only have to start with the last j^* each time. Thus the optimal cost is 260, about 4 percent cheaper than the best heuristic we tried.

To read off the policy here, we just read off the j^* column working backwards:

$$[[9]] = [[7]](8\ 9)$$
$$[[7]] = [[6]](7)$$
$$[[6]] = [[5]](6)$$
$$[[5]] = [[1]](2\ 3\ 4\ 5)$$

Thus the entire solution is $(1)(2\ 3\ 4\ 5)(6)(7)(8\ 9)$.

This is a simple example of a **dynamic programming** algorithm. (We did it intuitively first since dynamic programming has a bad reputation for being very difficult.) Dynamic programming algorithms recursively build new optimal solutions from old optimal solutions.

Updated Wagner-Whitin Algorithm. The updated Wagner-Whitin recursion is given by

$$C(1) = C(0,1),\ j^*(1) = 0$$

$$C(2) = \min\{\ C(0) + C(0,2);\ C(1) + C(1,2)\ \}$$

$$\ \cdot\ \cdot\ \cdot\ \cdot$$

$$C(n) = \min_{j=j^*(n-1),n-1}\{C(j) + C(j,\ n)\}$$

Define the optimal last regeneration point for an n period problem as $j^*(n.)$ Then the next to the last production point is $j^*(j^*(n))$ and so on. (Stop and make sure this makes sense to you.) Working backward gives the production plan. The improved algorithm follows from the fact that $j^*(n)$ is increasing, which we do not prove here.

The **regeneration set** idea, first developed by Lundin and Morton [1975], also tells us when we may guarantee that the first production (which is what we really want in a rolling horizon procedure) can be guaranteed not to change any further as n increases. This is called a **planning horizon**. It is beyond our scope to discuss these issues here.

2.4.4 Lot Sizing Exercises

Lot Sizing Heuristics.

1. Suppose a problem's bi-weekly demand pattern is relatively smooth, with seasonal factors no lower than 0.5 in the winter, or higher than 1.7 in the summer. Give the relative advantages and disadvantages (as best you can) of the following heuristics:

Table 2-3

Worksheet for Example 2-8

n	Cost Choices	C(n)	j*(n)
0			0
1	**(0 + 40)**	40	0
2	(0 + 110), **(40 + 40)**	80	1
3	(0 + 150), **(40 + 60)**, (80 + 40)	100	1
4	**(40 + 60)**, (80 + 40), (100 + 40)	100	1
5	**(40 + 90)**, (80 + 60), (100 + 50), (100 + 40)	130	1
6	(40 + 250), (80 + 180), (100 + 130), (100 + 80), **(130 + 40)**	170	5
7	(100 + 340), (100 + 220), (130 + 110), **(170 + 40)**	210	6
8	(130 + 250), (170 + 110), **(210 + 40)**	250	7
9	(170 + 130), **(210 + 50)**, (250 + 40)	260	8

   a. Lot-for-lot
   b. Simple EOQ
   c. Rolling EOQ
   d. Silver-Meal
   e. Least unit cost
   f. Part Period Balancing

2. Suppose a problem's bi-weekly demand pattern is wildly erratic, for example for orders for bullet-proof luxury cars. Give the relative advantages and disadvantages (as best you can) of the following heuristics:

   a. Lot-for-lot
   b. Simple EOQ
   c. Rolling EOQ
   d. Silver-Meal
   e. Least unit cost
   f. Part Period Balancing

3. Erratic demand patterns are typically known very poorly more than two or three months into the future. Why is this not much of a concern for such heuristics as Silver-Meal and Part Period Balancing?

4. A heavy machinery manufacturer makes a certain type of NC (numerically controlled) milling machine. Because of heavy demand, orders are solicited well in advance. Currently orders are predicted as follows:

Month	1	2	3	4	5	6	7	8	9	10
Orders	40	40	45	10	25	120	40	5	80	40

The holding cost is taken as 2 percent per month. The cost of a milling machine is 30K. Total setup cost for changing the entire line to produce this machine is about 125K (including initial relearning, trial runs on each machine, etc.). Solve this problem by:

   a. Lot-for-lot
   b. Simple EOQ
   c. Rolling EOQ
   d. What is the best solution? What percent-cost penalties do the others pay?

5. Solve problem 4 by:

   a. Least unit cost
   b. Silver-Meal
   c. Part Period Balancing

Assuming you have also solved problem 4 give a complete cost comparison of all the methods.

6. An MRP system, set up on a monthly basis, determines the following requirements for the next 12 months for an item ordered from an outside vendor: 6, 11, 6, 19, 11, 4, 19, 26, 15, 8, 3, 25. Current inventory is 8, and management's policy is to plan for an inventory of 4 at the end of 12 months. Assume a holding cost of $1 and a setup cost of $50. Determine a production plan and corresponding cost for:

   a. Rolling EOQ
   b. Part Period Balancing
   c. Silver-Meal
   d. Compare the accuracy of the methods

Wagner-Whitin/Planning Horizons.

7. Calculate the optimal policy and cost for a four-period dynamic lot size problem with demands of 10, 50, 84, and 25. The setup cost is $4000 dollars, and $h = \$30$ per unit per period.

   a. Enumerate all possible plans, using the method in this section; find the optimal plan and cost.
   b. Find the answer by the updated Wagner-Whitin Algorithm.

8. Answer problems 1, 2, and 3 for the updated Wagner-Whitin Algorithm.
9. Answer problem 5 for the Wagner-Whitin Algorithm.
10. Assume that the nine-period demand data in Example 2-9 is part of the infinite demand series 3, 7, 2, 0, 1, 4, 7, 7, 1, 2, 8, 1, . . . , repeating every 12 months. Scale the setup cost down to 4 and the holding cost to 1 in order to give you more room on your paper. (Compute $C(j,n)$ only as needed.)

    a. Do the full Wagner-Whitin algorithm with planning horizon machinery for as many periods as you have patience and energy.
    b. Does computational effort continue to be linear in the number of periods?

11. Re-solve problem 10 for a setup cost of 16. (This should about double the average lot size, as it would in any EOQ approximation.) What happens to the total computational effort per period as compared to the setup cost = 4 case?

2.5 UNCLE SAM'S SEAFOOD—REPRISE

The owner of Uncle Sam's Seafood, Jane Redman, feels that her overall inventories are too large, and that there is far too much loss due to price markdowns and outright spoilage of fresh foods. Furthermore, total storage space in the main freezers is also a serious problem. She hires an MBA student on a part-time basis from a local university. John has just completed a good course in operations management and is anxious to learn how to use it in practice.

After talking to Jane and her top staff a couple of times, John tells Jane that she has several types of problems: lot sizing, forecasting, and safety stocks. Given his limited time availability, he decides to concentrate on lot sizing for the near future, since that seems relatively simple, and requires less analysis and computer software than the others.

The bulk of the freezer items (90 percent of the volume) is stable in demand year around. John temporarily allocates 10 percent of the storage to the less stable items, and then turns to lot sizing for the stable freezer items, giving them a common capacity constraint of 90 percent of available freezer capacity. After some discussion with Jane about her cost of capital, that is set at 18 percent. Freezer space is about 8 percent and spoilage about 4 percent, giving a total holding cost of 30 percent. Since this is somewhat rough, John decides to try the values 20 percent, 30 percent, and 40 percent and see how much difference it makes. For each item he estimates demand and wholesale cost from the average figures for the preceding year. As far as ordering from a vendor, typical costs are $50 per order (including phone calls), and $2 in addition for each item on the order. Thus formulas (15a, 15b, 15c) apply in aggregating items from the order. He determines the setup as 50 plus 2 times the number of items, aggregates the demands directly, and then takes an aggregate holding cost, which is the weighted average of the individual holding costs.

This typical order size is then taken as the Granddaddy EOQ result for the aggregated order, which can be measured as a time between orders from the vendor. Next, if this time violates any shelf life, he will shorten this time appropriately. Finally, he must ask if the sum of orders so determined from all vendors adds to more than the 90 percent of capacity he has allotted.

Since the sum of the EOQs from all vendors exceeded allotted capacity by 50 percent, John applied the methods of Section 2.3.9, Multiple Products with Resource Constraints, to produce reduced EOQs to fit the freezer. Just as important, it gave him an effective storage cost of $9 per cubic foot, which also represents the value per cubic foot of buying more storage capacity. Since Jane had valued storage cost at only $4, John asked her to either raise this figure or consider buying more storage capacity. After talking further with John, and with her banker, Jane decided to invest in additional cold storage of about half the amount first indicated by the model, since here extra storage was only valued at $5.50, and she decided that this was closer to her true feelings about storage. After this things quieted down again. At one point John worried whether shelf-life constraints should be further reduced, but Jane assured him that the existing ones were adequate.

The remaining items in the freezer all centered around Thanksgiving and Christmas, had roughly the same seasonal pattern, and were ordered from the same vendor. So John aggregated them also, and applied the Silver-Meal heuristic for the dynamic lot sizing model, to see what the unconstrained ordering volume pattern would be. During the Christmas-New Year period the unconstrained volume rose to a maximum of 152 percent of capacity. Since John did not have a dynamic lot sizing model available which handled storage constraints, he simply experimented with raising the implicit storage cost until the volume constraint would be met. However, after $12.00 per cubic foot, further increases in the price did not bring the maximum volume below 128 percent. Finally John looked more closely at the data, and realized that with time buckets of a week, the solution had reduced to lot-for-lot. Christmas week itself was 128 percent of capacity! After ascertaining from Jane that a split twice-a-week delivery was reasonable, he put a patch in the computer program to handle this situation. Valuing storage at the agreed upon $5.50, he then found the maximum storage requirement (at New Years Day) down to 112 percent. This was not deemed a problem given the new freezer units already being planned.

John then turned to the problem of ordering fresh fish, shrimp and lobster, given the difficulty of forecasting, and the dangers of markdowns and spoilage. This problem seemed somewhat more difficult; he promised Jane to return in two weeks with some ideas.

Inventory Models with Uncertain Demands

3.1 INTRODUCTION

3.1.1 Overview

In Inventory Chapter 1, we classified the motives for holding inventory. We discussed the first two motives, setup costs/times and other production economies of scale, in Inventory Chapter 2. Here we look at an entirely different type of motive derived from protecting ourselves with safety stocks against uncertainties—demands which may be larger than expected, or order arrivals or production which may be smaller or later than expected. Situations which require both lot-sizing and safety stocks usually combine the simpler models in some direct way.

3.1.2 Quantifying Uncertainty

In order to clarify what we mean by uncertain, probabilistic, or random in the context of inventory systems, we consider an example.

Example 3-1. Sack's 7th Avenue has a forecasting system which smoothes a forecast of mean demand by exponential smoothing, and also keeps track of the forecast errors for forecasting a week ahead. For a particular stable product with no trend, the forecast errors over a 52-week period have been:

Quarter 1		−20	−5	−11	+6	+1	+8	−2	+7	+11	+15	+5	+12	−9
Quarter 2		+14	+5	+16	−7	+1	+5	−3	0	−4	+8	−14	−7	+3
Quarter 3		−3	+8	−8	−1	−15	−2	0	0	−8	+4	0	−6	−8
Quarter 4		−15	−2	0	+1	+4	−5	+1	−4	+16	+1	−6	−5	+1

This tabulation of forecast errors has no obvious pattern; we could not use it to improve our demand forecast in a given week. However, we can get some idea of how demands will be distributed upwards and downwards from our forecast. One way to do this is to look at a histogram of the errors as illustrated in Figure 3-1.

We might use the observed frequency histogram to estimate the probability that any given future forecast error will have a given value. This is quite useful in setting safety stocks in inventory control. For example, suppose Sack's always orders the product shown in Figure 3-1 one week ahead with negligible lead time, and that current average sales are 46. And suppose Sack's has the policy that enough inventory should be on hand so that the probability of not having enough is only 10 percent. Looking at the frequency diagram, 90

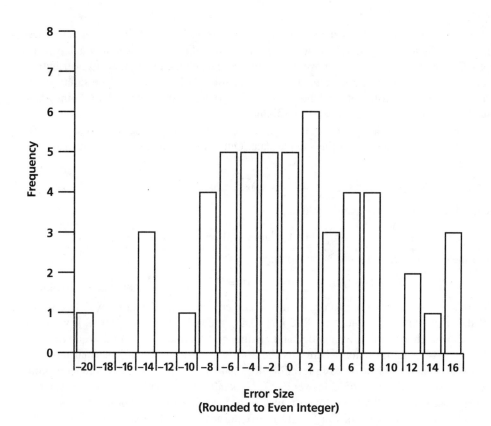

Figure 3-1

Frequency Histogram for
Forecast Errors of a Product
at Sack's 7th Avenue (Over
52 Weeks)

**Error Size
(Rounded to Even Integer)**

percent of the errors (47 of the 52) did not exceed 12. Or more precisely, looking at the original data, 90 percent of the errors did not exceed +11. Thus, if Sack's orders enough to raise next week's inventory to 57 (46 + 11), an adequate safety stock should result.

Although empirical frequency histograms give us a great deal of insight and can be used directly in inventory control, we tend not to use them for several reasons. First, a complete histogram must be kept for every item. If there are, for example, 50,000 items, this is not practical either in computer storage or computation time. Second, many inventory control situations require combining different probability distributions together, which is extremely cumbersome using histograms. For these reasons, we approximate discrete demand histories and errors by continuous distributions which are functions of two or three parameters, such as a mean and standard deviation. Then only these parameters need to be stored. The full distribution or parts of it can be recreated as necessary from one or two tables stored in the computer.

The normal distribution is by far the most used distribution in inventory control, for a number of reasons:

1. The normal distribution is specified completely by its mean μ and its standard deviation σ.
2. The normal distribution makes a relatively good approximation to many distributions, simply by setting the means and standard deviations equal.
3. The Central Limit Theorem says roughly that if a large number of random variables are added together, the result has nearly a normal distribution.
4. It is easy to find the distribution of a sum of normal variables.

There are two difficulties with using the normal distribution as an approximation to most demand distributions. First, demand is modeled as nonnegative in inventory models, and yet the normal distribution always takes on negative values. This can be minimized as a problem by keeping the probability of a negative value less than, say, 0.05. Thus, we would avoid having σ amount to more than 0.5 times as much as μ.

The second difficulty is related. Because real distributions are truncated at zero, they have fat tails to the right. That is to say, if the normal distribution has only a 1 percent probability of an observation above 2.33 standard deviations, the real world distribution may very well have 3 to 5 percent. The practical solution is to compute the safety stock from the normal distribution, and then increase it somewhat. We discussed this point when we discussed errors in the Forecasting Module.

Thus, for the Sack's 7th Avenue example, we would estimate the mean and standard deviation (or variance) from the sample data. Our estimate for the mean forecast error would be:

$$E_{av} = (1/_n)\sum_{i=1,n}E_i$$

Our estimate for the variance would be:

$$s^2 = (1/(n-1))\sum_{i=1,n}(E_i - E_{av})^2$$

For the data picture in Figure 3-1 we obtain:

$$E_{av} = (1/52)(-23) = -0.44 \qquad \sigma = [1/51(3383)]^{0.5} = 8.14$$

Thus, over the past year our forecasts have averaged almost 0.5 units low, with two-thirds of the errors within the interval [–8.6, 7.7]. Using the normal approximation, if we want 90 percent chance of covering demand in the next period, we would want to have $46 + (-0.44 + 8.14z)$ units, where z is the 90th percentile of the unit normal table, or $z = 1.28$, which yields a stocking level of $(46 - 0.44 + 10.42) = 56$. This compares quite reasonably with the histogram answer of 57, especially since small errors in the inventory level cause even smaller errors in cost, just as for the EOQ lot sizing problem.

The above calculation of s^2 is for illustrative purposes only. In practice we would probably smooth both the demand D_t and the mean absolute forecast error and then use the conversion that $\sigma = 1.25\text{MAD}$.

3.1.3 Chapter Summary and Preview

In Section 3.2 we visit Uncle Sam's Seafood again to investigate the difficult question of how much fish and other fresh seafood to order given that demand is quite uncertain, overstock tends to spoil, and understocking loses valued customers.

In Section 3.3 we look at periodic review models, where ordering is done regularly. We first look at one-decision models, first discussing the myopic approach, then the classic newsboy model, and finally general one-period models. Next we turn to multi-period models, and show how the myopic approach helps solve these more complicated models. In Section 3.4 we look at continuous review models, where inventory levels are monitored continuously, and reordering takes place whenever inventory drops below a predetermined trigger level. In Section 3.5 we visit Uncle Sam's Seafood for the last time.

3.2 UNCLE SAM'S SEAFOOD—YET AGAIN

John did not actually return to see Jane Redman, the owner of Uncle Sam's Seafood, until four weeks later. He found that probabilistic inventory models were indeed applicable to the difficult problem of forecasting and inventory control. However, these models were somewhat more difficult than he had expected and took some real effort to master. In addition, he guessed that a full scale forecasting system might be too complex for Jane's needs, and so he spent some time thinking about simpler forecasting procedures.

John came armed with professional looking slides. He wanted to discuss the big picture of the problem before getting into any gory details. His talk went something like the following:

"Jane, as near as I understand it, fresh fish, oysters, shrimp, lobsters are all flown in so that delivery is made approximately two days after the order is placed. These items are immediately placed on ice for sale. A big order is put out for sale on Saturday morning for the weekend crush and a smaller order Wednesday morning. Saturday fish is marked down 20 percent for quick sales on Tuesday morning, while Wednesday fish is marked down 20 percent for quick sales on Saturday. Marked-down fish that isn't sold within another two days is discarded. While this policy is conservative, we shouldn't consider changing it since Uncle Sam's values its reputation for high quality. Loss of sales due to stockouts is considered roughly the loss of gross markup on the lost sales. Currently there is no formal forecasting system. As I understand it, Jane, you determine all orders on an individual basis, using your long experience and knowledge of the current market.

Unfortunately, although overall demand for fresh seafood is rather constant from year to year, there is a great deal of weekly fluctuation, due to fluctuating availability and prices, competitors' sales, and so forth. Many times you are overstocked, and mark down a large quantity of fish 20 percent. Fairly often the overstock lasts more than two days, and that final leftover is thrown away. On the other hand, when you are understocked you consider that you lose the lost profit (gross markup) on the customers turned away. Since you have a PC in the office, I propose to develop a very simple forecasting/inventory system for fresh seafood, one that is not too difficult to maintain, and allows you to override the system when the recommendations do not seem good."

After a few more hours of discussion, Jane approved the project, and they agreed verbally on the amount John would be paid for putting this system together.

3.3 PERIODIC REVIEW MODELS

3.3.1 Overview

Inventory systems that allow ordering inventory only once a week, once every other week, or once a month are very important practically in wholesale and retail ordering and in MRP systems on the shop floor. While systems which order the instant new inventory is needed (continuous review) are theoretically better because they are more timely, in practice periodic review inventory systems have a number of advantages.

In the first place, ordering periodically automatically produces a typical lot size equal to demand in one period. Thus, the lot-sizing issue may be finessed if the period is of about the right length. In the second place, if there are large numbers of different low volume items, it will likely not be economical to keep a running tally on every small item, ordering each precisely when it hits some trigger point. In the third place, when a group of items are ordered in common from a vendor, they will have different EOQ ordering formulas, which ignores a large joint cost in ordering. Thus, it makes better sense to order these in unison. Fourth, MIS reasons of reporting and control make weekly or biweekly reporting useful.

However, there are a number of mathematical disadvantages to making models of periodic review systems. Almost all periodic review models require the lead time to be a simple integer multiple of the basic review period. Setup costs are much harder to analyze; distribution of demand is usually assumed for convenience to be independent from period to period, which is not very realistic. Many of these mathematical difficulties can be eliminated by using the fact that optimal solutions to many different types of inventory systems are, at least approximately, myopic. We will develop the myopic approach and show that the results are the same or nearly the same as traditional methods. Then we will sketch a number of more complex models for which it is now known that near-myopic models are optimal.

3.3.2 One-Decision Models

The Myopic Approach. Myopic models are often described as "one-period" models, but this is inaccurate; in fact they are **one-decision models**. In the Granddaddy EOQ model, there are no periods at all. But we showed that if we chose as the first lot time a period just long enough to minimize average costs per unit time for that lot, then we obtained the optimal solution to the infinite horizon problem. That is, we showed that we could optimize one lot at a time, in a forward fashion, rather than solving the whole problem simultaneously (or backward). The myopic approach thus fits very nicely with rolling horizon procedures. When we looked at time varying demand, we found that all the heuristics proposed were myopic. None of these heuristics are one-period but they are all one-decision.

We look next at the newsboy model, which forms the same underpinning for inventory problems with uncertain demands that the Granddaddy EOQ result does for inventory problems with known demands.

The Newsboy Model. We introduce the newsboy problem with an example.

Example 3-2. On Sundays, Professor Matt Gruenberg of Walla State University, who teaches operations management, operates a busy newsstand for his friend Jack, who owns the stand. Jack likes to have Sundays off and gives Matt two-thirds of the Sunday profits, as well as giving him free rein to order the various Sunday newspapers. In particular, the New York Times costs Matt $1.25 per paper, and he sells it for $3.00. Leftover papers are sold back to the supplier for $0.25 per paper. Matt has kept records of New York Times sales over the past two years. Sales have increased about 35 percent a year. He uses an exponential smoothing model with trend and smoothed absolute error. Currently his forecasting model suggests that Sunday sales of the New York Times have a mean of 325 and a standard deviation of 156. He is willing to approximate sales as having a normal distribution. How many papers should Matt order if he wants to maximize expected profits?

At first, it looks as though Matt should order the mean, or 325 papers. However, note that if Matt ordered one more paper, he would lose $(1.25 - .25)$ or $1.00 if he doesn't sell it. On the other hand, if he does sell the extra paper, he makes $(3.00 - 1.25)$ or $1.75. Since he is about equally likely to sell or not sell another paper, our intuition tells us he should buy it, therefore 325 is too small an order.

This problem is an example of the newsboy model, in which there is no starting inventory, a single product is to be ordered once, there are opportunity costs of not satisfying demand over a given time period and of leftover inventory at the end.

Let U be the opportunity cost of needing a unit but not having it.
Let D be the opportunity cost of having the unit but not needing it.
Let y be the amount to be ordered (decision variable).
Let $F(y)$ be the probability that fewer than y will be sold, so that $1.0 - F(y)$ is the probability that greater than or equal to y will be sold.

F is called the cumulative distribution of demand. We have defined it carefully so that the newsboy model we are working out will be correct for either a continuous distribution of demand (such as the normal) or a discrete distribution of demand (such as a histogram of last year's sales). Appendix A gives a brief review of probability theory. A table of the normal distribution is also given in Appendix G.

The Solution, Common-Sense Style. Matt doesn't like all the math in most inventory models, and decides to work out the correct answer using his common sense. He conceptualizes the decision to buy each additional newspaper as a separate (marginal) decision. The first paper is almost certain to be sold, so the decision to buy it is worth almost U, or perhaps $1.74996. The second is slightly less likely to be sold, and slightly more likely to be salvaged, so he assumes it is worth $1.7498. Each paper will be worth somewhat less: for continuous distributions the marginal paper at the optimum should be worth exactly zero; that is

$$-(\text{Prob. Selling})U + (\text{Prob. Not Selling})D = 0$$

(For a discrete distribution, it will be the last paper for which this is *greater or equal to zero*.) But $F(y)$ is exactly the probability of not selling y, and $1 - F(y)$ is the probability of selling y or more. Thus, we have

$$-(1.0 - F(y^*))U + F(y^*)D = 0$$

which may be easily solved to yield the newsboy equation:

$$F(y^*) = U/(U + D) \tag{1}$$

This formula is as central in probabilistic inventory as the EOQ square root rule was for deterministic inventory.

$U/(U + D)$ gives the percentile on the demand distribution which Matt should order up to; in his case $(1.75)/(1.75 + 1.00) = 0.64$. For the unit normal distribution the 0.64 percentile is given by $z = 0.36$. Thus, to maximize his expected profits, Matt should order $y^* = \mu + z\sigma$ or $y^* = 325 + (0.36)(156) = 381$ papers.

Of course, the number of papers to buy depends upon the relative costs of being over and under. If Matt could only get $2.25 for the *New York Times*, then $U = D = 1.00$, and the point estimate should be made at the 50th percentile, giving $y^* = 325$ papers. If there were price controls so that Matt could get only $1.75 for the papers, then $U = 0.50 and $D = 1.00. The 33rd percentile would then give $y^* = 325 + (-0.43)(156) = 258$. Matt would actually order fewer papers than he expected to sell! On the other hand, if the selling price were $5.25 then $U = 4.00 while $D = 1.00. Then z for the 80th percentile is $z = 0.84$, giving $y^* = 456$.

One-decision models which can be modeled reasonably well as newsboy problems do not only come up in short horizon problems. The decision of how much money to commit to R&D for a given product (given a single decision) depends on the estimated distribution of total demand over the life of the product, and can be modeled quite well using newsboy ideas.

In the next section, we look at somewhat more general one-decision models, where, for example, there is a starting inventory before ordering is done, or unfilled demand may be filled at higher cost at the end of the time period. We solve the model using little mathematics by recognizing a newsboy model within the mathematical formulation. Our long range strategy is to view one-decision inventory models as single units in many decision models. Thus, we need to consider cases where there is inventory carried into a one-period model, as well as inventory carried out. To be useful, we need a simple result that works for every possible incoming and outgoing inventory.

One-Period Models. We look here at problems with no setup costs on ordering, and linear ordering costs.

Formal Model. The model is as follows. We start with some inventory from some previous situation of x, and must order up to some y which will depend on x. We want to determine the optimal order $y^*(x)$ for every x. Some random amount u will actually be demanded: $F(u)$ is the cumulative distribution of demand, $f(u)$ is the density of demand (assumed continuous). There are two cases.

Case 1. If there is more demand than y, a second order can be placed at the end of the period to exactly cover it. This is the backlogging case, and ending inventory in this case is given by $(y - u)$ (negative means backlogged demand).

Case 2. In this case excess demand is lost, so ending inventory is zero for excess demand. Ending inventory in this case is given by $(y - u)^+$, where the + simply means replace negative ending inventory by zero. Any leftover inventory is salvaged at the beginning of period 2, returning an amount $s <= c$ per unit. In the backlogging case only, excess demand may be satisfied at the beginning of period 2 at a cost c. The model is net present value (NPV) in the sense that period 2 costs are discounted by a factor $\alpha <= 1.0$. α is defined as $1/(1 + r)$ where r is the cost of capital. It is useful to note that $(1 - \alpha) = r/(1 + r)$, which is almost exactly r.

We define $y^*(x)$ as the optimal order-up-to level as a function of the opening inventory in the problem and $G(x)$ as the optimal cost for the problem, again as a function of x. Finally, the costs in the problem are: each unit ordered costs c, each unit of ending inventory costs h, each unit of stockout costs p (p is larger for the no backlog case), each unit of salvage brings s.

We first write out the expected cost to be minimized for the no backlogging case:

$$G(x) = \min_{y >= x}\{c(y - x) + (h - \alpha s)\int_{u=0,y}(y - u)f(u)du + p\int_{u=y,inf}(u - y)f(u)du\} \quad (2)$$

(For the backlogging case, we simply replace p by $(p + \alpha c)$.) We state this equation in words to give intuition: "The minimum cost G, which depends on x, is the minimum cost for all choices of final order-up-to level y greater than or equal to x. This cost is comprised of the variable ordering cost per unit c times the order quantity, plus holding, less salvage return on expected ending positive inventory, plus the stockout penalty cost, times the expected amount of stockout." (We assume c and h and p to occur in this period, and thus do not discount them; we assume salvage is paid "next period" and so discount it. The rationale will become clearer for this when we hook one-period models together later. We could try to be prettier and have holding costs and penalties paid throughout the period in a random manner, with varying continuous discounts, leading to a more complex statement, but it is easier just to manually adjust h and p somewhat to reflect this if this refinement is desired.)

For Case 2, the backlogging case, the only change is that p times the expected stockout is replaced by $(p + \alpha c)$ times the expected stockout. This is because stockouts must be reordered at the beginning of the next period at a cost of c per unit, discounted back to the present time.

Why do we have this unusual backlogging possibility in a single-period model? For one thing, there are one-period situations where backlogging can be covered, possibly at extra cost. But more important, the results for the backlogging case will allow us to hook our one-period results directly into our later study of many-period models.

We omit the long mathematical solution of this problem, but just note that the solutions finally reduce to solving the following newsboy equations:

$$\text{NBL} \quad F(y^{**}) = (p - c)/[(p - c) + (c + h - \alpha s)] \quad\quad\quad = U/(U + D) \quad (3a)$$

$$\text{BL} \quad F(y^{**}) = [p - c(1 - \alpha)]/[(p - c(1 - \alpha)) + (c + h - \alpha s)] = U/(U + D) \quad (3b)$$

Equation (3a) is a no-backlogging case, and equation (3b) is a backlogging case.

We can find these results directly by our original newsboy analysis with a lot less work. Look at the no-backlogging case. For any unit demanded but not sold we pay p in stockouts, less c for never having ordered it. For any unit ordered but not sold, we pay c plus holding h, less a salvage value αs.

For the backlog case, the opportunity cost if the unit isn't needed is exactly the same. If the unit does stock out, however, a term αc must be added to our costs since we will order and deliver the unit at the beginning of period 2. (Notice it is not clear which U is larger, however, since p will be much smaller for the backlogging case, tending to compensate for the αc term.)

Although, classically, periodic review models have been solved with discounting, the average cost formulation gives the same answers and is really much easier to use. In the

EOQ model we used h as the total direct plus interest cost per period, whereas in periodic models it is customary to define h as the direct holding cost only. Thus, h in average cost formulations is equivalent to $h + rc$ in discounted formulations (see Table 3-1). Just putting $\alpha = 1$ in (3a) and (3b) gets the right answers for this case!

In the average cost formulation p corresponds to the old U and $h + v$ corresponds to the old D. p is the opportunity cost of stockout, h is the opportunity cost of holding, and v is the opportunity cost of salvaging.

Example 3-3. The Giant Gopher supermarket buys lettuce on Monday, which lasts until the following Sunday night, when it is salvaged by selling it to pet owners. This week GG can buy lettuce for $4.00 a box, and must decide how much to buy. The total holding cost for a box of lettuce is 0.5 percent a week, which is half direct holding and half the cost of capital. In some situations the customers will not wait until next week if there is no lettuce, and then the stockout cost is the lost revenue of $10.00 a box, plus an estimated $1.00 in lost goodwill. In some situations the customers will wait until next week if there is no lettuce, and then the stockout cost is just the $1.00 in lost goodwill. A box of week old lettuce brings about $1.20 in the pet market. What is the optimal probability for Giant Gopher to be in stock in each of the two cases?

Solution. Use average cost analysis. We can calculate

$$(h + v) = [(0.005)(4.00) + (2.80)] = 2.82$$

$$\text{NBL } (p) = (10.00 + 1.00) - 4.00 = 7.00$$

$$\text{BL } (p) = 1.00 = 1.00$$

Finally

$$\text{NBL } F(y^{**}) = (7.00)/[(7.00 + 2.82)] = 0.71$$

$$\text{BL } F(y^{**}) = (1.00)/[(1.00 + 2.81)] = 0.26$$

Thus, when customers are impatient and can get lettuce elsewhere, Giant Gopher should order more than expected demand, enough so that there would be no stockouts 71 percent of the time. On the other hand, if customers are loyal and can save up their need for lettuce, Giant Gopher should order much less than expected demand, just enough so that there would be no stockouts 26 percent of the time.

The produce manager of Giant Gopher got a chance to pick up 25 cases of good lettuce from the wholesale district at only $3.00 a box. His solution of the newsboy model had indicated that his optimal stocking level was 78. How many more cases should he buy?

Solution. The savings on the 25 cases is irrelevant, since it is a sunk cost. Since $y^{**} = 78$, and $x = 25$, the manager should order $(y^{**} - x)^+ = 78 - 25 = 53$. If the amount bought at the special sale price had been 90, then the subsequent regular order should be $(78 - 90)^+ = 0$. (Of course the large amount of cheap lettuce would probably induce the manager to lower the selling price and change the demand distribution. This is outside our scope here.)

Discounted Costs		Average Costs	
$h + c(1 - \alpha)$	$= h + rc$	h	
$p - c(1 - \alpha)$	$= p - rc$	p	(B.L.)
$p - c$		p	(N.B.L.)
$\alpha(c - s)$		v	
c		0	(sunk)

Table 3-1

Discounted Formulations versus Average Cost Formulations

Rounding Issues. Our newsboy analysis applies for discrete distributions as well. The only minor problem is that if the newsboy $U/(U + D)$ is 0.70, on the discrete distribution we may find $F(101) = 0.684$, and $F(102) = 0.705$. We just need to remember a simple rule: **For discrete distributions choose y^* such that it is the lowest integer satisfying $F(y^*) >= U/(U + D)$. That is, always round up.**

This is slightly different from the case where demand is continuous, but here we are only allowed to order in units, for example, cases. This leads to the **heuristic rule: If demand is continuous, but ordering must be in even lots, then round the newsboy answer to the nearest lot.**

3.3.3 Multi-Period Models

The underlying assumption made in one-decision models, such as the newsboy problem, is that the item perishes quickly (or becomes out-of-date or out-of-season) and cannot be used to satisfy demand in subsequent decision periods. In the vast majority of industrial, wholesale, and retail environments, however, products are more durable, or have more stable demand, so that inventory left at the end of a period (decision) can be stored and be available for future demands.

We will show that our basic newsboy (myopic) approach is easily modified intuitively to handle the multi-period problem. The trick is just to consider the multi-period problem to be a series of independent one-period problems which can buy and sell from each other. Then each one can be analyzed in the newsboy framework. We omit the very complex mathematical models, which get the same answer.

The myopic newsboy approach can handle many multi-period problems quite easily. For example, assume there is a manager in each period. This manager can buy inventory from the previous period, or she can order inventory for c per unit and get instantaneous delivery. What is a fair price to pay the previous period? Clearly, as long as the leftover inventory from the previous period is no more than the amount she was going to buy anyway, she will be willing to pay c per unit. Any units bringing inventory above the desired level will be worth somewhat less than c, and each additional unit will be worth a little less.

Now suppose all the periods are identical looking, except for the actual demand realized. By symmetry, every period will have the same order-up-to level y^{**}. The previous period experienced some non-negative demand u. Thus, ending inventory was less than y^{**}, and therefore she will buy the inventory since she was going to buy y^{**} anyway.

This means that the multi-period model does not differ from the one-period model, except that the salvage value is c rather than some smaller s.

Thus, for example, the multiperiod no-backlogging solution is:

$$F(y^{**}) = U/(U + D) = (p - c)/[(p - c) + (h + c(1 - \alpha))]$$

or in average cost terms

$$F(y^{**}) = p/(p + h)$$

You should be able to write the corresponding results for the backlogging case.

Example 3-4. The Start Rek Computer store sells the very popular video game "Mario Brothers in Hyperspace." They order this item monthly. Unsold copies of the game are kept for sale in future months. Customers who want to buy the game when it is out of stock will almost always wait until the following month. The manager buys the game for $20.00 and sells it for $35.00. The holding cost is taken as 3 percent per month on the purchase price. A loss of goodwill of $5.00 is estimated when a customer must wait. Monthly demand for this item is forecasted as having a mean of 50 and a standard deviation of 25, and the manager thinks a normal distribution is reasonable. The manager currently has 72 copies of the game on hand. How many should he order?

Solution. Here we have $U = p = \$5.00$ and $D = h = (0.03)(20) = \$0.60$. $F(y^{**}) = 5/5.6 = 0.89$, which corresponds to $z = 1.23$. $y^{**} = u + z\sigma = 50 + (1.23)(25) = 81$. Thus, he should order $(81 - 72) = 9$.

Delivery Lags. Let us look again at the basic many-period inventory model with backlogging, with the one change that, after ordering, a lead time of λ periods is required before delivery of the order. Suppose we order each period. It can be proved mathematically that the myopic solution is optimal for this problem. We simply assume this here; we also simplify our life a bit by using the average cost formulation. Let the current time be $t = 0$. We have x_0 on hand, and there are previous orders to arrive at times $1, 2, ..\lambda - 1$ of $z_1, z_2, .. z_{\lambda-1}$. We wish to decide on an order z_λ. This order will not help stockouts before time λ. By the same token, later orders can take care of time $\lambda + 1$ on, so we do not need to order now for these periods. Thus, our myopic decision is to protect the *review* period which is period λ. (Roughly the **review period** is defined as the period our order must protect). Let $F_{1,\lambda+1}(y)$ be the cumulative distribution of demand for the next $\lambda + 1$ periods, and $F_R(y)$ be the distribution of demand in the review period. Now the marginal unit we decide to order, called y^{**}, will save a backlogging cost of p if we were going to stockout in period λ, and a cost of h if we were not going to stockout in period λ.

We can't determine the probability of stockout in the review period in the usual way, because we don't know what the starting inventory will be for the review period. However, since we are backlogging, we know we must cover all the demands for $\lambda + 1$ periods, and therefore the probability of not stocking out in the review period is the same as the probability that all the resources of $(x_0 + z_1 + z_2 + .. + z_{\lambda-1}) + z_\lambda$ are sufficient to cover the $\lambda + 1$ period demand.

Define *system stock* as $x_s = x_0 + \Sigma x_t$, that is, **system stock** is all inventory on hand or currently to arrive. Define the order-up-to level as $y = x_s + z_\lambda$. Define $T(y)$ as the distribution of total demand over all $(\lambda + 1)$ periods. The solution is to solve the newsboy equation: $T(y^{**}) = p/(p + h)$. Order $z_\lambda = (y^{**} - x_s)^+$. Because of the backlogging assumption, we do not care what the review period demand distribution is. We must provide protection for all $\lambda + 1$ periods.

Note that while in mathematical formulations we are restricted to the lead time being an integer multiple of the review period; in practice this is not likely to be the case. The myopic assumption does not really need this integer assumption, so long as we can find the distribution of demand over the sum of the lead time and the review period (F_H), which is a standard forecasting problem. It is common practice to assume that the standard deviation for $\lambda + 1$ periods is $(\lambda + 1)^{0.5}$ times the standard deviation for one period. However, errors are correlated due to the forecasting process. (The actual standard deviation will be between $(\lambda + 1)^{0.5}$ and $(\lambda + 1)^{1.0}$ times the standard deviation for one period.)

Example 3-5. The Start Rek Computer store makes much of its revenue from the (DOS) IMAKLONE personal computer. Because of its popularity, ordering is done every two weeks. The lead time is 3.5 weeks. The computer is obtained from the vendor for $800, and retails for $1300. Holding is estimated at 26 percent per year or 0.5 percent per week. The customer will wait for out-of-stock computers, but suffers about $150 in personal inconvenience on average. The two-week demand for the computer is normal with mean of 100 and standard deviation of 42. The 5.5 week demand for the computer is normal with mean of 275 and standard deviation of 85. There is current inventory of 122 computers and an outstanding order of 50. How many computers should be ordered now?

Solution.

$$T(y^{**}) = 150/(150 + 0.01(800)) = 150/158 = 0.95, \text{ so } z = 1.65$$

Thus,

$$T(y^{**}) = 275 + (1.65)(85) = 415$$

$$x_\lambda = 415 - 50 - 122 = 243$$

The manager should order 243 computers. Note that 243 computers are more than the manager needs in order to cover the review period. However, previous inventories are low, and the order is also to cover some expected stockouts before this order arrives.

3.3.4 Periodic Review Exercises

One-Decision Models.

1. In Example 3-1, compare the histogram method with the normal approximation if Sack's wanted the probability of no stockout to be:

   a. 50 percent
   b. 98 percent
   c. 99.9 percent
   d. What are the strengths and weaknesses of each?

2. In Example 3-1, suppose only Quarter 2 data were available. Answer problem 1 again. What point does this make about the sample size?

3. Giant Gopher keeps careful records of lettuce sales and of the various costs that would allow it to decide how much lettuce to purchase. Why might its decisions be inaccurate? What would management have to do in addition to measuring the true demand for lettuce?

4. The Holiness Battalion buys ingredients for soup for its soup kitchen every day. The daily demand for soup is random; the cumulative distribution estimated from previous experience is shown in the following table.

Gallons of Soup Used In One Day	Cumulative Probability
0	0.10
5	0.15
10	0.20
15	0.35
20	0.60
25	0.80
30	0.90
35	0.95
40 or more	1.00

It costs $2 a gallon to make soup; leftover soup is discarded. When soup runs out, the kitchen feeds canned goods instead, at an estimated cost of $6 to replace each gallon of soup.

   a. Based on the discrete distribution given above, how many gallons of soup a day should be prepared? (Interpolate.)
   b. Do you think a normal approximation would work well here? Why or why not?

5. In problem 4,

   a. Compute the mean and variance of the discrete distribution given there (no interpolation necessary).
   b. Determine the optimal number of daily gallons of soup using a normal approximation.

6. Giant Gopher has four 24-bottle cases of Hyper Catsup on hand. It plans to discontinue the line in two weeks, and is having a sale to move this merchandise. Marketing personnel estimate the sale will have a normal demand with a mean of 200 bottles and standard deviation of 100. One more purchase of Hyper Catsup is planned for this sale. The purchase price is $0.90 a bottle, and the sale price is $1.50. Holding cost is $0.005 per week. Leftover catsup will be returned to the manufacturer and yield $0.40 a bottle. How large should the order be?

Multi-Period Models.

7. Why are multi-period models difficult mathematically? Why are they often quite easy intuitively?

8. Solve the IMAKLONE Example 3-5 for the following variations:

   a. Excess demand is lost; the penalty includes the lost revenue and the same loss of goodwill.
   b. Fifty percent of excess demand is lost, fifty percent is backlogged (**Hint**: Average the two stockout penalties.)

9. Suppose demand is uniformly distributed between 0 and 100.

   a. What are f(x) and F(x) in this case?
   b. Solve Example 3-5 for this distribution of demand.
   c. How do the two answers differ? Why?
   d. Answer (c) if the manager were to order to the 99th percentile of demand.

3.4 CONTINUOUS REVIEW MODELS

3.4.1 Overview

Our first complication of the Granddaddy EOQ model was to keep demand deterministic, but allow it to be seasonal, which led us to lot-sizing models. Basic continuous review models make the reverse extension: allow the realism that demand is probabilistic, but restrict the mean and standard deviation to be constant throughout the year. If the item is a large volume one, it may be practical to keep a running track of the inventory level at all times. The resulting version of the Granddaddy EOQ model is called a **continuous review model** or sometimes a **two bin inventory policy** or an **order point model**.

Continuous review systems are appropriate for large dollar volume items, where the higher cost of continuous computer surveillance is offset by the holding and stockout savings implicit in more precise and timely ordering. The ability to order exactly when the trigger point is hit also depends on single item ordering from the vendor; coordinating orders to a vendor for group setup savings destroys the precision necessary to make a continuous review system effective. Continuous review systems are easier to model overall than periodic review systems. This is partly because the myopic character of the solution is clearer, and approximations have been employed since the start. Lead times are not assumed to be fixed or integer, and appropriate demand distributions are not assumed to be independent.

In Section 3.4.2 we will develop the basic stationary demand model with setups and no backlogging. The result is almost identical to the results we developed for the periodic case. In fact, we show that the current solution may be obtained from the other solution, first by adding a leadtime to the periodic review model, and then by letting the period size go to zero. The backlogging model may be derived in a similar fashion, but we omit it for lack of space. In Section 3.4.3 we discuss models in which the service level is specified by the manager instead of being optimized. The Type 1 Service model limits the probability of stocking out in the lead time. The Type 2 Service model limits the proportion of demand which can stockout overall.

3.4.2 Optimal Service Models

Introduction. If we are continuously keeping track of the inventory level, why do we need to modify the Granddaddy model at all? Why not simply produce Q^{**} whenever the inventory level falls to zero? Even though the times between ordering/producing now vary, wouldn't the *average* number of setups per year still be D/Q^{**} and the *average* inventory still be $Q^{**}/2$?

The answer to this lies in the fact that the receipt of new inventory always *lags* the decision to produce or reorder, typically by two to six weeks. Thus, the reorder must be made before inventory gets to zero, and allowance must be made for the possibility that demand could randomly happen to be large during this **lead time period**.

No Backlogging Model. Now we are assuming a continuous monitoring of the inventory level and stationarity of demand, so that the inventory level should be a complete description of the state of the system. Thus, if at some point in time when the level has dropped to s we decide to order some Q^*, then, by complete symmetry, any other time the level drops to s we should also order Q^*. Thus, our main task will be to find what s and Q^* should be.

We will proceed by making a common sense first cut, and then gradually improve our answer. We can think of the Granddaddy EOQ model as a **first cut**, where we set $Q^* = Q^{**}$ from the economic lot size model and set $s = Dt$; that is, the product of the demand rate and the lead time, which gives the expected demand in the lead time LT. This is not a bad start, but it makes no allowance at all for demand variability. We need some kind of safety stock to allow for the possibility that demand is high during the lead time.

How can we get a second cut? Clearly, s should represent something like the "maximum" reasonable demand over the lead time. Thus, a second cut would be to leave $Q^* = Q^{**}$, but set s by, for example, $F(s^*) = 0.95$. If we assume a mean demand over the lead time of 200, and a standard deviation of 50, this would lead to $z^* = 1.65$, and $s^* = 200 + (1.65)(50) = 283$. (In practice we may decide the tail is somewhat fatter than normal, and use a z of 2.0 or even 2.5, depending on our experience.) Thus, our second cut is to increase s from 200 to 285.

The value of 95 percent here is supplied by the manager or our previous experience. We may get a third cut by calculating an economic value for s. In order to do this we must make some further assumptions. First of all, we must assume that the lead time is relatively small by comparison with the average time between orders (the average lot time). That is, our assumption is that $LT << Q^*/D$. (Note that the lead time may be a random variable, so we avoid calling it λ.) This basically assures us that we will not be ordering when there is already an order out, which would complicate our thinking considerably. This simple case is shown in Figure 3-2. (If the lead time is longer, or is very variable, there may then be outstanding orders. The proper time to order in this case is when *inventory on hand plus inventory on order* gets down to s. However, it is no longer clear what setting $F(s^*) = 0.95$ means, exactly.) Assuming that, in fact, our lead time is always shorter than the time between orders, we will have precisely one exposure to stocking out between each two orders, or an exposure for each setup cost.

Let p be the stockout cost (average cost case). Now suppose we have a reorder point of s and are considering increasing it by one unit. This will save us one unit of stockout D/Q^* times a year. Each time, our probability of stocking out is $1.0 - F(s)$. Thus, our total yearly stockout savings would be $p(D/Q^*)(1 - F(s))$. On the other hand, except for the very rare stockout times, we will have on average one more unit in inventory at a yearly cost of h. At the optimum, these should exactly balance out so that $h = p(D/Q^*)(1 - F(s^*))$. Solving, we obtain:

Figure 3-2

Inventory Level Over Time in
a Continuous Review System

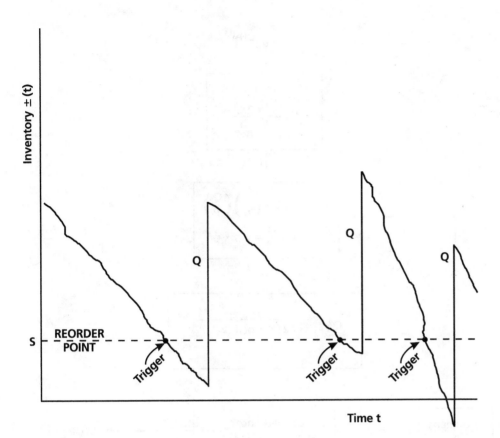

$$F(s^*) = 1.0 - (h/p)(Q^*/D) \qquad (4)$$

As an example, if $K = 4$, $D = 512$ per year, $h = 1$, and $p = 4$, then

$$Q^* = [2(4)(512)/(1)]^{0.5} = 64$$

$F(s^*) = 1.0 - (1/4)(64/512) = 1.0 - (1/32) = 0.969$. Set the reorder point to have a 3.1 percent stockout over the lead time.

Finally, as a fourth cut, we need to get an improved estimate for Q^*. Remember that Q^{**} from the Granddaddy model is given by $Q^{**} = [2KD/h]^{0.5}$. The main thing that changes here is that it costs us stockout costs in addition to K as part of our fixed costs for each cycle. Thus, the total fixed cost each time becomes $K + p(ESO(s^*))$ where ESO is an abbreviation for the amount of stockout during the lead time, which, of course, depends on the s we have chosen. This then updates Q^* to

$$Q^* = [2(K + pESO(s^*))D/h]^{0.5} \qquad (5)$$

where

$$ESO(s^*) = \int_{u=s,\inf}(u - s^*)f(u)du \qquad (6)$$

Thus, equations (4), (5) and (6) define our solution. As before, we can start with Q_1 as the EOQ solution, solve (4) to get s_1 and so on. This process is illustrated in Figure 3-3. Note that the first time through, the Q_1 we will get is precisely the Granddaddy EOQ value (which for large setup values K is often quite good enough). Then we calculate the s_1 corresponding to our third cut. We then can calculate an improved $ESO(s_1)$ and repeat the process, calculating Q_2, and then s_2, and so forth. Because convergence is monotonic, when two rounds give almost the same answer, it is safe to stop.

Figure 3-3

Iterative Solution of
Continuous Review Model

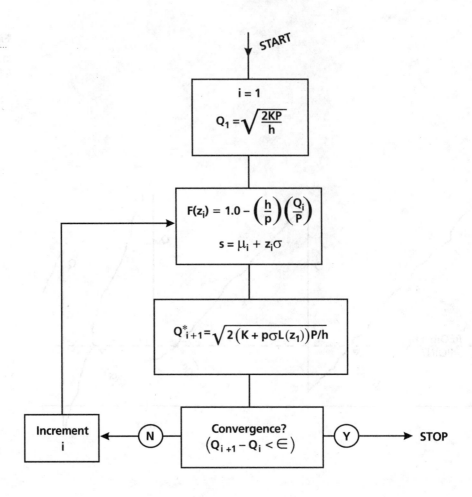

Table 3-2 illustrates the abbreviated table for $F(z)$ and $L(z)$.

Table 3-2

Abbreviated Table of $U(z)$
the Unit Normal Cumulative
Distribution and $L(z)$ the Unit
Normal Loss Function

z	F(z)	L(z)	z	F(z)	L(z)
.15	.560	.328	1.1	.864	.0686
.05	.520	.374	1.2	.885	.0561
.10	.540	.351	1.3	.903	.0455
.20	.579	.307	1.4	.919	.0367
.25	.599	.286	1.5	.933	.0293
.30	.618	.267	1.6	.945	.0232
.35	.637	.248	1.7	.955	.0183
.40	.655	.230	1.8	.964	.0143
.45	.674	.214	1.9	.971	.0111
.50	.692	.198	2.0	.977	.0085
.55	.709	.183	2.1	.982	.0065
.60	.726	.169	2.2	.986	.0049
.65	.742	.155	2.3	.989	.0037
.70	.758	.143	2.4	.992	.0027
.75	.773	.131	2.5	.994	.0020
.80	.788	.120	2.6	.9953	.0015
.85	.802	.110	2.7	.9965	.0011
.90	.816	.100	2.8	.9974	.0008
.95	.829	.0916	2.9	.9981	.0005

Example 3-6, Part 1. Java Jeff's is a popular coffeehouse that sells gourmet coffees and other foods. One of the items that Jeff sells is a very popular Columbian amaretto coffee bean in a three-pound bag. The coffee costs Jeff $10 a bag, and retails for $25. Excess demand is lost to the coffeehouse across the street; stockouts are costed at lost revenue plus $3 in goodwill. Bookkeeping expenses for placing an order are about $20.00. Jeff sells about 50 bags during the replenishment lead time of three months. Jeff's cost of holding is 20 percent per year. Demand is not very seasonal, but there is a standard deviation of demand during a lead time of 25 bags. Demand may be assumed to be described by a normal distribution. On what basis should Jeff order?

Solution. We wish to determine the optimal values of the reorder point s and the lot size Q. We start by finding the deterministic EOQ. Since demand averages 50 per three months and is steady, we must have $D = (50)(4) = 200$. Thus, $Q_0 = [2(20)(200)/(0.2)(10)]^{0.5} = 63.2$, and the average lot time is 3.8 months, which is longer than the lead time, as required.

Next we calculate s_1 from equation (4):

$$F(s_1) = 1.0 - (h/p)(Q_0/D) = 1.0 - (2/(25 - 10 + 3))(63.2/200) = 0.965$$

Thus, $z_1 = 1.81$, and $s_1 = 50 + (1.81)(25) = 95.2$.

Next we determine $ESO(s_1)$. From Table 3-2, $L(1.81) = 0.0140$. (It is not necessary to interpolate carefully; the normal assumption is not accurate anyway.) Thus, $ESO(95.2) = \sigma L(1.81) = (25)(0.0140) = 0.35$.

Now we are ready to go back and determine an improved Q_2. From equation (5):

$$Q_2 = [2(K + pESO(s_1))D/h]^{0.5} = [2(20 + 18(0.35))200/(2)]^{0.5}$$
$$= [2(26.3)(200)/2]^{0.5} = 72.5$$

Q_2 is about 15 percent larger than Q_1, so we must continue.

$$F(s_2) = 1.0 - (2/18)(72.5/200) = 0.960$$

Thus, $z_2 = 1.75$, and $s_2 = 50 + (1.75)(25) = 93.8$. s_2 is only about 2 percent down from s_1 which is encouraging.

Next we need $ESO(s_2)$. $L(1.75) = 0.0162$, so $ESO(93.8) = (25)(0.0162) = 0.405$.

$$Q_3 = [2(20 + 18(0.405))200/2]^{0.5} = [2(27.3)(200)/2]^{0.5} = 73.9$$

Q_3 is only about 2 percent larger than Q_2. Since we know costs are not too sensitive to small errors, we probably could stop. However, we do one more round to study the convergence.

$$F(s_3) = 1.0 - (2/18)(73.9/200) = 0.959$$

Thus, $z_3 = 1.74$, and $s_3 = 50 + (1.74)(25) = 93.5$. This time s changed only 0.3 percent.

Now we get $ESO(s_3)$. $L(1.74) = 0.0164$, so $ESO(93.5) = (25)(0.0164) = 0.410$. $Q_4 = [2(20 + 18(0.410))200/2]^{0.5} = 74.0$. Q_4 is only 0.1 percent larger than Q_3. (Note that while we thought we might still be 2 percent or more off at the last iteration, convergence is actually geometric, so it was quite safe to stop at the previous iteration.)

Thus, Jeff should order when his stock gets down to 94, and should order 74 at that time.

Example 3-6, Part 2. Java Jeff is trying to gain an understanding of his inventory process and would like to know the following:

1. Average annual holding cost, penalty costs, and setup costs associated with the Columbian Amaretto
2. Total costs as a fraction of cost of sales
3. Average time an order lasts before reordering
4. Safety stock, proportion of demand met, proportion of cycles with a stockout

Solution.

1. Holding cost is half of the lot size plus safety stocks = $h(Q/2 + (s - \mu)) = 2(74/2 + (94 - 50)) = \$162.00$ a year. ($74 for lot size inventory, $88 for safety stock inventory.) Penalty costs are cost per cycle times number of cycles $p\text{ESO}(s)(D/Q) = 18(0.405)(200/74) = \$19.70$ a year. Setup costs are each setup times number of cycles $KD/Q = 20(200/74) = \$54.05$. Total costs are $\$162.00 + 19.70 + 54.05 = \$235.75$.

2. Costs as a percentage of wholesale sales = $235.75/[10(200)] = 11.8$ percent.

3. Average time between orders = $[Q/D](12) = 4.4$ months.

4. Safety stock = $(s - \mu) = 94 - 50 = 44$ units.

Percentage of demand met = $1.0 - \text{ESO}/Q = 1.0 - (0.405/74) = .9945$ or 99.5 percent. Proportion of cycles with stockout = $1 - F(s) = 1 - 0.959$ or 4.1 percent.

Note that the amount spent on lot sizing inventory is almost exactly equal to the sum of the amounts spent in setups and stockouts, as would be predicted by the Granddaddy EOQ model. But also notice that the amount spent on safety stock inventory is much larger than the amount spent on stockouts. This is somewhat unrealistic, since real-world distributions have much fatter tails than the normal distribution, and therefore have larger losses.

Approximation Method. A useful approximation method in practice, which avoids calculating $\text{ESO}(s)$, involves taking a good starting guess for Q_1, calculating s_1 from that, and then stopping. The good starting guess for Q_2 in turn can be obtained by any fairly crude estimate of the ESO.

Example 3-6, Part 3. Java Jeff lost his calculations, and was unwilling to go through them all again. However, he remembers that he meets 99 percent of demand in all coffees taken as a whole, and therefore is willing to guess that ESO = (1 percent)(lead time demand.) = 0.5. Thus, he estimates:

$$Q_1 = [2(20 + 18(0.5))(200)/2]^{0.5} = 76.2$$

$$F(s_1) = 1.0 - (2/18)(76.2/200) = 1.0 - .042 = 0.958$$

$$z = 1.73$$

$$s_1 = 50 + (1.73)(25) = 93.2$$

Thus, s_1 is only 0.3 percent off, and Q_1 is about 3 percent off. Since we know the EOQ is not sensitive to small errors, this is probably a very satisfactory answer, obtained with little effort.

3.4.3 Specified Service Models

We do not fully solve these somewhat more complicated models here, but discuss their nature, and roughly how they could be solved.

Fill Rate Service Constraint. Here it is specified that the proportion of demand lost during a year (which is the same as the proportion lost during a cycle) should be less than or equal to some a_r. Thus,

$$a_r = \text{ESO}(s)/Q; \text{ or } Q = \text{ESO}(s)/a_r \tag{7}$$

We work with the same set of equations (4), (5), and (6) that formed our solution for the basic continuous review model. We first solve equation (4) for p. This tells us the imputed stockout cost p that would be associated with a given Q^* and s^* being optimal. Then we substitute this value of p into equation (5). Then the new equation together with (6) form a system we can solve iteratively in the usual fashion.

Stockout Service Constraint. This model is somewhat easier to solve mathematically than the fill level model; iteration is not required. We specify service by requiring that the probability of not stocking out be $1 - a_s$, that is

$$a_s = 1 - F(s^*) \qquad\qquad (8)$$

This determines z^* which determines s^* and $ESO(s^*)$ and so on, using (4), (5) and (6) as usual.

3.4.4 Continuous Review Exercises

1. Java Jeff also sells imported gourmet tea. His finest Burmese Jasmine Tea costs him $9.00 for a 12 oz. canister. The tea sells at a 70 percent markup. Excess demand is lost. Stockouts are cost at lost revenue, plus a 1 percent chance of losing a customer, whose average future business is estimated to be worth $500 in profits. The setup cost for an order is $30.00 in bookkeeping expenses and $18 in time lost keeping orders on track. Jeff sells 20 canisters a month. The lead time is two months. The standard deviation of demand over the lead time is 40 percent of the average demand. Jeff costs inventory at 3 percent per month.

    a. On what basis should Jeff order, using the simple approximation method? (Guess ESO at 1 percent of lead time demand).
    b. What are his annual average holding cost, penalty costs, and setup costs for this policy?
    c. What are his costs as a function of total sales?
    d. What is his average time between orders?
    e. What is his safety stock proportion of demand met, and proportion of cycles with a stockout?

2. Re-do problem 1, but with the full iterative method. What percentage total cost improvement came from the more complete method?

3. Re-do problem 1, if Jeff even *more simply* approximates the order quantity as the Granddaddy model. What percentage worse in cost terms is the approximation here?

4. The Aviation Warehouse sells parts for repairing/upgrading airplanes to a number of regional flight service centers. One particular component, a popular transponder, is purchased from a vendor for $75.00. It is estimated that the cost of order processing and receipt is $100 per order. The company uses an inventory cost based on a 24 percent annual interest rate.

    Order lead time is two months. Lead time demand for the transponder follows a normal distribution with a mean of 28 and a standard deviation of 12. Unavailable transponders represent lost sales at an opportunity cost of $80.00.

    a. Give the optimal order policy Q^* and s^*.
    b. Give total annual cost and costs broken down into holding, setup, and stockout.
    c. Evaluate the cost of uncertainty for this model. (Find the total cost if a perfect forecast for the lead time were available. Express the excess cost of the probabilistic model as a percentage of the deterministic cost.)

5. The Aviation Warehouse has a new policy in problem 4 that items stocked out will be expedited and shipped second day UPS to the waiting customer. Customers will accept this backup policy. The total cost of expediting is $25.00 plus $10 in lost goodwill to the customer. Re-solve problem 4. (**Hint**: This is not a backlogging model).

3.5 UNCLE SAM'S SEAFOOD—FINALE

John returned to see Jane at Uncle Sam's Seafood two months later to discuss his design for a fresh fish forecasting and inventory control system, and to discuss some improvements on his recommendations for frozen fish and meats. John's ideas for the fresh fish system were divided into three parts:

1. A simple forecasting system
2. A simple ordering system
3. An evaluation system

Simple Forecasting System.   John determined that Uncle Sam carries 38 distinct fresh fish products, including 10 grades of shrimp, 5 grades of lobsters, and so on. These products are not particularly seasonal. For each product a detailed internal record would be kept. For each week for the last year, the following information would have been kept:

Saturday Order
forecast total demand
forecast full price demand
forecast total demand standard deviation
forecast full price demand standard deviation
recommended order quantity
actual order quantity
quantity received
full price demand
reduced price demand
unit cost
full unit selling price
reduced unit selling price

Wednesday Order
(SAME)

The information could be displayed at different levels of detail. For example, Saturday Shrimp 25 count could be displayed by week, by month, or just the current decision. The decision maker could change/override these decisions in a number of ways:

DSS Support Changes/Overrides.

1. Multiply an item forecast by a one-time multiplier
2. Multiply groups of items by a one-time multiplier
3. Change item forecast by a permanent factor
4. Change all items forecast by a permanent factor
5. Change costs, prices, item, or group by a one-time multiplier
6. Change cost, prices, item, or group by a permanent factor

Forecasting Method.

1. Simple six-month moving average on total demand and full price demand
2. Simple six-month moving average on actual past (forecast – actual) forecast errors, for total demand and full price demand

Simple Ordering System.   The system is composed of an automatic ordering algorithm, which uses the forecasts and costs. The user always inputs the final order, which may be the recommended order, a minor change of it, or a complete override.

Ordering Method.

1. A two-phase newsboy formulation
2. Let U_1 be full price opportunity cost stockout penalty, U_2 the reduced price stock-out penalty, and D the salvage penalty.
3. Let F_1 be the cumulative distribution of full price demand and F_2 be the cumulative distribution of total demand.
4. The optimal order quantity y^* satisfies:
   $$[U_1 - U_2]F_1(y^*) + (U_2 + D)F_2(y^*) - U_1 = 0$$
5. This is a simple search which can be quickly solved on the company's PC.

Evaluation System. The system keeps track of actual stockout costs, holding costs, and salvage costs. It also keeps track of the corresponding cost if the theoretical ordering method had been followed every time. This gives the user an opportunity to see how good the system really is, before trusting it too much.

Frozen Foods. John converted the EOQ system for frozen foods to a periodic review system. This required a knowledge of the distribution of demand over the lead time interval. He installed record keeping on the PC to begin accumulating actual demands during lead times.

Inventory Systems: New Directions

4.1 INTRODUCTION

Inventory system issues include setting an inventory control method's intensity by the dollar volume of the item, controlling lot-sizing and stockouts by system "control knobs," allowing appropriate user override of the automatic system, structuring and solving other decision support issues, and combining forecasting and inventory control.

Apart from inventory systems, there are several strategic issues in inventory which have been stressed by the Japanese, and which it is important to address here. The Japanese feel that inventories are essentially "evil," and that we should strive for zero inventories! This is the foundation idea for **Just-In-Time** (JIT.) They cite a number of reasons for this. One is that large inventories allow bad items to be hidden for a long time. Low inventories require all items to be used quickly, which reveals such items. Another reason is that inventories are buffers which allow for poor planning and coordination. But poor planning and coordination are very costly to the firm and should be eliminated.

The lot-size model takes setup costs as given and optimizes a tradeoff between setup costs and holding costs. A more strategic issue is how to improve the process to radically reduce setup costs, and thus reduce inventories and move toward JIT. A similar issue is that conventional inventory theory computes inventory needs based on lead time. However, a more strategic issue is how to radically reduce lead time to both dramatically reduce inventories and provide a competitive edge in giving quick response to the customer. This is called time-based competition. Finally, there are issues involved in the coming information superhighway between firms. This is called **EDI**, for **electronic data interchange**. The idea is that a firm might directly access the computer files of a customer to find out what the customer is likely to order. In return the customer would be given a discount. This raises obvious issues of privacy and even antitrust; nevertheless, EDI is coming.

4.2 INVENTORY PRODUCT GROUPS

4.2.1 Overview

Product groups arise in a number of ways. A group of items may all be ordered from the same vendor, and can thus share the order form, shipment, and often group price discounts. On the shop floor, a group of items may be similar enough to all have the same major setup cost, but require an additional minor setup cost. Or the items may be customer substitutes. Five colors and styles of otherwise identical stockings, for example, might not require that each carry a high safety stock, since the customer will accept a substitute at a very small goodwill cost.

The proper grouping is not always a trivial issue. If vendor grouping corresponds with substitution grouping, for example, things are relatively simple. But many times some of the items in the vendor grouping are not substitutes at all; similarly, several different vendors may supply similar stockings. Also, there is often substitutability "drift." Fancy sweaters and less dressy sweaters are somewhat substitutable. Less dressy sweaters and casual sweaters are somewhat substitutable. Casual sweaters and fashion sweatshirts are somewhat substitutable. Fashion sweatshirts and ordinary sweatshirts are somewhat substitutable. But the system should not assume fancy sweaters and ordinary sweatshirts are somewhat substitutable!

High and low volume items also often give trouble. If a group of five items all have the same major setup, but four of them can allow a three-month lot size, while the fifth needs a one-week lot size, then likely there should be two groups. (An alternative is a complex group which coordinates but contains members at multiples of the basic ordering frequency.)

The system quickly becomes useless if we try to represent all this complexity faithfully. It is best to catch as many relationships as possible with simple groupings, and to simply omit the rest. In cases where the manager recognizes that this creates problems, he/she can use the decision support features to override the system and make corrections.

4.2.2 Grouped Setup Costs

Grouped Ordering Setup Costs Model. Consider the following multi-product version of the basic continuous review model with no backlogging. Suppose there are m products to be ordered in common from the same vendor. Suppose the order setup cost for the entire order is K_0 and the line setup costs for each item are K_j. We define the (aggregated) group setup cost as:

$$K = K_0 + \Sigma_{j=1,m} K_j$$

We choose our product units in dollars, for easy aggregation. Let D_j be the forecast demand rate for product j per time unit, expressed in total dollars at wholesale. Then the aggregate demand for the group product is just

$$D = \Sigma_{j=1,m} D_j$$

Because the basic product unit for all products is \$1, all individual holding costs and the aggregate holding cost are just I, the common percentage rate of holding. Let $(1 + v)$ be the common markup on all products over wholesale. That is, a dollar's worth of wholesale product sells to the customer for $\$(1 + v)$. Let Q be the total lot size in dollars for all products. Let p be the common no-backlogging cost per wholesale dollar of lost sales. Define the individual reorder points s_j, yet to be determined. Define the aggregate reorder point s by $s = \Sigma_{j=1,m} s_j$. It is the total coverage against stockout for all products aggregated. Finally, define: $\mu = \Sigma_{j=1,m} \mu_j$ as the aggregate mean lead time demand, and define $\sigma = \Sigma_{j=1,m} \sigma_j$. (It may seem strange to add the standard deviations rather than the variances. However, the expected stockout from adding the products grows linearly, since each product stocks out separately.) Since all products have the same relative economics in terms of holding cost, penalty cost, lot size, and demand, we have:

$$F(z) = 1.0 - (I/p)(Q/D) = 1.0 - (I/p)(Q_j/D_j) \tag{1a}$$

Thus, given the aggregate order quantity Q, we can determine s and all s_j by:

$$s = \mu + z\sigma; \quad s_j = \mu + z\sigma_j \tag{1b}$$

Remember that each expected stockout is determined under the normal distribution assumption by:

$$ESO_j(s_j) = \sigma_j L(z) \tag{2a}$$

Thus, we may define ESO(*s*) by

$$ESO(s) = \sum_{j=1,m} ESO_j(s_j) = (\sum_{j=1,m}\sigma_j)L(z)$$

or

$$ESO(s) = \sigma L(z) \tag{2b}$$

Because of all our careful aggregation work, the formula for Q is simply:

$$Q = [2(K + p\sigma L(z))D/I]^{0.5} \tag{3}$$

However, remember that everything in this formula is either aggregated over products or reinterpreted somewhat:

- K is the sum of the order setup and all line setups
- s is the dollar sum of all the reorder points in dollars
- ESO is the total dollar expected stockout for a total dollar investment in reorder point, allocated to give every product the same z of protection
- p is a stockout cost per dollar stocked out
- D is the aggregate forecast demand rate in dollars
- I is the holding cost per dollar of product

Example 4-1, Part 1. Java Jeff gets three of his house brand coffees from a gourmet exporter in Brazil; call them A, B, and C. These all come in one-pound bags. All are labeled "Java Jeff's Private Label." The three mixes are labeled, in addition, "Smooth Gourmet," "Prime Gourmet," and "Extra-prime Gourmet." Jeff sells $1500 of A, $1000 of B, and $500 of C, all yearly, in wholesale value. Jeff marks up the coffees by 110 percent. Stockouts are lost sales. He figures this cost at lost revenue, with no allowance for goodwill. He figures holding costs at 36 percent per year. Jeff estimates there is about $40 cost in sending an order to Brazil, plus $5.00 for each item on the order. The lead time for an order is three months. The standard deviation of demand over a lead time is about 30 percent for product A, 35 percent for product B, and 40 percent for product C. What is the economic order quantity for each product, and their reorder points?

Solution.

- Aggregate setup cost $K = 40 + 5 + 5 + 5 = 55$.
- Aggregate demand $P = \$1500 + \$1000 + \$500 = \$3000$.
- The holding cost per dollar is 0.36.
- The stockout cost per dollar is $(2.10 - 1.0) = 1.10$.
- Mean demands in lead time are 0.25(1500), 0.25(1000), 0.25(500), or $\mu = 375 + 250 + 125 = 750$.
- Standard deviations are 0.3(375), 0.35(250), 0.40(125), or 112.5, 87.5, 50.
- The aggregate standard deviation is $\sigma = 112.5 + 87.5 + 50 = 250$.

We take our initial estimate of the aggregate Q from the Granddaddy Model (e.g., formula (3) with ESO = 0):

$$Q_0 = [2KP/h]^{0.5} = [2(55)(3000)/.36]^{0.5} = 957$$

We substitute this back into (1a) to get a value for z:

$$F(z_1) = 1.0 - (0.36/1.10)(956/3000) = 1.0 - 0.104 = 0.896$$

From a unit normal table, we get therefore that $z_1 = 1.26$. From this we can get the various reorder points, but this is just extra work until we finish the iterations to get z accurately. $L(1.26) = 0.0496$.

We now use (3) again:

$$Q_1 = [2(K + p\sigma L(z))P/I]^{0.5} = [2(55 + (1.1)(250)(.0496))(3000)/.36]^{0.5}$$
$$= [2(55 + 13.6)(3000)/.36]^{0.5} = 1069$$

Now we must iterate again. We go back to (1a) to get a better value for z:

$$F(z_2) = 1.0 - (0.36/1.10)(1069/3000) = 1.0 - (.327)(.356) = 0.884$$

From a unit normal table we get $z_2 = 1.20$ and $L(z_2) = 0.0561$.
   We now use (3) again:

$$Q_2 = [2(55 + (1.1)(250)(.0561))(3000)/0.36]^{0.5} = [2(70.4)3000/0.36]^{0.5}$$
$$= 1083$$

The first iteration changed Q by 10 percent, this time only 1 percent. It seems safe to stop. To get the individual order points, we just use $z = 1.20$:

$$s_1 = \mu_1 + 1.20\sigma_1 = 375 + (1.20)(112.5) = \$510$$

$$s_2 = \mu_2 + 1.20\sigma_2 = 250 + (1.20)(87.5) = \$355$$

$$s_3 = \mu_3 + 1.20\sigma_3 = 125 + (1.20)(50) = \$185$$

Finally, to get the individual Q_j, we simply apportion Q in the same percentage as the three products apportion dollar demand:

$$a_1 = 1500/3000 = 0.500; \ a_2 = 1000/3000 = 0.333; \ a_3 = 500/3000 = 0.167$$

$$Q_1 = a_1Q = (.500)(1083) = \$542$$

$$Q_2 = a_2Q = (.333)(1083) = \$361$$

$$Q_3 = a_3Q = (.167)(1083) = \$180$$

Note that we don't have the information to convert dollar sales into physical bags of coffee, since we are not given prices per bag. This information was not necessary to do the analysis, since using dollars as the units was so convenient.

Group Reorder Triggering. In the previous model, all products have been timed to reach their reorder points simultaneously. Unfortunately, since demand is probabilistic, this will never actually happen. One or two products will often have exceptional demand for one reason or another. They will need a new order, while products which still have half of their lot size remaining may find a new order very undesirable.

   A full analysis of this situation would be very complicated and expensive, so we present a two part procedure:

1.   Group Reorder Trigger Procedure
2.   Coverage Equalization Procedure

Group Reorder Trigger Procedure. The idea is not to trigger an order just because one item prematurely reaches its single reorder point. On the other hand, we do not wish to allow extensive stockouts. At first, a reasonable compromise trigger would be to order when the aggregate inventory $x = \sum_{j=1,m} x_j$ drops below the aggregate reorder point $s = \sum_{j=1,m} s_j$. Unfortunately, this gives items which are stocking out no more influence than similar items which are somewhat overstocked. To make a simple correction for this, we bias our measure of aggregate inventory to give larger influence to items which are stocking out. We define aggregate "stockout adjusted" inventory by

$$x_{sa} = \sum_{j=1,m}[\mu_j + (x_j - \mu_j)^+ - (M + 1)(\mu_j - x)^+] \tag{4}$$

This equation is left as an exercise, to show that this is equivalent to

$$x_{sa} = x - M \sum_{j=1,m} (\mu_j - x)^+ \tag{5}$$

That is to say, the stockout adjusted inventory is the usual aggregate inventory, less a penalty multiple M times the total amount by which any items have inventory levels which are less than their mean demand over the lead time. This leads to a **triggering heuristic: Place a group order (to be determined later) whenever the adjusted inventory falls below the group reorder point, that is, when $x_{sa} <= s$.**

M is a control parameter to be set by the manager. If M is close to zero, the system will not be very sensitive to a single item being in trouble. If M is large, for example 5 or 10, then any item which reaches its reorder point will trigger the system. The manager will typically need to gain experience by trying different values. A value of $M = 2$ or 3 might seem like a compromise starting point.

Example 4-1, Part 2. For coffee types A, B, and C, Java Jeff had reorder points of $510, $355, and $185 respectively, with mean lead time demands of $375, $250, and $125. Thus, $s = \$1050$. He used an aggregate triggering method with $M = 3$. At one point x_1 became $510 and so triggered an order point. However at this point x_2 was $410 and x_3 was $250. Thus, no product was critical, and adjusted inventory was $1170, so that the aggregate reorder point was not triggered.

Next x_1 had dropped to $410, x_2 was $400, and x_3 was $240. Thus, $x_{as} = \$1050$, which just triggered the aggregate reorder point, and a full order was made.

At a different time x_1 had again dropped to its order point of $510, but the other two products had more sluggish demand, so that $x_2 = \$505$, and $x_3 = \$350$. No product was critical, and the aggregate x was $1365, considerably above $s = \$1050$. By the time x_1 had dropped to $375, x_2 had dropped to $450, and x_3 to $325. Product A was becoming critical, and aggregate inventory was $1150, still not triggering the aggregate reorder point. By the time x_1 had dropped to $350, x_2 had dropped to $425, and x_3 to $300. Now $x_{as} = x - 3(\mu_j - x_j)^+ = 1075 - 3(25) = 1000$, which triggered the order. (In a transactions-based system, these calculations would be made after each transaction for any of the products.)

Coverage Equalization Procedures. The plan, in a multi-product group situation, is for all products to run out simultaneously. Due to forecast errors, the plan will never exactly be realized. At the time of a reorder, we are likely to face an inventory situation as shown in Figure 4-1.

All careful ordering heuristics for the above situation are of the "coverage equalization," sometimes called the "fill equalization" philosophy. The idea is simply to equalize the weeks of coverage for all items, insofar as possible. The order is built sequentially, filling the greatest need first, and then the next greatest need, and so on.

Generic Coverage Equalization Procedure.

1. Fill all products below their reorder point to their reorder point.
2. Is the total order size cutoff reached? If so, exit.
3. Fill product or products currently at lowest weeks coverage, preserving that equality, until either the cutoff is reached or the coverage level of one or more new products is reached.
4. Return to 2.

Thus, in Figure 4-1, the procedure would first raise inventory for Product A to its reorder point. Next it would raise it to the same week's coverage as Product B. Next it would raise Products A and B at the same time rate until they reach the coverage of Product C. Then, finally, all three products would be raised simultaneously, preserving the time coverage.

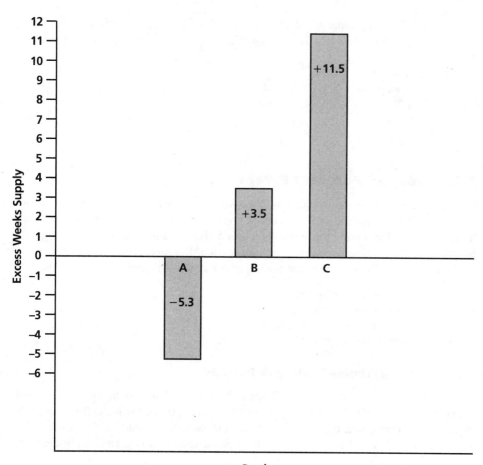

Figure 4-1

Weeks Supply in Excess of
Re-Order Point by Product

We have not yet explained the termination procedure for this heuristic. The simplest one, usually implemented in practice, is to terminate when the total order reaches Q^*, the aggregate optimal order. This works quite well when the coverages are not too far out of normal (say if total excess inventories are not more than $0.5Q^*$).

If the situation is badly out of balance, it is better to use the Silver-Meal heuristic, since the out-of-balance condition in essence produces a seasonality type situation. We leave statement of the Silver-Meal heuristic for this situation as an exercise.

Example 4-1, Part 3. Remember that at the time of the order trigger, Java Jeff had 350 units of Product A on hand compared with a reorder point of 510, 425 units of Product B on hand, compared with a reorder point of 355, and 300 units of Product C on hand, compared with a reorder point of 185. What sort of an order should Jeff place?

Solution. (We use 50 weeks in a year for computational convenience.) Demand for Product A is 1500/50 = $30 per week; demand for Product B is $20 per week; demand for Product C is $10 per week.

Thus, in terms of weeks supply in excess of the reorder point, A is at –5.3 weeks, B is at 3.5 weeks, and C is at 11.5 weeks. Excess supplies are 70 + 115 = 185, which is less than 0.5 times the standard Q^* of 1083. So we build an order of $1083.

Step 1. Raise inventory of A to zero. Cost = $160.
Step 2. Raise inventory of A to 3.5 weeks. Cost = $105.
Step 3. Raise inventory of A and B to 11.5 weeks. Cost = $400.

Step 4. Remaining order to be placed = $1083 – 400 – 105 – 160 = $418. Group demand = 30 + 20 + 10 = 60 a week. Raise all inventories to $11.5 + (418)/(60) = 18.5$ weeks.

Step 5. Summary of orders:

A 30(18.5 – (–5.3)) = $ 714
B 20(18.5 – 3.5) = 300
C 10(18.5 – 11.5) = 70

Total order $1084

4.2.3 Grouped Forecast Errors

Overview. There are many situations when we would like to be able to forecast the distribution of demand for individual demands given the distribution for the product group, or to obtain the distribution for the product group given distributions of demand for each product. That is, we desire to scale over **aggregation/disaggregation**.

Situations for which aggregation scaling of demand distributions is useful include:

- Efficiency of the forecasting system
- Safety stocks for substitutable products
- Group advertising, storage considerations
- Aggregate modeling in general

Methods of Aggregate Scaling of Demand.

Demand Independence. In this method, we assume the demands for the different individual products are completely independent. Let $\mu_1, \mu_2, \ldots, \mu_m$ be the mean demands of the individual products, and $\sigma_1, \sigma_2, \ldots, \sigma_m$ be the individual standard deviations. Then assuming normality and independence, the group distribution is normal with mean and standard deviation:

$$\mu = \Sigma_{j=1,m}\, \mu_j$$

$$\sigma = [\Sigma_{j=1,m}\sigma_j^2]^{0.5}$$

As an example, if each of three products had a forecast with mean 20 and standard deviation 10, then the group forecast under independence would have a mean of 60 and a standard deviation of 17.

Independence is an extreme assumption, because if the products are at all similar, they will have common uncertainty about popularity of the group. Another way of saying this is that the group forecasting process introduces a correlation in the forecasts. However, independence is useful in that it establishes a *lower bound* on the possible group standard deviation.

Perfect Demand Correlation. At the other extreme, if the products are very similar, so that common uncertainty about the line popularity is large, and if the volumes are also large, so that randomness is not an important factor, then the forecasts will be close to perfectly correlated, and the standard deviations will just add:

$$\sigma = [\Sigma_{j=1,m}\sigma_j]$$

Under this assumption, the group mean would be 60 as before, but the group standard deviation would go up from 17 to 30. Complete correlation is useful in that it establishes an *upper bound* on the possible group standard deviation.

Fixed Power of Demand. This method, attributed to R.G. Brown, tries to get a compromise between the two extremes, by assuming

$$\sigma = (\mu/\mu_j)^a\sigma_j, \text{ where } 0 <= a <= 1.0$$

The value of a is obtained by regression on past data; a typical value is $a = 0.7$. Using that value in our example, we would have

$$\sigma = (60/20)^{0.7}(10) = (2.16)(10) = 21.6$$

The trouble with this method is that the power coefficient is very sensitive. For large volumes it tends to be close to 1.0, for small volumes it tends to be close to 0.5.

Two Component Demand Scaling. This method, developed by the author, also compromises between the two extremes: $\sigma = [A\mu + B\mu])^{0.5}$ where μ is any mean. A is fit as the average number of units in a transaction, allowing B to be fit for any known distribution. The resulting formula can then be used for extrapolation.

Suppose, in our example, that the average transaction size $A = 1.0$. Then, fitting one of the products

$$10 = [(1)(20) + B(20)^2]^{0.5}, \text{ giving } B = .20$$

Thus, our estimated formula is

$$\sigma = [\mu + 0.20\mu^2]^{0.5} = [60 + (.2)(60)^2]^{0.5} = 27.9$$

It is critical here that units are assumed to be sold individually. If the average order size were 4, then

$$10 = [4(20) + B(20)^2]^{0.5}, \text{ giving } B = 0.05$$

Then our estimated formula would be

$$\sigma = [4\mu + 0.05\mu^2]^{0.5} = [4(60) + 0.05(60)^2]^{0.5} = 20.5$$

The advantage of this method is that it considers both the pure randomness component of errors and the forecast component. It is easy to fit and gives random answers for small forecasts and highly correlated forecasts for large forecasts. Its main disadvantage, at this point, is that it has not been widely tested.

4.2.4 Grouped Stockout Costs (Substitutability)

A major shortcoming in inventory theory has been the treatment of how to plan safety stocks when demand for one product may often be filled by another at relatively small implicit or explicit cost. For example, a customer may want six pairs of brown socks, but may be convinced with relatively little prodding to take three pairs of brown socks and three pairs of black socks in the same size and style. Or the customer may want four white shirts from a certain manufacturer at \$19.50, but may gladly accept four slightly better quality shirts which retail for \$22.50, which will be given to him for \$19.50 to avoid bad feelings.

If there are n substitutable products, a conventional approach would need about n^2 probabilities of substitution, with n^2 corresponding costs. Then safety stock levels could not be optimized separately, but would require at least an n-variable dynamic programming formulation. Here we cut through much of this mathematical forest by a rather simple approach, the group substitution ordering heuristic.

1. Solve the group problem as in 4.2.2, assuming no substitution is allowed.
2. Make a choice for a method for obtaining the group standard deviation from the individual standard deviations.
3. Solve the group problem assuming costless substitution.
4. Using some managerial weight β choose a solution which weights β on the costless solution and $(1 - \beta)$ on the full cost solution.

Example 4-1, Part 4. We already solved the original Java Jeff problem assuming no substitution is allowed in the first part of Example 4-1. We summarize this solution first, and then go on to the other three points discussed in the previous paragraphs.

1. **Assume there is no substitution (review).**

   We found in the original Java Jeff problem that, assuming no substitutability, the group standard deviation for calculating the group reorder point was just the sum of the individual standard deviations. That is,

   $$\sigma = \sigma_1 + \sigma_2 + \sigma_3 = 112.5 + 87.5 + 50 = 250$$

   As the final solution, we obtained $Q = 1083$ and $s = 1050$; the safety stock portion of this is $ss = 1050 - 750 = 300$.

2. **Choose a group standard deviation method.**

   As an example, we arbitrarily pick the method assuming independence between the individual products. (The other methods will be looked at in the exercises.) This yields for the grouped distribution of demand over the lead time

   $$\mu = \mu_1 + \mu_2 + \mu_3 = 375 + 250 + 125 = 750$$

   $$\sigma = [(112.5)^2 + (87.5)^2 + (50)^2]^{0.5} = 151$$

   (versus 250 for completely correlated).

3. **Solve the group problem, assuming costless substitution.**

   With costless substitution, we may truly solve the problem as a single product with a smaller standard deviation than the direct sum of the standard deviations, just as in the no substitution problem. At the end, we can give equal coverage to each product for the sake of balance (although this has no effect on the model given costless substitution).

   Now we may repeat the original calculations, up to the point that the Q_1 formula needs the reduced value for σ inserted:

   $$Q = [2(55 + (1.1)(151)(.0496))(3000)/.36]^{0.5}$$
   $$= [2(55 + 8.2)(3000)/.36]^{0.5} = 1026$$
   $$F(z_2) = 1.0 - (0.327)(1026/3000) = 0.888$$

   From our tables, we get $z_2 = 1.22$ and $L(z_2) = 0.0558$. Then $Q_2 = [2(55 + (1.1)(151)(.0558))(3000)/.36]^{0.5} = [2(64.3)3000/0.36]^{0.5} = 1035$.

   Again, it is safe to stop here, for the same reasons as before. We use $z = 1.22$. Thus, to get the group reorder point, we have

   $$s = \mu + 1.22\sigma = 750 + (1.22)(151) = 750 + 184 = 934$$

   In going from no substitution to full substitution, lot-sizing inventories on average will be reduced from 542 (0.5(1083)) to 518 (0.5(1035)). Safety stock inventories equal the reorder point minus the mean demand over lead time. Thus, safety stock inventories will be reduced from 300 (1050 – 750) to 184 (934 – 750). Thus, total average discretionary inventory is reduced from 842 (542 + 300) down to 702 (518 + 184), a reduction of 17 percent. You will be asked in the exercises to show what the reduction is in terms of total costs.

4. **Take a weighted average of the two solutions.**

   In practice we do not expect that products will ever be fully substitutable. We let management choose a control β, $0 < \beta < 1.0$, and form a compromise solution which is a weighted average of the two solutions. Suppose that Java Jeff chooses $\beta = 0.5$. Then the final solution he would obtain would be $Q_{av} = 0.5(1083) + 0.5(1039) = 1061$, and $s_{av} = 0.5(1050) + 0.5(934) = 992$.

   The compromise safety stock would be $ss_{av} = 992 - 750 = 242$. This safety stock should be apportioned according to the standard deviation of each product. Since the total standard deviation is 250, we would use $z = 242/250 = 0.97$ for each product.

Thus,

$$s_1 = 375 + (0.97)(112.5) \quad = 484$$

$$s_2 = 250 + (0.97)(87.5) \quad = 335$$

$$s_3 = 124 + (0.97)(50) \quad = 173$$

4.2.5 Inventory Group Exercises

Grouped Setup Costs.

1. Restinghouse Corporation Tube Division makes four styles of 3/4-inch 20-foot nuclear tubes for reactors, known as alpha, beta, gamma, and delta. These four types of tubes are quite similar, and all cost $20 per tube. Restinghouse sells 10,000 of alpha per year, 4000 of beta, 4000 of gamma, and 2000 of delta. The average sale size is 100 tubes. Restinghouse sells the tubes for $35 each. There is no backlogging. The stockout cost is lost revenue, plus $5 for goodwill. It takes about 12 hours of machine time to set the machine up for the group, and another 0.5 hour to adjust the machine for each product. The production lead time is about 12 percent of a year. The standard deviation of demand over the lead time is about 360 for alpha, 240 for beta and gamma, and 160 for delta. What are the economic order quantities for the products, and their reorder points?

2. Consider again problem 1. At the time that delta inventory reaches its reorder point, gamma inventory is four weeks' supply above its order point, beta is ten weeks above its order point, and alpha is one week above its order point. Assuming that an aggregate triggering method is used with $M = 2$, and assuming that demands continue from here on at their normal average rate, project the four individual inventory situations when the adjusted inventory dips below the aggregate reorder point.

3. In problems 1 and 2, use a coverage equalization procedure to make a total aggregate order equal to Q^* from problem 1, while equalizing the inventory situation you found in problem 2 as well as possible.

Grouped Forecast Errors.

4. Estimate the distribution of demand over the lead time for problem 1 for each of two methods:

   a. Independent demand
   b. Completely correlated demand

5. Estimate the distribution of demand over the lead time for problem 1 for each of the following two methods. In each case extrapolate from each of the individual products separately, and comment on the consistency of the extrapolation for the two methods:

   a. Power law extrapolation of demand
   b. Two component extrapolation of demand

   In the last two methods, you will get somewhat differing answers depending on which of the four products you scale up from.

Grouped Stockout Costs (Substitution).

6. In problem 1, re-solve the problem under the assumption that the four styles of pipe are perfectly substitutable. Then assume that the pipe manufacturing manager wants a solution which is a two-third weighting on the substitutable solution and one-third on the non-substitutable solution. Produce that compromise solution.

7. Re-solve problem 1 with the stockout penalties multiplied by
   a. 0.75
   b. 0.55
   c. 0.25
   d. Plot a curve for Q^* as a function of the stockout multiplier, and another for s^*. Plot the Q and s from problem 6 on the graphs for comparison purposes. What do you conclude?

4.3 INVENTORY SYSTEMS

4.3.1 Overview

A forecasting/inventory system is much more than a large number of individual products (SKUs for "stockkeeping units"), each forecast and controlled separately. Items with similar seasonal patterns derive benefits by grouped forecasting. Items with a common vendor or job shop resource derive benefits by grouped sharing of a common setup cost. Items with high substitutability derive benefits by sharing safety stocks. The relative cost of a given sophistication of control is much lower for high dollar volume items than low dollar volume items. Many items have multiple levels of groupings. For example, a given style of shoe may come in different colors and different sizes.

Groupings discussed previously for different purposes may result fortuitously in the same group for seasonal pattern, vendor, and substitutability. Unfortunately, in many cases these groupings conflict with each other and compromises must be made. Sometimes these groupings are made judgmentally, and sometimes automatically, by measuring similarity of patterns, for example. How should grouping, and compromises for different groupings, be done?

Turning to informational issues, the manager does not want to be snowed under with output looking at every one of perhaps 100,000 items manually. How does one design a system which thinks in an aggregate manner by lines and vendors, and yet gives detail when it is desired? We will try to take at least an initial look at these and similar questions in this section.

4.3.2 Hierarchical System Structure

A typical wholesale or retail distributor who carries a broad class of consumer goods thinks of his/her offerings in a hierarchical fashion. A typical detailed item or SKU (stockkeeping unit) might have the eight levels of classification shown in Table 4-1, for example. (This differs from establishment to establishment.)

Consider a particular women's blouse, for example. It might be classified by the following categories:

Company—Ralph's Discount Department Store
Department—Women's Clothing

Table 4-1

Merchandise Hierarchy

Merchandise Hierarchy
Company
Department
Line
Vendor
Family
Article
Color
Size

Line—Spring Fashion
Vendor—Ace Fashion Clothing
Family—Youth Fashion Blouses
Article—Particular Blouse Style and Pattern
Color—Red and White
Size—10

The item would be identified by a long code identifying each level in turn. The size itself may be complicated in some cases; for example, shoes might be represented both by size and width, jeans both by waist and length, and shirts by neck size and sleeve length. Sometimes the lower levels of the classification are missing. For example, a particular type of radio would be represented by an article number, but no color or size. All items are coded down to the article level.

It would be very nice for forecasting purposes, for example, if all items from the same vendor within a line had pretty much the same seasonal pattern, so that the same grouping used for group forecasting could also be used for group ordering. Unfortunately this is often not the case. Ordinary umbrellas, for example, might have a fairly even seasonal pattern, while top-of-the-line umbrellas might sell heavily at Christmas.

In the same way, it would be nice if all items from the same vendor within a line had little substitutability with any items outside the line, and heavy substitutability within the line (or none). This is not often the case. A single vendor may sell umbrellas and rain boots, for example, which are not very good substitutes (they are really complements). On the other hand, vendors even in different lines may sell rain boots, hiking boots, and dress boots, which may be fairly substitutable for some customers.

Another problem is that a high volume item may be ordered together with a number of low volume items from the same vendor. The high volume item may have an EOQ such that it is necessary to order it every week, even if the full order setup K must be paid each time, as well as its own line setup cost. But even if management piggybacks the high volume item, and considers the K setup to be free for it, the other items may not be able to justify ordering more often than every two months, even just to cover their line setup K_j. From a modeling point of view, it may be cheapest to order the one item every week, and to have a group order of all items every two months. However this may cause confusion. The manager is likely to prefer considering them as two groups, even at a theoretically higher cost.

Thus, in practice, grouping requires careful thinking and a number of compromises. Successful groupings are usually done by hand, by an experienced manager. Attempts to do such complex groupings algorithmically by computer have not been very successful in the author's opinion. This remains an important area of potential research.

4.3.3 ABC Analysis

Introduction. ABC analysis concerns sorting items by decreasing importance to the firm, which is assumed to be measured by yearly dollar sales volume. The high volume items are then to be managed carefully, and the low volume items are to be managed in a low cost fashion. This analysis unfortunately ignores the complications brought on by grouping and the hierarchical structure of merchandise in the first place. We first present the classical ABC analysis, and next discuss briefly how grouping issues affect the analysis.

Exchange curves concern a process by which the manager can change the costs for all products simultaneously and simply, and use this changeability as a control knob to effect tradeoffs between frequency of ordering and lot sizing inventory or between safety stocks and stockout fill rates.

Classical ABC Analysis. There is a clear tradeoff between the cost of implementing and operating an inventory control system and the size of the savings that system is expected to make. In real inventory systems there is a vast difference in profitability for different products. A fancy system may be justified for a profitable item, but not for other less profitable items. It certainly doesn't pay to spend more on controlling the item than its gross revenue.

The approach called **ABC Analysis** classifies items into three categories of significance by the following method:

1. Calculate the price times yearly demand for each SKU in the inventory system. Call this value **dollar volume**.
2. Sort the entire SKU list in order of decreasing dollar volume, and calculate the cumulative dollar volume of the items in a new column.
3. Label the items comprising approximately the top 70-80 percent of the cumulative value (perhaps 20 percent of the SKUs) **A items**. Label the items comprising the next 15-20 percent of the cumulative value (perhaps 30 percent of the items) the **B items**. Label the items comprising the last 5-10 percent of the cumulative value (perhaps 50 percent of the items) **C items**.

Example 4-2, Part 1. Wally's Wholesale Warehouse supplies a number of retail department stores in New York City. Wally stocks 72,500 items. A random sample of the items is shown in Table 4-2, with their price, yearly demand, and associated dollar volume. Note the great spread in the dollar volumes.

When the inventory manager sorted the items by decreasing dollar volume and calculated cumulative dollar volume, she was able to do the ABC analysis shown in Table 4-3. Then when she graphed the cumulative percentage of the items versus the cumulative percentage of total dollar volume, she found the rather standard ABC curve shown in Figure 4-2.

The basic point of the classic ABC analysis is that since **A items** account for most of the sales, these items should be taken care of more carefully. Perhaps some **A items**, so called "big ticket" items like refrigerators and stoves, should be handled with a continuous review system. More sophisticated forecasting might be appropriate. More care might

Table 4-2

Dollar Volume of 25 Random SKU's at Wally's Wholesale Warehouse

Product Code	Yr. Demand	Price	Dollar Volume
23A-6x5	650	$8.00	$5200.00
Tick-79xxx	310	30.00	9300.00
Tick-82y	30	115.00	3450.00
Fash-aa6	14	13.10	183.40
Hard-7708	295	2.25	663.75
Hard-661	45	2.75	123.75
Tick-889	51	98.50	5023.50
888-6	21	1.75	36.75
Misc-7786	388	0.98	380.24
Fash-aa19	651	4.40	2864.40
Misc-0001	25	7.50	187.50
Men-54J	66	6.33	417.78
Misc-99	158	0.79	124.82
Men-54J2	695	0.72	500.40
Child-j6	55	1.93	106.15
Child-j9	14	6.05	84.70
Child-jj1	91	3.98	362.18
Men-667	120	58.00	6960.00
Misc-7799	50	0.30	15.00
Misc-11j	71	0.80	56.80
Hard-7009	210	0.62	130.20
Fash-ba6	120	35.00	4200.00
Fash-ba24x	876	1.59	1392.84
Hard-70x	15	13.00	195.00
Fash-fx6	38	75.00	2850.00

Product	Demand	Price	Dollar Volume	Cumulative $ Volume	Cumulative $ %
Tick-79xxx	310	30.00	9300.00	$9300.00	20.7
Men-667	120	58.00	6960.00	16260.00	36.3
23A-6x5	650	8.00	5200.00	21460.00	47.9
Tick-889	51	98.50	5023.50	26483.50	59.1
Fash-ba6	120	35.00	4200.00	30683.50	68.4
Tick-82y	30	115.00	3450.00	34133.50	76.1
Fash-aa19	651	4.40	2864.40	36997.90	82.5
Fash-fx6	38	75.00	2850.00	39847.90	88.9
Fash-ba24x	876	1.59	1392.84	41240.74	92.0
Hard-7708	295	2.25	663.75	41904.49	93.4
Men-54J2	695	0.72	500.40	42404.89	94.6
Men-54J	66	6.33	417.70	42822.59	95.5
Misc-7786	388	0.98	380.24	43202.83	96.3
Child-jj1	91	3.98	362.18	43565.01	97.1
Hard-70x	15	13.00	195.00	43760.01	97.6
Misc-0001	25	7.50	187.50	43947.51	98.0
Fash-aa6	14	13.10	183.40	44130.91	98.4
Hard-7009	210	0.62	130.20	44261.11	98.7
Misc-99	158	0.79	124.82	44385.93	99.0
Hard-661	45	2.75	123.75	44509.68	99.3
Child-j6	55	1.93	106.15	44615.83	99.5
Child-j9	14	6.05	84.70	44700.53	99.7
Misc-11j	71	0.80	56.80	44757.33	99.8
888-6	21	36.75	111.00	44794.08	99.9
Misc-7799	50	0.30	15.00	44809.08	100.0

Table 4-3

ABC Analysis on Same Items Ranked by Dollar Volume

be taken in specifying exact parameters for the inventory model. More surveillance by the departmental inventory managers to intervene in the automatic system would probably be appropriate also.

For **B items** inventories might be reviewed periodically. Group control would be more appropriate; group intervention and surveillance might be more appropriate than individual surveillance. Somewhat less complicated forecasting might be appropriate. **C items** might use large lot sizes and simple large groups, with demand within the group estimated by simple fixed percentages. In some cases ordering in simple fixed percentages without tracking individual forecasts might be appropriate. For expensive **C items** with very low demand or with customization, the best policy is often simply to order these items after they have been demanded.

Example 4-2, Part 2. Wally's inventory manager next runs the ABC analysis on the full 72,000 inventory items to verify the stability of the A and B boundary definitions. She finds that breaking the categories at 20 percent and 50 percent of the items works very well for the full inventory problem.

There do seem to be some difficulties, however. In many cases, items from a vendor which have always been ordered together are a mixture of the A, B, and C categories. The manager is unwilling to split the group or to treat these items differently. In other cases, low volume **C items** are complementary to high volume A items. The manager worries if these should not be coordinated somehow.

Hierarchical ABC Analysis. In the simple world of independent products, each ordered or produced individually, with separate simple setup costs, the simple ABC analysis performs admirably. However, if it is obvious that the eight items which are ordered from a vendor should be ordered on a joint basis to share a single joint setup cost, then dividing the eight items into A, B, and C categories makes no sense whatever. They should be forecast and controlled as a group, automatically having the same level of control.

Figure 4-2

ABC Distribution of Value
Curve for Wally's Wholesale
Warehouse

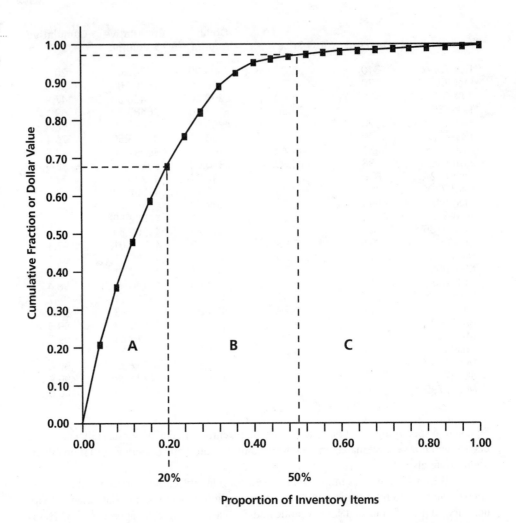

If the inventory manager has previously done groupings which are compromises between common seasonal patterns, common vendors, and similar issues, then the hierarchical modification of the ABC analysis is relatively straightforward. She should simply aggregate individual items in the group into an aggregate group dollar volume, and treat these groups as individual items in an ABC analysis procedure, producing finally A groups, B groups, and C groups.

4.3.4 Decision Support Issues

Introduction.   Thirty or forty years ago, many large automated inventory systems were built, but most of them failed for one reason or another. If the builders were sensitive to the department managers' concerns that the automatic system would make too many mistakes, then the manual system and the automatic system were operated in parallel. There was nothing to force the managers to use the system, and so they mostly ignored it. Eventually an expensive system would die on the vine. Occasionally, the system was forced on the managers without any reasonable way to override it. After the system made a few serious mistakes, the managers had sufficient ammunition to shoot it down.

Cash register order-entry saved the day. Everyone appreciated the great convenience of inexpensive and accurate data collection into a large and accurate database. The system was assured of survival irrespective of what happened in terms of automatic ordering. In this more comfortable environment, the automatic ordering system could be gradually improved until it worked.

The issue of when to override the system, at what level, and how to assure that the manager tries to use the system are still very important. The following paragraphs look at desired attributes of these systems, and the question of how the manager can change the system easily to adjust to changing circumstances.

Easy Access to Information. Another headache of large inventory systems is the tendency to print out reams and reams of detailed information on every SKU, expecting the manager to absorb it. As we have said, the inventory system is hierarchical. The manager should be able to query the line level, for example, and get sales by vendor and percentage deviation of vendors from forecast. He should then be able to focus on a bad vendor and get more detail, and so forth. These kinds of queries should all be on-screen, with printout reserved for occasional special situations. This is a major issue discussed in MIS courses; we do not belabor it further here.

Easy Explanation of Automatic Decision. The manager should be able to understand an order by querying a simple explanation involving on hand, on order, group parameters, and reorder points, etc. This should again be hierarchical at different levels of aggregation as desired.

Easy Override of Automatic Decision. The manager should be able to change an order easily. This could be at different levels: changing a single order, changing the formula for the single item in general, or changing a group order. At the other extreme, the manager should easily be able to increase all setup costs in a line by 20 percent to decrease ordering frequency, or increase all stockout costs for a vendor for one month by 30 percent, and so forth. This is often discussed under the name **exchange curves**, however, the principle is very broad and general.

While it is important for the manager to be able to make changes, she should not be allowed to override the system so frequently as to make it useless. Thus, an advanced system might keep an audit trail of changes made, for audit by an independent person every three months or so. Either too infrequent or too frequent changes could call the attention of the oversight senior manager.

Easy Reports for Top Management. Although top management should be able to query the system directly, many times top echelon personnel prefer predigested written reports. It should be easy for managers to generate whatever type reports are desired in a convenient and readable form.

4.3.5 Systems Exercises

1. Why is it useful for companies to organize their product lines in a hierarchical structure? How might this hierarchical structure differ for different departments in retail or wholesale merchandise? How might this hierarchical structure differ for a job shop? An assembly line?
2. What are the sources of conflict in grouping items in an inventory system? Give two or three specific hypothetical conflicts, and suggest how the manager might resolve them.
3. Describe the classic ABC classification system. What is the purpose of classifying items in this manner? What would be the primary use of such a classification system to a retailer? In a job shop? A high speed transfer line?
4. Describe modifications of the classic ABC classification system to consider the hierarchical system structure, and in particular grouping issues. What is the simplest way to introduce this modification? What problems remain?

5. Consider the following list of items sold in the Fly-boy Pilot's Catalogue.
   a. Rank the items in decreasing order of annual dollar volume.
   b. Classify the items as A, B, or C.
   c. Are there any items here which might be grouped as coming from the same vendor?

Item	Price	Yrly Demand
1. Goggles	$51.00	400
2. Leather Cap	75.00	110
3. Leather Jacket	210.00	100
4. Leather Seat Cover—back	150.00	30
5. Leather Seat Cover—seat	130.00	30
6. Sheepskin Seat Cover—back	175.00	30
7. Sheepskin Seat Cover—seat	155.00	50
8. Airsick Bags-six	3.10	100
9. Airsick Bags-box	11.50	250
10. Pilot/Co-pilot headset	310.00	10
11. Passenger Earphones	125.00	30
12. Mounted Compass	150.00	640
13. Windshield Wipes	4.00	500
14. Trail mix	1.79	550
15. Gorp	1.79	200
16. Dried apples	2.21	200
17. Dried apricots	2.21	100
18. Supplemental cushion	75.00	20
19. Supplemental back support	55.00	30
20. Fuel tester	17.00	100
21. Independent altimeter	420.00	20
22. Transponder	650.00	20
23. Radio model 3x67	450.00	40
24. Radio model 3x68	820.00	610
25. Flyboy Magazine Subscription	36.00	110

6. In problem 5, you have just learned that Flyboy has eight vendors.

   a. Classify the 25 items into eight vendor groups as best you can. Explain your reasoning in interesting cases.
   b. Assuming your classification to be correct, rank the eight groups by the ABC method.
   c. Assuming a good classification, how could Flyboy use your ranking?

7. Flesh out some of the Decision Support suggestions in the text.

   a. Discuss in more detail a flexible executive report writer that would generate the information desired in a comprehensible fashion.
   b. Discuss in more detail how a summary audit trail could be kept to see quickly which managers were changing the automatic answers too little or too much.

4.4 NEW DIRECTIONS IN INVENTORY

4.4.1 Introduction

The Japanese argue that inventories are *evil* because they cause:

   a. Confusion and poorer process control on the shop floor
   b. Poorer communication and coordination between departments
   c. Inadequate pressure to improve the production process
   d. Poorer response to changing customer taste

Whereas the United States remains the leader in basic research and new product invention, Japan maintains leadership in continual improvement of the product and of the process for making it. This has allowed them to maintain leadership in product quality, time to market, and cost although the U.S. auto industry has been doing well recently.

Just-In-Time means literally that goods or WIP should be delivered exactly when they are needed, which would obviously mean zero inventory (except transit). It is used also to mean a broader set of tools and philosophies to help maintain continued process improvement, including Kanban, special relationships with buyers, broadly trained workers, sensitivity to process problems, and so forth. We will touch on these other issues lightly in our discussion.

The Japanese Challenge. Everyone is aware, to some degree, of the major inroads the Japanese have made and are continuing to make in U.S. markets, including automobiles, electronics, cameras, computer hardware, machine tools, and aerospace. In automobiles, the United States has fought back strongly.

This cannot be laid to the inferiority of American workers. There are many examples where the Japanese have taken over an American plant, kept the same workers, laid off half of management, and doubled productivity! Some of the elements of the Japanese philosophy include:

- **Worker-Flexibility.** Rather than being specialized, workers are trained to do many different tasks, making for a flexible process and reduced WIP.
- **Jidoka-Quality at the Source.** If a bad unit is made, it is not set aside. The entire process is stopped, and everyone looks to find the problem. This again reduces WIP and does not allow continued production of bad goods.
- **Just-In-Time Production.** An item is produced exactly when it is needed (a bit exaggerated). This works best for repetitive manufacturing, so all processes are designed to be repetitive manufacturing. Kanban control systems were developed for this situation.
- **Uniform Plant Loading.** Confusion and shock waves from changing things are avoided by having exactly the same thing made every day. One way to do this is to establish a standard mix of products to be made every day.

Adoption of JIT in the United States. There has been widespread adoption by U.S. management of JIT, at least in form. In many cases manufacturers have asked their suppliers to deliver exactly as needed. If the supplier complied, however, it usually meant that the supplier was forced to keep higher inventories. In turn the supplier eventually passed the higher cost on to the manufacturer, so that the savings were somewhat illusory. Many manufacturers have managed to reduce WIP inventories significantly in places within the organization, without implementing the strategic purpose of continued process improvement intended.

At the same time there have been many genuine stories of successful implementation. Harley Davidson completely reorganized itself in the Japanese manner, and has improved its motorcycles from being 50 percent defect free to 99 percent defect free. Xerox reduced its number of suppliers from 5000 to 400, and reduced copier part inventories by $240 million.

4.4.2 Just-In-Time

Overview. Just-In-Time is a strategic philosophy which is concerned not with inventory levels per se, but with promoting an environment in which the way of producing goods can keep improving over time. Drastic inventory reductions are only one tool to this end. If inventories are low, then it will not be possible to hide badly produced units in the floor inventory. The Japanese use the analogy that bad units are like rocks hiding in the water. If the water level is lowered, the rocks will show. Then everyone will be forced to fix the process, rather than to let it slide. This analogy is illustrated in Figure 4-3.

Figure 4-3

"Bad" Inventory as Rocks in
the Water

**Excessive Inventories
Hide Problems**　　　　**Low Inventories
Show Problems**

Similarly, if there are small inventories between two departments, or between a company and it suppliers, then the two departments will be forced to coordinate their scheduling instead of depending on the buffer to fix things. Also, if there is little inventory, the customer will be able to receive more things made to order, rather than having to accept something in the inventory which doesn't really fit.

JIT and EOQ. It is often suggested that JIT and EOQ are in conflict, because EOQ suggests a square root balance between setup costs and inventory costs, and JIT suggests inventory should be zero! There is really no conflict, because the two situations are apples and oranges. EOQ is a short run tactical decision. Given a setup K and holding costs h, then order $Q^{**} = [2KD/h]^{0.5}$. The Japanese would not disagree with this, but would simply suggest that the tradeoff between a fixed setup and a fixed holding cost is not strategic. The Japanese would say to change the setup cost and whatever else is possible to make inventories very low. Then a number of strategic advantages will accrue which are not mentioned in the EOQ formula. One way to make the two goals work together is to achieve radical lowering of the setup cost.

JIT and Kanban. **Kanban** is simply a practical manual system for implementing JIT, developed by Toyota. Kanban uses a system of cards; in fact, the word means *card* or *ticket* in Japanese. The Kanban system has been a major factor in making Toyota profitable. A typical system uses two kinds of cards: withdrawal Kanbans and production ordering Kanbans. The production Kanban authorizes the manufacturing of a container of parts. The withdrawal Kanban authorizes the withdrawal and movement of those parts. The number of pieces in a container is fixed. When production rates change, containers can be added to or deleted from the system. The idea of safety stock is limited to 10 percent of one day's demand.

The flow of Kanban cards between two machine centers is shown in Figure 4-4. Two parts are being made, A and B, and they are stored in containers next to the machine center. When the next machine starts to use part A from a full container, an employee takes the withdrawal Kanban from the container and travels to the machining center storage place. The worker finds a container of part A, removes the production Kanban, and replaces it with the withdrawal Kanban, which authorizes moving the container. The freed production Kanban is then placed in a niche by the machining center as production authorization for another set of parts to be made. Parts are made in the order in which cards are placed on the rack, which makes the set of cards in the rack into a dispatch list.

The same idea can be used to authorize vendor shipments. If both the customer and the vendor are using the Kanban system, the withdrawal Kanban becomes the shipping document, while the production Kanban at the vendor's plant regulates production at that point.

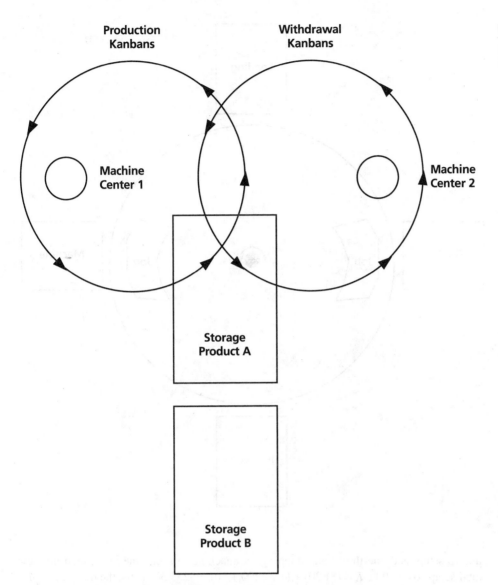

Figure 4-4

Card Movements in a Kanban

4.4.3 Tools for Implementing JIT

Overview. JIT is a very ambitious philosophy, which is very difficult to implement. It requires very low inventories, so that something must be done to lower setup costs to make that practical. It requires short lead times in production and in design, so that new approaches must be designed to make that possible. It requires tight coordination between a plant and its suppliers and between the plant and its customers. Again, new techniques must be found to make this work. We discuss some of these techniques in this section.

Setup Cost Reduction. In our inventory work, we have typically just specified a setup cost K for setting up a machine. In practice, things are a little bit more complicated than that. Suppose that currently time on the machine is valued at $200 an hour, while the person doing the setup has a value of $20 an hour. Suppose the worker spends eight hours setting up the machine, and that nothing else can be produced during this time. Then we might reasonably value the setup cost as $K = 8(200 + 20) = \$1760.00$.

When the shop has a new way to reduce setup time, what is usually meant is to reduce time lost on the main machine. Figure 4-5 shows a rotating plate, which allows one part to be machining, while the next part is being set up off-line. If it still takes eight hours off

Figure 4-5

A Device for Setup Cost
Reduction

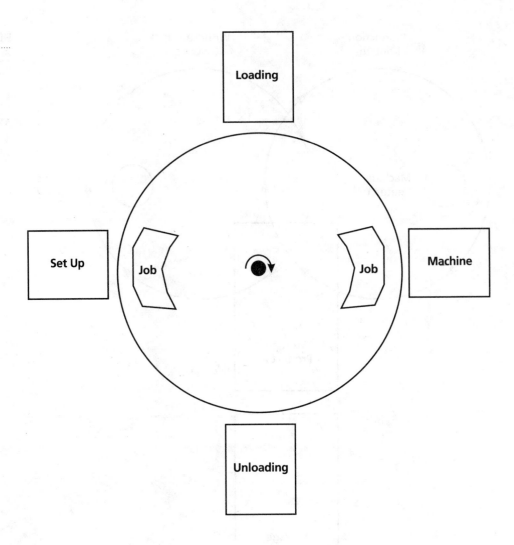

line to setup, and one-third hour stopping the machine to rotate the plate, then the new total setup cost will be $K = (8)(20) + (1/3)(200 + 20) = \$233.33$. Thus, the new device has reduced setup costs by a factor of 7.5. However, more commonly, it will be reported that setup times have been reduced by a factor of 24!! Remember this, the next time you hear of very dramatic reductions.

Of course, this is not the whole story. The new rotating plate device has to have full setup equipment. Thus, we must try to find the amount we are saving per year and calculate a rate of return on our investment.

There are models which make the setup cost K in the EOQ formula a function of investment in setup cost reduction, and then optimize both investment and the setup cost in one fell swoop. This is a rather strange mixture of tactical and strategic models. It perhaps makes more sense to have engineers design various actual possible equipment for setup reduction, and then to cost out rates of return for various shop situations.

Time Based Competition. The term **time based competition** means to offer the customer shorter lead times as a way of improving the attractiveness of the product. This can be at two levels:

Level 1. Shortening production lead times—that is, shortening the time from receipt of the order until the final delivery of the order.

Level 2. Shortening new product development lead times—that is, shortening the time from inception of a new product idea until it is available for sale. The first is tactical, the second is strategic. We talk briefly about the first issue; the second is outside of our scope in this textbook.

Shortening Production Lead Times. The most common traditional method for shortening production lead times is to carry final product inventories and supply orders from that. The Japanese would argue that such inventories decouple the customer from the production process, so that we expect the customer to take what is available, rather than being sensitive to nuances of modifying the product. That inventory often hides defective units, in much the same way the large floor WIP can. Thus, JIT would suggest that final inventories not exist or be very lean.

The more strategic way to shorten production lead times is to redesign the entire process, including paperwork handling, authorization of various steps, etc., to reduce **information inventories**, that is, piles of paperwork that the particular job paperwork must wait for. By switching to JIT in terms of *information flow* the paperwork part of the lead time can be reduced. By reducing setups and more strategic scheduling on the shop floor, waiting in queue at machines can also be drastically reduced.

Electronic Data Interchange (EDI). Satellites, fiber optic cable, and sophisticated communications software are increasingly linking various plants within a company more tightly together, linking plants with their suppliers, and plants with their customers. These kinds of tighter communication allow more coordinated scheduling, and reduced inventories; that is, in a nutshell, JIT.

For example, a plant linked with its customer's computers can see exactly when the customer plans to order. This allows a much more accurate production plan for the plant, and reduced WIP and final inventories. The customer gains better service and lower prices. Similarly, a plant linked with its suppliers can see exactly when the supplier will be able to deliver, again facilitating low raw material inventories. Plants linked with sister plants can make quick dynamic changes as to which plants should supply which customer and again minimize inventories.

EDI raises obvious challenges as well. How can the software be written so as to maximize useful communication while minimizing the danger that privacy will be invaded in areas which are not appropriate for the other company to know? A rather different issue which must be resolved is: as companies cooperate more and more automatically via their computers, at what point is competition lessened? This issue is likely to be raised more than once in the near future.

BIBLIOGRAPHY

General/Books

Brown, R. (1967). *Decision Rules for Inventory Management.* New York: Holt, Rinehart Winston Inc.

Brown, R. (1977). *Materials Management Systems.* New York: John Wiley & Sons.

Goyal S., and A. Satir (1989). "Joint Replenishment Inventory Control: Deterministic and Stochastic Models," *EJOR* 38, 2–13.

Graves, S., et al. eds. (1992). *Handbook in Operations Research and Management Science, Volume 4, Logistics of Production and Inventory.* Amsterdam: Elsevier Science Publishers.

Li, L. (1992). "The Role of Inventory in Delivery Time Competition," *Management Science* 38, 182–197.

Morton, T., and D. Pentico (1993). *Heuristic Scheduling Systems.* New York: John Wiley & Sons.

Silver, E. (1981). "Operations Research in Inventory Management: A Review and Critique," *Operations Research* 29, 628–645.

Silver, E., and R. Peterson (1985). *Decision Systems for Inventory Management and Production Planning*, 2nd ed. New York: John Wiley & Sons.

Wight, O. (1974). *Production and Inventory Management in the Computer Age*. Boston: Cahners Books.

Deterministic Articles

Arcelus F., and J. Rowcroft (1992). "All-units Quantity-freight Discounts with Disposals," *EJOR* 57, 77–88.

Atkins, D., M. Queyranne, and D. Sun (1992). "Lot Sizing Policies for Finite Production Rate Assembly Systems," *Operations Research* 40, 126–14.

Campbell, G., and V. Mabert (1991). "Cyclical Schedules for Capacitated Lot Sizing with Dynamic Demands," *Management Science* 37, 409–427.

Crowston, W., and M. Wagner (1973). "Dynamic Lot Size Models for Multi-Stage Assembly Systems," *Management Science* 20, 14–22.

Dobson, G. (1988). "Sensitivity of the EOQ Model to Parameter Estimates," *Operations Research* 36, 570–574.

Elmaghraby, S. (1978). "The Economic Lot Scheduling Problem (ELSP): Review and Extensions," *Management Science* 24, 587–599.

Lippman, S. (1971). "Economic Order Quantities and Multiple Set-Up Costs," *Management Science* 18, 39–48.

Lundin, R., and T. Morton (1975). "Planning Horizons for the Dynamic Lot Size Model: Protective Procedures and Computational Results," *Operations Research* 23, 711–734.

May, J. (1974). "A Linear Program for Economic Lot Sizes Using Labor Priorities," *Management Science* 21, 277–286.

Moily, J. (1986). "Optimal and Heuristic Procedures for Component Lot-Splitting in Multi-Stage Manufacturing Systems," *Management Science* 32, 113–125.

Newson, E. (1975). "Multi-Item Lot Size Scheduling by Heuristic, I and II," *Management Science* 21, 1186-1194, 1194–1204.

Porteus, E. (1986). "Optimal Lot Sizing, Process Quality Improvement and Setup Cost Reduction," *Operations Research* 34, 137–144.

Rosenblatt, M. (1981). "Multi-Item Inventory System with Budgetary Constraint: A Comparison between the Lagrangan and the Fixed Cycle Approach," *International Journal of Production Research* 19, 331–339.

Salomon M., L. Kroon, R. Kuik, and L. Van Wassenhove (1991). "Some Extensions of the Discrete Lotsizing and Scheduling Problem," *Management Science* 37, 801–812.

Schussel, G., and S. Price (1970). "A Case History in Optimum Inventory Scheduling," *Operations Research* 18, 1–23.

Smunt, T., and T. Morton (1985). "The Effects of Learning on Optimal Lot Sizes: Further Developments on the Single Product Case," *Institute of Industrial Engineering Transactions*, 33–37.

Sohn, K., and H. Hwang (1987). "A Dynamic Quantity Discount Lot Size Model with Re-sales," *EJOR* 28, 293–297.

Wagner, H. M, and T. M. Whitin (1958). "Dynamic Version of the Economic Lot Size Model," *Management Science* 5, 89–96.

Zipkin, P. (1991). "Computing Optimal Lot Sizes in the Economic Lot Scheduling Problem," *Operations Research* 39, 56–63.

Stochastic Articles

Arrow, K., T. Harris, and T. Marschak (1951). "Optimal Inventory Policy," *Econometrica* 19, 250–272.

Arrow, K., S. Karlin, and H. Scarf (1958). *Studies in the Mathematical Theory of Inventory and Production*. Stanford, CA: Stanford University Press.

Bishop, J., Jr. (1974). "Experience with a Successful System for Forecasting and Inventory Control," *Operations Research* 22, 1224–1231.

Gross, D., and A. Soriano (1969). "The Effect of Reducing Lead-time on Inventory Levels— Simulation Analysis," *Management Science* 16, B61–77.

Hartung, P. (1973). "A Simple Style Goods Inventory Model," *Management Science* 19, 1452–1458.

Krajewski, L., B. King, L. Ritzman, and D. Wong (1987). "Kanban, MRP, and Shaping the Manufacturing Environment," *Management Science* 33, 39–57.

Lovejoy, W. (1990). "Myopic Policies for Some Inventory Models with Uncertain Demand Distributions," *Management Science* 36, 724–738.

Morton, T. (1971). "The Near-Myopic Nature of the Lagged Proportional Cost Inventory Problem with Lost Sales," *Operations Research* 19, 1708–1716.

Ravindran, A. (1972). "Management of Seasonal Style-Goods Inventories," *Operations Research* 20, 265–275.

Scarf, H. (1963). "Analytical Techniques in Inventory Theory," *Multi-Stage Inventory Models and Techniques* ed. H. Scarf, D. Gilford, and M. Shelly. Stanford, CA: Stanford University Press.

Wagner, H. (1974). "The Design of Production and Inventory Systems for Multi-facility and Multi-warehouse Companies," *Operations Research* 22, 278–291.

Applied Articles

Aggarwal, S. (1981). "Purchase Inventory Decision Models for Inflationary Conditions," *Interfaces* 11, 4, 18–23.

Backes, R. (1980). "Cycle Counting—A Better Way for Achieving Accurate Inventory Records," *Production and Inventory Management* 21, 36–44.

Baker, R., and T. Urban (1991). "Deterministic Fixed Order-level Inventory Models: An Application for Replenishment of Radioactive Source Materials for Irradiation Sterilizers," *EJOR* 50, 249–256.

Belobaba, P. (1989). "Application of a Probabilistic Decision Model to Airline Seat Inventory Control," *Operations Research* 37, 183–197.

Cohen R., P. Kamesam, P. Kleindorfer, H. Lee, and A. Tekerian (1990). "Optimizer: IBM's Multi-Echelon Inventory System for Managing Service Logistics," *Interfaces* 20, 11, 65–82.

Edwards, J., H. Wagner, and W. Wood (1985). "Blue Bell Trims its Inventory, *Interfaces* 15, 1, 34–52.

Grunwald, H., and L. Fortuin (1992). "Many Steps Towards Zero Inventory," *EJOR* 59, 359–369.

Inman, R., and S. Mehra (1990). "The Transferability of Just-in-Time Concepts to American Small Business," *Interfaces* 20, 2, 30–37.

Lee, H., C. Billington, and B. Carter (1993). "Hewlett-Packard Gains Control of Inventory and Service through Design for Localization," *Interfaces* 23, 4, 1–11.

Martin, C., D. Dent, and J. Eckhart (1993). "Integrated Production, Distribution, and Inventory Planning at Libbey-Owens-Ford," *Interfaces* 23, 3, 68–78.

Millet, I. (1994). "A Novena to Saint Anthony, or How to Find Inventory by Not Looking," *Interfaces* 24, 2, 69–75.

Tedone, M. (1989). "Repairable Part Management," *Interfaces* 19, 4, 61–74.

Scheduling

3

Introduction to Scheduling

1.1 SCHEDULING IS CRUCIAL!

1.1.1 Resistance to Scheduling

In the 1950s and '60s business executives paid relatively little attention to high tech scheduling. This was due to a number of factors:

    a. The need for scheduling could be reduced with buffer raw materials, WIP, and finished goods.
    b. The mathematics of large problems were very difficult.
    c. Schedulers were leery of computers.
    d. Top management was wary of system builders.
    e. Each installation must be almost custom.
    f. There was secrecy among software houses.
    g. Computers were too small, too slow, and too clumsy.

Many of these issues do not apply now.

    a. JIT is widely recognized as strategic, so buffers are no longer "cheap."
    b. Large problems can now be solved adequately by heuristic techniques.
    c. Schedulers today are more comfortable with computers.
    d. Top management is still very wary.
    e. Today computers are very adequate to the task.

In summary, it seems times are propitious for building inexpensive but sophisticated PC-based systems at the scheduling level.

1.1.2 Global Competition, Scheduling, and JIT

The Japanese long-range strategic concerns for continuous product improvement in terms of quality and cost, reducing shop and design throughput time, and increasing system flexibility and coordination now permeate the consciousness of the entire global business community. In turn, the Japanese have argued successfully that a Just-In-Time (JIT) philosophy of inventory management is a central ingredient toward achieving these goals. Thus, JIT also becomes strategic. There are a number of ways in which JIT can help achieve the strategic goals previously mentioned.

    a. Reducing the cost of the increasing complexity and rapid obsolescence of products
    b. Leading to more rapid learning to eliminate process flaws

    c. Accommodating customer desires for shorter lead times with easier change orders

    d. Providing improved flexible reaction to changes in product mix

    e. Providing more flexible reaction to emergency floor problems

    f. Providing rapid awareness of changes in quality and sources

The strategic importance of JIT in turn impacts the perceived cost of scheduling buffers. Before JIT it was considered reasonable to have large work-in-process buffers and finished goods stocks to absorb scheduling errors and to decouple complex systems. The resulting simpler scheduling sub-systems could be managed adequately by human schedulers. But if JIT is strategic, then reducing or eliminating these buffers is strategic and so accurate scheduling becomes strategic!

Without the comfortable large buffers, the human scheduler must struggle to adapt to the whole larger system. At best, this leads to a lessened ability to deal with the system in as much detail; at worst, the broad understanding of the problem may be lost as well. This situation is made worse by the fact that the system itself is now typically changing rapidly and becoming more complex.

1.1.3 Broad Scheduling Approaches

It is possible to improve scheduling by a number of means:

    a. **Human experts**—We have already explained that the expert will face greater difficulties due to reduced buffers, rapid system change, and increased system complexity. On the other side, however, humans have great common sense, intuitive thinking abilities, and "big picture" thinking.

    b. **Expert systems**—In stable situations expert systems can duplicate humans quite well. However, they are quite rigid and are not good at controversial or changing situations.

    c. **Mathematical systems**—Long solution times may be required in mathematical systems; writing programs for every possible situation may be a problem. Mathematical systems can be quite accurate and are not rigid.

    d. **Mixed systems**—Decision Support Systems using the best of human and computer expertise seem to be the best long term solution.

1.1.4 Chapter Summary and Preview

Section 1.2 gives a very general picture of just what scheduling is. Section 1.3 provides an overview of the levels of analysis within a scheduling problem (hierarchy), a categorization of the types of manufacturing scheduling, and other non-manufacturing scheduling examples. Section 1.4 discusses a number of past approaches to scheduling. Section 1.5 is a summary of the full Scheduling Module.

1.2 WHAT IS SCHEDULING, ANYWAY?

1.2.1 Overview

We tend to think of scheduling in terms of work-in-process in front of machines on the shop floor. The truth is that planning and scheduling pervade our economic and personal life in many ways. (Planning and scheduling are both really terms for the same thing, although we tend to use "planning" as being less detailed and "scheduling" as being more detailed.) Such activities as developing a rocket to go to the moon, getting all those term papers done more or less on time, waiting in line at the bank, making an airline reservation, building twenty tract houses, getting four software projects done without causing excessive demand on the best software engineer, getting six executives together for a meeting, and running a steel foundry all use very much the same principles of scheduling.

Scheduling always involves accomplishing a number of different things which tie up various resources for varying amounts of time. The resources are not unlimited by any means. The things to be accomplished may have names like **jobs**, **assignments**, **projects** or **tasks**, and are composed of elementary parts such as **activities**, **operations** and **delays**. Activities require certain amounts of resources for defined lengths of times. There is usually a common time for everything, called the **process time**. Resources can also be decomposed into smaller parts called **machines**, **workers**, **paint**, **cells**, **transport**, or **delays**.

Scheduling problems are very often made much more difficult because of rules or **constraints** that specify which sorts of things can or cannot be done and under what circumstances. Since these complexities can make the system very hard to solve, it is natural to try to look at simpler versions of the problem first to gain insight. If the solution does not seem to be very sensitive, we may just use the simpler solution, or modify it a little bit to fit.

1.2.2 How to Recognize a Good Solution

Deciding whether a particular schedule (detailed plan) is a good one is also a difficult question. We would like to specify a payoff or objective to maximize or minimize in order to deal with this question. However, there may be several different payoffs operating at the same time and it may be difficult to compromise among them. Furthermore, many times the payoff may be rather intuitive and difficult to quantify.

For instance, a manufacturing shop usually deals with four major types of objectives, which are quite different:

    a. **Throughput** is an important objective when the shop has more business than it can handle, desires to make maximum use of its capacity, most out-of-pocket costs are sunk, and customers have little power. The most important throughput objective is **Makespan**. (We will explain these objectives later.)

    b. **Out-of-pocket costs** is an important objective when product cost is critical and there are many costs which can be changed in the short run. The most important out-of-pocket cost objective is **Net Present Value**.

    c. **Turnaround** or **flow time** is an important objective when customer desires are paramount and fast delivery is desired. Flow time objectives include **Weighted flow time** or **Maximum flow time**.

    d. **Contracted delivery** or **due dates** is an important objective when customer desires are paramount and delivery matching the contract time is desired. Due date objectives include **Weighted tardiness** or **Maximum tardiness**.

A problem is that quantifying the importance of these objectives depends on quantifying customer desires, which is quite difficult. One method would be to look at solutions for several different strengths of customer desires and see how sensitive the solution is. A different solution is to provide customers with questionnaires designed to elicit the strength of their preferences.

1.2.3 Kinds of Decisions

There are a number of kinds of decisions which the scheduler must make. These decisions are discussed in the following paragraphs.

Sequencing. Suppose six jobs are waiting in front of a machine; the question is which to do next. Clearly, other things equal, jobs which are more important should go first. Similarly, jobs which don't require much of the machine's time should be given preference. Jobs which have been in the shop a long time, or which are likely to be tardy, should also be given preference.

Releasing. There are a number of motives for *not releasing* raw material to the production floor until just before it is needed. These include:

    a. Work in process (WIP) on the floor incurs inventory charges at a higher rate than raw material.
    b. There is limited space on the floor for WIP.
    c. Obsolescence, damage, and confusion cause high WIP to be expensive.

The motives *for releasing* are much the same as the motives for giving a job high sequencing priority.

Routing. If a job has a number of operations which can be done in different orders, which ordering should be used? If an operation has a choice of three machines with different process times and values of machine time, which machine should be chosen? Should a job be sent to the flexible manufacturing cell or be done by an expert on a manual all-purpose machine? The answers to these questions will determine how a job is routed.

Lotting. Very often there is a setup time involved before an operation can be run on a machine. Also, the setup time usually depends on which item was run previously. A common situation is that the items may be divided into groups. Within groups there is little setup time required, perhaps one-half hour. Between groups there is a larger setup time of perhaps five to ten hours, depending on the two groups.

Clearly, we have a motive to run as many items in the same group as possible, to get many cheap setups. At the same time, if we carry this too far we will be running items with little current priority to get this advantage and ignoring items in other groups which do have such priority. Thus, there is a tradeoff (similar to the EOQ idea) on lot size versus timeliness of the jobs.

1.3 LEVELS AND TYPES OF SCHEDULING

1.3.1 Overview

Levels of Scheduling. Whether a group of assets is considered to be a single resource (or not) for doing scheduling depends on whether internal decisions are being made seriously, or are simply given by some fixed simple rules that we need not consider. Thus, a given job shop might be considered to be a number of resources when modeled in detail; if we move up a level, we may only be concerned with what to release to the shop and when. This can be repeated several times, leading to a classification of manufacturing problems at several levels. We present such a scheme with five levels in Table 1-1.

While all these levels can be considered to have a type of scheduling in that they all have issues of sequencing, timing, routing, etc., it is easy to exaggerate this similarity. There are a great many scheduling models at Level 4; in fact, these models are the main subject of this scheduling module. In trying to model at other levels it is useful to recognize both the similarities and the differences. Careless use of a Level 4 model at a different level can be a big mistake. In Section 1.3.2 we will discuss the five levels in a little more detail.

Types of Level 4 Scheduling. We have just given an overview of different levels of scheduling in terms of time horizon and aggregation. Here we will fix our attention on

Table 1-1

Classification of Scheduling
Levels

Level	Examples of Problems	Horizon
1. Long-Range Planning	plant expansion plant layout plant design	2–5 years
2. Middle-Range Planning	production smoothing logistics	1–2 years
3. Short-Range Planning	requirements plan shop bidding due date setting	3–6 months
4. Scheduling	job shop routing assembly line balancing process batch sizing	2–6 weeks
5. Reactive Scheduling/ Control	hot jobs down machines late material	1–3 days

Level 4 scheduling environments, which range from small, complex, custom job shops to high-speed, low-variety transfer lines, from discrete parts manufacturing to continuous process situations. Table 1-2 gives a brief summary of these scheduling environments.

Table 1-2

Scheduling Environments

Type	Characteristics
1. Classic Job Shop	Discrete, complex flow, unique jobs, no multi-use parts
2. Open Job Shop	Discrete, complex flow, some repetitive jobs and/or multi-use parts
3. Batch Shop	Discrete or continuous, less complex flow, many repetitive and multi-use parts, grouping and lotting important
4. Flow Shop	Discrete or continuous, linear flow, jobs all highly similar, grouping and lotting important
5. Batch/Flow Shop	First half large continuous batch process, second half typical flow shop
6. Manufacturing Cell	Discrete, automated grouped version of open job shop or batch shop
7. Assembly Shop	Assembly version of open job shop or batch shop
8. Assembly Line	High volume, low variety, transfer line version of assembly shop
9. Transfer Line	Very high volume and low variety linear production facility with automated operations
10. Flexible Transfer Line	Modern versions of cells and transfer lines intended to bring some of the advantages of high volume production to job shop items

1.3.2 Levels of Scheduling

Level 1: Long-Range Planning. At the two- to five-year planning horizon, *jobs* are mostly large *projects* and include design, sizing, and location of new capacity (plants, warehouses, assembly lines, foundries, and the like) and the expansion, redesign, and layout of current facilities. Activities are any smaller pieces of these activities such as designing electrical systems or installing walkways. Needed resources include financing, engineering, management, crews, and land. Often several such projects are being carried out at once, with many concurrent and interfering activities, so that sequencing and timing issues are clearly important. Examples of routing issues include alternate sources of financing and alternate vendors.

However, at Level 1, forecasting dominates the scene much more than at lower levels. Which products will be popular five years from now? How fast will technology move? Will the new assembly line have a chance of being obsolete in four years? Furthermore, as discussed in the Forecasting Module, long range forecasting models are inherently very inaccurate.

Level 2: Middle-Range Planning. At the one- to two-year horizon, scheduling methods have been somewhat more productive. Production smoothing deals with reconfiguring resources over time to balance capacity facing highly seasonal demand loads. Types of reconfiguration which are possible include hiring, firing, layoff, subcontracting, overtime, opening and closing lines, and shifting manpower between shops. Sequencing, timing, and routing are definitely necessary to produce a production schedule. Both deterministic and probabilistic models have been used successfully at Level 2. Although forecasting issues are still very important, issues of grouping, aggregation, and disaggregation are probably most central.

Level 3: Short-Range Planning. At the three- to six-month time horizon, models of interest include material requirements planning (MRP), shop bidding, setting/negotiating due dates, and order forecasting. While MRP is discussed in detail in the Planning Module, it is an important topic and we sketch it here. MRP uses the production smoothing plan and order forecasting to produce a **master schedule**, which is a period-by-period forecast of what needs to be produced by product type. Each piece of the master schedule is then broken down into components and moved backward in time to show time-based requirements for inputs and so forth.

Level 4: Scheduling. At the two- to six-week time horizon, scheduling is concerned with a rather detailed level of the shop. The MRP system sends down to the floor a forecast of job arrivals, with due dates, quantities, and the activities necessary to do them. The full schedule for a six-week period might be developed once a week, with only the first week of each schedule actually used. The rest is just to make sure the current week's plans fit properly in future weeks' activities. We will not spend more time discussing scheduling here, since this will occupy most of the rest of the module. Dominant issues at the scheduling level are probably sequencing, timing, and routing, although forecasting deserves more attention than it has typically received.

Level 5: Reactive Scheduling/Control. At the one- to three-day horizon, the more detailed level of reactive scheduling and control, the central issues are emergencies, glitches and other short-term problems, including machine breakdown, late arrival, and poor materials. Very detailed constraints binding activities and resources that might be glossed over at Level 4 must be treated. Most activity is involved in correcting the Level 4 schedule for these problems.

1.3.3 Types of Manufacturing Scheduling

Classic Job Shop. A typical example of a job shop (also called a "closed" shop) is a machine tool milling company. Each order is unique with a unique routing. Operations are performed sequentially on a lot of parts, which stay together throughout the shop. All floor inventories are identified with a single job. Scheduling is highly complicated with no obvious repetitive patterns.

The structure of the classic job shop appears in many different settings; for example, research and development of the space shuttle and non-standard paperwork that flows across your desk. However, the analogies with the classic job shop must not be overdrawn. The space shuttle, for example, has tremendous issues of forecasting and reconfiguration.

Open Job Shop. An example of an open shop is the production of mainframe computers, each of which is slightly different. The term "open job shop" is often simply taken to mean a shop that produces to final inventory rather than directly to customer order. Here we use it in the broader sense of where some of the WIP may be identical for different orders and so it makes sense to keep an inventory of it, or to steal from one order to another. The space shuttle would be between an open and closed shop. A builder of tract houses runs an open shop.

Batch Shop. A good example of a batch shop is a garment factory, another is a manufacturer who supplies various small parts to other manufacturers. A batch shop is essentially an open shop with a large amount of duplication in work-in-process and final inventory due to overlap between customer orders. Thus, large batch processing becomes feasible to take advantage of economies of large batches (lot sizing).

Flow Shop. A good example of a flow shop is a paper company which does not make its own pulp. A flow shop is basically a batch shop with a single route (linear flow). Flow can be discrete or continuous. In the simplest case there is a unique machine which does the first activity in each job, another that does the second and so on. In a more complex **compound** flow shop, each machine may be replaced by a set of parallel machines. Each job can choose one from the first cluster, one from the second and so on. There are few pure flow shops.

Batch/Flow Shops. A paper company which does make its own pulp is a good example of a (compound) batch/flow shop. A surprisingly large number of production processes take the following form: the first half is a large continuous batch process, where the raw and early intermediate materials are "cooked." The second half is a more typical compound flow shop. A tomato packing cannery, for example, first cooks the tomatoes in huge kettles connected by piping; this system is not usually a single route (not linear). The second half involves bottling or canning the food on several parallel high-speed (flow) lines.

Manufacturing Cell. The manufacturing cell makes an attempt to combine the low cost and efficiency of a flow shop with the flexibility of the job shop. Basically, items to be produced in the larger shop are grouped into similar families. Each family is serviced by one cell, which is typically an automated handler or conveyor surrounded by a cluster of machines. The machines themselves are computer controlled and are quite flexible in the activities that can be performed.

Assembly Shop. A good example of an assembly shop is an optical company which makes custom and semi-custom telescopes to order. It is just an open/batch shop in which parts are assembled to make sub-sub-assemblies, which in turn are combined to make sub-assemblies and so on. The open shop issues of labeling and cannibalization of work-in-process remain important here.

Assembly Line. A good example of an assembly line is the assembly of automobiles. It is basically an assembly shop combined with high volume and low product variety, giving it many of the characteristics of a flow shop. A conveyor belt moves the work in process along the line to the workers or machines, with no buffer inventory except at the start of the line. Production is efficient but rigid.

Transfer Line. Transfer lines are used in making light bulbs, hardware, toys, games, and paint, among many other items. It is a very high volume and very low variety production line, often very linear. Whereas assembly lines use a large amount of human effort, the transfer line is usually almost completely automated. Since there are no buffers, rejects must be dealt with later.

Flexible Transfer Line. Whereas the manufacturing cell tries to bring efficiency to the open shop, the flexible transfer line tries to bring flexibility to the transfer line. More clever buffers, computer control, and transport devices allow items to be processed in different orders on the line. Thus, larger product variety can be accommodated at smaller volumes for each. A number of companies have pilot projects for such concepts.

1.3.4 Types of Scheduling Exercises

1. Give an example of a long range strategic problem where:

   a. It makes no sense to plan for more than two or three years.
   b. It makes sense to plan for ten years.
   c. It makes sense to plan for twenty years.

2. Consider your desk as a one-machine (you) job shop, with many jobs competing for your attention:

   a. Make up a situation with competing jobs and deadlines and discuss how you would sequence these jobs.
   b. Now invent some problem or glitch in your schedule and discuss how you would make a reactive rescheduling of these jobs.

3. Find an example for each of the following types of shops not given in the text. Explain your example clearly.

   a. Open job shop
   b. Batch/flow job shop
   c. Assembly shop
   d. Assembly line
   e. Transfer line

4. Explain these examples of non-manufacturing scheduling:

   a. A software shop with multiple simultaneous projects
   b. A TV news program
   c. Congress with committees and multiple bills
   d. Your choice

1.4 SCHEDULING APPROACHES

1.4.1 Overview

In the following section, we define a number of scheduling terms.

Scheduling Terms.

Interval schedule—A schedule with specific times which are not expected to slip. Needed when several important resources must be coordinated. Schedule often has gaps and inefficiencies.

Dispatch schedule—A schedule which normally slips somewhat without problems. Organized more by priorities than by starting times. Schedule tends to be compact.

Non-delay dispatch schedule—A schedule for which resources are never held idle to wait for an important job.

Critical job schedule—The most important job is scheduled first throughout the shop, then the next most important is scheduled second and so forth. Schedule tends to leave gaps.

Critical resource schedule—The overused resource is scheduled carefully and other resources scheduled to fit.

Bottleneck schedule—Same as the critical resource (bottleneck) schedule.

Critical operation schedule—Looking inside the jobs, the activity/resource pair with the highest priority is scheduled first.

Forward scheduling—To schedule forward in time (simulation). Produces compactness at the possible expense of missing critical future due dates. It is usually a dispatch schedule.

Backward scheduling—To schedule backward from the due date. This usually minimizes tardiness at the expense of not being currently feasible. It is used mostly for interval and critical jobs.

Heuristic dispatch scheduling—A forward dispatch method where at each decision point choices are made by some heuristic priority rule.

Bottleneck dynamics—A more advanced forward dispatch method that forecasts and solves due date problems and critical resource problems dynamically.

Combinatorial scheduling—Seeks to evaluate all possible schedules (some completely, some by arguing that some schedules are inferior). Methods include branch-and-bound and dynamic programming. The advantage here is the attempt to find perfect answers. Disadvantages include prohibitive computation and storage for large problems and lack of any solid intuition as to how to modify the solution for emergency glitches.

Broad Scheduling Approaches.

Manual (interval)—Involves a human scheduler, in cases for which precise timely matching of activities and resources is necessary, such as launching a rocket.

Manual (dispatch)—Involves a human scheduler, in cases for which timing can be changed somewhat but overall priorities remain coherent, such as in much of discrete parts manufacturing.

Simulation (dispatch)—Computerizes a very simple form of manual-dispatch scheduling, where choices are made one at a time using simple rules.

Mathematical (exact)—Formalizes the scheduling problem mathematically and solves it exactly. The problem is usually simplified to make it solvable, such as using linear programming to solve production smoothing problems.

Mathematical (heuristic)—Approximately solves a mathematical formulation at much lower computational cost. There is a great variety of these methods, some of which we will study.

Pure expert system—Computerizes a more realistic version of manual dispatch scheduling using artificial intelligence ideas by trying to copy what the expert actually does.

Mixed AI/OR/DSS systems—Basically tries to use the best features of expert systems, mathematics, and decision support systems (DSS).

1.4.2 Past Approaches to Scheduling

In the past, several different approaches to scheduling were developed. Some of these methods, as well as their strengths and weaknesses, are discussed in the following paragraphs.

The Human Expert. It is a popular misconception that manual approaches are simplistic. Actually, acquiring expertise as a scheduler can take many years on the floor. Such expertise does not always transfer easily into a different shop, or even survive a large restructuring of the current shop.

Strengths of manual scheduling include:

a. Easy mixing of experience and formal rules
b. Broad common sense for dealing with difficult situations

Weaknesses of manual scheduling include:

a. The inability to rapidly explore a large number of alternatives
b. Difficulties in mixing expertise (committee problem)
c. Difficulties in handling change (future shock)
d. Increasingly complex shops (data overload)

Computer Simulation. The simulation approach became popular in the 1960s as computers became available. Simulation tends to replace a fairly simple kind of manual-dispatch method, using formal rules to make choices at each decision point in the simulation.

Strengths of simulation include:

a. The ability to model realistic systems at modest programming/computational costs
b. A more natural way to extend to a decision support system

Weaknesses of simulation include:

a. Solutions which may not even be close to optimal
b. A possibility of no benchmarks to say how good solutions are

More advanced methods based on simulation resolve some of these difficulties.

Branch-and-Bound. To use this method, one essentially forms a decision tree which branches at each decision, so that eventually there are as many branches as all possible solutions to the problem (it could become huge). One could not afford to evaluate every possible solution, but the method includes procedures to prune away branches and whole parts of the tree which cannot contain the solution.

Strengths of branch-and-bound include:

a. The ability to formulate very complex and realistic problems
b. The ability to solve small problems exactly
c. The fact that it is the basis for modern approximations, discussed later

Weaknesses of branch-and-bound include:

a. The inability to solve large problems
b. The fact that difficulty grows exponentially in problem size
c. The fact that faster computers are not the answer

Neighborhood Search. This method first requires a good starting solution. From there, we try all possible ways of changing that schedule slightly and compute how much each variation helps or hurts the solution. If none helps, we are finished. Otherwise, we take the best improvement as the new starting solution and repeat the whole procedure. This is really a special example of a non-linear programming method called "hill climbing."

Advantages of neighborhood search include:

 a. It is much faster than branch-and-bound.
 b. It is often quite accurate, especially with a good starting solution.
 c. It is the basis for modern heuristics, discussed later.

Disadvantages of neighborhood search include:

 a. It achieves only a local optimum.
 b. It has little intuition about sensitivity to problem changes.

Other Classical Methods. Other methods which have sometimes been used in the past include Lagrangean relaxation and dynamic programming.

1.4.3 New Approaches to Scheduling

Overview. Neighborhood search is often called an **intensification** strategy—we single-mindedly do what seems best at the moment. Another approach, random sampling, involves trying solutions without regard to what has worked so far. This is called a **diversification** strategy—it's time for a change, try to get a little variety, take a chance. A problem with no structure suggests using diversification; one with lots of structure suggests intensification. Neighborhood search is a pure intensification strategy; branch-and-bound and dynamic programming insist on lots of diversification to make sure every possibility is explored. Many modern techniques use mixtures of the two strategies. We turn to some of these next.

Tabu Search. Glover [1990] is considered the father of tabu search. In its simplest form, tabu search is simply neighborhood search together with a list of recent positions, the tabu list. Repeating recent moves is not allowed and one may move even if the best move makes things temporarily worse. (Of course we save the best move to date.) It becomes necessary to limit the total number of moves, since there is no longer a natural termination point.

   Note that the original neighborhood search method, which is pure intensification, has been modified to diversify rather than stay at a local optimum.

Simulated Annealing. In its simplest form, simulated annealing is simply neighborhood search, except that when all nearby positions are evaluated to decide the next move, a random amount is added to the evaluation, producing some tendency to occasionally try apparently bad moves. Thus, some randomness is added to the search procedure in a way that encourages exploration as well as immediate improvement. It is again necessary to limit the total number of moves.

   Note that the original intensification method has been modified to diversify occasionally, but at every move rather than only at local optima, as is the case with tabu search.

Beam Search (Partial Enumeration). Beam search is a method for approximately searching decision trees originally developed by the Artificial Intelligence (AI) community. Beam search is rather like a branch-and-bound procedure. Instead of waiting to throw away branches that are sure to be useless, however, we may throw away parts of the tree that are *likely* to be useless. One essential factor is to have a good measure of what "likely" means; another is to throw away parts that save a lot of effort without taking much risk. The net result is that we develop a number of solutions simultaneously (the beam) as we move down the tree. The beam represents diversification, while throwing away unlikely portions is intensification.

Bottleneck Dynamics. Basically, bottleneck dynamics (BD) estimates prices (delay costs) for delaying each possible activity within a shop and, similarly, prices (delay costs) for delaying each resource in the shop. Thus, if we expedite a job, we can calculate the benefit for getting it done earlier and the cost of using the resources earlier to accommodate it. The benefit/cost ratio becomes the job's priority at the machine. Since the problem is not convex, such prices can only be approximate. Thus, the tasks for BD become:

a. Look for a number of different ways to estimate prices easily.
b. Demonstrate by extensive computer testing and other validation that some of the approximate pricing procedures work well.

BD is primarily an intensification procedure, although searching aspects are easily added.

Other Modern Methods. Other modern methods which we will not consider here include genetic algorithms, OPT, shifting bottleneck, expert systems, and neural networks.

1.44 Scheduling Approaches Exercises

1. Compare the branch-and-bound and neighborhood search. How are they alike? How are they different?
2. Do you think it would be possible for a system to utilize both a human scheduling expert and computer simulation? If so, explain how they might work together.
3. Explain likely intensification and diversification procedures in terms of:

   a. Dating to find a wife/husband
   b. Finding your way across a strange large city without a map
   c. Playing a slot machine
   d. Driving to work on a long commute

4. Compare tabu search and simulated annealing. How are they alike? How are they different?
5. Explain why one might use something very much like beam search in some cases in the following real life situations:

   a. Dating to find a wife/husband
   b. Searching for a job
   c. Building a portfolio of stocks and bonds

1.5 SUMMARY AND PREVIEW OF THE SCHEDULING MODULE

In Scheduling Chapter 2, Section 2.1 an introduction is provided to one-machine sequencing with an explanation of why one-machine results are the key to understanding more complicated scheduling problems. In Sections 2.2 and 2.5 a Company Application Scenario is developed to show a practical situation which requires essentially the solution to a one-machine problem. In Section 2.3 the foundations of one-machine sequencing are developed; in 2.4 more modern approaches are developed.

In Scheduling Chapter 3, Section 3.1 we give an introduction to the topic of multiple-machine sequencing with a discussion of resource aggregation issues. In Sections 3.2 and 3.4 we present a couple of Company Application Scenarios to illustrate some actual scheduling problems involving several machines. In Section 3.3 we develop heuristics for flow shops and job shops.

In Scheduling Chapter 4, we look at somewhat more realistic job shops. In Section 4.2 we give a Company Application Scenario which is non-classical—a computer card sector. In Section 4.3 we consider open shops, assembly shops and continuous shops, as well as pull systems and Just-In-Time systems. Finally, in Section 4.4 we develop an introduction to flexible manufacturing systems, including multiple machines per resource cases and multiple resources per activity cases. In Appendix J we give a brief development of a classic result for the two-machine flowshop problem with a makespan objective: Johnson's Algorithm.

CHAPTER 2

One-Machine Scheduling

2.1 INTRODUCTION

2.1.1 One-Machine Problems are the Key!

Many large real-world scheduling problems have the following characteristics:

a. There are a number of jobs to do.
b. Each has a certain importance.
c. Each must be completed in a reasonable time frame for it.
d. Each job consists of a number of individual activities.
e. Each activity competes with other similar activities for a unique resource (machine).
f. The scheduling problem is too large to solve perfectly.

One of the great achievements of scientists is to break such a problem down into building blocks that can be solved nearly perfectly. Another of the great achievements is to be able to put these building blocks back together to re-create the full problem. (This is actually quite complicated, since the blocks have connections to each other.)

The most obvious building block for scheduling is the one-machine problem with jobs arriving over time (dynamic). Even this problem is too difficult to solve directly in many cases. We need to remove some of the constraints in the problem, to further simplify it. This is called a **relaxation**. One type of relaxation, the **static** problem, removes the arrival time constraints and allows all activities to be available from the beginning. A second type of relaxation, the **preemptive** problem, allows an activity to be interrupted and finished later, which gets rid of the difficult lumpiness in the problem. These simplifications are relatively easy to solve and to understand. They are not always very useful in themselves; however, they do provide help in building solutions for the full scale dynamic one-machine building block.

2.1.2 Summary and Preview of the Chapter

In Section 2.2 and Section 2.5 we discuss a Company Application Scenario—Super Science Servers. In Section 2.3 we lay the foundations for one-machine sequencing, including a large number of classic dispatch heuristics. In Section 2.4 we discuss more modern methods of one-machine sequencing, including neighborhood search methods, manual search, simple neighborhood search, tabu search, and simulated annealing.

2.2 COMPANY APPLICATION SCENARIO— SUPER SCIENCE SERVERS

Super Science Servers (SSS) is a rather large scientific laboratory which does custom analysis of material samples for many clients. Clients meet initially with the SSS customer representative to jointly create a work order. This work order specifies the exact work to be done, including technical tolerances and other specifications. It also gives the relative urgency of the job, the due date (if any), and the price for the work. The representative later adds an importance index for the job. This might often be simply the dollar value of the job times the relative urgency, although the representative might increase or decrease this value to reflect how highly the customer is valued, for example.

Recently, Sue Slotnick, the manager of the lab, has become somewhat concerned. Most of the equipment that SSS owns has a relatively low utilization and there are usually adequate personnel to perform tests quickly. However, two of the pieces of equipment are having scheduling problems: the tunneling microscope and the micro assayer.

The tunneling microscope is an extremely delicate instrument that can "see" atomic details of a material's surface. The instrument works by guiding a very fine needle across the surface, applying a charge and utilizing quantum effects. The procedure is so delicate that the machine is being repaired about 40 percent of the time, while the queue of current jobs simply waits. Even the procedure of analyzing the sample itself is quite delicate. There is an initial setup time for a sample, while the microscope is being adjusted to the new type of sample. But this is not very important, since by far the largest amount of time is spent making a sweep across the sample, checking whether it is good or not, making another sweep and so on. The work order might call for 10 good sweeps, but it might take 15 to 30 sweeps to produce 10 good sweeps. The manager of SSS wants to know a good scheduling procedure to improve the average flow time (time from order arrival to delivery), which has been rather bad lately as the volume of work for the microscope has grown.

The micro assayer is a combination melting crucible/chemical quantitative analysis apparatus. This instrument works by first melting the sample, putting it into solution and then running it through a complicated set of chemical procedures with a series of test tubes, beakers, tubings, and so forth. In contrast with the tunneling microscope, the micro assayer breaks down rarely. Some components are indeed delicate, but they are simply replaced every run. Also, a given micro assay is relatively predictable as to time. The run is typically repeated three times for statistical purposes, but the time for each is quite well known. On the other hand, the setup time for starting a new sample is rather large and is quite variable, depending mostly on whether the previous sample was somewhat different or very similar. The manager would like somehow to run similar samples in a sequential cluster. On the other hand, if this is carried too far, urgent items in a different cluster may have to wait too long and become tardy. Micro assay customers typically negotiate due dates with the laboratory and expect them to be met. The client is also typically happier if the work can be returned before the deadline. Thus, the manager's concern is to develop a decent sequence for the samples which will compromise between the desire to minimize setups and the desire not to hold tardy jobs unnecessarily. Sue decides to employ a scheduling consultant. A friend suggests that the firm of Gray, Skize, Skize, and Skize does good work in this area. Sue calls the consulting firm and Dr. Gray agrees to come out in two weeks and spend a couple of days studying the situation to make a preliminary recommendation.

2.3 ONE-MACHINE SEQUENCING—FOUNDATIONS

2.3.1 Overview

The Big Picture. A machine (station, resource, processor, etc.) processes **jobs** (operations, tasks, assemblies, etc.) one at a time. There is an **objective** (cost, penalty, etc.) for each job based on its completion time. Typically, our overall objective is to find the right **sequence** (ordering, priorities, etc.) for the group of jobs, either to minimize the sum of the costs for the jobs or, sometimes, the maximum cost of any job.

We just consider jobs already in the **queue** (line, etc.) at the current time ($t = 0$) or arriving over some **horizon** ($t = 0$ to H). We suppose there to be n of these jobs and often want to refer to some generic one, which we call j. Our task (in the non-preemptive case) is to put these n jobs in the right sequence in order to minimize costs or customer dissatisfaction. (The **preemptive** case is slightly different. Here we are allowed to remove jobs while they are processing, start a more urgent one and finish the preempted job later. It turns out that we will usually preempt only when an important job arrives, so that our task in this case would be to choose the next job either when a job finishes or when a job arrives.)

Each job j has a known arrival or ready time r_j. Sometimes all the arrival times are assumed to be 0, that is, all jobs of interest were already available (in the line) at the start. This is called the **static** case. There *are* situations in the real world when all jobs are available from the start, such as a very long line at a movie, when everyone arrived well in advance. If at least some of the jobs arrive later, this is called the **dynamic** case. Most real problems are dynamic. Many times we still solve the static problem because it is easier. Many other times we solve the easier static problem first to give us some idea of approaches to solve the dynamic problem.

Each job j has a known **processing time** on the machine p_j. Whether it has a long or short processing time doesn't change the job's importance. (If processing time is variable, it is very often reasonable to simply use the expected process time.) A job's own processing time is a sunk cost as far as it is concerned. One job's processing time does influence other jobs, however. If the job is processed early and has a long processing time, all other jobs after that wait that extra amount of time. Another way of putting this same idea is that putting a job first delays all other jobs in direct proportion to p_j.

Each job j has a known importance or **weight** on the machine w_j. If the time is measured in days, w_j might be expressed in dollars per day, for example. It might be work-in-process, holding cost of inventory, or value to the customer per day in receiving the order later, or explicit penalty for tardy delivery and so on.

Each job j has a known expected delivery time or **due date** from the machine d_j. If d_j is not given explicitly, it is usually assumed to be 0. (Sometimes all jobs may be given a common due date.)

Given the sequence in which jobs are to be processed on a machine, it is important to be able to calculate the cost for each job of that sequence. The **completion time** C_j of a job is the time at which job j finishes on the machine. It won't be able to start until the previous job finishes. It also won't be able to start until it arrives. For a **regular objective**, each job always prefers to finish earlier rather than later. (This is much easier to deal with mathematically.) For all the regular objectives we will consider, the job will always start as soon as possible for its turn, so we may calculate in turn the completion time of each job for that sequence. However, Just-In-Time type objectives are **non-regular**, since jobs do not want to finish early (discussed later). The **flow time** F_j of job j (also called cycle time) is the time from job arrival to job completion; that is, customer waiting time.

Turning to costs related to due dates, the **lateness** L_j of a job is the amount a job finishes past its due date (positive or negative). When lateness is positive, it is also called **tardiness** T_j. When lateness is negative, its tardiness is zero. In a similar way, when lateness is negative its magnitude is called the (positive) **earliness** E_j. Note that earliness and tardiness are never negative and that when one is strictly positive, the other is zero.

To make this a little clearer, we consider a couple of examples. If a job arrives at time 5 and completes at 25, with a due date of 21, its flow time is 20, its lateness is +4, its tardiness is +4, and its earliness is 0. If instead it completed at 18, its flow time is 13, its lateness is –3, its tardiness is 0, and its earliness is +3.

Problem Relaxations.

General. As we have said, the general (dynamic) one-machine problem is too difficult to solve exactly in most cases. In applied mathematics, science, and engineering, a very common way to study difficult problems is to simplify them by *relaxation*; just ignore some of the difficulties in the problem and solve the rest. (Literally, to relax a problem is to remove part of its constraints, just as a person might relax by taking off a constricting garment.)

[As an example of relaxation, consider the problem of minimizing $f(x) = 20 - 2x + 8x^2$ with the constraint that x is an integer. First, relax the problem by ignoring the fact that x must be an integer and solve the resulting problem by calculus:

$$f'(x) = -2 + 16x; \quad f''(x) = +16$$

with minimum at $x = 1/8$; $f(1/8) = 20 - 2/8 + 8(1/8)^2 = 19.875$. It is obvious that the relaxed and original problems increase smoothly in both directions around $x = 1/8$. Thus, a little thought will convince us that the solution to the original integer problem was either $x = 0$ or $x = 1$. Since $f(0) = 20$ and $f(1) = 26$, the solution to the original problem must be $x = 0$.]

Clearly, if we start with a cost minimizing problem and relax it, the solution will be reduced or stay the same. We say that the relaxation solution is a *lower* bound for the original problem. If the optimal solution to the original problem is not known, this lower bound is useful in evaluating how good any heuristic for the original problem is. For example, if a heuristic solution gives a value of 15.3 and there is a known lower bound of 15.2 (solution to a relaxed problem) the heuristic cost can be no more than 0.1 from the cost of the optimal solution.

Static vs. Dynamic. The static problem is a relaxation of the dynamic problem. The dynamic problem has a constraint for each job specifying the earliest time it can start. The static problem removes these constraints by making all jobs available from the start. While, as we have said, the static case is sometimes realistic, it is more often simply useful in helping us find good approximations for the dynamic problem.

Preemptive vs. Non-preemptive. The preemptive problem is a relaxation of the non-preemptive problem. This is because the non-preemptive problem has a constraint for each job saying that once it is started, it must be finished without interruption. Preemption is actually allowed in some real problems, but it is more often important in allowing good bounds/insight for the non-preemptive problem.

We may distinguish two kinds of preemption:

a. **Cost-at-End (CAE):** Costs or rewards are not assigned until the entire job is finished. (The whole job is tardy or none of it is tardy, for example.)

b. **Spread Cost (SC):** Costs or rewards are assigned to each piece in proportion to the size of the piece. (For example, 40 percent can be processed first and be on time and then 60 percent can be processed later and be tardy.)

(CAE is reasonable for certain types of real problems; SC is usually the better relaxation for giving insight.)

2.3.2 Objectives in Scheduling

We first give some formal definitions for measures of schedules we have introduced above: (For the one-machine case we use "job" and "activity" interchangeably.)

Completion time C_j—The time at which activity j finishes.

Due date d_j—The time at which activity j is due to finish.

Arrival time r_j—The time at which activity j arrives.

Flow time F_j—The time activity j spends in the shop.

$$F_j = C_j - r_j$$

Lateness L_j—The time by which j's completion exceeds its due date (can be negative):

$$L_j = C_j - d_j$$

Tardiness T_j—Same as the lateness if that is positive; otherwise equal to zero.

$$T_j = \max \{0, L_j\}$$

Earliness E_j—Same as the negative of lateness if lateness is negative; otherwise equal to zero.

$$E_j = \max \{0, -L_j\}.$$

Weight w_j—The importance of a particular job, used in averaging these measures over all activities.

The flow time for a customer is the time between submitting his order and receiving the finished order, and thus is an important measure of customer service. The flow time is also almost directly proportional to the average WIP for the activity and thus is an important measure of shop inventory costs. The lateness measure and the flow time measure at first glance seem quite different, since the former measures due date performance and the latter doesn't. However, the two measures create identical schedules, as we shall see.

The tardiness measure for a customer penalizes us for being past the due date, but gives no reward for being early. This measure is quite important in practice; many objectives measure the amount and frequency of tardiness. The earliness measure reflects the fact that some orders may not be desired before they are due (Just-In-Time). This leads to a non-regular objective function. Typical objective functions are formed in one of three ways:

1. Taking a weighted average of one of these measures
2. Taking a maximum or minimum of one of these measures
3. Taking some mixture of these

In the following we use the same symbol w_j for the weight of activity j for different objectives, even though the actual weights are likely to differ. This simplifies notation.

Utilization Objectives. The only utilization objective with very wide use is

$$\textit{Makespan } C_{max} = \max \{C_j\}$$

The schedule with the smallest makespan is the one in which the entire set of jobs (jobs = activities, in the one-machine case) is finished first. The intuitive idea is that finishing the current group of jobs earlier will allow new jobs to start earlier and thus get the most done over a long period of time. For more complex shops, there is another utilization objective called **Economic Makespan**, which we will not discuss here.

Flow Time/Lateness Objectives.

Flow time. The two most important flow time objectives are weighted flow time and maximum flow time:

$$\textit{Weighted Flow time } F_{wt} = \sum w_j F_j$$

$$\textit{Maximum Flow time } F_{max} = \max \{F_j\}$$

The schedule with the smallest weighted flow time is the one with the smallest average of the flow times, weighted by the importances of the jobs. This measures the average turnaround performance of the shop and also the average inventory if the weights are proportional to the dollar values of the orders.

The schedule with the smallest maximum flow time is the one for which the job with the worst flow time is better off than the job with the worst flow time in any other schedule. This can be important if customers are not very sensitive to average performance, but become increasingly upset for a very long turnaround job.

Lateness. The two most important lateness objectives are weighted lateness and maximum lateness:

$$\textit{Weighted Lateness } L_{wt} = \Sigma w_j L_j$$

$$\textit{Maximum Lateness } L_{max} = \max \{L_j\}$$

The schedule with the smallest weighted lateness is, it turns out, the same as the schedule with the smallest weighted flow time discussed previously. In fact, we shall see later that weighted flow time and weighted lateness differ by a simple constant (the weighted average due date less the weighted average arrival date).

Once again, the schedule with the smallest maximum lateness is the one for which no job has too large a lateness. Maximum lateness and maximum flow time do not differ by a constant.

Tardiness Objectives.
The three most important tardiness objectives are weighted tardiness, maximum tardiness, and weighted number of tardy jobs.

$$\textit{Weighted tardiness } T_{wt} = \Sigma w_j T_j$$

$$\textit{Maximum tardiness } T_{max} = \max \{T_j\}$$

$$\textit{Weighted number of tardy jobs } N_{wt} = \Sigma w_j \delta(T_j)$$

(where $\delta(T_j) = 1$ if $T_j > 0$, $\delta(T_j) = 0$ otherwise)

The weighted tardiness objective is the same as the weighted lateness objective, except that no credit is given for negative lateness. For each tardy job we multiply the weight times the amount of tardiness and add. The only difference for the weighted number of tardy jobs is that we just add up the weights of the tardy jobs. The rates in the former case are a rate per unit-time tardy; in the latter case we pay a large one-time charge when the job becomes tardy.

The maximum tardiness and the maximum lateness objectives are very similar. If the maximum lateness is positive it is clearly equal to the maximum tardiness. If the maximum lateness is negative, then the maximum tardiness is zero.

Weights. It is often difficult in practice to estimate weights accurately. Since re-scaling all weights up or down does not really affect any of the objective functions we have talked about, many authors choose to require $\Sigma w_j = 1.0$. There is nothing wrong with this practice algebraically, except that it obscures the fundamental fact that weights are about "dollars per unit time" or simply "dollars."

For lack of anything better, users often assume all the weights are equal, that is $w_j = 1/n$ (n being the number of jobs). To show this usage we would replace F_{wt} by F_{av}. Unfortunately, this process obscures the actual rewards and penalties which are a part of the job situation. Difficulty in estimating w_j does not detract from the urgency of measuring it as well as possible.

The weight w_j in a flow time situation represents the cost of delaying activity j for, say, one day. This should be related to the interest rate, the value of the item (or value added);

it should also be related to the clout of the customer. It seems to be somewhat easier for practitioners to estimate w_j by

$$w_j = (r/365)D_jA_j$$

where r is the yearly interest rate (simple), D_j is the dollar value of the activity and $A_j > 1$ is a customer priority factor. The weight for a tardiness situation might be the flow time rate multiplied by a tardiness factor of perhaps 5 or 10.

2.3.3 Some Exact Results

The following propositions have the implicit requirement that the objective function be "regular"; that is, earlier completion of every job is always preferred. (We discuss the "nonregular" early-tardy [JIT] problem later.) Where it does not cause confusion, we number the jobs by their order in the schedule being considered.

General Results.

Proposition 1. For the dynamic case, $C_j = \max\{C_{j-1}, r_j\} + p_j$.

This proposition says simply that the job will start when both the previous job has finished and the current job has arrived. The job then takes p_j to be processed and be finished.

From Proposition 1, if we know the ordering of a schedule, we can find completion times and thus evaluate how good the schedule is. Unfortunately, if there are n jobs, there are $n!$ orderings. Now 5! = 120 which we could certainly solve with a lot of work. But 10! = 3.6 million, 15! = 1.3 trillion. Thus, we must look for good methods, both exact and approximate, which are more clever and therefore faster.

Proposition 2. For the static case, Proposition 1 simplifies to $C_j = C_{j-1} + p_j$ or equivalently $C_j = \Sigma p_i$ (for $i = 1, j$).

If all jobs have already arrived then the total time until j is completed will be the sum of its processing time and that of previous jobs.

Example 2-1, Part 1. A skilled machinist, Grinder Jim, has gone into business for himself and has a small shop with a lathe, two kinds of milling machines, a grinder, and a sander. He can operate only one machine at a time and hence this is the limiting factor. One Monday morning, he has five jobs left to do, numbered in the order they came into the shop. He considers these jobs roughly equally important. Processing times and due dates for the jobs in hours are given below.

Job	Length in Hours	Working Hours Until Due
1	11	61
2	29	45
3	31	31
4	1	33
5	2	32

Grinder Jim usually just does jobs in order of their arrival. He is worried that the shop is pretty heavily loaded, and wonders how well first-come first-served (FCFS) will perform this time.

Solution. There are apparently five machines, and no job is ever held up for the lack of a machine. Grinder Jim is the unique limiting resource and hence he is the single machine in a formal sense. Since all jobs are available when we are considering how to solve the problem and none are given yet to arrive, this is a static problem. Since Jim usually uses the FCFS discipline, let us find out how good a schedule it is in this case.

Job #	Process	FCFS Schedule Completion	Due Date	Late	Tardy
1	11	11	61	–50	0
2	29	40	45	–5	0
3	31	71	31	40	40
4	1	72	33	39	39
5	2	74	32	42	42
Totals		268	202	66	121
Average		53.6	40.4	13.2	24.2
# Tardy = 3					

The makespan of Grinder Jim's schedule is 74, signifying that all the work will be finished in 74 work hours. The average time the jobs will be done in is 53.6 hours, the average time they are due is 40.4 hours (not under our control), and the average lateness giving credit for earliness will be 13.2 hours. The average tardiness not giving credit for earliness will be 24.2 hours.

Utilization Results. We define a **dispatch** scheduling policy as one which always schedules some available job as soon as the machine is empty. (This constitutes non-delay. "Don't hold the machine empty even a short time for an arriving 'hot' job.")

Proposition 3. For the dynamic case and the makespan objective, any dispatch schedule (non-delay schedule) will give an optimal solution.

All jobs must be finished to define the makespan, so there is no hot job to wait for. For similar reasons, it doesn't matter which job is done next among the available jobs.

Proposition 4. For the static case, any permutation schedule whatever is optimal for the makespan objective; in fact $C_{max} = \Sigma p_j$.

For the static case, all jobs are available, so that all permutation schedules are dispatch. Now apply Proposition 3.

Example 2-1, Part 2. The schedule that Grinder Jim would usually take gives him a makespan of 74, which is just the same as any other permutation schedule would give him. However, Grinder Jim is not at full capacity so makespan does not seem like the right measure. He wonders about the effect of using other schedules.

Flow Time/Lateness Results.

Proposition 5. For the static case and the weighted flow objective, if all the process times are 1.0, an optimal sequence of jobs must satisfy $w_1 >= w_2 >= w_3 >= \ldots >= w_n$.

We have that $F_{wt} = (1)w_1 + (2)w_2 .. + (j)w_j + (j+1)w_{j+1} + \ldots + nw_n$. (The first job waits only for itself, the second job for the first two jobs and so on.) Thus, if we interchange any w_j and w_{j+1} in an optimal solution the weighted flow is increased by $w_{j+1} - w_j$. But the schedule is optimal, implying that $w_j <= w_{j+1}$. This is true for any pair.

Proposition 6. For the static weighted flow problem, an optimal sequence of jobs must satisfy $(w_1/p_1) >= (w_2/p_2) >= (w_3/p_3) >= \ldots (w_n/p_n)$.

First assume the p_j to be all integers. Replace job j by p_j jobs of length one and weights (w_j/p_j). (A relaxation). Now schedule all the resulting joblets using Proposition 5. All the highest w_j/p_j will be at the front of the line. Note that if two activities of the same priority are interspersed we can reorder them to occur together. Thus, we can reunite the joblets to obtain a non-preemptive cost as low as our preemptive solution. Hence the non-preemptive solution is optimal.

If the p_j are not all integers, we simply make the units arbitrarily small to make them as close to integers as desired in percentage terms.

A simple example may clarify the idea.

Example. Suppose there are three projects sitting on a consultant's desk. Project 1 will pay $40,000 and requires 400 hours to complete. Project 2 will pay $15,000 and requires 20 hours to complete. Project 3 will pay $800 and requires 5 hours to complete. The consultant estimates that each hour a project is delayed in completion costs him about 0.3 percent of the value of the project in lost customer goodwill. Thus, flow time is a good objective.

$$w_1/p_1 = (0.003)(40,000)/(400) = \$0.30/\text{hour customer waits}$$

$$w_2/p_2 = (0.003)(15,000)/(20) = \$2.25/\text{hour customer waits}$$

$$w_3/p_3 = (0.003)(800)/(5) = \$0.48/\text{hour customer waits}$$

Thus, by WSPT (Weighted Shortest Processing Time) the consultant should do the middle-sized project first, the smallest project second and the biggest project last. Note also that if the relative urgency of Project 1 had been 3 percent rather than 0.3 percent per hour, Project 1 should be scheduled first.

Proposition 7. In the static or dynamic problem, the objectives of weighted completion time, weighted flow time, and weighted lateness all have WSPT as their optimal schedule. *Now* $F_{wt} = \sum w_j(C_j - r_j) = \sum w_j C_j - \sum w_j r_j = C_{wt} - r_{wt}$ *where* r_{wt} *is the weighted average arrival time, a constant not depending on the schedule chosen. Also* $L_{wt} = \sum w_j(C_j - d_j) = \sum w_j C_j - \sum w_j d_j = C_{wt} - d_{wt}$ *where* d_{wt} *is the weighted average due date, a constant not depending on the schedule chosen. Since all three functions,* F_{wt}, L_{wt} *and* C_{wt} *differ only by a constant, they must all achieve their minimum using the same sequence, namely WSPT.*

Example 2-1, Part 3. On being told that SPT (shortest processing time rule, that is, WSPT with weights = 1) will minimize both average completion time and average lateness, Grinder Jim asks us to evaluate this schedule in this case. Now we sequence by increasing process time.

Job #	Process	SPT Schedule Completion	Due Date	Late	Tardy
4	1	1	33	−32	0
5	2	3	32	−29	0
1	11	14	61	−47	0
2	29	43	45	−2	0
3	31	74	31	43	43
Totals		135	202	−67	43
Average		27.0	40.4	−13.4	8.6
# Tardy = 1					

This is certainly a much better schedule than the FCFS schedule, since average lateness, average tardiness, and number of tardy jobs have all been reduced. But the total time for all jobs is still 74.

a. Average completion time has gone down from 53.6 to 27.0. (We know no schedule will do better on this. Why?)
b. Average lateness has gone down from 13.2 to −13.4.
c. Average tardiness has gone down from 24.2 to 8.6.
d. The number of tardy jobs has gone down from 3 to 1.

Grinder Jim sees that other scheduling rules besides his usual one may indeed pay off. He is a little unhappy, though, that one job has a tardiness of 43 hours. Customers often tolerate a little tardiness but get upset at a large tardiness. He wonders if it is possible to spread that tardiness around a little in order not to lose a customer.

Proposition 8. For the static case and the maximum lateness objective, the earliest due date rule (EDD) is optimal. That is, we should schedule the job with smallest d_j first.

Note that it would be enough to show that the job with the latest due date may be placed last. (Then we could place the next-to-latest due date next to last by the same rule, etc.)

Suppose that the optimal rule didn't place the latest due date job last, then move it to last. This helps the lateness of every job except the one moved last. If it does not now have the maximum lateness, then it has no effect. If it does now have the maximum lateness, then the job moved from the final slot would have had at least as great a lateness.

The amazing thing about this rule is that we don't need to know anything about process times to sequence the jobs. Thus, if three jobs have due dates of 6, 2, and 9 then they should be processed in order 2, 6, and 9, irrespective of whether processing times were 1, 2, 3; 6, 4, 2; or 7, 7, 7.

Note that the EDD rule helps prevent the embarrassment of very large lateness, but the rule is often rather poor in practice with respect to the objectives of weighted lateness or weighted tardiness. EDD may be of practical use to the scheduler if the top management intervenes only in cases where jobs are extremely late. Minimizing maximum lateness is also very important if all the activities have a common due date as inputs to a project downstream. In such a case it would not be good if one of the inputs was especially late.

It is also interesting that even if some of the jobs are fixed in position in advance, then putting the rest in EDD order around them will produce minimum maximum lateness for the non-fixed jobs. The proof is almost identical to that given for Proposition 8.

Tardiness Results.

Proposition 9. For the static case, the EDD rule is also optimal for the maximum tardiness objective.

Just rework the proof of Proposition 8 slightly.

Example 2-1, Part 4. On learning that the EDD rule is the best possible rule to use if he wants no customer to be extremely unhappy, Grinder Jim asks us to evaluate that schedule for him. Looking at the results, notice that compared to SPT we have reduced the maximum tardiness from 43 down to 18 and the average tardiness from 8.6 to 6.6. However, we have paid a high price in the average turnaround through the shop; the average completion time has gone up from 27.0 to 47.0. Also, the number of tardy jobs has increased from one to four.

Job #	Process	EDD Schedule Completion	Due Date	Late	Tardy
3	31	31	31	0	0
5	2	33	32	1	1
4	1	34	33	1	1
2	29	63	45	18	18
1	11	74	61	13	13
Total		235	202	33	33
Average		47.0	40.4	6.6	6.6
# Tardy = 4					

Proposition 10. For the static problem, the unweighted number of tardy jobs may be minimized by Hodgson's algorithm:

   Step 1. Order the activities in EDD order.
   Step 2. Find the first tardy job, call it k, in the sequence.
   Step 3. If there are no tardy jobs, stop; this solution is optimal.
   Step 4. Find the job among the first k with the longest processing time, and move it to the end of the list (tardy); return to step 2.

Putting the activities in EDD will minimize maximum tardiness and hence will produce a no tardiness schedule if one exists. If k is the first tardy job in the first k jobs then one of the first k jobs will be tardy in the optimal solution, since they are in EDD order and EDD would have produced zero tardiness if possible. Thus, we may remove one job to be tardy from the problem. Taking the longest one helps the remaining completion times the most.

As an example of Hodgson's algorithm, consider the job set in this table.

Job j	p	d
1	1	4
2	5	8
3	4	9
4	9	13
5	6	10
6	13	18

Following is a worksheet summarizing Hodgson's procedure.

Step 1. Initialize in EDD order 1-2-3-5-4-6.

Step 2. Find the first tardy job. Job 3 is first tardy one; we need not compute the rest of the table.

Job j	d	p	C	T
1	4	1	1	0
2	8	5	6	0
3	9	4	10	1

Step 3. Not operative; there is a tardy job.

Step 4. Job 2 is removed as the longest one among 1, 2, 3 (permanently tardy), giving the revised order 1-3-5-4-6-(2); return to step 2.

Step 2. Find the first tardy job. Job 5 is the first tardy one.

Job j	d	p	C	T
1	4	1	1	0
3	9	4	5	0
5	10	6	11	1

Step 3. Not operative.

Step 4. Job 5 is removed as the longest one among 1, 3, 5, giving the revised order 1-3-4-6-(2-5); return to step 2.

Step 2. Find the first tardy job. Job 4 is the first tardy one.

Job j	d	p	C	T
1	4	1	1	0
3	9	4	5	0
4	13	9	14	1

Step 3. Not operative.

Step 4. Job 4 is removed as the longest one among 1, 3, 4, giving the revised order 1-3-6-(2-5-4); return to step 2.

Step 2. Find the first tardy job. But there is none (ignore those at the end).

Job j	d	p	C	T
1	4	1	1	0
3	9	4	5	0
6	18	13	18	0

Step 3. Operative. Stop; the solution is optimal.

Thus, the optimal solution is 1-3-6-(2-5-4). (The parentheses mean that the tardy jobs can be done in any order.) Note that the number of tardy jobs problem often has more than one optimal solution. The procedure given here guarantees only to find one of them.

Actually, of course, in most realistic problems different activities have different importances; that is, we would like to solve the weighted number of tardy problem. This is very difficult to do exactly; however, we later give a proposition helpful in solving this problem either exactly or approximately.

Example 2-1, Part 5. Grinder Jim is fascinated by the fact that although EDD produces a worst tardiness of only 18, which is the best possible, and would produce a zero tardy case if one were possible, it produces four out of the five jobs as tardy. And, although SPT produces only one tardy job, it has a very large tardiness of 43. Jim wonders if it is possible to find a schedule with one tardy job with a smaller tardiness.

Solution. We can find the answer to Jim's question with a little spadework. (This example is a little more advanced.) Certainly the question of the placement of Job 3 is the most important, since it has the earliest due date and largest completion time. Consider putting it in the first position; order the rest of the jobs in EDD to minimize their maximum lateness.

Job j	Process	Completion	Due Date	Late	Tardy
3	31	31	31	0	0
5	2	33	32	1	1
4	1	34	33	1	1
2	29	63	45	18	18
1	11	74	61	13	13

It is not possible to have Job 3 first and have only one other tardy job. How about putting Job 3 second? Putting the others in EDD sequence around it, at least Job 3 and another job must be tardy. Putting it third or fourth leads to the same conclusion. Finally, putting it last allows all other jobs to be on time, but gives Job 3 a tardiness of 43. Note the Hodgson's solution and SPT solution are quite similar in this case.

Proposition 11. For the static weighted number of tardy jobs problem, an optimal solution has the following general form.

Step 1. Order the activities in EDD order.

Step 2. If there are no tardy jobs remaining, we are finished.

Step 3. Find the first tardy job, call it k, in the sequence.

Step 4. Choose *some job* to remove among the first k.

Step 5. Move that job to the end and revise the completion times.

Step 6. If the rest of the sequence still has a tardy job, return to step 4; otherwise go to step 2.

The proof is left as an exercise.

We clearly have a conflict. We would like to remove jobs with small weights so as to add little to the total weight of tardy jobs. At the same time we would like to remove jobs with long processing times. One likely heuristic is to remove jobs with the smallest value of w_j/p_j. We discuss this heuristic (WTD HODGSON) later.

The weighted tardiness problem is even harder than the weighted number of tardy jobs problem, in the sense that the unweighted version of the number of tardy jobs problem is easily solvable, while the unweighted version of the weighted tardiness problem is not. Yet it is a very important objective in practice. We give two propositions which will be helpful in designing heuristics.

Proposition 12. For the static weighted tardiness problem, if every sequence makes every job tardy, then WSPT is optimal.

If all jobs must be tardy there is no distinction between lateness and tardiness and WSPT optimizes lateness.

Proposition 13. For the static weighted tardiness problem, if there is at least one sequence with no tardiness, then EDD is optimal.

EDD will minimize the maximum tardiness; since that minimum is known to be zero, EDD must find it.

Propositions 12 and 13 might lead us to guess that WSPT would be a good heuristic for heavily loaded (and therefore very tardy) shops and that EDD would be a good heuristic for lightly loaded shops. There is some truth in this, but we will discover sharper heuristics using the same ideas in Section 2.3.4.

2.3.4 Dynamic Dispatch Heuristics

General Approach. We now know several scheduling rules that are optimal for static problems:

a.   Any rule for makespan
b.   WSPT for weighted flow time or lateness
c.   EDD for maximum lateness or tardiness
d.   Hodgson's rule for unweighted number of tardy jobs

While there are no easily computed scheduling rules that are optimal for the static weighted tardiness problem or the weighted number of tardy jobs problem, a number of heuristics have been proposed and tested for these static problems also.

With jobs arriving over time, the dynamic problem is much more difficult and there are rarely exact solutions for this case. However, there is a general procedure which works well fairly often to change good static heuristics into good dynamic heuristics.

Dynamic Dispatch Procedure.

1.   Choose a heuristic which works well for the static version of the problem. Set the time as the start of the problem.
2.   Consider the set of activities which are available to be scheduled; if an activity is available go to step 3; otherwise go to step 6.
3.   Schedule an activity from this set by the static heuristic and update time by the process time of the job scheduled.
4.   Update the set of available jobs.
5.   If all jobs have been scheduled, stop or go to step 2.
6.   Update time until the next arrival of an activity.

(Notice that a static heuristic can still change over time, for example, as the due date approaches. In such a case priorities must be recalculated each time a decision is made.) The intuition behind this procedure is that far future job arrivals don't affect priorities of current jobs very much, while current jobs behave toward each other much as in a static problem.

The Heuristics.
   RANDOM—The RANDOM Rule is just that: choose from the available jobs at each decision point at random; a useful "bad" benchmark.
   FCFS—First Come First Served is another "bad" benchmark. Yet in practice it is a common rule in waiting lines. One point that is often overlooked is that earlier jobs often have earlier due dates, so that FCFS is closer to an EDD-type rule.
   WSPT—As we have seen, the Weighted Shortest Processing Time Rule is optimal for the static weighted lateness and weighted flow time problems and is very good for heavily loaded tardiness shops. (We denote the priority of activity j by π_j.)

$$\pi_j = (w_j/p_j).$$

EDD—As we have seen, the Earliest Due Date Rule is optimal for the static maximum lateness and maximum tardiness problems and is very good for lightly loaded tardiness shops.

$$\pi_j = -d_j$$

That is, the priority of j goes down as its due date increases.

SLACK—The slack of a job is how early it would be if scheduled first; that is $S_j = (d_j - p_j - t)$. The slack rule simply schedules the job with the least slack first:

$$\pi_j = - (d_j - p_j - t)$$

where t is the time at which the current decision is being made. Note that while slack changes over time, the priorities of jobs as determined by their slacks all change by the same amount, so that slacks need be calculated only at one point in time. SLACK is commonly used in shops for tardiness objectives. Although it is not a very sharp rule for any common tardiness objective, it is simple to use and understand.

Example 2-1, Part 6. Grinder Jim notes that the schedules he has looked at have very different average tardiness: FCFS with 24.2, SPT and Hodgson's with 8.6, and EDD with 6.6. He has heard some schedulers use the least SLACK Rule and wonders how it would do for this problem. To refresh your memory, the data for Grinder Jim is given at the start of Example 2-1 just after Proposition 2 in Section 2.3.3.

Solution. Slack is defined as $S = (d - p - t)$. At the initial time $t = 0$, therefore, Job 1 has slack $61 - 11 = 50$, Job 2 has $45 - 29 = 16$, Job 3 has $31 - 31 = 0$, Job 4 has $33 - 1 = 32$, and Job 5 has $32 - 2 = 30$. Thus, we schedule Job 3 and advance the time to $t = 31$ to schedule the next job. (Note that we may continue to use the slacks of time zero, since the same amount of time gets subtracted off of each.)

Thus, we may simply order the jobs by their slack at time zero, from smallest to largest: 3, 2, 5, 4, and 1.

	P	C	d	L	T
Least SLACK Schedule					
Job j	**Process**	**Completion**	**Due Date**	**Late**	**Tardy**
3	31	31	31	0	0
2	29	60	45	15	15
5	2	62	32	30	30
4	1	63	33	30	30
1	11	74	61	13	13
Totals		290	202	88	88
Average		58.0	40.4	17.6	17.6
# Tardy = 4					

Grinder Jim sees that in this example the SLACK Rule behaves very badly in average tardiness, lateness, completion time, and number of tardy jobs. This example has actually been set up to make the SLACK Rule behave badly. However, it illustrates its main defect: Long jobs tend to be favored to go first, which makes other jobs wait excessively until they too become tardy.

WTD HODGSON—An effective weighted version of Hodgson's for the static case is illustrated below.

Weighted Static Hodgson Heuristic

1. Order the list by EDD.
2. Find the first tardy job k.
3. Remove the job $1 <= j <= k$ with smallest w_j/p_j; repeat until k is removed or there is no tardy job.

4. Repeat steps 2 and 3 as necessary.

For the dynamic case we make the following modifications.

Weighted Dynamic Hodgson Heuristic.

1. Order the list by the dynamic dispatch EDD heuristic.
2. Find the first tardy job k.
3. For each job j up to that point, let p_{jk} be the amount by which removing j would reduce C_k.
4. Remove smallest w_j/p_{jk} etc.

The following remaining heuristics were all designed for the weighted tardiness objective. All give the priority as (w_j/p_j) times a slack factor, but differ in the form of the slack factor.

WTD CRITICAL RATIO—The critical ratio rule has been quite popular in practice. The weighted rule is S_j is the slack of job j.

$$\pi_j = (w_j/p_j)[1/(1 + (S_j/p_j)]$$

Note that the priority is a function of S_j. Figure 2-1 gives a plot with respect to $-S_j$. It has three limitations:

1. The priority continues to rise rapidly after the job is overdue (going to infinity by the time $S_j = -p_j$).
2. The priority goes down too slowly (there is still a noticeable priority at slacks of 5 to 10 times processing time).
3. Slack is normalized by the processing time of the job itself, rather than by the competitors.

WTD COVERT—The COVERT Rule was invented by Carroll [1965] for the job shop. The weighted one-machine COVERT Rule is:

$$\pi_j = (w_j/p_j)[1 - (S_j)^+/kp_j]^+$$

(The notation $[\ \ ]^+$ means "expression is unchanged if positive, changed to zero if negative." That is, $[\text{Lateness}]^+ = [\text{Tardiness}]$).

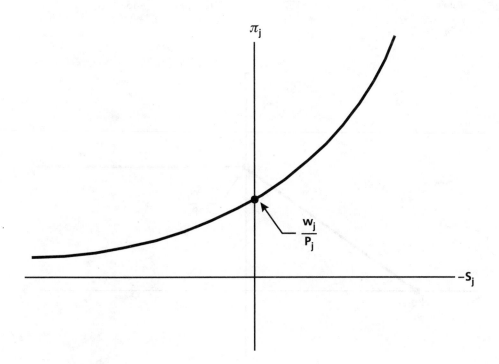

Figure 2-1

Priority versus –Slack for the Weighted Critical Ratio Heuristic

Note the parameter k, which makes the priority go down more slowly or more quickly. (It becomes zero at $S_j = kp_j$.) A typical value to be used might be $k = 2$ or 3 so that jobs having more than two or three times their processing time in slack would have zero priority. Figure 2-2 gives a plot with respect to $-S_j$.

R&M—Rachamadugu and Morton (see Morton and Pentico [1993]) developed the R&M heuristic in 1982 as a part of the early bottleneck dynamics methodology. It is similar to the weighted COVERT procedure, except that priority drops off more smoothly.

$$\pi_j = (w_j/p_j)[\exp\{-(S_j)^+/kp_{av}\}] \tag{1}$$

(p_{av} is the average processing time of the other jobs). A typical value of k for the static one-machine problem is $k = 2.0$. Figure 2-3 gives a plot of the priority as a function of $-S_j$. Intuitively, the formula for $k = 2$ may be explained as follows. If the slack is negative so the job is sure to be tardy, the job has full WSPT priority. If slack $= 2p_{av}$, then the priority is multiplied by $e^{-1} = 0.4$. If slack $= 4p_{av}$, then the slack is multiplied by $(0.4)^2 = 0.16$ and so on.

In testing on the one-machine problem, R&M has been found to be somewhat superior to WTD COVERT, basically because it is useful to give jobs some priority even though they have a lot of slack. (If only such jobs are available, we still want to know which is the better one to select.)

Similar heuristics for the job shop will be presented later. Rather than producing studies for the one-machine case, you may use the POMQuest software to gain experience on the relative merits of these heuristics.

Example 2-1, Part 7. Grinder Jim was interested that R&M seems to give consistently good results at low computational effort and asked to see the results of R&M on his problem.

Job #	Process	R&M Heuristic Completion	Due Date	Late	Tardy
4	1	1	33	−32	0
5	2	3	32	−29	0
3	31	34	31	3	3
1	11	45	61	−16	0
2	29	74	45	29	29
Totals		157	202	−45	32
Average		31.4	40.4	−9.0	6.4
#Tardy = 2					

Figure 2-2

Priority versus –Slack for the Weighted COVERT Ratio Heuristic

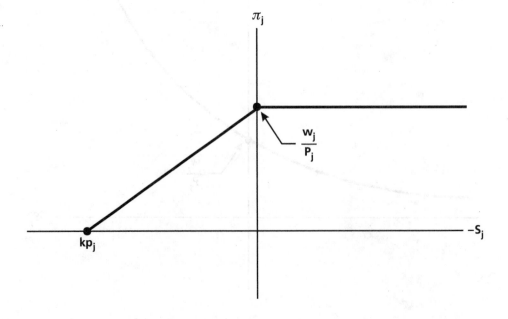

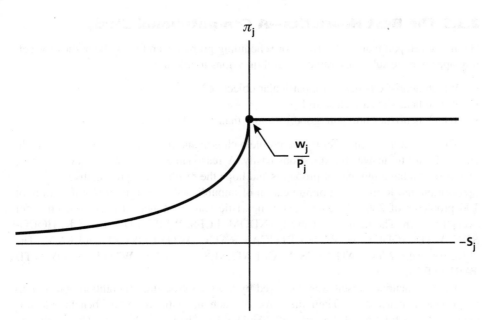

Figure 2-3

Priority versus –Slack for the R&M Heuristic

Thus, R&M with an average tardiness of 6.4 beats the second best tardiness of EDD, which was 6.6, by about 3 percent. R&M also has a much better flow time than competing low-tardiness heuristics.

Grinder Jim now decided he would likely use the R&M heuristic in the future, but wondered how far it was from the perfect or "optimal answer." He paid a student to get him the optimal answer by running it on an integer programming routine, which was possible due to the small size of the problem. (It is the fact that integer programming is not practical for large problems that makes heuristics important.)

Job #	Process	Optimal Schedule Completion	Due Date	Late	Tardy
3	31	31	31	0	0
5	2	33	32	1	1
4	1	34	33	1	1
1	11	45	61	–16	0
2	29	74	45	29	29
Totals		217	202	15	31
Average		43.4	40.4	3.0	6.2
# Tardy = 3					

The optimal solution has an average tardiness of 6.2, compared to 6.4 for R&M, a difference of about 3 percent. Notice also that it has a much higher average completion time and lateness. We show a comparison of the different heuristics on the problem in a summary table.

Heuristic	Schedule	Summary of Heuristics Average Completion	Average Tardiness	# Tardy
FCFS	1-2-3-4-5	53.6	24.2	3
SPT	4-5-1-2-3	27.0 best	8.6	1
EDD	3-5-4-2-1	47.0	6.6	4
SLACK	3-2-5-4-1	58.0	17.6	4
R&M	4-5-3-1-2	31.4	6.4 best	2
OPTIMAL	3-5-4-1-2	43.4	6.2	3

2.3.5 The Best Heuristics—A Computational Study

Having developed many objectives for scheduling problems and many heuristics for getting approximate solutions, rather natural questions to ask are:

- Which heuristic is best for a particular objective?
- Which heuristics are close to best?
- Which heuristics are quite good for more than one objective?

These answers often differ by the problem chosen and in most cases there is no mathematical way to answer the questions easily. A reasonable approach is to take average results over a large number of problems and hope the results are representative.

Morton and Ramnath (communication of unpublished study) in 1994 ran a study of 100 problems of 200 jobs each. Every heuristic was tried against every objective for every problem. The heuristics were RANDOM, FCFS, WSPT, EDD, SLACK, HODGSON, WTD HODGSON, WTD CRITICAL RATIO, WTD COVERT, and R&M. The objectives were WTD LATENESS, MAX LATENESS, # TARDY, WTD # TARDY, WTD TARDINESS.

The best heuristic result was improved by a search procedure (neighborhood search) to provide a benchmark. Then the error of each heuristic from the benchmark was expressed as a fraction of the error of RANDOM (a "bad" benchmark). The results are shown in Table 2-1.

a.   WSPT performed best for weighted lateness (and thus also for weighted flow) of the dispatch procedures (28 versus second place 40).
b.   EDD performed best for maximum lateness and thus also for maximum tardiness (11 versus second place 36).
c.   Hodgson's performed best for # tardy (13 versus second place 19).
d.   Weighted Hodgson's performed best for weighted # tardy (10 versus 19).
e.   R&M performed best for weighted tardiness (20 versus 26).

2.3.6 Foundations—Exercises

Problem Relaxations.

1.   Consider the problem of minimizing the function $f(x) = 12 - x + 0.25x^4$ subject to x being within 0.25 of an odd integer.

   a. Relax the problem to drop the "odd integer" constraint and solve the resulting problem using calculus.
   b. Roughly draw the function.
   c. Find the solution to the original problem and explain.

Table 2-1

Dynamic One-Machine
Computational Study

HEUR	WLATE	MLATE	#TARD	W#TARD	WTARD
RANDOM	100	100	100	100	100
FCFS	105	48	107	105	77
WSPT	**28**	230	83	52	40
EDD	106	**11**	107	104	58
SLACK	111	36	114	111	59
HODG	305	2897	**13**	19	4267
WHODG	297	2905	19	**10**	4136
WCRIT	112	78	117	115	73
WCOV	69	207	91	71	26
R&M	40	213	75	50	20

2. Consider the following heuristic for finding how many nails are needed for a new house: "*x.xx* pounds of nails per square foot of space times the square footage, times *yyy.y* nails per pound, rounded to the nearest nail, rounded up to the nearest package." To what extent is this like a relaxation process? To what extent is it not?

Objectives in Scheduling.

3. Consider the following seven-job problem with all arrival times 0, with processing times, job weights, and due dates for each one as shown.

Job j	1	2	3	4	5	6	7
p_j	8	8	6	4	2	6	8
w_j	2	2	2	2	1	1	1
d_j	10	10	16	20	12	12	25

Create any schedule with no preemption or idle time. Evaluate your schedule for each of the objectives we have discussed. Use the same weights for all objectives.

4. Consider your schedule in problem 3 and one of the objectives. Find any schedule which improves the value of that objective. Now repeat the exercise for each of the objectives.

5. Given a weighted tardiness objective, what methods could you use with your clients to try to figure out the appropriate weights?

Some Exact Results.

6. Eight jobs are to be carried out with a single resource. The weights, processing times, and due dates are given below.

Job	1	2	3	4	5	6	7	8
Weight	1	2	1.5	0.5	0.5	1.5	2	1
Process time	6	3	6	9	4	2	1	6
Due Date	32	25	20	15	25	10	5	35

Determine the ordering of the jobs to minimize:

a. Weighted flow time
b. Weighted lateness
c. Maximum lateness
d. Maximum tardiness
e. Fraction of jobs tardy
f. Makespan

7. Use the data of problem 6 but change the processing times to 7, 2, 7, 8, 5, 1, 2, and 5. (Add and subtract 1.)

a. Resolve problem 6 with the changed data.
b. How much are the solutions changed?
c. How much would it cost to erroneously use the solutions from problem 6 if the true data were as presented here?

8. A smithy makes custom glass objects in his shop and can make only one at a time. At the beginning of one 40-hour week, he finds that he has agreed to do six jobs that week. His assistant will make the deliveries, which take about one hour each. (We show promised delivery in terms of working hours into the future. Assume that projects can be left at the end of the day and started again the next day without much loss.)

Job	Hours Required	Promised Time
1	9.3	8
2	4.0	6
3	4.5	15
4	5.4	30
5	8.9	19
6	4.1	35

The smithy does not wish to weight the jobs. Determine the sequence in which he should perform the jobs in order to minimize:

a. Makespan
b. Mean unweighted flow time
c. Number of tardy jobs
d. Maximum lateness

9. In problem 8, suppose the smithy used the optimal solution for the number of tardy jobs, when actually he should have used the optimal solution for the mean unweighted flow time. What percentage penalty would this cost him?

Dynamic Dispatch Heuristics.

10. Use the data from problem 6. Find the best sequence you can to minimize weighted tardiness.

11. Using the data from problem 6 try the following heuristics to attempt to minimize weighted tardiness and find the percentage difference in each case from the solution you found in problem 10.

a. RANDOM
b. FCFS
c. WSPT
d. EDD
e. SLACK
f. R&M

12. In problem 8, find the best sequence you can to minimize unweighted tardiness and then compare it with R&M.

2.4 ONE-MACHINE SEQUENCING—MODERN METHODS

2.4.1 Neighborhood Search Methods

Overview. The computational effort required to exactly solve scheduling problems grows remarkably fast as problems grow larger. It is quite difficult for most of us to understand just *how* fast. There is an old story about the rajah who was very pleased with his advisor and offered him a large reward of the advisor's choosing. The clever man asked for one grain of rice on the first square of the chess board, two on the second, four on the third and so on. The rajah readily agreed. Now there would be roughly 0.5 million grains of rice on the twentieth square, which the rajah could handle. But there would be 1 million sets of 0.5 million grains of rice on the fortieth square, which would probably be very difficult to pay. Finally there would be 16 million sets of 0.5 trillion grains of rice on square 64, which is likely more than the world's production of rice over all the ages!

This shows us vividly the problem of exponential growth, which is shared by all exact methods, such as branch-and-bound. Neighborhood search is a rather general purpose heuristic technique which, if used thoughtfully, often produces very good results at practical computational costs. In its classic form, neighborhood search is very intensive (myopic); it just tries to improve the current solution as much as possible at each step. Modern versions of neighborhood search such as tabu search and simulated annealing mix intensification and diversification strategies.

We first discuss a rather simple manual (but computer assisted) approach to neighborhood search. Next we develop classical neighborhood search (with a modern twist or two). Finally we explore tabu search and simulated annealing.

Manual Search. The version of manual search that we are going to describe might better be called **computer assisted search**. First the user enters (or retrieves from problem storage) the data for the problem: objective function, number of jobs, individual jobs (job number, arrival date, due date, job weights). Suppose there are 12 jobs and the objective is weighted flow. Either the user or the computer enters an initial solution guess and the computer displays the objective for it. (All the data remains displayed to help the user make decisions, but we shall just show the current solution and objective.) Suppose the initial guess for the sequence is: 1-2-3-6-4-5-10-12-7-8-9-11 with objective 346. Perhaps the user feels that 10 should not have a very high priority and should come later in the sequence, giving: 1-2-3-6-4-5-12-10-7-8-9-11 with objective 342. Since the weighted flow has decreased, the user keeps moving 10 later, watching the answer as she does. She finds that the best place is next to the end: 1-2-3-6-4-5-12-7-8-9-11-10 gives 338, then 1-2-3-6-4-5-12-7-8-9-10-11 gives 336.

Next, she feels that since job 8 is due immediately, it should be moved forward. It seems to help to move it, but not before the first four jobs: 1-2-3-6-8-4-5-12-7-9-10-11 gives 287.

After more changes of this variety the user finally arrives at a sequence which she finds hard to improve: 3-2-1-6-8-4-5-9-7-12-10-11 gives 261.

The manual approach has the advantage of being under the complete control and understanding of the user. Of course, more automatic approaches better utilize the power of the computer.

Classic Neighborhood Search. In maximization problems, improving the solution a little bit at a time is called **hill climbing**. If we climb until all directions are "down" we might say we are at the top of the hill. This works well if there is only one hill; however, in practical scheduling problems there are usually many hills and some may be higher than the one we reach. (In scheduling we are usually minimizing, so that "hill climbing" should perhaps be "valley descending." We shall use the traditional term anyway.)

Classic neighborhood search climbs to the top of the hill and simply stops, even though we might not be on top of the right hill. Here we shall restrict ourselves to scheduling problems where the schedule is represented by a permutation of $1, 2, \ldots, n$.

Classic Neighborhood Search Procedure.

1. Choose a good starting solution (seed).
2. Look at all solutions close to the current solution (neighborhood).
3. If no such solution is superior, terminate.
4. Choose a better one as the new current solution.
5. Go back to step 2.

We look at these in turn.
Some methods of generating the neighborhood of a solution include:

1. **Adjacent pairwise interchange**—Suppose the current sequence is $1, 2, 3, \ldots n$. Then the neighborhood has $(n-1)$ solutions obtained by interchanging 1 and 2, interchanging 2 and 3, . . ., interchanging $(n-1)$ and n.
2. **General pairwise interchange**—Now we consider exchanging every possible pair, adjacent or not. Thus, there are $n(n-1)/2$ or on the order of n^2 choices.

This method is very expensive to use, especially for large n, but it is also more thorough.

3. **k-move**—A k-move considers moving any job up to k moves to the left or up to k moves to the right, or $(2k-1)n$ choices in all (there is duplication). k-moves are about as accurate as general pairwise interchange at about $(4k/n)$ the cost.

There are several choices on choosing the next solution.

a. Evaluate every solution in the neighborhood, and choose the best.
b. Take the first solution giving an improvement.
c. Find the 20 apparently best by an approximate method; exactly choose the best of these.

Example 2-2. We give a very small example here which is easy to do by hand. Consider three jobs in a static problem with weighted tardiness criteria.

Job j	p	d	w
1	1	4	1
2	2	2	1
3	3	3	1

There are three possible choices for the first job, two for the second job, and one for the third, or six total solutions. We choose adjacent pairwise interchange as our way of generating neighborhoods.

Suppose we take as our initial solution 1-3-2. We can work out the objective value for this solution in a table (or perhaps mentally):

Job j	p	d	C	L	T
1	1	4	1	−3	0
3	3	3	4	1	1
2	2	2	6	4	4
				Objective	5

As we work through the procedure, we will not show the details of calculating the objective for each solution. Also, we will abbreviate the situation above as 1-3-2 Value 5. Next we generate the neighborhood of 1-3-2. We can permute either the first and second, or the second and third, so the neighborhood always has two solutions: 3-1-2 Value 4, and 1-2-3 Value 4. Either is an improvement. Experience shows that the method of breaking a tie is not too important. Let us just choose the first, so that our new improved seed is 3-1-2 Value 4. The neighborhood of 3-1-2 is 1-3-2 Value 5 and 3-2-1 Value 5. Since no solution in the neighborhood can improve on our current solution, the method terminates at 3-1-2 Value 4. However, this is not optimal. The only one of the total of six solutions which we did not evaluate was 2-1-3 Value 3. If we use this instead as our starting solution, our neighborhood is 1-2-3 Value 4 and 2-3-1 Value 4. Thus, if we had started at 2-1-3 we would be starting at a better solution which was also a local optimum. Since there are only six possible solutions in our very small problem and the other five all have tardiness of 4 or more, 2-1-3 is in fact found to be optimal by *complete enumeration*. Note, however, that for a ten-job problem there would be 10! = 3,628,800 solutions to check and that for a 20-job problem there would be 20! = 2,432,902,008,176,640,000 solutions to check! Complete enumeration is not very practical.

Example 2-1, Part 8. Grinder Jim wondered in his problem whether neighborhood search added to the heuristics he already knew would be a sufficient improvement to be worth his effort. He learned and used the manual move routine in the software to evaluate schedules in the neighborhood of a given schedule. For his neighborhood method he decided to use adjacent pairwise interchange, to keep his calculations fairly manageable.

Iteration #1.

FCFS	Starting Solution	1-2-3-4-5	Value 24.2
	Neighborhood	2-1-3-4-5	24.2
		1-3-2-4-5	23.6
		1-2-4-3-5	18.2 *
		1-2-3-5-4	24.4

Iteration #2.

Better Solution	1-2-4-3-5	Value 18.2
Neighborhood	2-1-4-3-5	18.2
	1-4-2-3-5	16.6
	1-2-3-4-5	24.2
	1-2-4-5-3	12.4 *

Iteration #3.

Better Solution	1-2-4-5-3	Value 12.4
Neighborhood	2-1-4-5-3	12.4
	1-4-2-5-3	10.8 *
	1-2-5-4-3	12.6
	1-2-4-3-5	18.2

Iteration #4.

Better Solution	1-4-2-5-3	Value 10.8
Neighborhood	4-1-2-5-3	10.8
	1-2-4-5-3	12.4
	1-4-5-2-3	8.6 *
	1-4-2-3-5	16.6

Iteration #5.

Better Solution	1-4-5-2-3	Value 8.6
Neighborhood	4-1-5-2-3	8.6 *
	1-5-4-2-3	8.6 *
	1-4-2-5-3	10.8
	1-4-5-3-2	8.6 *

Thus, after five iterations, we terminate at the local optimum of 8.6 which is still 39 percent above optimum, but a real improvement over the original 290 percent! Grinder Jim tried the same calculations starting from the R&M initial solution:

Iteration #1.

R&M Starting Solution	4-5-3-1-2	Value 6.4
	5-4-3-1-2	6.4 *
	4-3-5-1-2	6.4 *
	4-5-1-3-2	8.6
	4-5-3-2-1	6.8

* means "best choice."

Thus, after one iteration, we terminate, already being at a local optimum. This result is typical of neighborhood search with an excellent start.

Grinder Jim made some other calculations which we do not report here in detail. He found that starting with the SLACK solution, neighborhood search required three iterations and obtained the optimum. He found that starting with EDD, neighborhood search required one iteration and obtained the optimum.

Tabu Search. The basic idea of tabu search, developed by Fred Glover, is quite simple. Why do we get caught at the top of the wrong hill? Because at that point all directions are down and we can't choose an improving step. How can this be fixed? Simple: always take the best move available, *even if this makes our solution a little worse.* Since we can't make our solution better right now (intensify), we might as well look around a little (diversify). Just in case we don't find anything better, however, we save our current solution as the *best to date*.

Now it is probably obvious that if we force ourselves down from the top of the hill, at the very next move neighborhood search will want to move us right back! The solution to this problem is to force ourselves to continue diversifying for a few moves. The approach that tabu search in its simplest form employs is to keep a list of our last m moves (Glover mentions $m = 7$) and not to allow them to be repeated while they remain on the list (they are currently "tabu"). Now there is no natural shopping rule, so we must now add a termination rule, such as 2000 iterations.

Example 2-1, Part 9. Grinder Jim wondered whether tabu search could noticeably improve his results for the R&M method and the SLACK method (adjacent pairwise interchange).

TABU SEARCH

Iteration #1.

R&M Starting Solution	4-5-3-1-2	Value 6.4
	5-4-3-1-2	6.4 *
	4-3-5-1-2	6.4
	4-5-1-3-2	8.6
	4-5-3-2-1	6.8

(We arbitrarily break ties by choosing the first minimal value obtained which is not tabu.) The best solution to date is then 5-4-3-1-2 Value 6.4. The solutions 4-5-3-1-2 and 5-4-3-1-2 are now tabu, so that neither will be chosen again.)

Iteration #2.

New Solution	5-4-3-1-2	Value 6.4
	4-5-3-1-2	6.4 Tabu
	5-3-4-1-2	6.4 *
	5-4-1-3-2	8.6
	5-4-3-2-1	6.8

Pick 5-3-4-1-2 instead of 4-5-3-1-2 because it is the best solution in the neighborhood which is not tabu. The best solution to date remains 6.4.

Iteration #3.

New Solution	5-3-4-1-2	Value 6.4
	3-5-4-1-2	6.2 Optimal
	5-4-3-1-2	6.4 Tabu
	5-3-1-4-2	8.6
	5-3-4-2-1	6.8

* means best choice

Thus, after three iterations, tabu search has improved R&M to the optimum. (Note that the method has no way of verifying that 6.2 is indeed optimal and it will continue searching for better solutions until told to quit.)

Simulated Annealing. Simulated annealing was developed in the process of studying annealing (heating, cooling, and recrystallization in metals) and hence has a different history than tabu search. Yet they are similar in modifying hill climbing or neighborhood search to avoid or escape local optima.

To understand annealing, suppose we are in neighborhood search, but that after evaluating all the possible solutions in the new neighborhood we do not always choose the apparent best move (the one giving the best value of the objective). Instead, we choose that best move with highest probability, the second best move with second highest probability, and so on. These probabilities go down according to the size of the improvement given by the move. (We do not give a more technical description of this point here.) The user can set a parameter k called the temperature. A high k causes a great deal of randomness and diversification. A low k gives little randomization and is thus similar to neighborhood search. Within a given search we could start with a high temperature to allow a lot of random exploration and then gradually lower the temperature to focus in on a local minimum. Then we could raise the temperature and start looking for another local minimum and so on.

Example 2-1, Part 10. By now thoroughly hooked, Grinder Jim wanted to know how simulated annealing would handle his problem. The following table gives summaries iteration by iteration, using the POMQuest software. (For illustrative simplicity we have left the temperature constant at $k = 1$).

ANNEALING TEMP=1	BEST SCHED	CUR VALUE	BEST VALUE
#1 FCFS	1-2-3-4-5	24.2	24.2
#2	1-2-4-3-5	18.2	18.2
#3	1-2-4-5-3	12.4	12.4
#4	1-4-2-5-3	10.8	10.8
#5	1-4-5-2-3	8.6	8.6
(skip)	. . .	. . .	. . .
#21	1-4-5-2-3	8.6	8.6
#22	5-4-3-1-2	6.4	6.4
#23	5-4-3-1-2	6.8	6.4
#24	5-4-3-1-2	6.4	6.4
#25	5-4-3-1-2	6.4	6.4
#26	5-4-3-1-2	6.8	6.4
#27	5-4-3-1-2	6.4	6.4
(skip)	. . .	. . .	. . .
#31	5-4-3-1-2	6.4	6.4
#32	3-5-4-1-2	6.2 Optimal	6.2

Simulated annealing took longer than tabu search to reach the minimum, primarily because it stayed at the local optima longer. It might be interesting to search with a higher temperature; for example a temperature of $k = 3$.

2.4.2 Tree Search Methods

Overview. Branch-and-bound (B&B) is a very general methodology for solving scheduling problems (and all sorts of other combinatorial problems). When computationally feasible, it is a very powerful method. Beam search and other partial enumeration methods are essentially approximate branch-and-bound methods for larger problems. The basic idea is to conceptualize the problem as a decision tree. From each decision choice point, called a **node**, for a partial solution (for example, which job to schedule last), there are a number of **branches**, one for each possible next decision (for example, which job to schedule next-to-last). Each branch leads to another node, which in turn branches for the next decision and so on. **Leaf nodes**, when all decisions have been made, represent complete solutions. If we compute the objective function for all the leaf nodes, the cheapest of these will be optimal. Of course, this will usually be far too expensive; we must limit the search. Branch-and-bound limits the search in an exact but expensive way; beam search uses an approximate but much less expensive method.

Branch-and-Bound. It is not our purpose to go very deeply into this method. Our purpose is just to give a good idea of how it works. There are two important variations:

    a.   Depth-first search
    b.   Best-first search

Example 2-1, Part 11. We will show how B&B works with our Grinder Jim example, using depth-first search. We repeat the problem data for convenience. Remember that the criterion is average (unweighted) tardiness per job.

Job j	p	d
1	11	61
2	29	45
3	31	31
4	1	33
5	2	32

We choose to make our decisions in reverse order, last job first, for reasons that will become clear. For the last job to be scheduled, we can choose 1, 2, 3, 4, or 5. Any job chosen last will finish at 74, so we can determine its tardiness. If Job 1 is chosen last it will have a tardiness of 13; so that the problem as a whole must have a tardiness of at least 13. Thus, any problem with last Job 1 will have an average tardiness of at least 13/5 = 2.6. This is called a **lower bound** for further branches in this part of the tree. Similarly, sequences ending in 2 have a lower bound of 29/5 = 5.8, those ending in 3 have a lower bound of 8.6, those ending in 4 have a lower bound of 8.2, and those ending in 5 have a lower bound of 8.4. We write the decisions to date in each node and write the lower bounds next to the nodes, as shown in Figure 2-4.

It is quite attractive for us to make further branching from node 1; on the other hand, it seems unattractive for us to branch from node 3, 4, or 5. To find the minimum tardiness for node 21 (last two jobs are 2 and 1, in that order), for example, we know that job 1 will finish at 74 and job 2 at 63 for a total known tardiness of 13 + 18 = 31, giving a lower bound on average tardiness of 6.2. We find 31 has a lower bound of 9.0, 41 of 8.6, and 51 of 8.8, as shown in Figure 2-5.

Our choice is now less obvious. The most interesting among our current branches is 21 with a lower bound of 6.2, but we have an older branch 2 with a lower bound of 5.8. This is where there are two main philosophies. In **depth-first search** we stay as deep as we can in the tree and so would pick 21. In **best-first search** we jump to the node which has the lowest lower bound (that we have not yet branched from) and hence we would choose node 2 with a lower bound of 5.8.

Here we are doing depth-first and branch on 21, giving 321 with a lower bound of 6.8, 421 with a lower bound of 6.4, and 521 with a lower bound of 6.6. Now 421 is the most promising; we branch on it to get 3421 with a bound of 6.8 and 5421 with a bound of 6.6. Branching on 5421 gives the solution 35421, with a solution value of 6.6.

Figure 2-4

Start of Branch & Bound
Decision Tree

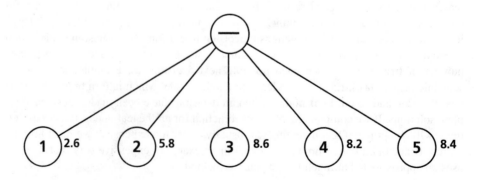

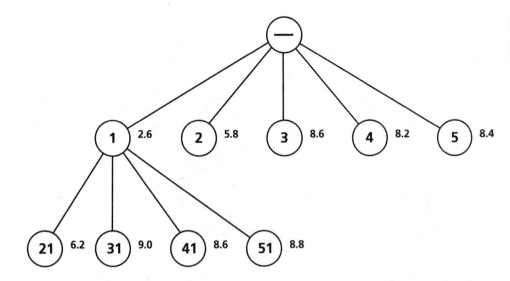

Figure 2-5

Continuation of Branch &
Bound Process

We can proceed through the tree and cross out all branches with lower bounds greater than or equal to 6.6. Since we have a full solution with value 6.6, we cross out 3421, 321, 521, 31, 41, 51, 3, 4, 5. The only node left to explore is 2. Expanding it gives 12 with a bound of 5.8, 32 with a bound of 8.6, 42 with a bound of 8.2, and 52 with a bound of 8.4. Again, the only node we can't yet cross off is 12. Expanding it gives 312 with a bound of 6.4, 412 with a bound of 6.0, and 512 with a bound of 6.2. All three of our new nodes are viable. We expand 412 into 3412 with a bound of 6.4 and 5412 with a bound of 6.2. Finally, we expand 5412 and get the solution 35412 with a value of 6.2. There are no viable remaining nodes to expand which could beat this. Thus, 35412 with a value of 6.2 is optimal. This is shown in Figure 2-6.

Depth-first search and best-first search differ only in their philosophy of which node to expand next. Perhaps we should give a little clearer statement.

Depth-First Search Algorithm

1. Choose the node at the greatest depth first and expand it.
2. At the same depth, choose the one with smallest lower bound.
3. Eliminate sub-problems with bounds above the current best solution.
4. Repeat until there are no sub-problems left to expand.

Best-First Search Algorithm

1. Always choose the node with smallest lower bound and expand it.
2. Eliminate sub-problems with bounds above the current best solution.
3. Repeat until there are no sub-problems left to expand.

In this particular problem, if we had always expanded the lowest bound node, we would have done less work. In general it is an open question as to which method works best and under what conditions.

Beam Search. The lower bounds we used in branch-and-bound give us one way of trying to estimate what is worthwhile. But they do not tell us the solution value to expect from pursuing a branch, only the very best we could hope for. Could we find a way to rather guess what to expect as the *likely* solution from that branch? If we could only know exactly the best solution value to expect from each branch at each stage, we could just keep picking the best branch going down the tree and end up exactly at the optimal solution! (This would be effort proportional to n rather than to $n!$.)

If we knew even fairly accurately how good a solution to expect from each branch at a node, we could take a chance and keep only the three branches with the best approxi-

Figure 2-6

Full-Depth First Branch &
Bound Solution

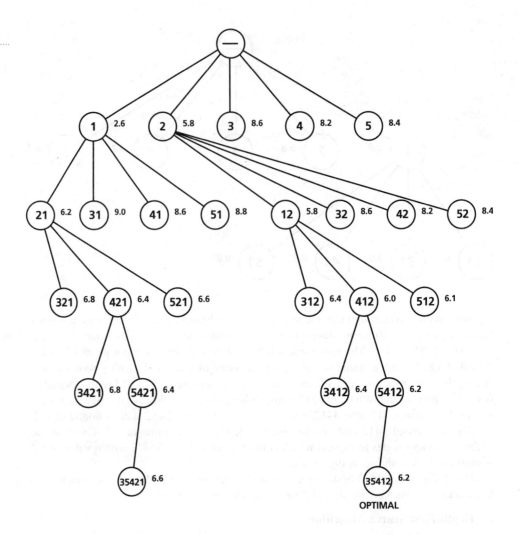

mate solution. Suppose we keep three at the first stage, in a five-job problem, which we expand to 12 (3×4) at the next level. Then again we keep the best three, which we expand to 9 (3×3) at the next level and so on. Of course, we could save more nodes for safety, or fewer for more speed. The number of nodes saved each time is called the **beam width** b. If there are n jobs, then the number of sub-problems considered is less than bn^2, a very practical size for modern computational speeds.

How do we give a good estimate of the value of the best solution starting from, say, node 54? This is really not too hard; we simply run any high-quality heuristic with the restriction "Jobs 5 and 4 at the end." We could use R&M giving 5 a priority of –100 and 4 a priority of –1000. R&M's running time is roughly proportional to the number of jobs. Thus, the total running time of beam search using R&M to estimate the solution values will be on the order of bn^3.

Although beam search is much faster than branch-and-bound for larger problems, it is still difficult to do by hand. The POMQuest software makes things much easier.

Example 2-1, Part 12. Let us look at Grinder Jim's problem once more to compare beam search with branch-and-bound. (The beam search software solves the problem forward: first choosing the first job, then the second and so forth. We stick to the backward method here to make easy comparison with the prior branch-and-bound result.)

In beam search, after we expand the first node we know the tardiness of the last job. Then we can run R&M, for example, for the rest of the problem. In this case our estimated likely cost if we put 1 last and scheduled perfectly otherwise is 2.6 (for job 1) + 5.2 (R&M

estimate of rest of jobs) = 7.8. Similarly, if we put 2 last our estimate is 5.8 + 0.8 = 6.6. If we put 3 last, our estimate is 8.6 + 0.0 = 8.6 (perfect estimate!). If we put 4 last, our estimate is 8.2 + 15.7 = 23.9. If we put 5 last, our estimate is 8.4 + 7.0 = 15.4.

If we trusted R&M perfectly, we would just put 2 last and proceed. However, we know there are errors, so we save nodes 1 and 2 and throw away the rest. On the next round, we expand to 21, 31, 41, 51, 12, 32, 42 and 52. Our two best choices will be 21 and 12. On the following round, we expand these to 321, 421, 521, 312, 412, and 512. We now get estimates of 6.2 for both 412 and 512 and throw away the other nodes. We finally obtain the optimal solution 35412 with a value of 6.2. This is illustrated in Figure 2-7.

2.4.3 Bottleneck Dynamics

Overview. Bottleneck dynamics is a new scheduling method based on supply and demand for the machine resource. One set of formulas estimates the time-varying value of extra capacity for each resource (basically a dual price). Essentially, the price which should be charged to a job desiring to use the machine is the cost of delaying all the other jobs already using the machine. Another set of formulas for each job estimates the value to that job of finishing earlier (which is the same as the delay cost to it of finishing later). It would be too complicated to develop these formulas here. But when specialized to the one-machine case and the weighted tardiness objective, this method gives the R&M formula, shown in equation (1). However, bottleneck dynamics is most powerful for more complicated multi-machine and multi-project problems and will be discussed in more detail later.

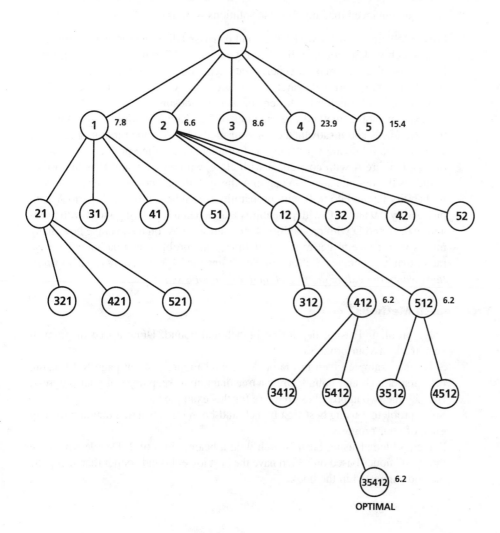

Figure 2-7
....
The Beam Search Solution

2.4.4 Modern Scheduling Exercises

Neighborhood Search Methods.

1. Consider the following scheduling problem with average tardiness objective.

Job j	p	d	w
1	1	1	2
2	6	8	4
3	3	9	8
4	9	12	1
5	7	18	5

    Solve this problem using:

    a. EDD (FCFS)
    b. WSPT
    c. Critical Ratio
    d. R&M with $k = 2.0$

2. Solve problem 1 using pairwise adjacent search with the following starting seeds:

    a. WSPT
    b. EDD
    c. R&M with $k = 2.0$

    Are you convinced that any of these solutions is optimal?

3. Solve problem 1 using a WSPT seed and pairwise adjacent search augmented by tabu search with a long tabu list. Limit yourself to 15 moves. What seems to be happening? Can you make a general statement about tabu search?

4. Sometimes neighborhood search results are improved by running the problem many times with randomly chosen seeds and choosing the best result. Suggest and explain another method you can think of for making multiple starts. What are the advantages and disadvantages of your method versus the random method?

5. Consider the following very simplified simulated annealing problem. The states of a system are A with cost 20, B with 30, C with cost 29, and D with cost 10 (which is the optimal state). When in A the system will choose to stay in A with probability 0.9 and go to B with probability 0.1. When in B it will go to A with probability 0.9 and to C with probability 0.1. When in C it will go to B with probability 0.01 and D with probability 0.99. Starting in A, on the average how many moves will it take to get to the optimum? (This problem is a pathological case rather than an average case for simulated annealing.) *Note: There are also situations where annealing does much better than tabu search.*

Tree Search Methods.

6. Solve problem 1 using depth-first branch-and-bound. Draw a tree diagram to keep track of your progress.

7. Solve the example given in the book (around Figure 2-4, on page S-40) using best-first branch-and-bound. Draw a tree diagram to keep track of your progress. How do the two approaches compare for this example?

8. Solve problem 1 using best-first branch-and-bound. Draw a tree diagram to keep track of your progress.

9. Solve problem 1 using beam search with a beam width of 2. Decide which are the "best" nodes based on which have the best lower bounds rather than using the method suggested in the book.

2.5 SUPER SCIENCE SERVERS—REPRISE

Dr. Gray spent three full days at Super Science Servers, talking extensively to Sue Slotnick and to several of the operators of the microscope and the assayer. He seemed especially interested in what sort of data was available on past arrivals, process times, flow times, and tardiness. He was a little disappointed to find that little of this information was available. He went back to Gray, Skize, Skize, and Skize's offices, did a little research and called Sue a few times on specific points which still weren't clear. Then he wrote a short report and set up a time to make a presentation to Sue and her staff.

"Thank you for taking the time to come and listen to me," Dr. Gray said. "I find that the tunneling microscope and the micro assayer pose rather different problems, so I would like to take them one at a time. First, the tunneling microscope: there seems to be general agreement that weighted flow is the appropriate objective. Thus, if the problem were deterministic and static, WSPT would be optimal, that is, schedule so that $w_1/p_1 > w_2/p_2 > w_3/p_3 > \ldots$. In the first place, the problem is not static; new jobs are arriving on an irregular basis. The standard procedure for such dynamic modifications is to apply a dynamic WSPT dispatch procedure. That is, choose the currently available job with the highest priority job by WSPT and schedule it. This is a good and robust procedure.

"Another important issue is the variability in the process times caused by the frequent machine breakdowns. I have made a little model here. Suppose the base processing time for job j is p_j and the probability of the machine breaking down is proportional to the processing time, that is, ap_j where a is a constant depending on the unreliability of the machine. Suppose each time the machine breaks down the average time to repair it is T. Then the total expected processing time for job j is $p_j + ap_jT = p_j(1 + aT)$. Thus, the expected processing times of all jobs are increased by a common factor and so if we use expected processing times, the relative priorities will not change. But as Baker [1974] points out, the WSPT rule is still correct if we put average (or good) processing times in the formula (static case is exact, dynamic case is a good approximation).

"Now what I have just said depends on the constant a being the same for all jobs. This is a good place to start, but we should begin keeping records of job types, base processing times, setup times, and breakdown frequencies and lengths. We should also keep careful records of prices and urgencies for various customers, so that eventually we can improve this model. For the moment, a very adequate course is simply to utilize dynamic WSPT with current weights and base processing times. Keep it simple (when possible)!

"Turning to the micro assayer, one of our main problems is determining an appropriate objective function. Both flow time and tardiness seem to be important. I have chosen weighted flow/tardy as the objective function, with the tardiness cost a fixed multiple M of the weighted flow cost:

$$\pi_j = [w_j/p_j][1 + M\exp\{-(S_j)^+/kp_{av}\}]$$

That is, this priority starts at the weighted flow value of w_j/p_j and increases to $(M + 1)$ times this as the due date is approached.

"Finally, the micro assayer has much the same issues of gathering data from now on for future improvements. I will not talk about them now, but they will appear in my written report."

CHAPTER 3

Multiple Machines Scheduling

3.1 INTRODUCTION

3.1.1 Overview

We have argued that a good way to solve scheduling problems is to break them down into sub-problems, such as one-machine and/or one-resource problems, and learn how to solve them. We have, in fact, learned a great deal about solving one-machine/resource problems in Scheduling Chapter 2.

Some types of multiple-machine problems are given by *flow* shops and *job* shops. Here the job has a chain of operations in series, which must be done on differing machines in a certain *route* through the shop. (Flow shops differ from job shops in that they have a single route for all jobs.) Here the technique we will learn is basically decomposition. We break the shop down into individual machines and correct for the effects of other machines through such variables as machine prices and job lead times. While earlier texts typically develop a separate theory for flow shops and job shops, we simply treat flow shops as a special case. However, there are some classic results for the special case of the static flow shop with makespan objective, which are presented in Appendix J.

Resource Aggregation Issues. Aggregation is a pervasive feature of our thinking process. For detail purposes we may think of days or even seconds, but for a larger view of history we need to think in terms of years or even centuries. The foreman thinks of individual workers, the scheduler in terms of crews, the CEO in terms of the size of the work force.

Aggregation is powerful in terms of letting us reason about a larger problem; however it almost always involves errors due to suppressing detail. This tradeoff is very critical. There are company presidents who are strictly "big picture" and those who "micro-manage." Before the advent of computers, fiber-optic networks, and communication satellites, all major decisions had to be made in a very aggregated fashion. Now it is often possible for the computer to consider the problem in a more detailed fashion, summarize the results, and communicate them across the country in a matter of minutes.

For this reason, many mathematical researchers into scheduling disdain aggregation entirely, on the expectation that the computer can arbitrarily solve huge detailed models and summarize the results meaningfully, all in a short time. The nature of scheduling models, however, is that exact solution of large problems will always elude us, no matter how large or fast our computer. We must continue to use an intelligent mixture of detailed models and aggregate models in scheduling.

In Sections 3.2 and 3.4 we consider a Company Application Scenario—a nuclear control rod shop at Exotic Metals Corporation. In Section 3.3 we present various heuristic methods for dealing with flow shops and job shops.

3.2 COMPANY APPLICATION SCENARIO—
NUCLEAR CONTROL ROD SHOP

Jack Nichols is the general manager of the Parkington Plant of the Exotic Metals Corporation, which is located in Bonnington, Kentucky. In the past few months he has been concerned that Bob Barkeley, the senior scheduler for the Nuclear Control Rod Shop within the Parkington Plant, is about to retire in two years. Barkeley, in conjunction with the superintendent of the shop and two manufacturing engineers, has scheduled the shop manually for over thirty-five years. Nichols worries that no one is trained to replace Barkeley and wonders if it is not time to put a more formal scheduling system in place.

The Nuclear Control Rod Shop produces precision zircalloy rods about 1.5 inches in diameter and 20 feet long for controlling nuclear reactions in reactors. The customer is another division of Exotic Metals located in Atlanta (Exotic Atomics). Rated at 15 million feet of control rods per year, the facility makes rods of several diameters, composing and finishing to close specifications and very tight standards. The application of the product demands high levels of performance due to safety considerations in reactors.

The manufacturing procedure is roughly as follows: Each incoming rod blank (2000 lb.) is **extruded** or **pilgered** four times. That is to say, the prototype rod is drawn through dies four times to slowly reduce the diameter and is cut into pieces repeatedly to produce about 475 four-pound tubes. (There is some scrap.) Each time the diameter is reduced the process is said to have made a **pass**. Such a pass consists of pilgering, then smoothing the ends, pickling the rod with acid to clean it, and tempering the rod in an annealing furnace to reduce the stresses induced by extrusion and produce the required mechanical properties. At the end of four passes there are final straightening and finishing steps. At various points in the process the rods have to undergo tests for chemical, mechanical, corrosive, and metallurgical characteristics.

Some of the scheduling complexities of this manufacturing procedure include: major and minor setups for the pilgers, the ability to use the same pilgers at different places in the process (in some cases), batch processing (annealing furnaces), and the ability to supplement furnace capacity with a second furnace. The full cycle time for the four passes and final finishing work is about 35 days. Due dates are rather soft since the shop maintains large lot-sizing inventories due to the high setups involved in pilger changeover. Order release to the floor is under the control of a committee composed of a high-level planner from the control rod shop and a similar planner from the nuclear plant in Atlanta.

In addition to his worries about replacing Barkeley, Mr. Nichols feels it is necessary to make major cuts in work-in-process (WIP). There has been a dictum from top management of Exotic Metals to implement JIT. This has been passed down as a simple statement to reduce WIP by 40 percent!

Details of the Problem. Jack Nichols talked to Ed Eastwood, the Vice-President of Manufacturing, and requested consulting assistance, preferably someone with some prior experience with the nuclear control rod shop. Ed pointed out that Dr. Bob Redwood in the corporation's operations research group had a good theoretical scheduling background and also four or five years of experience on several different shop floors in the corporation. He suggested that Bob investigate the nuclear control rod shop thoroughly, and after designing a fairly simple theoretical scheduling system, make a full set of presentations both to corporate and to the control rod shop. At this point they could decide whether to try to build a computerized scheduling system or to train a replacement scheduler, using the new insights. Jack Nichols thought this a good approach and so they went ahead.

After several weeks of living on the floor of the control rod shop and absorbing all he could from Barkeley and others, Bob Redwood made the following observations: All lots basically follow the same route, although some operations may choose among more than one machine and several operations utilize the same machine (annealing furnace). With a few exceptions, the process seems to be a complex flow shop (all jobs roughly following a single route), with compound operations (parallel machines) and reentrant machines (same machine for more than one operation).

The situation is shown in Figure 3-1. In the diagram, (a) emphasizes the flow shop structure, while (b) emphasizes the reentrant problem (multiple flows to the furnace). As a flow line, there are four passes in series with the first three passes having three compound machines in series, the last pass having just pilgering. Each pass except the last has the same sequence:

1. **Pilger.** Extrude rod and cut. A pilger stage consists of multiple pilgers in parallel. Pilgers have minor setups for the same rod family and major setups for a different family.
2. **Clean/Debur.** Remove dirt, acid bath for final cleaning, remove tailings from cut. This is not a bottleneck; treat it as a fixed delay for a stage (no waiting).
3. **Annealing.** Heat to restore crystalline structure. This employs the batch process: up to 12 lots, which must be of the same family, are annealed at once. Usually one furnace serves everything (reentrant). Compatible lots from different passes can be annealed together.

Figure 3-1

Two Schematics of the
Control Rod Process

(a) Flow Shop Structure

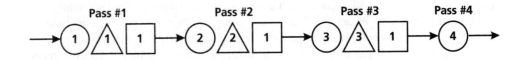

(b) Job Shop Structure

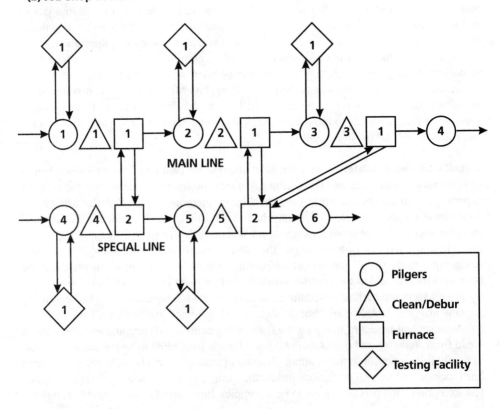

First pass pilgering requires about four hours; there are two dedicated pilgers. The second pass takes about six hours, using two to four pilgers. The third pass takes 15 hours and uses four pilgers, although extras can be brought in as needed. The fourth pass takes 55 hours and uses 10 to 12 pilgers.

The main annealing furnace usually does the mainline products for all passes. It handles four lots minimum and 12 lots maximum per batch and requires 9.5 to 15 hours a batch.

The backup furnace has been used in an entirely separate flow line for special products such as Matte orders, which require separate handling. This is an older furnace with different procedures and 20 hours average processing time. It has excess capacity, but management has resisted using the backup furnace for the mainline products, citing the longer processing time, quality questions, and difficulty in having enough product to fill the furnace.

Bob Redwood received feedback on his description of the shop, which allowed him to make a few corrections and improvements. He then went back to corporate headquarters to first make a capacity analysis to pinpoint the bottlenecks in the control rod floor setup, then design a scheduling system approach and return to make another presentation in a month. If his approach proved acceptable to management, he would design an interactive scheduling system. Actually building and implementing the resulting system would require the support of an outside software house.

3.3 FLOW AND JOB SHOPS

3.3.1 Overview

Both flow shops and job shops have multiple machines. In a flow shop, all jobs follow the same routing (sequence of machines) through the shop. In a job shop there may be many routings. A job shop may be "nearly" a flow shop if there are only a few similar routes, or if aggregating clusters of machines would produce a flow shop, and so on. Flow shops are easier to work with in terms of practical modeling, however the same heuristics work for both and we treat them together, simply using the term "job shop."

Classic job shops have restrictive definitions for computational reasons. All jobs and machines are available at time zero (static). Each job has a number of operations less than or equal to the number of machines. The operations are performed in strict serial order on a unique machine in each case.

Classic Job Shop Notation, Charts, and Graphs. A job shop has m machines, indexed by k, all available at time 0, each of which has some flexibility as to type of operation, but can do only one operation at a time. At time zero the n jobs, indexed by j, are all available. Job j consists of q_j operations in series, indexed by i. To specify the problem we must give an input table of p_{ji}, the processing time of operation i of job j, (see Table 3-1). If the operation is implicit, p_{jk} may be used as a shorthand for the processing time of job j on machine k. We also must specify k_{ji}, the machine on which operation i of job j is to be run, as shown in Table 3-2.

Table 3-1

Example of Processing Times

		Operation		
		1	**2**	**3**
	1	4	3	2
Job	2	1	4	4
	3	3	2	3
	4	3	3	1

Table 3-2

Example of Machine Routing

		Operation		
		1	**2**	**3**
	1	1	2	3
Job	2	2	1	3
	3	3	2	1
	4	2	3	1

The constraints for assigning an activity or operation to start are:

a. The job's previous operation must have finished.
b. The machine must be free.
c. The job must have top priority among those available.

Going back to our example, it is important to understand that small to middle-sized problems are often better understood using one or more kinds of Gantt charts. The horizontal axis represents time and there are several horizontal bars. In a machine Gantt chart, each bar represents a machine; in a job Gantt chart, each bar represents a job. In these figures the operation code is as follows: the first digit is the job number, the second the operation number, and the third, the machine; that is, algebraically, *jik*. A feasible schedule must not schedule two jobs on the same machine at the same time; it must also not schedule an operation before its predecessor is finished.

We illustrate Gantt charts for a feasible solution our example in Figures 3-2 and 3-3. Figure 3-2 shows this schedule in terms of what time the various jobs are on the given machine, while Figure 3-3 shows at what times the operations of a given job are processed.

(You will be asked to explain why this schedule is feasible in the exercises.) Of course, we have shown only one possible schedule for this problem. We could tighten up this schedule by moving things to the left as far as possible. To do better, we would have to have an objective function to tell us how good a solution is. Then we have to specify procedures to get very good solutions among feasible ones, either exactly or by heuristics.

3.3.2 Dispatch Heuristics

One-Pass Dispatch Heuristics. With simple dispatch heuristics, we always schedule an empty machine whenever there are one or more jobs available, using the highest priority job.

Static priorities may be calculated for all time in advance. Examples include earliest global due date, first job in the shop, or highest job weight.

Dynamic priorities must be calculated each time a job is chosen. Examples here include R&M, COVERT, and least slack.

Local priorities depend only on the situation at the current machine. An example is SPT.

Figure 3-2

Machine Gantt Chart

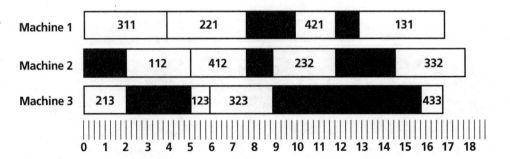

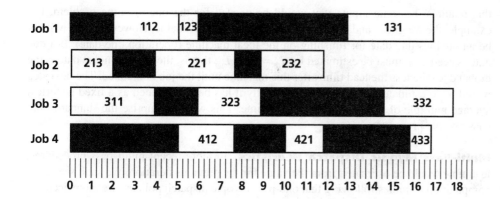

Figure 3-3

Job Gantt Chart

Forecast priorities depend on both the situation at the local machine and on a forecast of the job's remaining experience. Examples for this are Critical Ratio, COVERT, and R&M.

Although we have listed many of these rules elsewhere and many have primarily historical interest, it will be useful to list many of them in Table 3-3. (We define only new ones here.)

One-Pass Myopic Dispatch Heuristics. Myopic procedures are high quality one-pass dispatch heuristics that make the decision at each machine to optimize (or approximately optimize) the one-machine problem for the appropriate objective function. To do

Table 3-3

Job Shop Dispatch Heuristics

RANDOM	Random choice
FCFS	First come to the machine, first served
FASFS	First arrival at shop, first served (smallest r_j)
WSPT	Weighted shortest processing time
LWKR	Least work remaining (sum of remaining process time)
WLWKR	Weight divided by LWKR
TWORK	LWKR before any processing (total work)
WTWORK	Weight divided by TWORK
FOFO	First off first on. Put a job on the machine that can finish it first (not dispatch; a routing rule).
EDD	Earliest global due date
ODD	Operation due date
ODDC	Operation due date from common artificial due date
MST	Minimum slack time
S/OPN	Minimum slack time per remaining operation
AWINQ	Anticipated work in next queue. Highest priority goes to the job whose next machine is short of work (similar to bottleneck dynamics).
WTDCOVERT, R&M	Weighted tardiness heuristics (see Section 2.3.4).

this requires the same inputs that would be needed for the one-machine problem. For example, the weight w_j and local processing time p_{jk} are available. However, there will not be an obvious due date for finishing on the local machine (operation due date). If a due date is needed, it must be estimated by $d_{jk} = d_j - LT_{jk}$; that is, the operation due date is the global due date less the lead time after this machine until the job is finished. The next step would be to estimate the lead time. Classically it has been estimated as a fixed historical average multiple of the remaining process time. This would comprise the standard one-pass myopic procedure.

Multi-Pass Myopic Dispatch Heuristics. In more recent multi-pass procedures, lead time would be estimated from the value for the previous iteration. We shall see in the computational studies following that one-pass myopic dispatch policies are more accurate than other one-pass dispatch policies and that multi-pass myopic dispatch policies are even more accurate.

3.3.3 Bottleneck Dynamics

We sketch the extension of bottleneck dynamics (BD) to the job shop case very briefly. Bottleneck dynamics estimates relative priorities for various activities at a machine in terms of a benefit/cost analysis for each such activity. These priorities are estimated dynamically in a sophisticated fashion, considering both current and future shop congestion. In order to do this, BD must do all of the following:

1. Estimate the value of resources a given job must use to finish in terms of current congestion.
2. Combine these properly to estimate the implicit *cost* of giving this job priority among those waiting.
3. Estimate the implicit *benefit* of expediting the job in terms of its current value and expected lateness.

More specifically:

1. The appropriate current price of using a machine is estimated from queuing approximations.
2. The remaining cost of finishing the job is then estimated by $\sum_{m=i,M} R_{k(m)} p_{jk(m)}$; that is, the sum of the price times the processing time on each remaining machine. Any dispatch which includes the term (w_j/p_j) in its priority formula can be improved by replacing it by $w_j/\sum_{m=i,M} R_{k(m)} p_{jk(m)}$.
3. The value of expediting the job is the product of its weight w_j and a measure of urgency depending on its current slackness, which depends on its estimated remaining lead time through the shop.
4. The lead time can be estimated by simulating the shop several times to get improving estimates.

We discuss the lead time estimation idea in more detail.

Lead Time Estimation. A number of heuristics are based on a job's slack; that is, how much the job would finish before its due date if expedited. For the one-machine problem, the slack is known, simply as $S_j = d_j - p_j - t$. However, in a flow shop or a job shop, it is not enough to subtract process time on this machine from the time left. We must also subtract likely waiting time and process time on remaining machines, which we call $S_{jk} = d_j - p_{jk} - LT_{jk} - t$. Or in words, "The slack of job j waiting in the line for machine k is its due date, less its processing time on the current machine, less its lead time, less the current time."

Lead Time Iteration.

1. Choose any initial estimate of lead times (e.g., $LT_{jk}(0) = 0$).
2. Perform a dispatch simulation using some heuristic procedure.
3. Record the objective function obtained, $F(n)$ for iteration n.
4. Record actual (ex post) lead times, $LT_{jk}(n)$ for iteration n.
5. If the termination* condition is satisfied, go to step 7.
6. Go to step 2.
7. Report the objective value and scheduling policy for the iteration giving the best value of the objective function.

*(For example, five iterations since new best solution obtained.)

We do not have the space to develop this important new methodology further here. A full development is given in *Heuristic Scheduling Systems*, by Morton and Pentico [1993].

3.3.4 Search Methods

There are many other multi-pass methods besides lead time iteration and bottleneck dynamics. All of these methods try to get better answers by generating many solutions instead of one, usually at the expense of much increased computation time. Neighborhood search methods, including tabu search and simulated annealing, start with a good solution and progressively improve it. Both standard beam search and neighborhood search are usually prohibitively expensive in the job shop environment, since about half of a full simulation of the problem is necessary to evaluate a single interchange. Here we will discuss important exceptions, including the makespan objective.

Neighborhood/Tabu/Annealing Search. Neighborhood search methods (tabu search and simulated annealing are really just variations) are less practical for flow shops than single-machine problems and are less practical for job shops than flow shops. The basic reason is that neighborhood search works with complete solutions. From a given full solution, we compute the value of moving to a number of nearby complete solutions. If any improves the solution, we take that as our new base case and so on. This procedure is inherently more difficult for job shops, since the computational cost of trying out a local move is about one half a full simulation of the job shop. There are several exceptions to this:

a. Restriction to simple types of policies
b. Restriction to makespan objective
c. Faster estimation (as opposed to computation) of move cost

Neighborhood search is comparatively practical for the flow shop if we consider only permutation sequences. There are then only as many permutations as for a one-machine problem, although each is more expensive to evaluate. The analogous case for the job shop would be to consider only dispatch permutation sequences. In this discipline, a permutation sequence determines a global priority rule: no matter what the machine, job a has priority over job b, which has priority over job c. Now there are no more possible permutations than for the one-machine case; however, each move requires on average one half simulation of the full job shop, which becomes much more expensive. Small shops can probably still use the method.

For the makespan criterion, the cost of evaluating a move can be reduced to solving a shortest path problem, for which extremely fast algorithms are available. For makespan some effective tabu/annealing methods have been created. (See the computational studies in Section 3.3.5.) For other criteria, the best hope is to find much faster methods to exactly or approximately calculate the effect of a pairwise interchange in a job shop.

3.3.5 Computational Studies

In this section we discuss simulation studies to evaluate various kinds of heuristics in a number of different job shop settings. First we present classic simple dispatch studies developed by Conway [1967] and Carroll [1965] for the average flow and average tardiness objectives. Next we give more recent iterated myopic dispatch studies attributed to Vepsalainen and Morton [1987, 1988] for the weighted tardiness problem. Next, we briefly review a number of new studies on the makespan problem by Adams, Balas, and Zawack [1988], Van Laarhoven, Aarts, and Lenstra [1992], and Dell'Amico and Trubian [1991]. In the final section we present a number of bottleneck dynamics studies by Morton, Kekre, Lawrence, and Rajagopalan [1988], and unpublished studies by Morton and Lawrence in 1994 and Narayan, Morton, and Ramnath in 1994.

Classic Dispatch Studies.

Average Flow. Flow objectives were studied thoroughly in the 1960s and 1970s due to the fact that myopic dispatch policies (SPT or WSPT) are so simple and robust and do not need lead time iteration. However, these early studies used mostly rather bland shops with nearly equal and static load on machines, so that conditions favorable to bottleneck methods were not really tested.

Conway [1967] performed a rather elaborate study with the average flow objective. There were nine machines and about 9000 jobs were simulated using 30 different rules. Table 3-4 reports part of the results of this study. (The table reports average WIP instead of average flow; however, these differ only by a constant factor.)

Note that SPT is by far the best rule tested. It is not a coincidence since SPT is known to provide the optimal solution for the static one-machine problem. This is called a **myopic** rule; we have argued that iterated myopic rules are very robust in the job shop. There is no need for iteration here, since the rule does not use estimates of due dates, slacks, or prices.

The second best rule, AWINQ, has some similarities to a modern bottleneck dynamics rule, since it rewards jobs for which the next machine has a low workload. Bottleneck dynamics, on the other hand, also takes into account the work content on other future machines, as well as the job's work content on these machines. We shall see later that bottleneck dynamics is able to make further improvements over SPT. Conway was also able to get improvements over SPT by taking weighted combinations of SPT and LWKR or SPT and AWINQ. These combinations are also somewhat similar to bottleneck dynamics in spirit.

Average Tardiness. Carroll [1965] first studied the mean tardiness objective to test his COVERT heuristic that was described in Section 2.3.4. His priority function for the unweighted case is $\pi_{jk} = [1/p_{jk}][1 - S_{jk}{}^+/hLT_{jk}]^+$. The first term is the SPT rule. The second term discounts the priority if the job has a large slack compared to the estimated lead time. The larger the h, the larger the slack must be to lower the priority. Table 3-5 shows his results for a job shop with eight machines operating at 80 percent utilization.

It is clear from the table that COVERT was by far the best rule tested and that COVERT can be fine tuned by adjusting the rate of decay of the priority function using

Table 3-4

Performance of Simple Dispatch Rules for Average Flow

Rule		WIP
FCFS	first come to the machine	58.9
FASFS	first arrival in shop	57.5
LWKR	least work remaining	47.5
AWINQ	least work in next queue	34.0
SPT	shortest processing time	23.2

Rule		Av. Tardiness
FCFS	first to machine	36.6
FASFS	first in shop	24.7
S/OPN	slack per remaining operation	16.2
SPT	shortest operation first	11.3
TSPT	truncated SPT	4.6
COVERT	$h = 1.0$	2.5
COVERT	$h = 0.5$	1.4

Table 3-5

Comparison of Simple Dispatch Rules for Average Tardiness

the h parameter. SPT is good on the average because it is good in getting the average job through the shop quickly. However, a long operation arriving when a machine is busy can wait a very long time and thus become tardy, which hurts SPT. TSPT is a modification which expedites the long job when it has waited "too long." This produces a rule which is a decent competitor with COVERT. We turn next to more modern rules which can improve on COVERT.

Iterated Myopic Study.

Weighted Tardiness. Vepsalainen and Morton [1987, 1988] carried out myopic dispatch studies with lead time iteration for weighted tardiness, both for the flow shop and for the job shop, reported here. They considered both COVERT (corrected for the weighted tardiness case) and R&M as likely candidates for the myopic heuristic, since both have rather similar performance for the one-machine case and dominate any other simple dispatch heuristics. They also considered both heuristics with and without lead time iteration. Without lead time iteration, lead times were estimated as a fairly carefully estimated average multiple of remaining process time. (This careful estimation would be unlikely to be carried out in practice and thus the benefits of LTI are likely understated.) The study also considered a formula method for estimating the lead time as a function of shop load; however, the results were inconclusive and have not been reported here. FCFS, EDD, S/OP, and WSPT have been included as benchmarks.

In Table 3-6 six separate shop loads are shown: 80 percent, 90 percent, and 97 percent utilization and loose (*L*) or tight (*T*) due dates. Three types of shops are averaged together in this table: a uniform shop, a shop with correlated operation sizes in a job, and a shop with bottlenecks.

Notice that none of the benchmarks is competitive, although WSPT does well in high utilization tight due date situations, as would be predicted. It still averages almost 100 percent more weighted tardiness than WCOV or R&M. For both, WCOV and R&M lead time iteration saves about 7 or 8 percent. In addition, R&M with iteration saves about 4 percent in addition over WCOV with iteration. It must be remembered that this study was performed before bottleneck dynamics was fully developed. We will see that BD can dramatically improve on these results.

Rule		(Table Value is Weighted Tardiness)						
		80-L	80-T	90-L	90-T	97-L	97-T	AV.
FCFS	first to machine	0.28	0.76	1.17	2.33	3.39	5.98	2.318
EDD	early due date	0.02	0.35	0.20	1.66	1.90	4.47	1.433
S/OP	slack/operation	0.02	0.27	0.08	1.59	1.50	4.06	1.253
WSPT	weighted SPT	0.11	0.25	0.35	0.56	0.71	1.08	0.510
WCOV	weighted COVERT	0.02	0.10	0.06	0.34	0.29	0.78	0.265
R&M	exponential decay	0.02	0.10	0.05	0.33	0.29	0.75	0.257
WCOVL	iterated WCOV	0.01	0.09	0.05	0.31	0.29	0.73	0.247
R&ML	iterated R&M	0.01	0.08	0.04	0.29	0.27	0.73	0.237

Table 3-6

Comparing Iterated Myopic Methods for the Weighted Tardiness Job Shop

It is also interesting to ask "How robust are these results?" How would these heuristics perform if the true objective were somewhat different? As an example, if the true objective were percentage of tardy jobs, a manager might accept a weighted tardiness objective without thinking much about it. How much harm would be done? Table 3-7 compares some weighted tardiness heuristics.

In this case WSPT tends to look quite good, since it puts long jobs to the end, which is roughly what the myopic Hodgson's rule would have done. In fact, WCOV is only about 1 percent better than WSPT, which does especially well in high utilization, high tardiness cases. The effect of lead time iteration is now about 4 to 7 percent (down from 7 to 8 percent previously). Finally, R&M with iteration is now a full 25 percent cheaper than WCOV with iteration. A likely problem for COVERT is that it assigns 0 priority to jobs with a certain amount of slack, while it should still place longer jobs last.

Recent Makespan Studies.

Overview. In this section we present a number of high computation, high accuracy job shop studies for the makespan objective function. It is no coincidence that almost all high cost/high accuracy studies of the job shop are for the makespan objective. The special structure of the makespan objective makes this possible in several ways:

a. There is a fast, exact myopic solution for the one-machine dynamic makespan problem developed by Carlier [1982].
b. Simulations of the effect of a pairwise interchange may be reduced to solving a longest path algorithm, for which there are very efficient algorithms.
c. Bottleneck machines and bottleneck jobs may be more sharply defined.

Shifting Bottleneck. The shifting bottleneck method put forth by Adams, Balas, and Zawack [1988] (ABZ) involves successively improving an estimate of the bottleneck machine or machines by solving successive one-machine problems by Carlier's algorithm. The basic shifting bottleneck algorithm, called SB-I, is fast and quite accurate. It has the nice property that in many easy cases it can verify that the solution is optimal. If not, there is a more demanding procedure called SB-II, something like beam search, which the user can use in addition if desired.

ABZ then conducted a study to test the method. As their first benchmark they took eight classic heuristics from the literature, ran all eight and reported the best solution as "best of eight dispatch," or 8DISP. As their second benchmark they ran a randomized heuristic (RDISP) which decided which dispatch heuristic to use randomly at each position, setting probabilities proportional to their priorities. They then ran SB-I. If optimality was guaranteed, they stopped, otherwise they ran SB-II.

They ran 40 test problems, mostly with 5 or 10 machines and 10 to 30 jobs. The shop was static and machines were uniformly chosen. Using the intensive SB-II as the standard, the average excess cost of each alternative was 8DISP 9.7 percent, RDISP 5.8 percent, SB-I 2.3 percent, and SB-II 0 percent. In terms of computational cost, SB-I was about the same as 8DISP, RDISP took 33 times as long and SB-II took only 16 times as long.

Table 3-7

Comparing Some Weighted Tardiness Heuristics if True Objective Is Percentage of Tardy Jobs

	(Table Value is Percent of Tardy Jobs)						
Rule	**80-L**	**80-T**	**90-L**	**90-T**	**97-L**	**97-T**	**AV.**
FCFS	16.5	36.8	34.3	60.9	52.3	76.4	46.2
EDD	5.1	31.4	20.4	67.2	51.0	80.5	42.6
S/OP	5.3	36.1	19.7	74.5	54.2	85.1	45.8
WSPT	12.7	24.3	20.1	32.1	24.1	36.8	25.0
WCOV	6.7	22.4	15.2	40.0	25.7	44.3	24.7
R&M	4.3	18.4	8.6	30.2	18.8	35.4	19.3
WCOVL	5.0	22.4	12.9	35.4	24.8	37.8	23.1
R&ML	3.7	17.2	8.2	29.0	17.8	35.1	18.5

While the shifting bottleneck method is clearly a serious contender for makespan, this particular study has some limitations:

   a. 8DISP and RDISP are not state-of-the-art dispatch rules for a benchmark. Operation due date (with common due date) with lead time iteration is the appropriate myopic dispatch rule.
   b. The static uniform job set limits the generalizability of the results.

Simulated Annealing. Van Laarhoven, Aarts, and Lenstra [1992] (VLAL) have applied simulated annealing to the job shop problem. It is important not to try all pairwise interchanges from a given position since there are about mn of them and evaluating each is fairly expensive. They prove a number of important results, such as the fact that two jobs, neither on the current critical path, do not need to be considered for interchange. Many of the remaining evaluations can be screened by an approximate evaluation and the remainder by a fast longest path evaluation.

Remember that simulated annealing has a "temperature" setting. At high temperature the procedure explores a lot and hence is rather unstable. At low temperatures it is stable, but moves to correct mistakes slowly. VLAL compared their procedure with the fancier ABZ procedure SB-II on the same 40 problems tried by ABZ and discussed above, except that they restricted their attention to "hard" problems which SB-I did not solve exactly. VLAL ran their procedure five times and took the best result. At a temperature where simulated annealing repeated five times and took about as long as SB-II, they did about as well. When they repeated at a low temperature, they took about five times as long as SB-II, but improved ABZ results by about 1 to 3 percent.

Thus, simulated annealing would seem to qualify as an intensive computational procedure for makespan that is about as effective as the shifting bottleneck method. (After all, SB-II could have been run five times as long also!) Both methods are undoubtedly being improved, so it is an open question which will be faster eventually. It is also an open question whether either would be computationally feasible for realistically large problems, such as a dynamic shop with 40 machines and 200 jobs.

Tabu Search. Dell'Amico and Trubian [1991] have recently developed a strong tabu search approach to the job shop makespan problem. It seems to outperform both the shifting bottleneck method and simulated annealing at this point. There are perhaps four main issues in designing a tabu search algorithm:

   1. A good initial heuristic for a starting solution
   2. A randomizing procedure to allow multiple runs
   3. Working with small neighborhoods and efficient computation
   4. Other technical issues

Initial Heuristic. The algorithm used a hand-crafted heuristic which schedules part of the operations forward in time and part backward in time. (The heuristic is interesting, but other strong candidates such as SB-I or iterated ODDC could have been considered.)

Randomized Starting Points. At points within the algorithm the routine becomes blocked and the deadlock is broken randomly. Thus, rerunning the routine produces different answers. (Again, more systematic randomization might have been considered.)

Small Neighborhoods, Efficient Interchanges. Dell'Amico and Trubian use all the basic methodology developed by VLAL for simulated annealing. In addition, they sharpen those results in several ways.

Technical Issues. Some of the technical issues, which we do not discuss, include rules for changing the tabu list length, rules for removing items from the tabu list, restarting from the current best solution if the current direction seems unpromising, and when to terminate the search.

In Table 3-8 we show the results for five individual problems (ABZ5 to ABZ9) for which comparisons could be made between tabu search and the shifting bottleneck method. The first two columns show the number of jobs and the number of machines, respectively. The third column shows the best result known from the literature, using very high computational methods. For the first two problems, this is the optimal solution and for the last three it is the best lower bound known. The next four columns show the percentage that a given heuristic is above the best known heuristic, for the basic shifting bottleneck method (SB-I), the advanced shifting bottleneck method (SB-II), tabu search with a single try (TS-1), and tabu search with five tries (TS-5).

Tabu search gives disappointingly little improvement for five times the effort, so we do not discuss TS-5 further. SB-I, while very fast, does very badly on the harder problems. Thus, we compare SB-II with TS-1, which seem to be the best representatives of each method. As it happens, SB-II and TS-1 required similar amounts of computation times, so the comparison is especially easy. For the two easy problems both methods are very accurate; however on the three difficult problems, TS-1 is far superior. It thus seems the method of choice at the moment, although both methods are undoubtedly being improved and it is difficult to forecast this competition.

Bottleneck Dynamics Studies.

Job Shops with Release Times. Morton, Kekre, Lawrence, and Rajagopalan [1988] first developed an early version of bottleneck dynamics, called SCHED-STAR. It used repeated simulation to iterate slacks and prices by a post-iteration analysis. However, the methods used to calculate both prices and priorities have been improved since that time.

In their study, the authors used a net present value (NPV) objective which was somewhat similar to an early-tardy objective. The decision process chosen was twofold:

  a. Choose a release time for the job (to avoid earliness).
  b. Prioritize the job and schedule as usual.

The experimental design was quite complex, involving five shop types, six shop load levels, and 40 replications, for 1200 problems. The dispatch heuristics compared were:

  a. Critical Ratio—CR
  b. Weighted Covert—WCOVERT
  c. (Ow/Morton) Early/Tardy—E/T
  d. Bottleneck Dynamics—SCHED-STAR

The types of shops which were investigated were (5 machines):

  a. Single machine
  b. Smooth flow shop
  c. General flow shop
  d. Ordinary job shop
  e. Bottleneck job shop

E/T and SCHED-STAR have their own internal methods for setting the due date (when priority goes from negative to positive). Critical ratio and WCOVERT were given three choices for release heuristics:

Table 3-8

Tabu Search Makespan Job Shop Study

Problem	n	m	OPT(LB)	SB-I	SB-II	TS-1	TS-5
ABZ5	10	10	1234	5.8	0.4	0.3	0.2
ABZ6	10	10	943	2.0	0.0	0.1	0.0
ABZ7	20	15	(651)	12.1	9.1	3.8	2.5
ABZ8	20	15	(627)	23.4	14.2	9.1	8.1
ABZ9	20	15	(650)	15.5	13.1	7.7	6.0

a. Immediate release—IR
b. Average queue time release—AQT
c. Queue length release—QLR

The release methods are ordered in terms of sophistication. Immediate release gives a basic standard. AQT assumes the required lead time is a multiple of the total processing time. QLR is more complex and takes current queue lengths in the shop into consideration.

Two SCHED-STAR heuristics were tested. SCHED-STAR used just initial estimates for prices and lead times. SCHED-STAR* used iterated pricing and lead times. Table 3-9 reports the results of the study, reporting a normalized NPV. Thus, a negative result means the shop lost money over the period.

Summary. Using grand averages, SCHED-STAR*'s performance came out on top, with a normalized NPV performance of 100 percent. The non-iterated version of SCHED-STAR came in second at 91 percent. WCOVERT-STAT came in third at 68 percent. WCOVERT came in fourth at 62 percent; EARLY-TARDY came in fifth at 57 percent.

Since SCHED-STAR is particularly designed as a bottleneck procedure, it is interesting also to see its performance for the bottleneck shop. Here again SCHED-STAR* came out on top with 100 percent. The non-iterated version SCHED-STAR came in second at 78 percent. WCOVERT came in third at 72 percent; WCOVERT-STAT came in fourth at 53 percent; and EARLY-TARDY came in fifth at 34 percent.

Some conclusions may be drawn: For the conditions of this study SCHED-STAR is superior to WCOVERT, which in turn is superior to EARLY/TARDY and CRITICAL RATIO. Iteration is worth 10 to 20 percent, depending on the bottleneck condition. DYN is an inferior release heuristic. (This is a surprising result and may well mean the formulas for taking queue length into account need to be improved.)

Comparative Dispatch Study. Lawrence and Morton, in an unpublished study in 1993, set out to validate a unified set of hypotheses about dispatch methods. In the following hypothesis "myopic" means the dispatch policy which would be optimal (or very nearly optimal) for the dynamic one-machine problem; "iterated myopic" means the myopic dispatch policy with lead time iteration; "bottleneck dynamics" means the iterated myopic policy with dynamic price iteration.

Hypotheses.

1. The myopic policy performs better than other simple dispatch policies.
2. The iterated myopic policy performs better than the myopic policy.
3. Bottleneck dynamics performs better than the iterated myopic policy.

(Reporting Normalized NPV) Shop Type					
Heuristic	**Single Machine**	**Sm. Flow Shop**	**Gen. Flow Shop**	**Job Shop**	**Bot. Job Shop**
C. RATIO	−0.73	0.18	−0.13	−0.07	−0.19
−STAT R.	−0.75	0.16	−0.14	−0.08	−0.18
−DYN R.	−0.87	0.04	−0.34	−0.43	−0.49
WCOVERT	−0.06	0.38	0.20	0.31	0.23
−STAT R.	0.09	0.39	0.23	0.29	0.17
−DYN R.	−0.01	0.33	0.16	0.11	−0.03
EARLY-TARDY	0.08	0.36	0.22	0.21	0.11
SCHED-STAR	0.16	0.47	0.31	0.36	0.25
SCHED-STAR*	0.16	0.50	0.34	0.39	0.32

Table 3-9

Release/Tardy Job Shop Study

The study was carried out for five objective functions: weighted flow time, weighted tardiness, maximum tardiness, weighted fraction tardy, and makespan. For these the myopic policies were taken to be: WSPT, Rachamadugu & Morton, Operation Due Date (true due dates), Weighted Modified Hodgson's Rule (modified for dynamic case), and Operation Due Date (constant due dates). There was also a pool of competing heuristics.

Three types of shops were tested. In the *bottleneck job shop*, each job visited each of the ten workstations in random order; one machine was the bottleneck in that operations required twice the time on it than on other machines. In the *limited resources job shop* there were three resources, of bottleneck strengths 1.0 , 2.0, and 3.0. Jobs had variable numbers of operations leading to highly variable resource usage and prices over time. In the *industry example*, created by Bitran and Tirupati, the authors recreated their ten workstation, thirteen product manufacturing network, which models an actual production facility in the semi-conductor industry.

Each cell in the following table is the average of 20 replications. One heuristic here, Weighted Modified Hodgson's Rule, may be unfamiliar. Basically, in Hodgson's Rule one orders jobs by ODD, finds the first tardy job, removes the longest job not later in the sequence, and iterates the procedure. In the weighted version one removes the one with the smallest weight/processing time. In the modified version one corrects for the dynamic arrival of the jobs.

Note that in 14 of the 15 objective/shop type conditions in Table 3-10, the hypothesis is fully confirmed. Note also that the relative strengths of these effects varies considerably over these 15 different treatments. While the hypothesis is robust, clearly much more experimentation would be necessary to predict the relative importance of myopic policies, lead time iteration and bottleneck dynamics under varied shop conditions.

Table 3-10

Myopic, Iterated Myopic, Bottleneck Performance by Objective and Shop Type

OBJECTIVE	HEUR NAME	BOTTLE SHOP RES	LIMITED SHOP	INDUSTRY EXAMPLE	AVG.
(Table value is performance over benchmark)					
WEIGHTED FLOW TIME					
#2 Dispatch	CR RATIO	137.2	162.7	132.1	**144.0**
Myopic Dispatch	WSPT	100.5	115.3	102.4	**106.1**
Iterated Myopic	WSPT	100.5	115.3	102.4	**106.1**
Bot. Dynamics	WSPT-P	100.0	100.0	100.0	**100.0**
WEIGHTED TARDINESS					
#2 Dispatch	WCOV	110.2	119.7	117.4	**115.8**
Myopic Dispatch	R&M	107.6	117.1	116.2	**113.6**
Iterated Myopic	R&M-I	100.6	113.2	102.6	**105.5**
Bot. Dynamics	R&M-I,P	100.0	100.0	100.0	**100.0**
MAXIMUM TARDINESS					
#2 Dispatch	SLACK	105.0	101.4	125.7	**110.7**
Myopic Dispatch	ODD	103.0	100.0	112.5	**105.2**
Iterated Myopic	ODD-I	100.0	100.0	100.0	**100.0**
Bot. Dynamics	—	—	—	—	—
WTD FR TARDY					
#2 Dispatch	WSPT	150.0	169.2	125.5	***148.2**
Myopic Dispatch	WMHR	119.4	119.2	140.4	***126.3**
Iterated Myopic	WMHR-I	100.0	100.0	100.0	**100.0**
Bot. Dynamics	—	—	—	—	—
MAKESPAN					
#2 Dispatch	SLACK	100.3	100.9	117.0	**106.7**
Myopic Dispatch	ODD	100.3	100.0	104.6	**101.6**
Iterated Myopic	ODD-I	100.0	100.0	100.0	**100.0**
Bot. Dynamics	—	—	—	—	—

*Reversal of Hypothesis

3.3.6 Flow and Job Shop Exercises

Overview.

1. Give a practical example of a shop which is:

    a. Quite complex yet basically a flow shop
    b. Only two machines, yet basically a job shop
    c. What is the defining characteristic?

2. How would input Tables 3-3 and 3-4 need to be modified to handle:

    a. Re-entrant machines
    b. Alternate routings
    c. Compound machines

3. Generate all non-delay schedules (no machine is left deliberately idle) for the following problem with two machines, three jobs, and two operations per job. (While there could conceivably be 36 schedules, there are actually only a few.)

		Processing Times Operation			Routings Operation	
		1	**2**		**1**	**2**
	1	1	3		1	3
Job	2	2	1	Job	2	1
	3	2	2		1	2

4. Pick one of the schedules from problem 3 and show the job and the machine Gantt charts for it.
5. Which of the schedules in problem 3 has the minimum makespan? Average flow?

Dispatch Heuristics/Bottleneck Dynamics.

6. Create an interesting job shop problem with makespan objective, three machines, four jobs, and two operations per job.
7. In problem 6 choose a single ordering of the jobs. Try to use this as a pure permutation sequence rule. Are there any problems?
8. In problem 7 modify the heuristic to a dispatch permutation sequence. Is the makespan improved? If so, by how much?
9. Choose three or four simple dispatch heuristics and run them on your problem. Explain why the heuristic which did the best did so on intuitive grounds.
10. Create an interesting job shop problem with weighted flow objective, three machines, five jobs, and two operations per job. Solve it by the myopic dispatch heuristic.

Search Methods.

11. Solve problem 6 with the dispatch permutation discipline, using neighborhood search. Use as the neighborhood all adjacent pairwise interchanges on any machine. Start from a clumsy initial solution.
12. Repeat problem 11, but start with the best solution you have available.

Computational Studies.

13. Give two or three weaknesses in the computational research you have studied in this chapter. If you were to conduct research in this area, what might you do to remedy some of these problems?

3.4 APPLICATION SCENARIO—REPRISE

In six weeks Bob Redwood returned to the shop floor to make a preliminary presentation to Ed Eastwood, Jack Nichols, and Bob Barkeley. A summary of what he had to say follows.

Capacity Issues. Processing in the shop goes on for 24 hours a day, 6 days a week, with Sunday sometimes available in emergencies for the backup furnace. On average, 4 lots a day or 24 lots per week pass through the shop. Each of 2 pilgers at the first stage can handle 36 lots per week, each of 2 to 4 at the second stage can handle 24 lots per week; thus, these stages have excess capacity. Each of four pilgers at the third stage can handle 10 lots, giving a utilization of 65 percent. Each of, say, 12 fourth-stage pilgers can handle 2.2 lots per week giving 91 percent utilization. *This is high enough so that the fourth stage can sometimes be a bottleneck.* Finally, the main furnace averages 12 hours per run, so it can handle 12 runs per week of 12 lots each. Records show a run averages half full or six lots. Each lot in turn requires three separate runs through the furnace. Thus, the furnace seems to average 100 percent capacity for a six day week. *Thus, the furnace would seem to be the principal bottleneck, with the fourth stage the secondary bottleneck, although a more careful analysis should be done later.*

First Cut Simplifications.

1. Treat the main furnace with its products and the backup furnace with its few products as separate problems. To capture occasional use of the backup furnace for the main line, treat backup capacity as a parametric variable to study its importance. This turns a complex job shop problem into two complex flow shop problems, which is much simpler. As justification note that:

   a. Barkeley has serious reservations about using the backup furnace.
   b. The analysis becomes simpler and more intuitive.

2. Initially ignore the possibility of moving pilgers between stages and allowing pilgers to be reconfigured (major setup) for different product groups. Treat the minor setups by a myopic bottleneck analysis. As justification note that:

   a. These types of changes are usually handled at a higher level rather than on the floor.
   b. The analysis becomes simpler and more intuitive.

3. Add average amount of breakdowns to processing times followed by a deterministic analysis.

   a. Later simulation can check the robustness of this assumption.

Basic Analysis. Bob Redwood summarized the suggested analysis as follows:

1. Treat the main furnace part of the shop as a compound flow shop with one re-entrant batch machine (annealing furnace). There are ten stages: three in the first pass, three in the second pass, three in the third pass, and one in the fourth pass.
2. The first stage of each pass is a group of parallel pilgers, clustered into groups of equal machines, each of which can handle a subfamily of jobs. There is a minor setup within members of a subfamily.
3. The second stage of each pass is a pickling phase with excess capacity. It is treated as a single high-capacity machine for simplicity.
4. The third stage of the first three passes is the same annealing furnace. It takes 4 to 12 jobs at a time with rules as to which jobs can be processed together.
5. We assume the furnace does not wait for jobs when it has four or more available.
6. We suggest a bottleneck dynamic analysis of the resulting compound flow shop. See Morton and Pentico [1993].

7. Prioritize the furnace as follows:

   a. First prioritize jobs as if the furnace were 12 equal parallel machines.
   b. For each class of jobs, form the potential highest priority total load.
   c. Schedule the load with the highest priority.

Discussion. The reaction of Ed Eastwood, Jack Nichols, and Bob Barkely was favorable on the whole. However, Ed Eastwood, who had a background in Systems Engineering, was a bit worried about splitting up the shop into two lines and analyzing them separately. He also pointed out that jobs often left the line to go to a testing facility; this had been left out of the analysis. Jack Nichols was more worried about the expense of programming and implementing a system.

Bob Redwood suggested that he prepare a more integrated job shop version of the analysis and come back in two weeks, prepared to compare and defend the two approaches. However, he was not willing to make cost estimates until the desired system was a little better defined. This met with general agreement.

Job Shop Formulation. Sixteen days later Bob Redwood returned. He got out the overhead projector, and put up the diagram on the screen that is shown in Figure 3-4. To construct this job shop diagram in an intuitively appealing way, Bob first showed the regular pilger line and the special pilger line as two separate flow shop lines. Secondly, he connected the main furnace (3) and the old furnace (11) to show the possibility of interchange between them. The testing facility is actually several machines in series with a single queue, but he showed it as a single resource to keep the diagram from getting more complicated. Then he used arrows to show possible interconnections to and from each pilger to the testing facility. The resulting model still looks almost like two flow shop lines, with the exception of a routing choice between two furnaces and a common testing facility.

Figure 3-4

Nuclear Control Rod Shop—
Job Shop Version

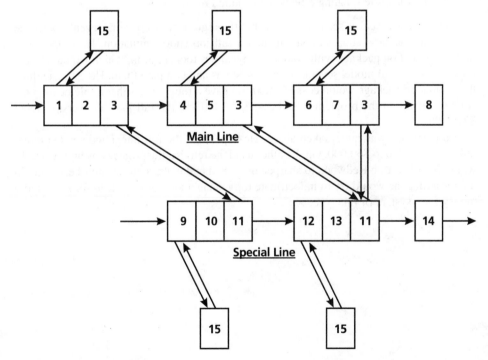

3 = Main Furnace   1,4,6,8,9,12,14 = Pilgers
11 = Old Furnace   2,5,7,10,13 = Clean/Deburr
15 = Testing Facility

Mr. Redwood said that the arguments for ignoring possible sharing of load between two furnaces and simply modeling two flow shops include:

1. Simplicity and ease of understanding a flow shop compared to a more complex job shop
2. Personnel resist putting primary line material onto the second line
3. The main furnace capacity can be varied up and down to see how the extra capacity would affect this. He said the following arguments could be given in answer:

   a. Two flow shops with cross connections are not nearly as complicated to design heuristics for as a general job shop.
   b. The dislike of using the other line could be treated as a cost and quantified within the bottleneck dynamics framework.
   c. If simulation indicates the other line should be used even with the penalty, this is a strong statement to reconsider the problem.
   d. Simulation can help personnel to understand more clearly the advantages and disadvantages of integration.

Arguments that the testing facility should be ignored include:

1. Testing is rare and relatively known in duration and not under the scheduler's control.
2. Therefore, it can simply be fudged in as extra average processing time at the pilgering stage.
3. The average, or possibly random drawings from the processing time distribution should be used in the simulations.

Arguments that the test facility must be part of the simulation include:

1. Delay time is highly variable.
2. This leads to queuing effects not captured by averages.

Mr. Redwood said it seemed to him that the arguments were fairly evenly balanced between simple flow shop simulations and a full job shop simulation. He proposed to build a simulation package with bottleneck dynamics tools built in, which would be flexible, and be able to model several types of systems and compare them. He estimated that the simulation package would cost $50,000. He gave a rough guess that implementing the simpler version of the problem would cost $150,000 and the full job shop version about $225,000.

Ed Eastwood was rather taken aback. He hoped that the full integrated version might only cost $50,000 to $60,000. On the other hand, he felt that the project was highly worthwhile. He asked Bob Redwood to sharpen his pencil and make a more careful estimate. In the meantime, he would try to indoctrinate top management into the need for some more money for a system of this type.

CHAPTER 4

Beyond the Classic Job Shop

4.1 INTRODUCTION

Up to this point we have made a lot of simplifying assumptions, all of which fall under the heading "classic job shop." We have basically assumed that each job is customized and starts through the shop as a response to a given customer order with a known due date. In particular, each piece of WIP in the shop is assumed to have a unique fixed intended customer; it cannot be pirated to make a later hot job. We have assumed that a resource consists of a single machine and that it takes a single machine or resource to perform an activity.

In this chapter we briefly consider some of these extensions. In Section 4.2 we look at a Company Application Scenario—a computer card line for International Computer Makers (ICM). In Section 4.3 we look at various kinds of shops we have not considered before, including open, assembly, and continuous shops, push and pull systems, Just-In Time, and *kanban*. In Section 4.4 we look briefly at flexible manufacturing systems

4.2 COMPANY APPLICATION SCENARIO— INTERNATIONAL COMPUTER MAKERS

International Computer Makers (ICM) is an enormous computer conglomerate with manufacturing facilities worldwide. It has historically enjoyed its greatest profits from mainframe computers, although it is also a very large manufacturer of workstations, PCs, and software. Its plant in Minneapolis makes (motherboard) computer boards for assembly into mainframe computers at other plants in Canada, the United States, Mexico, and Brazil.

The Minneapolis computer board line is very long; it is both automated and quite flexible. It is actually a series of 22 sectors. Given an operator at each machine at each stage, each sector is in itself a compound flow line, with an initial queue and sequencing and release decisions. However, it is not economic to staff enough operators to man every machine at every stage. Furthermore, many of the operators are trained to be able to operate machines at several different stages.

A computer board is an interchangeable module in a computer, which might have 10 to 20 such boards, each worth about $25,000. The composition is highly variable. It usually includes layers of circuit board wiring, with groups of hardware chips and software chips. Boards coming into a sector are often very different. A particular type of board will usually be made one or two at a time. There are also always many "test boards" on which engineering is testing design modifications, and also boards going through to fix flaws found in testing or by a customer. It is fairly important to be able to forecast the process time of each board in each sector. Engineering personnel have worked out a fairly careful regression scheme to forecast times from the features on the particular board.

Given an assignment of operators to the different stages on the line, it is easy to determine the effective capacity of each stage (proportional to the number of operators assigned, up to the maximum number of machines). If then we know the lead times of each board through the rest of the shop, we may do a modified bottleneck dynamics procedure as follows:

    a. Use deterministic times, increased for average rework.
    b. Simulate the sector for each job that is reasonable to go on next.
    c. Choose for each of these jobs the smallest simulated delay not causing jamming.
    d. Get loads on each stage by adding up all loads estimated for future jobs.
    e. Estimate prices of each stage by dynamic queuing approximation.
    f. Calculate each job's bottleneck priority.
    g. Start the job with the highest priority at the correct delay time.

To complete this analysis, we would still have to deal with the questions of where the lead times come from and how the proper operator assignment is obtained. But this would lead us too far afield.

4.3 OTHER TYPES OF SHOPS

4.3.1 Overview

In open shops, assembly shops, and continuous shops there is not a one-to-one matching between a given existing piece of work-in-process on the floor and a single fixed customer order. We consider this issue in Section 4.3.2. Two major points of view about modern shops center around push versus pull philosophies. We consider this issue in Section 4.3.3.

4.3.2 Open, Assembly, Continuous Shops

Open Shops. If many customers order similar items, and need shorter lead times than would be possible if the item were made "to order" (made after the order), then it is appropriate to keep a final stock of inventory for these types of items and to fill orders from this final stock. A rather similar problem is keeping track of conflicting orders. If there is WIP on the floor in terms of two batches of 75 each, and one customer wants 110 while the other requires 80, how is the conflict resolved? And how can bookkeeping be designed to allow use of priority heuristics and our other tools?

Scheduling with Final Inventories. When there are stocks of final goods, we modify the records for existing orders and forecast orders as follows:

    a. List known orders by increasing priority.
    b. List forecasted orders by increasing (forecasted) due date.

(We simply show forecasted orders as spaced on average by $1/D$ where D is the demand rate, and having an average importance.) We forecast out as far in the future as we would be willing to produce.

We allocate (match in the records) existing inventory against these phantom demands. The system treats leftover phantom demands as orders causing new items to be put into production. See Figure 4-1. Whenever there is a change, all the labeling and record keeping is changed dynamically. For example, if an item is returned by a customer, it will be labeled against a phantom demand, causing canceling of an order to the floor (unless it is already started).

Figure 4-1

Open Shop (Make-to-Stock)

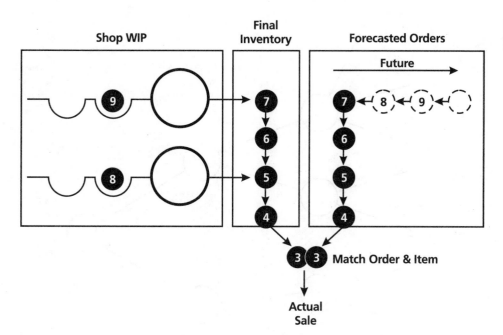

Competing Customer Problem. Suppose there is no final inventory on the floor, but work-in-process in order of increasing remaining lead time of 100, 50, 100, 100. There is a single existing medium priority customer who wants 175. She is assigned all 100 of the first, all 50 of the second, and 25 of the third. This WIP is now given her priorities in terms of scheduling decisions on the floor. Note that nothing is split physically, but the bookkeeping can get complicated. For example, now suppose a very high priority customer appears who wants 125. She would be assigned the 100 from the first and 25 from the second. The first customer would be reassigned the remaining 25 of the second, 100 of the third, and 50 of the fourth. The priority of the first lot would now be high, the second lot would be a mixture of high and medium priorities (high-medium priority), and so forth.

An important issue here is how complicated to let the bookkeeping get before making some approximations.

Assembly Shops. In an assembly shop, the structure of the operations forms a tree, as shown in Figure 4-2. Sub-sub-assemblies are assembled in sub-assemblies, which finally are assembled into the final product. Bottleneck dynamics for this kind of process is similar to that for a project shop, discussed in the Project Management module. Here we are mostly interested in the bookkeeping issues.

All activities coming before a given activity (called its initial set), when completed, always create a sub-assembly of actual work in process. In a classic project shop these sub-assemblies would all be distinct, and it would be clear which eventual job or project they were to be a part of. However, in an assembly shop with many similar final products, a particular sub-assembly may be suitable for several different final products.

If a dispatch heuristic is trying to see whether a new sub-assembly can be carried out, it looks to see if all the predecessors have been completed. Due to duplications, there may be several different possible pieces of WIP sitting on the floor which would allow this high priority activity to go ahead, but none of which are currently labeled as part of this particular high priority job. Thus, we clearly must have a procedure to relabel WIP to allow this activity to proceed. This is basically a relabeling problem, but a little more complicated. We have to basically perform the following on an iterative basis:

a. Lead time estimation
b. Pricing

Figure 4-2

Assembly Product
Operations Structure

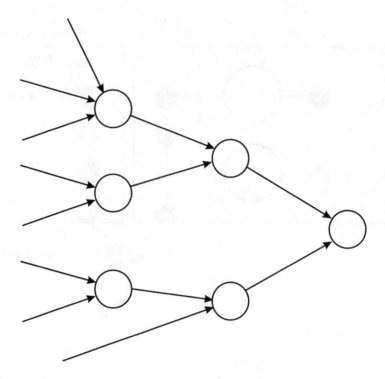

c. Simulation of the solution
d. Iteration

Continuous Shops. Up to this point we have been talking almost entirely about **discrete part manufacturing**: a job or assembly comes in integer multiples of a standard piece. On the other hand, **continuous manufacturing** has the identifying characteristic that a large batch of tomato soup, molten steel, or paper is manufactured and can be divided up in all sorts of ways into final needs. In this sense, a cola canning line might be called **quasi-continuous** since the discrete unit is very small.

A common misconception is that the process of turning out product continuously over time is what defines "continuous." Although the idea of making products continuously over time is of importance, the primary point about continuous products is the fine divisibility, and hence the difficulty of defining WIP for a particular job in advance. Cake mixes, paper pulp, and molten steel are often made in stationary batches, but are continuous processes. An automobile assembly line makes cars more or less continuously over time, but is a discrete process. Paper roll manufacture and continuous steel casting make product continuously and are continuous processes. The issues are those of final jobs looking at WIP.

All the processes we have mentioned share the common characteristic that they are made in batches. The batches for continuous casting or paper may be large, but quite finite, and setup costs for a batch are not small. The largest cost in starting a batch is often that the process must be adjusted until the paper or steel being produced is as desired. The beginning part of the batch until the adjustment is made is scrap and part of the setup cost. In some cases the process has to be stopped to put a new batch on, in some cases it doesn't. This also makes it clear that a classification "batch" versus "continuous" really doesn't make sense. It would have to be "stationary time batch" versus "continuous time batch."

Top Priorities versus Waste. In deciding which jobs to put in a batch, we will generally have two conflicting purposes:

    a.   Assign jobs in order of highest priority.
    b.   Fit with as low a percentage of waste as possible.

Suppose we are planning a certain kind of paper with a batch of 50,000 feet. If we simply fit by the highest priority jobs, we might end up using 42,000 feet. This is fine if we can replan the roll for 42,500. Otherwise 8000 feet might be too much waste, and we might try to solve the integer programming problem of fitting as much as possible into the roll (bin packing problem).

Relabeling Problem. A complex relabeling problem can occur when a hot job or just everyday shifts in lead times and prices cause us to replan the uses of a given molten heat (or batch), for example. We sketch here a few thoughts on the one-machine problem.

Consider the case where all jobs can be made from the same kind of batch. For simplicity we restrict our attention to the weighted flow case. Let n jobs j arrive over time with processing time p_j, arrival time r_j, due date d_j, and weights w_j. The machine currently has a price R; the entire batch has a (relative) volume of 1.0. If we schedule some subset X of the n items, it wastes a fraction $v(X)$ of the batch, and uses $1.0 - v(X)$. The imputed machine cost of this waste is $v(X)Rp$. Assume the waste material can be reprocessed at a cost Q, independent of the amount (raw material cost only here). Expediting a job to be part of the batch is worth w_j per time unit expedited; the interest cost to the job of being part of an earlier batch is IRp.

Thus, the net value of running a particular batch of jobs X can be given by

$$\pi(X) = [\Sigma_X w_j] - IR\overline{p} - v(X)Rp + Q$$

We should then put the subset X into the batch which maximizes this expression. This fitting function $v(X)$ may be complex and require integer programming to exactly optimize, for example, optimal cutting of a roll of paper into individual orders. Heuristics are widely used for this purpose.

4.3.3 Pull Systems, Just-In-Time

Push Systems Versus Pull Systems. In a classic **push** system (which we have studied), a customer order causes all the following, more or less in order:

    a.   Creation of initial paperwork
    b.   Negotiation of due date with customer
    c.   Job release to shop floor
    d.   Dynamic calculation of priorities
    e.   Push of job through shop by priorities
    f.   Completed job to customer

In a **pull** system a customer order causes the following:

    a.   Completed job to customer from final inventory
    b.   Instruction for last machine to take unit from WIP and create a new unit for final inventory
    c.   Order from that machine for a unit of WIP from the next-to-last machine
    d.   And so forth

The pull system has a number of advantages and disadvantages:

Advantages.
    1.   Lead time from order to delivery is short and automatic.
    2.   Lead time to replace final inventory is short and automatic; and so on back through the floor.

3. WIP inventories are essentially constant.
4. There is no confusion in the shop.

Disadvantages.

1. There must be only a few products and high volume, to make it practical to keep WIP for each in front of all machines.
2. There can be no demand surges to swamp the system.
3. Machine failures cannot be tolerated. (The Japanese would say this is an advantage.)

In summary, neither push systems nor pull systems will be best in all shops. It is important to study the characteristics of the shop and design the system accordingly.

Just-In-Time (JIT). The Japanese first saw important strategic concerns which caused them to prefer pull systems. But even more important, they have actively changed products and processes to bypass the disadvantages of pull systems. They were the first to argue that manufacturers should aim for zero inventories as a strategic goal. This philosophy is called just-in-time (JIT), since if product were finished just in time to be shipped, there would be no need for final inventories; if raw materials were delivered just in time for first stage manufacturing, there would be no need for raw material inventories, and so on.

The Japanese motives have now been largely adopted by globally competitive companies everywhere. Adopting JIT is strategic because:

a. A defective product can no longer be hidden in WIP on the floor.
b. There is quick tracing to the worker or machine causing problems.
c. There are resulting repeated small improvements to the production system.
d. There are high long-term learning improvements to costs, quality, and flexibility.

Note that pull systems help a JIT system to be successful, since pull systems produce constant level, easily controlled inventories.

4.3.4 Shop Type Exercises

Open, Assembly, Continuous Shops.

1. Set up a small open shop: two machines, one product with two operations, and a final inventory. It should also have forecasted sales, weighted flow objective, ten jobs in process (some from known orders, some from forecasted orders), and dynamic arrivals. Illustrate relabeling issues by running a little simulation to see the effect of a new hot order or similar effect.
2. Set up a small assembly shop with three machines, two products, two final inventories, forecast sales, weighted flow objective, ten pieces of WIP in different states, dynamic arrivals. The two products are red wheelbarrows and black wheelbarrows. Machine 1 makes a basic wheelbarrow, Machine 2 paints a basic wheelbarrow red, Machine 3 paints a basic wheelbarrow black. Illustrate relabeling issues as you did in problem 1.

Pull Systems, Just-In-Time.

3. Create a small two-machine flow shop with one product. Suppose no more than one item of WIP is allowed in front of each machine, and one item in final inventory. Let both process times be 2.0 and raw material have a lead time of 2.0. Operate by a pull system. Do a manual simulation for:

   a. A time stream of demands which works well.
   b. A time stream of demands which does not.

4. Convert problem 3 into a push system. No permanent inventories are kept at machines; when an item is taken from final inventory, a new one is started from the beginning. What differences do you note?

4.4 FLEXIBLE MANUFACTURING SYSTEMS

4.4.1 Overview

We have met several situations before where a multiple machine grouping actually comprises a single resource, since there is a single external queue and decision to be made. The great advantage of these multiple machine but single resource problems is that since they possess a single queue to be sequenced, determining only a single optimal permutation sequence is required, and all the search techniques for the one-machine case may be used. This is an overstatement, however, since evaluating a pairwise interchange requires a simulation of the entire system. Furthermore, it may be necessary to estimate a delay time before a job enters the system, even if it is known to be next.

Turning to activities which, on the other hand, require multiple resources, these are comparatively easy if dispatch methods are appropriate. One simply adds resource costs across the various resources to get the cost in a standard benefit/cost analysis. Unfortunately, if careful coordination of several expensive resources is required, interval scheduling will become necessary, rather than dispatch heuristics. This may introduce secondary idleness for the other resources, the cost of which must be added to the resource cost.

In summary:

a. Conventional methods can sometimes be "stretched" to deal with more complex problems.
b. That "stretching" is subject to decreasing returns.

4.4.2 Multiple Machines per Resource

Machines with External Setup. Large or computerized machines are so expensive that it is undesirable to hold them idle while the next job is being set up. Setup is usually a somewhat simpler matter that does not use the entire capability of the machine. We discuss one scheme for processing one job while the next one is being set up. The situation is pictured in Figure 4-3.

There is a turntable, say 10 feet in diameter, in front of the main machine (or machine complex). The turntable is split in half by a vertical divider. Each half has a duplicate of the holding jigs, and duplicates of any part of the machine needed in the setup. Two jobs may be mounted at once. One has previously been set up and is ready to process, the other is ready for setup. Suppose that setup is scheduled to end exactly as the other job is finished being removed from processing.

A little thought makes it clear that this problem is equivalent formally to a two-machine flow shop with no delays, where we delay new jobs so that they may be processed through both machines without waiting. A central proposition for this case is given in [Morton and Pentico 1993, pp. 511–513]. They also extend the model to the case where there are several machines, all sharing the same external setup.

Line of Parallel Machines. As preparation for the rest of the International Computer Makers Scenario, a simplified version of that scenario is given here. Consider a compound flow shop with a set of equal machines at each stage. There may be different numbers of machines at each stage, with zero or one operators. The effective capacity of each stage is proportional to the minimum of the number of machines and the number of operators. All internal queues are very short. The ordering of jobs does not change once the scheduler

Figure 4-3

One Machine with External
Setup Station

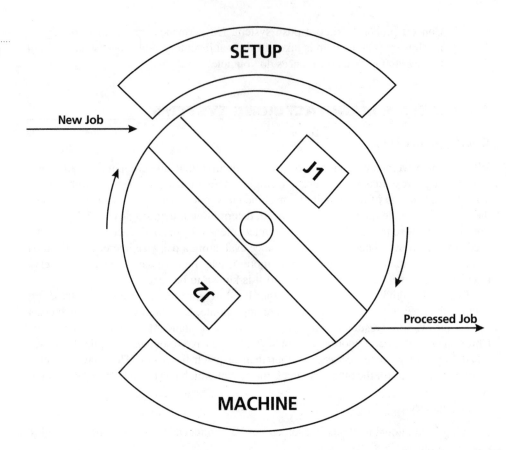

chooses the next job and the delay before entering it after the last one into the line. We gloss over some difficult stochastic issues, except to note that if a stage operates more slowly at some point than usual, jamming can occur.

One thing needed for an analysis is some kind of simulator that can forecast present and future positions of jobs currently being processed and can estimate the amount and type of potential jamming if a new job entered at a particular point in time. This is quite difficult computationally; one possible simplification is to use the following two heuristics:

Heuristic to Estimate Delay.

1. Pick a job to go next.
2. Estimate a crude delay.
3. Enter the job with this delay and simulate to find the amount of conflict.
4. Adjust the crude delay by the amount of conflict.

Sequencing by Neighborhood Search.

1. Choose an initial sequence by a simpler heuristic.
2. Simulate and cost the sequence, using proper delays.
3. Interchange two jobs.
4. Simulate and cost, etc.

This procedure is discussed more carefully in [Morton and Pentico, 1993, pp. 515–516, 526–530].

Flexible Manufacturing Cells. We look at just one example of a flexible manufacturing cell. Look at Figure 4-4. Instead of a revolving turret as in an external setup situation, we have an elliptical transporter with a number of positions, buckets, hooks, or harnesses for each job. There are a number of machines around the belt.

Each machine has a queue position of length one that can be used to store that job until it is appropriate for the machine to start, work on the job, and store it until the belt can take it away. There is a load-unload position for the FMC, also located on the belt, that is manned by a couple of workers. It handles arriving and departing jobs, and places them on or off the belt. It also provides supplementary storage in case arrival and departure are irregular. Finally, this can be used as a work area for workers to reconfigure jobs with different jigs, etc.

Let us follow a hypothetical job through the FMC. Job AX-372-C arrives at the load area and waits until its turn on one of the machines (3). It is loaded on the belt to arrive just as the second (3) machine becomes free. Five operations are performed on it by (3). Then it is returned to the belt, to be worked on next by machine (2). However this machine is initially busy, so the job is stored on the circling belt for awhile. The belt gets too full, and so the job is returned to the storage area. Finally it becomes top priority for machine (2) and is returned to the belt just in time to arrive when (2) becomes free. After (2) finishes with it, it is placed back on the belt, and returned to storage for refixturing before going to a (1) machine. It is finally sent back to the load/unload area to depart to another part of the shop.

This problem is relatively easy to handle by bottleneck dynamics if storage on the belt and in the loading area are in good supply. The problem is analogous to a mixture of skip shops and reentrant shops. If storage is more constrained, addition of a simulator might be required.

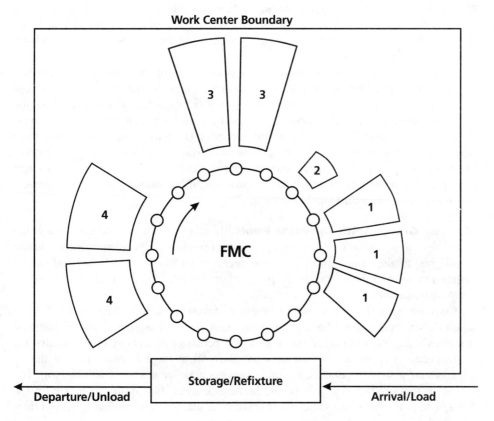

Figure 4-4
....
Flexible Manufacturing Cell

4.4.3 Multiple Resources per Activity

Situations where completing an activity requires multiple (fairly divisible) resources can be handled quite reasonably if there is no serious problem with getting the resources to all be available at the same time. We simply aggregate the value of all resource usage and use our standard benefit/cost analysis. If the price of all resource k available is R_k, and activity ij will use fraction f_{ijk} of resource k, then the total amount of resource usage to perform activity ij with processing time p_{ij} would be simply

$$p_{ij}\Sigma_{k=1,m}f_{ijk}R_k$$

However, bottleneck dynamics is less useful, without some modifications in, let us say, assigning classrooms, instructors, and students simultaneously to the activity "learn POM," all of which have schedule constraints and must match each other exactly. It is also less useful in assigning skilled operators to machines.

Multiple Resources—Modifications of the Dispatch Method. When we are scheduling several resources for a common activity, we will often make an interval "reservation" (often simply called a schedule). If no resource suffered any wastage from this schedule, then the formula for the total resource usage given previously still applies. However, if some resource has suffered some idleness by leaving gaps in the rest of its own schedule or by more complicated interchanges of low- and high-priority items, then simply "price times activity times length" will give too low an estimate of that resource usage. If changes forced in the rest of that resource's schedule are straightforward, then they may be costed out. For example, extra idle time caused by the main schedule in question can be costed at the lost time multiplied by the resource's price and added into the estimation of the total cost. These issues are discussed more thoroughly in Morton and Pentico [1993 pp. 520–523].

Machines with Unique Operators. If there is a unique operator assigned to a single machine, then a decision to use the machine is a decision to use the operator, and vice versa. Thus, we may treat them as a single resource and use our usual heuristic pricing methods without any change.

On the other hand, suppose the operator is in charge of three machines. Activities arrive for specific machines. The operator must choose which of the three machines to use next, and must devote his full attention to it until it is finished. Under this situation, the operator becomes the single resource, and he may mentally combine the three lines, sequencing the grand line by some priority scheme. The only contribution of the three machines to the analysis is to give appropriate processing times. Since the problem structure made the operator the limiting resource, prices of the machines are irrelevant. If there is a significant travel time from machine to machine, it becomes a problem in sequence-dependent setup times on a single machine.

Machine Groups with Operator Pools. In other situations there may be a group of machines to be staffed on a shift. Suppose some operators are very experienced and can be assigned to almost any machine. Some operators have some experience and can be assigned to some of the machines. Some operators are new and can be assigned only to one or two machines.

Consider again the International Computer Makers scenario in Section 4.2. For the sake of discussion, say we have a compound flow line with K stages, and N_k identical machines at stage k. Looking at future jobs over perhaps the next day or so, say that the load forecast is L_k machines (fractions are allowed) at stage k. Now if n_k of the N_k machines are assigned operators, the utilization per machine at stage k will be L_k/n_k. The largest of these utilizations will be the bottleneck stage. Our desire to maximize the throughput of the line is the same as minimizing the maximum utilization L_k/n_k. But minimizing L_k/n_k is clearly the same as maximizing n_k/L_k.

Now let i represent an operator, and I the total number of operators. Let v_{ik} be 1 if i can work the machine at stage k, and 0 otherwise. In the same way let x_{ik} be 1 if i is assigned to stage k, 0 otherwise. Finally, let there be a dummy stage 0. All operators not needed to work will be assigned stage 0, as a dummy.

Proposition 1. The operator assignment problem given just above can be solved using the maximin version of the generalized assignment algorithm as follows:

$$\max[\min_{k=1,K}\{n_k/L_k\}]$$

s.t.
$$\sum_{i=1,I} v_{ik} x_{ik} = n_k, \qquad k = 0, \ldots, K$$
$$\sum_{k=0,K} x_{ik} = 1, \qquad i = 1, \ldots, I$$
$$n_k <= N_k, \qquad k = 1, \ldots, K$$
$$x_{ik}, v_{ik} \text{ are 0 or 1}$$

Machines with Permanent Tool Assignment. If there is a rotary magazine holding perhaps 20 different tools for a machine and the magazine rotates to the tool needed for a particular job, then the machine and the tools are really not separate resources. However, for a fixed way the tools are stored in the magazine, there will be a sequence-dependent setup time problem (setup time equals travel time of the tools), which is beyond our scope to discuss here.

A more interesting case arises if the arriving jobs tend to use the tools preferentially in particular patterns. For example, each arriving job might have four serial activities, all to be done on the same machine with different tools. In such a case we will be interested in optimizing the placement of the tools in the magazine, as well as optimizing the sequence of jobs processed. This is somewhat like the operator assignment problem. For a fixed sequence of jobs, one could solve for the tool ordering. For that ordering, one could find the optimal sequence, and so forth, alternating back and forth.

Shared Tooling. In a more complex flexible manufacturing cell, each of three machines might have its own magazine for tools, holding perhaps 20 tools each. In addition there could be a central automatic tool handling magazine holding 50 tools. Each machine can request a tool from the central magazine, or send back a tool not needed to make space. The central magazine can request a tool a different machine wants.

This is quite complex. The four machines and 60 or 70 tools all represent distinct resources and several decision makers. A simple rule often proposed for one of the user machines is:

Rule 1: Don't ask for a tool until it is needed immediately.
Rule 2: Transfer out a tool with greatest expected time until next use.

4.4.4 Flexible Exercises

Machines with Operators.

1. An operator tends two machines, which have a fifteen-minute walk between them. The objective is to minimize average flow time. Machine A has jobs of 15, 30, 30, and 45 minutes to be completed; Machine B has jobs of 10, 20, 30, and 60 minutes. The operator starts at machine A. Find a reasonable solution to this problem as best as you can.

2. In problem 1 argue that there is an optimal solution which has the form:

   a. Put both lines in SPT order.
   b. Alternatively process blocks in SPT order in A, B, A, . . .

3. Use problem 2 to find the best solution you can for the problem in problem 1. Can you argue that your solution is optimal?

4. Consider a compound flow shop with four stages, each with three equal parallel machines. There is a pool of eight operators, two of whom are senior and can handle any machine, one who can handle stages 1 and 3, and one who can handle stages 2 and 4. The other four are specialized to stage 1, stage 2, stage 3, and stage 4, respectively. The total loads at the four stages are 50, 75, 150, and 75, respectively.

   a. Find an operator assignment that works and evens the load as well as you can.
   b. Explain your heuristic methodology as best you can.

Machines with Tooling.

5. There are eight jobs waiting for a machine with a small tool magazine. These jobs are being processed to minimize average flow time. They have processing times 10, 15, 15, 20, 30, 35, 40, and 40 minutes respectively, and require tool 1, 2, 3, 1, 2, 3, 1, and 2, respectively. To change between tools 1 and 2 or 2 and 3 requires five minutes. To change between tools 1 and 3 requires ten minutes. Tool 1 is in place at the start. Argue a result analogous to that in problem 2.

6. Solve the problem in problem 5 by three different heuristic methods. Compare the three objective function values achieved.

   a. Straight SPT across all machines, ignoring setup problem.
   b. Do all the jobs with one tool in a large batch. Optimize within each batch, and to order the batches.

7. For problem 5 find the very best solution you can manually, using the general form of the optimal solution you learned in problem 5. How does your heuristic compare with those in problem 6? Explain your heuristic as best as you can.

BIBLIOGRAPHY

A. General References

Baker, K. R. (1974). *Introduction To Sequencing and Scheduling*. New York: John Wiley.

Conway, R. W., W. L. Maxwell, and L.W. Miller (1967). *Theory of Scheduling*. Reading, MA: Addison-Wesley.

French, S. (1982). *Sequencing and Scheduling: An Introduction to the Mathematics of the Job Shop*. New York: John Wiley.

Morton, T. E., and D. W. Pentico (1993). *Heuristic Scheduling Systems*. New York: John Wiley.

Muth, J. F., and G. L. Thompson (1963). *Industrial Scheduling*. Englewood Cliffs, NJ: Prentice Hall.

B. One Machine—Foundations

Gupta, S. K., and J. Kyparisis (1987). "Single Machine Scheduling Research," *Omega* 15, 207–227.

Moore, J. M. (1968). "Sequencing n Jobs on One Machine to Minimize the Number of Tardy Jobs," *Management Science* 17, 102–109.

Sidney, J. B. (1972). "A Comment on a Paper of Maxwell," *Management Science* 18, 716–717.

Smith, W. E. (1956). "Various Optimizations for Single State Production," *Naval Research Logistics Quarterly* 3, 59–66.

C. One Machine—Modern Methods

Aarts, E. H. L., and P. J. M. Van Laarhoven (1985). "Statistical Cooling: A General Approach to Combinatorial Optimization Problems," *Philips Journal of Research* 40, 193–226.

Dell'Amico, M., and M. Trubian (1991). "Applying Tabu-Search to the Job-Shop Scheduling Problem," Politecnico di Milano, Italy.

Dobson, G., and U. S. Karmarkar (1989). "Simultaneous Resource Scheduling to Minimize Weighted Flow Times," *Operations Research* 37, 592–600.

Eglese, R.W. (1990). "Simulated Annealing: A Tool for Operational Research," *European Journal of Operational Research* 46, 271–281.

Glover, F. (1990). "Tabu Search: A Tutorial," *Interfaces* 20, 4, 74–94.

Lawler, E. L., and D. E. Wood (1966). "Branch and Bound Methods: A Survey," *Operations Research* 14, 699-719.

Ow, P. S., and T. Morton (1988). "Filtered Beam Search in Scheduling," *International Journal of Production Research* 26, 35–62.

Potts, C. N, and L. N. Van Wassenhove (1985). "A Branch and Bound Algorithm for the Total Weighted Tardiness Problem," *Operations Research*, 33, 363–377.

Van Laarhoven, P. J. M., E. H. L. Aarts, and J. K. Lenstra (1992). "Job Shop Scheduling by Simulated Annealing," *Operations Research* 40, 112–129.

Zhou, D. N., V. Cherkassky, T. R. Baldwin, and T. R. Olson (1991). "A Neural Network Approach to Job Shop Scheduling," *IEEE Transactions on Neural Networks* 2, 175–179.

D. One Machine—Advanced Topics

Adams J., E. Balas, and D. Zawack (1988). "The Shifting Bottleneck Procedure for Job Shop Scheduling," *Management Science* 34, 391–401.

Baker, K. R., and G. D Scudder (1990). "Sequencing with Earliness and Tardiness Penalties: A Review," *Operations Research* 38, 22–36.

Carlier, J. (1982). "The One Machine Sequencing Problem," *European Journal of Operations Research* 11, 42–47.

Carroll, D. C. (1965). "Heuristic Sequencing of Single and Multiple Component Jobs," Ph.D. Thesis, Sloan School of Management, M.I.T., Cambridge, MA.

Dobson, G., U. Karmarkar, and J. Rummel (1987). "Batching to Minimize Flow Times on One Machine," *Management Science* 33, 784–799.

Elmaghrabi, S. E. (1968). "The Machine Scheduling Problem—Review and Extensions," *Naval Research Logistics Quarterly* 15, 587–598.

Gavett, J. W. (1965). "Three Heuristic Rules for Sequencing Jobs to a Single Production Facility," *Management Science* 2, B166–B176.

Karmarkar, U. S. (1987). "Lot-Sizing and Sequencing Delays," *Management Science* 33, 419–423.

Lawler, E. L. (1973). "Optimal Sequencing of a Single Machine Subject to Precedence Constraints," *Management Science* 19, 544–546.

Potts, C. N., and L. N. Van Wassenhove (1985). "A Branch and Bound Algorithm for the Total Weighted Tardiness Problem," *Operations Research* 33, 363–377.

Silver, E. A., and H. C. Meal (1973). "A Heuristic Selecting Lotsize Requirements for the Case of a Deterministic Time-Varying Demand Rate and Discrete Opportunities for Replenishment," *Production and Inventory Management* 14, (Second Quarter), 64–77.

Smith, W. E. (1956). "Various Optimizations for Single State Production," *Naval Research Logistics Quarterly* 3, 59–66.

Vepsalainen A., and T. E. Morton (1987). "Priority Rules and Leadtime Estimation for Job Shop Scheduling with Weighted Tardiness Costs," *Management Science* 33, 1036–1047.

E. Multi-Machine Scheduling—Bottleneck Methods

Adams, J., E. Balas, and D. Zawack (1988). "The Shifting Bottleneck Procedure for Job Shop Scheduling," *Management Science* 34, 391–401.

Carlier, J., and E. Pinson (1989). "An Algorithm for Solving the Job Shop Problem," *Management Science* 35, 164–176.

Goldratt, E. M. (1990). *What's This Thing Called Theory of Constraints?* Milford, CN: North River Press.

Meleton, M. P. (1986). "OPT: Fantasy or Breakthrough?" *Production and Inventory Management* 27, (Second Quarter) 13–21.

F. Flow Shops

Campbell, H. G., R. A. Dudek, and M. L. Smith (1970). "A Heuristics Algorithm for the n Job m Machine Sequencing Problem," *Management Science* 16, 630–637.

Dudek, R. A., S. S. Panwalkar, and M. L. Smith (1992). "The Lessons of Flowshop Scheduling Research," *Operations Research* 40, 7–13.

Graves, S. C., H. C. Meal, D. Stefek, and A. H. Zeghmi (1983). "Scheduling of Re-Entrant Flow Shops," *Journal of Operations Management* 3, 197–207.

Gupta, J. N. D. (1972). "Heuristic Algorithms for Multistage Flow Shop Problems," *AIIE Transactions* 4, 11–18.

Johnson, S. M. (1954). "Optimal Two and Three-Stage Production Scheduling with Setup Times Included," *Naval Research Logistics Quarterly* 1, 61–68.

Palmer, D. S. (1965). "Sequencing Jobs Through a Multi-Stage Process in the Minimum Total Time—A Quick Method of Obtaining a Near Optimum," *Operational Research Quarterly* 16, 101–107.

Ow, Peng Si (1985). "Focused Scheduling in Proportionate Flowshops," *Management Science* 31, 852–869.

Vepsalainen, A., and T. E. Morton (1987). "Priority Rules and Leadtime Estimation for Job Shop Scheduling with Weighted Tardiness Costs," *Management Science* 33, 1036–1047.

G. Job Shops

Adams, J., E. Balas, and D. Zawack (1988). "The Shifting Bottleneck Procedure for Job Shop Scheduling," *Management Science* 34, 391–401.

Carroll, D. C. (1965). "Heuristic Sequencing of Single and Multiple Component Jobs," Ph.D. Thesis, Sloan School of Management, M.I.T., Cambridge, MA.

Dell'Amico, M., and M. Trubian (1991). "Applying Tabu-Search to the Job Shop Scheduling Problem," Politecnico di Milano, Italy.

Lozinski, C., and C. R. Glassey (1988). "Bottleneck Starvation Indicators for Shop-Floor Control," *IEEE Transactions on Semiconductor Manufacturing* 1, 147–153.

Manne, A. S. (1960). "On the Job-Shop Sequencing Problem," *Operations Research* 8, 219–223.

Morton, T. E., S. Kekre, S. Lawrence, and S. Rajagopalan (1988). "SCHED-STAR: A Price Based Shop Scheduling Module," *Journal of Manufacturing and Operations Management* 1, 131–181.

Uzsoy, R., L. A. Martin-Vega, C. Y. Lee, and P. A. Leonard (1991b). "Production Scheduling Algorithms for a Semiconductor Test Facility," *IEEE Transactions on Semiconductor Manufacturing* 4, 270–280.

Van Laarhoven, P. J. M., E. H. L. Aarts, and J. K. Lenstra (1992). "Job Shop Scheduling by Simulated Annealing," *Operations Research* 40, 112–129.

Vepsalainen, A., and T. E. Morton (1987). "Priority Rules and Leadtime Estimation for Job Shop Scheduling with Weighted Tardiness Costs," *Management Science* 33, 1036–1047.

Vepsalainen, A., and T. E. Morton (1988). "Improving Local Priority Rules with Global Leadtime Estimates," *Journal of Manufacturing and Operations Management* 1, 102–118.

H. Beyond the Classic Job Shop

Agnetis, A., C. Arbib, M. Lucertini, and F. Nicolo (1990). "Part Routing in Flexible Assembly Systems," *IEEE Transactions on Robotics and Automation* 6, 697–705.

Arbel, A., and A. Seidmann (1984). "Performance Evaluation of Flexible Manufacturing Systems," *IEEE Transactions on Systems, Man and Cybernetics* SMC-14, 132–140.

Arbib, C., M. Lucertini, and F. Nicolo (1991). "Workload Balance and Part-Transfer Minimization in Flexible Manufacturing Systems," *International Journal of Flexible Manufacturing Systems* 3, 5–15.

Berkley, B. J. (1991). "Tandem Queues and Kanban-Controlled Lines," *International Journal of Production Research* 29, 2057–2081.

Berkley, B. J., and A. S. Kiran (1991). "A Simulation Study of Sequencing Rules in a Kanban-Controlled Flow Shop," *Decision Sciences* 22, 559–582.

Box, R. E., and D. G. Herbe, Jr. (1988). "A Scheduling Model for LTV Steel's Cleveland Works' Twin Strand Continuous Slab Caster," *Interfaces* 18, 1, 42–56.

Buzacott, J. A., and D. D. Yao (1986). "Flexible Manufacturing Systems: A Review of Analytical Models," *Management Science* 32, 890–905.

Buzacott, J. A., and J. G. Shantikumar (1980). "Models for Understanding Flexible Manufacturing Systems," *AIIE Transactions* 12, 339–350.

Chan, B. W. M. (1992). "Tool Management for Flexible Manufacturing," *Intelligent Manufacturing* 5, 255–265.

Chandra, J., and J. Talavage (1991). "Intelligent Dispatching for Flexible Manufacturing," *International Journal of Production Research* 29, 2259–2278.

Daniels, R. L., and R. K.Sarin (1989). "Single Machine Scheduling with Controllable Processing Times and Number of Jobs Tardy," *Operations Research* 37, 981–984.

Diaz, A., L. Sancho, R. Garcia, and J. Larraneta (1991). "A Dynamic Scheduling and Control System in an ENSIDESA Steel Plant," *Interfaces* 21, 5, 53–62.

Dupont-Gatelmand, C. (1982). "A Survey of Flexible Manufacturing Systems," *Journal of Manufacturing Systems* 1, 1–16.

Fry, T. (1990). "Controlling Input: The Real Key to Shorter Lead-Times," *International Journal of Logistics Management* 1, 7–12

Glassey, C. R., and R. G. Petrakian (1989). "The Use of Bottleneck Starvation Avoidance with Queue Predictions in Shop Floor Control," Research Report ESRC 89–23, University of California, Berkeley, CA.

Glassey, C. R., and M. G. C. Resende (1988a). "A Scheduling Rule for Job Release in Semiconductor Fabrication," *Operations Research Letters* 7, 213–217.

Gravel, M., and W. L. Price (1988). "Using the Kanban in a Job Shop Environment," *International Journal of Production Research* 26, 1105–1118.

Inman, R. R., and R. L. Bulfin (1991). "Sequencing JIT Mixed-Model Assembly Lines," *Management Science* 37, 901–904.

Jaikumar, R. (1974). "An Operational Optimization Procedure for Production Scheduling," *Computers and Operations Research* 1, 191–200.

Karmakar, U. S. (1989). "Capacity Loading and Release Planning with Work-In-Progress (WIP) and Leadtimes," *Journal of Manufacturing and Operations Management* 2, 105–123.

Kimura, O. and H. Terada (1981). "Design and Analysis of Pull System, a Method of Multi-Stage Production Control," *International Journal of Production Research* 19, 241–253.

Krajewksi, L. J., B. E. King, L. P. Ritzman, and D. S. Wong (1987). "Kanban, MRP and Shaping the Manufacturing Environment," *Management Science* 33, 39–57.

Leachman, R. C. (1986). "Preliminary Design and Development of a Corporate-Level Production Planning System for the Semiconductor Industry," OR Center, University of California, Berkeley, CA.

Lefrancois, P., and M. C. Roy (1990). "Estimation of Mean Flow Time in a Rolling-Mill Facility," *Journal of Manufacturing and Operations Management* 3, 134–152.

Mejabi, O., and G. S. Wasserman (1992). "Basic Concepts of JIT Scheduling," *International Journal of Production Research* 30, 141–149.

Miltenburg, J., and G. Sinnamon (1992). "Algorithms for Scheduling Multilevel Just-In-Time Production Systems," *IEE Transactions on Design and Manufacturing* 24, 121–130.

Morton, T. E., S. Kekre, S. Lawrence, and S. Rajagopalan (1988). "SCHED-STAR: A Price Based Shop Scheduling Module," *Journal of Manufacturing and Operations Management* 1, 131–181.

Mukhopadhyay, S. K., B. Maithi, and S. Garg (1991). "Heuristic Solution to the Scheduling Problems in Flexible Manufacturing Systems," *International Journal of Production Research* 29, 2003–2024.

Rabinowitz, G., A. Mehrez, and S. Samaddar (1991). "A Scheduling Model for Multirobot Assembly Cells," *International Journal of Flexible Manufacturing Systems* 3, 149–180.

Roundy R., W. Maxwell, Y. Herer, S. Tayur, and A. Getzler (1988). "A Price-Directed Approach to Real-Time Scheduling of Production Operations" Technical Report No. 823, School of Operations Research and Industrial Engineering, College of Engineering, Cornell University, Ithaca, NY.

Sabuncuoglu, I., and D. L. Hommertzheim (1992). "Dynamic Dispatching Algorithm for Scheduling Machines and Automated Guided Vehicles in a Flexible Manufacturing System," *International Journal of Production Research* 30, 1059–1079.

Sarker, B. R., and J. A. Fitzsimmons (1989). "The Performance of Push and Pull Systems: A Simulation and Comparative Study," *International Journal of Production Research* 27, 1715–1731.

Schweitzer, P. J., A. Seidmann, and P. B. Goes (1991). "Performance Management in a Flexible Manufacturing System," *International Journal of Flexible Manufacturing Systems* 4, 17–50.

Sengupta, S., and R. P. Davis (1992). "Quality Implications of Machine Assignment Decisions in a Flexible Manufacturing System," *Applied Mathematical Modelling*, 16, 86–93.

Sethi, S. P., C. Sriskandarajah, G. Sorger, J. Blazewicz, and W. Kubiak (1992). "Sequencing of Parts and Robot Moves in a Robotic Cell," *International Journal of Flexible Manufacturing Systems* 4, 331–358.

Spearman, J. L., W. J. Hopp, and D. L. Woodruff (1989). "A Hierarchical Control Architecture for Constant Work-In-Progress (CONWIP) System," *Journal of Manufacturing and Operations Management* 3, 147–171.

Spence, A. M., and D. J. Welter (1987). "Capacity Planning of a Photolithography Work Cell in a Wafer Manufacturing Line," *Proceedings of the IEEE Conference on Robotics and Automation*, 702–708.

Stecke, K. E. (1989). "Algorithms for Efficient Planning and Operation of a Particular FMS," *International Journal of Flexible Manufacturing Systems* 1, 287–324.

Sullivan, G., and K. Fordyce (1990). "IBM Burlington's Logistics Management System," *Interfaces* 20, 1, 43–64.

Sumichrist, R. T., and R. S. Russell (1990). "Evaluating Mixed-Model Assembly-line Sequencing Heuristics for Just-in-Time Production Systems," *Journal of Operations Management* 9, 371–390.

Suri, R., and W. Dille (1984). "On Line Optimization of Flexible Manufacturing Systems Using Perturbation Analysis," First ORSA/TIMS Conference on Flexible Manufacturing Systems, Ann Arbor, MI.

Veermani, D., D. M. Upton, and M. M Barash (1992). "Cutting-Tool Management in Computer-Integrated Manufacturing," *International Journal of Flexible Manufacturing Systems* 4, 237–265.

Wang, L., and W. E. Wilhelm (1992). "A Recursion Model for Cellular Production/Assembly Systems," *International Journal of Flexible Manufacturing Systems* 4, 129–158.

Wittrock, R. J. (1989). "The 'Orchard' Scheduler for Manufacturing Systems," IBM Research Report RC 15275, IBM T.J. Watson Research Center, Yorktown Heights, NY.

Younis, M. A., and M. S. Mahmoud (1992). "An Algorithm for Dynamic Routing in Flexible Manufacturing Systems Under an Unpredicted Failure," *Applied Mathematical Modelling*, 16, 141–147.

Project Management

Introduction to
Project Management

1.1 WHAT IS PROJECT MANAGEMENT?

A project is any group of activities with a common goal, for which we try to control costs, resource usage, completion time, and quality of the output. Very large one-time projects often run into billions of dollars. Examples include a nuclear power plant, the Alaska oil pipeline, the Polaris submarine, the Apollo moon program, the Gulf War, and the Concorde, to name a few. However, large (one-time or multiple) projects in the range of millions to hundreds of millions of dollars are more common and undoubtedly have a larger total economic impact. Examples include new plants, schools, office buildings, genetic modification research programs, some types of electronic research and development, bridges, and highways. Projects in the thousands to one million dollar range are even more numerous and include building houses, remodeling offices, modernizing wiring and plumbing, establishing a small PC cluster, and so on. Small and very small projects are too numerous to try to catalog. For example, getting to work in the morning can be considered a project, with such activities as shower, brush teeth, put on shoes, dry hair, and so on.

Project management is a broad multi-level activity which involves strategic planning, middle- and short-term planning, scheduling, and control. (The terms as we use them here are analogous to the five-level classification of job shop scheduling problems, except that here it is more customary to speak of control rather than reactive scheduling.) As is the case for job shop scheduling, the scheduling and control levels are not necessarily the most important. We will first give a broad introduction to project management at all levels from strategic planning to control. Next we present the foundation of project scheduling without considering resource constraints. Then we consider the case of project scheduling with resource constraints from several points of view. Finally we discuss broader issues surrounding scheduling such as project design and strategic project control.

Most of the formal work in project management has focused on large one-time projects which we shall focus on also. However, the newer techniques we will develop for project scheduling apply to smaller multiple-project situations as well. Project management tends to be a very involved process, requiring the careful coordination of experts in a number of areas. It is important that the individual parts of the process be carefully organized. It requires developing and manipulating a great deal of data and reports. The scheduling and control portion (Levels 4 and 5) of project management have benefited greatly from the PC revolution. In the old slow mainframe days, only the largest projects could afford computerized help. Now it is available to all; quite sophisticated project management software is available on the PC for under $500.

A large one-time project may be defined as a group of tasks, to be performed in a definable period of time, to meet particular objectives. It possesses most of the following characteristics:

1. It possesses a unique and one-time set of tasks.
2. It will have a specific start and end.
3. The work can be broken into specific tasks.
4. Some tasks cannot start until others have finished.
5. It will have a budget, both in terms of cash and other resources.
6. Some resources will be shared with other projects.
7. It will often cross organizational boundaries.

In Section 1.2 we briefly discuss issues in strategic project management; that is, the management of projects which are large enough to significantly affect the survival of a company. In Section 1.3 we give an introduction to basic graphical and quantitative tools for planning and scheduling projects. Section 1.4 gives a brief summary of the rest of the module.

1.2 STRATEGIC PROJECT MANAGEMENT

1.2.1 Overview

Project management provides a necessary tool for carrying out the overall strategy of a firm. Therefore, it must also be considered in the full context of the organization and its larger strategy. Project management is a powerful tool that can help manage the many boundaries or interfaces among the different areas of a firm.

1.2.2 Project and Matrix Management

Morris [1988] argues that managing project interfaces or boundaries between different functional control spheres is key to project success. He argues first that project management should address the project as a system and identify:

- The subsystems of the project
- The interfaces on each subsystem needing management
- How to manage each interface

Choosing the amount of "pulling together" across an interface calls for a considerable amount of judgment. Subsystems which are in constant contact and interaction require regular human contact (liaison) in order to achieve an appropriate amount of integration, while those that just follow on from one another may be able to follow external plans and schedules alone.

Possible Methods to Achieve Liaison. In order of increasing strength, each of the following may be used to achieve liaison:

1. **Liaison position**—This person facilitates communication only. She has no authority and little responsibility.
2. **Task force**—A group is formed just for the purpose of the task, then disbands.
3. **Special team**—This is a task force that deals with recurrent issues.
4. **Coordinator**—This is a liaison person who has some formal authority. He cannot direct anyone to do anything, but he might control the budget, etc.
5. **Project coordinator**—A coordinator who has additional authority to direct people to take actions or decisions.
6. **Matrix organization**—the staff is accountable simultaneously to both the project (integrating) manager and the functional manager being integrated.
7. **Mixed project form**—A single project manager is put at the head of both the functional side and the project side.

Matrix vs. Project Manager. In matrix management, both the project manager and functional managers have authority and responsibility over work done on the project. The functional manager is more responsible for what gets done and who is assigned to do it; the project manager decides when the work is needed and how much funds will be allocated for the work. The person actually doing the work is often caught in the middle between his or her two bosses when there is conflict (for example, on how much should be spent). Matrix structures often make for a good deal of conflict and tend to have shifting interfaces.

It is generally agreed that the project manager form offers stronger leadership and unity of command and is better for large, difficult projects. It is also agreed that the matrix organization is more economical on resources; hence it is often unavoidable. The mixed mode with a full-fledged project manager controlling both the project side and the functional side as shown in Figure 1-1 is sometimes used to achieve both of these advantages at once.

1.2.3 Role of Projects in Implementing Strategy

King [1988] points out that many business strategies fail due to poor implementation. Since the way that strategies are actually implemented is by carrying out projects, this points up that good project execution is essential to corporate strategy.

Figure 1-1

Mixed Mode: Simultaneous
Project Management and
Matrix Management
Structure

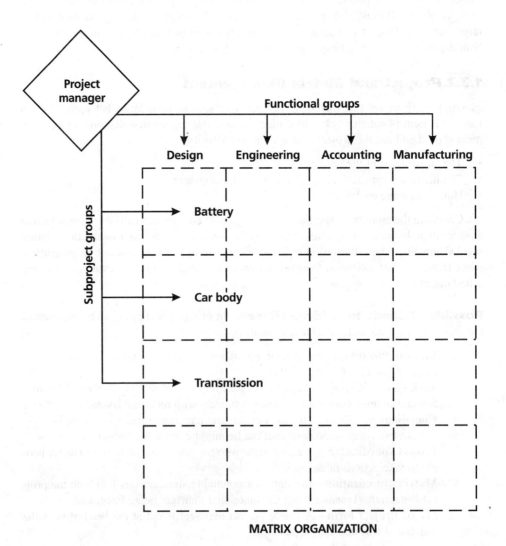

King further defines the choice elements of corporate strategy:

- **Mission**—The widely defined comparative advantage of the organization
- **Objectives**—Broad future targets of the company
- **Goals**—Specific future targets with time factors involved
- **Projects**—Resource-using activities to implement strategies and goals
- **Resource Allocations**—Allotment of resources to units, strategies, and projects

The mission must be defined carefully, since it gives scope to the other choices. A mission statement such as "we publish university business texts" is perhaps too narrow. An attempt should be made to capture generic strengths which retain flexibility as to new directions in the future. "We create and distribute educational materials world-wide" leaves more scope. The mission is the top of the hierarchy of choices; objectives are next, followed by strategy, goals, and programs/projects. Figure 1-2 illustrates strategic choice elements for a publishing company.

King [1988] argues cogently that a good approach for evaluating and choosing projects must be consistent with the higher level strategic choices which the company has made. In particular, it should be evaluated by the following criteria:

1. Does the project take advantage of a company's strength?
2. Does it avoid a company's weakness?
3. Does it help get a comparative advantage over a competitor?
4. Does it keep internal consistency among existing projects?
5. Does it address a mission-related opportunity?
6. Is the level of risk acceptable?
7. Is the level of risk consistent with existing policy guidelines?

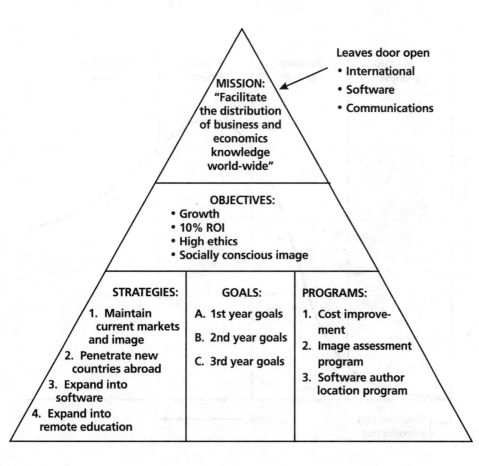

Figure 1-2

Strategic Choice Elements for a Publishing Company

King goes on to present an example of a strategic project/program evaluation methodology, which we do not present here.

1.2.4 Life-Cycle Management

Cleland and King [1988] point out that all projects have a natural life cycle from birth to death and that changes inherent in the life cycle cause shifting interfaces and broad changes over time which dramatically increase the need for the project management approach. This life-cycle property is also shared by product sales and systems development. We first discuss these broader concepts briefly and then move on to life-cycle management.

Life-Cycle Theories and Concepts. The product sales life cycle is probably the best known. Between the point of introduction and the final removal from the market (replacement by another product is more complicated) there are roughly four phases, as illustrated in Figure 1-3.

1. Introduction
2. Growth
3. Maturity
4. Decline

Actually, a product must go through research and development stages before it is introduced on the market. If we add these phases to the product we would have a larger cycle similar for products/projects/processes.

Figure 1-3

Product Sales Life Cycle

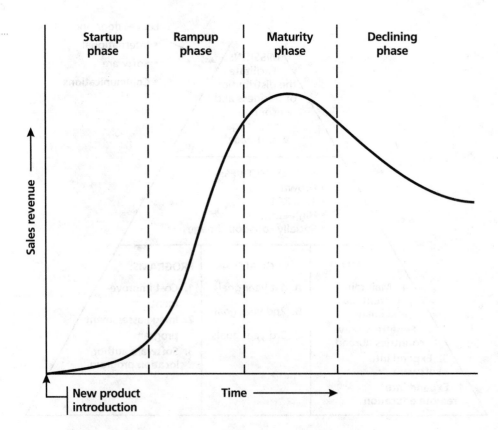

Full Product/Projects/Processes Life Cycle.

1. **Pre-design phase**—The product/project idea is born and given early evaluation. Early forecasts of performance, cost, and time aspects are made, as well as of organization and resource requirements. There is a high mortality rate in this phase.
2. **Design phase**—A much more detailed design of the project/product is developed and its feasibility and desirability are determined.
3. **Pilot testing phase**—An actual prototype of the product, system, or difficult pieces of the project are made, tested, and redesigned as necessary.
4. **Startup/Introduction phase**—The product is introduced or the main project is started up.
5. **Rampup/growth phase**—Product sales grow, and the product is expanded to its full volume.
6. **Mature phase**—Sales are full, as is the project effort size.
7. **Rampdown/decline phase**—Sales decline, phasing the project out.
8. **Termination/divestment**—The product is removed, the project is stopped, and the system is sold.

Management of the Life Cycle.   Cleland and King [1988] argue that the traditional branching tree control structure within an organization is simply not designed to cope with the ever changing management requirements dictated by the life-cycle changes within a large project. The fact that various input and output measures vary over the project's life suggests that project management must focus on universal project dimensions such as *cost, time* and *performance* (quality).

As an example of how interface problems vary over the life of a project, consider the two functions of R&D (Research and Development) and production over the life-cycle of a given product. Before the introduction of the product, R&D must be closely matched with production. R&D may be doing reliability tests which will lead to engineering changes. Production will be doing production design and process planning, which may be affected seriously by engineering changes. Thus, good communication is essential to avoid wasted resources in production.

On the other hand, in the growth phase R&D is likely to be focusing on developing the next product, while production will be ramping up production and producing long runs to avoid production losses due to setups. Thus, there will be relatively little explicit conflict between R&D and production at this phase. (On the other hand, if R&D does not consult extensively with production on good designs for the next product, there will be future conflict on the next product!)

In the decline phase, R&D will be in the design phase on the new product and will withdraw all R&D from the declining product. Production will be heavily involved in cost control. Again there will tend to be no apparent conflict, but good managers will make sure production is adequately consulted on the new design.

It is clear from our example that a full project management structure which focuses on future products as well as current products can help R&D to interact in a more useful fashion.

1.2.5 Strategic Exercises

Project and Matrix Management.

1. Write a couple of sentences on each of the following topics:

   a. What are the strengths of matrix management for accomplishing a large project versus using a project manager?
   b. What are the weaknesses?
   c. How does the mixed mode address these weaknesses?
   d. Does the mixed mode have any new weaknesses?

2. Secretaries at a university are sometimes examples of matrix management. The supervisor corresponds to functional management, while each professor represents a separate "project." Both have authority over the secretary.

   a. Discuss the strengths of this arrangement.
   b. Discuss the weaknesses.
   c. Would the mixed mode make sense?

Role of Projects in Implementing Strategy.

3. Pick a university you have some familiarity with. Try to write out a "reasonable" mission for it. Do the same with objectives and with goals. What are some projects the university has (or might have)? What resources are being competed for? Which of these projects seem consistent with the mission, objective, and goals? Which do not?

4. Revise problem 3 to be more consistent with your own value system. Describe some of the projects you might undertake to achieve these ends. What sorts of problems might you have?

Life-Cycle Management.

5. Pick four related well-known products that have been around for quite awhile and attempt (guessing is O.K.) to draw their life-cycle curves on a common time scale. You may want to show how the introduction of a product impinges on the cycle of an existing product and so on.

1.3 TOOLS FOR PLANNING, SCHEDULING, AND CONTROL

1.3.1 Overview

From now on, we shall focus on project scheduling (Level 4) in detail. Mostly we focus on the simpler case where there is a single project. That is, there are not two or more work goals competing for the same resources. We define a "simple" project as one in which project completion time is restricted by the order in which activities must be completed rather than by competition of the activities for resources. We consider simple projects in Project Management Chapters 1 and 2 and resource-constrained projects in Project Management Chapter 3. Control of projects (Level 5) is briefly discussed in Chapter 4.

History of Network (Critical Path) Methods. Henry Gantt first invented the Gantt Bar Chart around 1900. (See Figure 1-4 (a).) In its simplest form, each activity is represented by a bar with length equal to its processing time. Each activity uses one row of the graph, while the horizontal axis represents time. The user must make sure that no activity starts until its predecessors have finished. If this is done carefully and activities are started as early as possible, completion of the last activity will give the minimum duration for the project. Although it does not represent precedence constraints directly, the Gantt chart is user friendly and is used in all major software packages as a visualization aid. Note on the figure that actual completion points can be marked on the chart, showing which activities are ahead of and which are behind schedule. A Polish researcher named Adamiecki [1931] added a clever means of showing precedence constraints on the bar chart, but most people are apparently unaware of this work.

In the 1950s, the Project Evaluation and Review Technique (PERT) was developed for use in the Polaris submarine project by Malcolm et. al. [1959]. Independently, the Critical Path Method (CPM) was developed for a large duPont project by Kelly and Walker [1959]. Both used standard types of network precedence diagrams and developed

Figure 1-4(a)

Gantt Chart

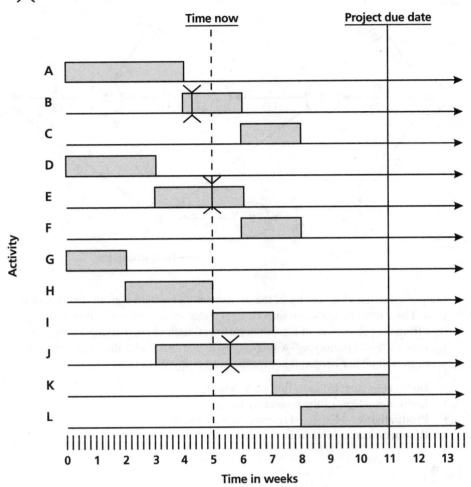

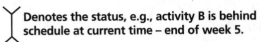

Denotes the status, e.g., activity B is behind
schedule at current time – end of week 5.

techniques for finding the longest path (critical path) for a project. PERT's network
form is shown in Figure 1-4 (b). In the standard PERT network diagram, activities are
represented by *arrows* and precedence relationships are shown by other activity arrows
pointing to the start of the activity, represented by a circle called an **event**. While this
type of network diagram shows precedences well, it loses the ability to show scaled
activities at the time they occur. The time-scaled network keeps both the correct time
scaling and accurate presentation of precedence constraints, as shown in Figure 1-4(c).
However, it is not used too frequently due to the difficulty of drawing it initially and
modifying it. Most graphical packages present both the Gantt chart and the network
graph as an alternative.

1.3.2 The Work Breakdown Structure (WBS)

The first step in drawing a network graph for a project is to list all activities which have
to be performed and to specify which must be completed before others can start (precedence relationships). A complicating factor is that we may want differing levels of detail
for differing purposes. An aid to this process is to organize the activities in the form of a
multi-level tree structure, called a work breakdown structure (WBS). The detailed level of
the work is basically a large number of work breakdown units or packages, each of which

Figure 1-4(b)

Network Diagram

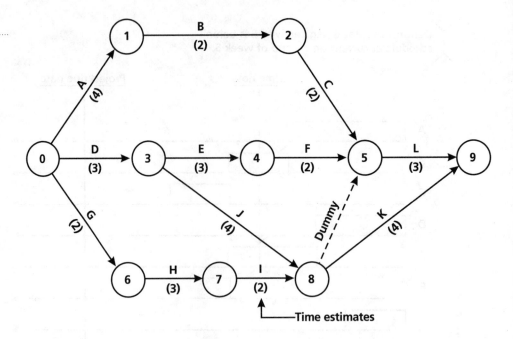

—Time estimates

is a particular detailed activity of the project and lies within a given function of the company. These units of work can then be aggregated in various ways to show the project as seen from the perspective of a given department, such as engineering, or as a major activity, such as "build prototype." A properly designed WBS will allow these groups to communicate and gather needed input for the project (by WBS unit):

- **Budgets**—Expected cash flows per period
- **Estimates**—Cost of the project by facility
- **Productivities**—Expected resource effectiveness
- **Resource usage**—Resources needed per WBS package

Figure 1-4(c)

Time-Scaled Network

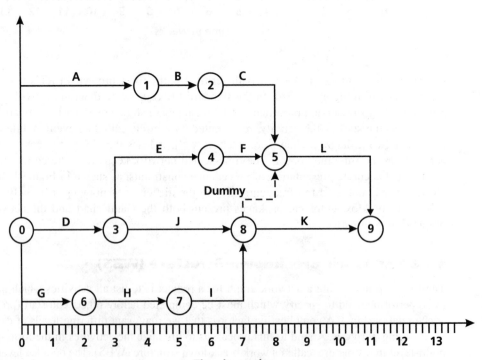

Time in weeks

If this full structure is maintained, consistent reports at all levels can be produced easily. Also, updating of any information allows the entire project to be updated; updated project networks at any level are easily constructed.

A good coding design is necessary for a useful WBS system for project control or accounting. The code should have a common meaning to all users. The top level would represent the whole project among other projects; one digit might be sufficient. The second level of the code could be the relevant major subsystems, such as design user interface, design algorithms, design platform compatibility, code user interface, code algorithms, code platform compatibility, debug user interface, etc. Two digits might be necessary for this. The code design algorithms, in turn, might be broken down into critical path algorithm, resource leveling, and so on, requiring one digit. This, in turn, might be broken down by programmer assignments, as shown in Figure 1-5.

Reports should be easily generated from the WBS structure, whether the user wants automatic reports or the ability to retrieve desired data easily.

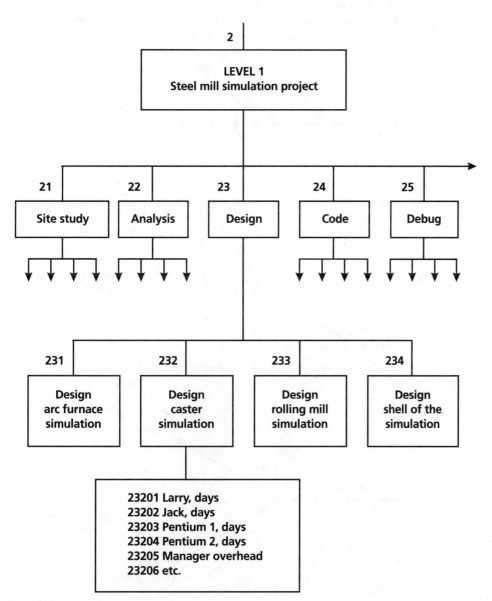

Figure 1-5

Work Breakdown Fragment for Software Project

1.3.3 Network Tools for Project Scheduling

Classic Network Tools. Networks are made up of **nodes** (circles) and **directed arcs** (arrows). In the classic **activity-on-arc (AOA)** network, each arc represents an activity and each node represents an event. It is important to be very clear about the distinction between activities and events. An **activity** is a process with a starting time, an ending time, and a duration; **events** are points in time having no duration, and which signal the start or the completion of one or more activities. For example, in the development of a prototype computer chip for anti-lock brakes, "pilot testing the chip" might be an activity, while "conditions O.K. to start the chip" would be an event.

The symbols $A < B$ are read as "A is a *predecessor* of B" and mean that B cannot start until A is finished. The appropriate AOA network representation of this is shown in Figure 1-6(a). Event 1 (the node marked **1**) represents logical permission for A to start; event 2 represents the completion of A, but it also represents the logical permission for B to start. Finally event 3 represents the completion of B.

If two activities C and D can be carried on at the same time (concurrently), but $C < E$ and $D < E$, the appropriate network representation is given in Figure 1-6(b). The interpretation of node 6 here is either that both C and D have been completed or that there is logical permission for E to start, these two statements being equivalent. In the same way, if F < G and F < H, where G and H can be concurrent, then the network representation is given in Figure 1-6(c). (Consider what the two interpretations of event 9 would be.)

Figure 1-6(a)

Simple Network Diagram

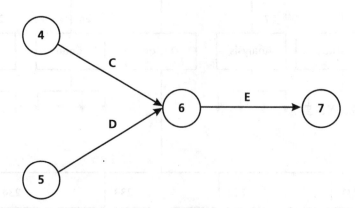

Figure 1-6(b)

Multiple Predecessors

Figure 1-6(c)

Multiple Successors

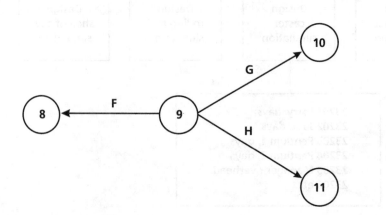

There are several *classic formation rules* for standardizing the construction of AOA networks:

1. There should be a single starting event (node).
2. There should be a single completion event.
3. The ending event of an activity should have a larger number than the starting event.
4. No two activities may have the same starting event and ending event.

It is not difficult to take any AOA network and change it to conform to these rules. For example, if there are multiple starting events, add a *dummy* "grand start" node and connect it by arrows to each starting event. Let these activities also be dummy, with zero processing times. If there is more than one completion event, a dummy "grand completion" event can similarly be added.

To get the numbering of events to follow rule 3, number the starting event as 1. Conceptually do all the activities in any legal order. Any time an event has all its predecessors satisfied, number the event by the next available integer.

Rule 4 may be problematic for the classic AOA network. For example, consider the simple project in Table 1-1 (planning and holding an open house) and the network representation in Figure 1-7(a).

For informal purposes or hand calculations, this network diagram is sufficient. However, large classic network computer programs often identify an arc by its starting and ending event and here (2,3) is ambiguous.

There are several ways out of this difficulty:

1. Number the duplicated arcs: (2,3)-#1 and (2,3)-#2 and so on.
2. Aggregate the activities to a single activity.
3. Include a dummy activity of 0 duration, shown as a dashed arc in Figure 1-7 (b).

The dummy activity allows the same logical relationships to be shown without violating rule 4. (Problem 3 will introduce another use of dummy activities, which is to cope with overlapping [but not identical] sets of predecessors for two activities.) Given these conventions, the problem of creating an appropriate network for a problem requires two types of inputs:

a. A detailed list of the individual activities
b. A specification of the precedence relations

To help provide this data, the following questions might be answered for each activity.

Activity	ID	Predecessors
Plan open house	A	—
Make and send invitations	B	A
Buy and prepare refreshments	C	A
Hold open house	D	B, C

Table 1-1

Planning and Holding an Open House

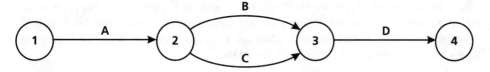

Figure 1-7(a)

Network for Planning and Holding an Open House

Figure 1-7(b)

Adding a Dummy to
Standardize the Network

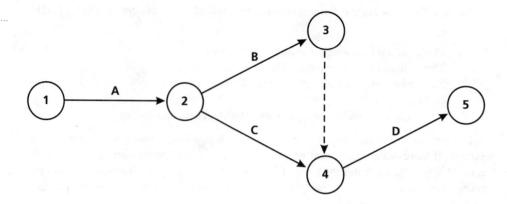

- What must happen before it can start?
- What can start once it is finished?
- Which activities can be done at the same time?

Finally, we introduce a number of concepts for classic networks which have to do with how much delaying a given activity will (or will not) delay the completion of the project:

1. The *early start time* of an activity is the earliest the activity will logically be able to start if all predecessors (and their predecessors) start as soon as they can and require exactly their expected times to complete.
2. The *early finish time* of an activity is just its early start time plus its own expected process time.
3. The *late start time* of an activity is the latest the activity will logically be able to start without delaying the project, assuming all its successors (and their successors) require exactly their expected times to complete.
4. The *late finish time* of an activity is just its early finish time plus its own expected process time.
5. The *total float* of an activity is its (late start time) – (early start time).
6. The *critical path* of a project is a chain of activities from start to finish which all have zero float. (Such activities are called critical.)

Newer Network Tools.   A number of newer network tools and tool revisions have made improvements in graphical representation possible, allowing most of the advantages of Gantt charts and AOA graphs to be combined. In addition, a number of types of logical relationships between activities are now possible that were not practical before.

Activity-On-Node (AON) Networks.   The AOA network method presented previously was the system first utilized in the development of PERT and is still used today. However, activity-on-node has a number of advantages and forms the foundation for precedence diagramming, which we describe next.

AON reverses the roles of arrows and activities. Now activities are shown as nodes (usually boxes rather than circles) and arrows show the precedence relationships directly. Events now just become the beginning or the end of an activity. Thus, the box shape makes it easy to point to events, as we shall see. Look again at Figure 1-7(b), our open house example. Note that we required five activities (one a subtle dummy) and five events to model this problem. Note also that we lost the symmetry between B and C. Figure 1-8 shows how much simpler the diagram is for AON.

Figure 1-8

AON Network for Open
House Example

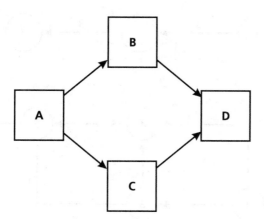

Scheduled Dates. In many projects some resources or materials won't be available until a scheduled date. Thus, the corresponding activity will not be able to start before a given date. This is denoted as **NET:** Not Earlier Than (date).

In most large projects there are, in addition, completion points of major parts of the project, called **milestones**, which will often have their own due dates. Such constraints are denoted as **NLT:** Not Later Than (date).

Sometimes a date must be precisely met. This is denoted as **ON:** Exactly ON (date) = NET and NLT.

All large software packages handle these sorts of internal date constraints. When there are no resource constraints, they can actually be handled rather easily while doing the usual calculations to get the critical path. We shall return to this in Section 2.3.3.

Precedence Diagrams. A major advantage of the AON formulation is that it can be extended to more powerful types of precedence relationships. For example, if a plasterer is plastering a building, requiring eight days, and the painter is subsequently painting it, requiring ten days, there appear to be only two activities. Yet we certainly would not like to calculate the total time required as 18 days, since we may overlap the activities and start the painting a day or so after the plastering (to allow drying). Precedence diagrams give us a powerful way to diagram these situations economically.

Precedence diagrams first appeared in 1964 in an IBM user's manual. Crandall [1973] has carried the ideas much further. There are basically four types of lag precedences to consider. All may have negative lags (leads). In all of the cases the lags refer to a lag between a predecessor i and the activity of interest j.

1. $SS_{ij} = x$ means that i must start x time units before j starts. (In our example plastering must start one day before painting.)
2. $FF_{ij} = x$ means that i must finish x units before j finishes.
3. $FS_{ij} = x$ means that i must finish x units before j starts.
4. $SF_{ij} = x$ means that i must start x units before j finishes.

(Note that the usual precedence constraint is equivalent to $FS_{ij} = 0$.)

Consider again our simple project consisting of plastering and painting a building. Each task is estimated to take three days, one day each for the first, second, and third floors. A classic network diagram allowing no overlapping is shown in Figure 1-9(a). It shows the time to execute as six days. Now suppose we allow overlapping with a one-day lag. This is shown by a time-scaled AOA network diagram in Figure 1-9(b). Now four days are required. Notice that a dummy activity and a total of seven activities are required to diagram this very simple project. This could be quite clumsy in a large diagram with a thousand major activities! The identical diagram is shown as an AON diagram in Figure 1-9(c), which still requires six activities. (Note that the arrows here were not allowed to represent lags.)

Figure 1-9(a)

AOA, No Overlapping

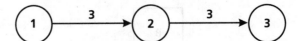

Figure 1-9(b)

Time-Scaled AOA,
Overlapping

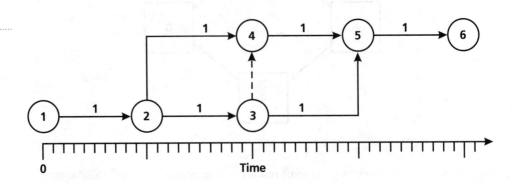

Figure 1-9(c)

AON, Overlapping

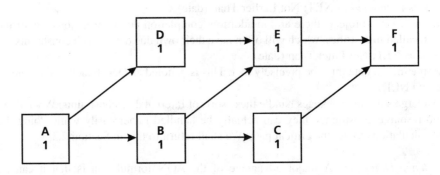

Precedence diagrams can represent this problem with only two activities, as shown in Figure 1-9(d). Notice that the beginning and ends of the activity are really treated as events in Figure 1-9(d), which gives a very clear picture of what is going on.

1.3.4 Aggregating Networks

A large project may easily have 10,000 or more activities and hundreds of different resources. It is not useful to graph such a large network on a single piece of paper. It is a tremendous task to enter that much data into a computer. Even the best heuristic algorithms would be computationally incapable of handling problems of this size. But there is a larger

Figure 1-9(d)

Precedence Diagram

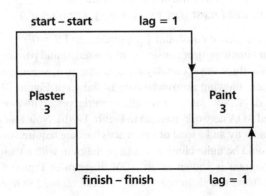

difficulty; how can the computer present this much output data in a form that the manager can grasp and determine intuitively what the solution means? The human mind is marvelous when dealing with the "big picture," but is easily swamped by excessive detail. For that matter, how can the manager decide intuitively whether the solution is probably correct, or whether it has a bad "feel" so that the formulation and programming should be checked again?

Aggregation and Hierarchical Management. This problem existed long before the computer. The project manager doesn't think in terms of 10,000 activities and 200 resources. Looking at the big picture, he/she thinks of blocks of activities, gives them names, and treats them much as if they were individual activities. The result is a much smaller project network of perhaps 25 (aggregated) activities and 4 (aggregated) resources.

Now consider one of the aggregate activity blocks, for example, Prototype. There might be an engineering manager of prototypes who manages this part of this project and of several other projects. He is responsible to the project manager for getting the prototype done on time, on budget, and with good quality. He in turn depends on a number of engineers to do various parts of the prototype. He might break the aggregate prototype block down into 20 smaller activities. (We have shown only five for simplicity.) A particular engineer might be in charge of several of these blocks.

Figure 1-10 first shows the block as the project manager sees it and then shows how the prototype block is broken down.

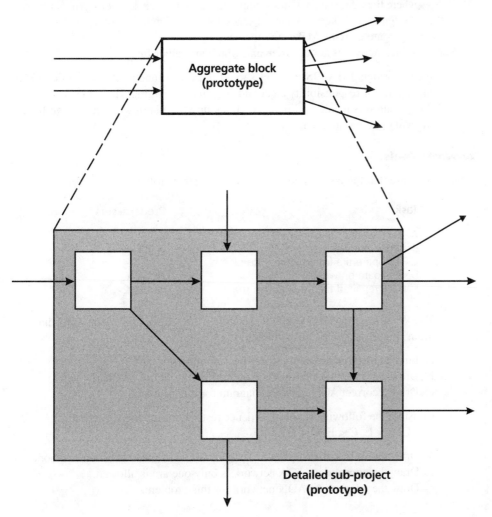

Figure 1-10

Aggregate Project and Breakdown of Prototype Activity

There is a technical problem here in how to aggregate the predecessor and successor arrows. The author has worked out a reasonable solution using precedence diagram ideas, but there is not space to discuss this here.

A final question: What is the relationship between the hierarchical project structure we have just discussed and the work breakdown schedule? The answer is easy in theory, but not so easy in practice. The multi-level project breakdown and the work breakdown structure should be identical. However, it could conceivably be useful for the detailed WBS to be more detailed than the detailed activities. For example, the WBS might be primarily accounting oriented and accounting could need fine detail. On the other hand, it could be conceivably useful for the lowest level activities to be more detailed than the lowest level WBS. For example, managers might be given an overall budget of resources and would not want the system to be second guessing them all the time. It is important that the different uses be consistent across the company.

1.3.5 Tool Exercises

Work Breakdown Structure.

1. Suppose you are embarking on a project on taking a course in production.

    a. Detail all the different activities that would be involved, including registration, buying the textbook, etc.
    b. Organize these activities in a two-level Work Breakdown Structure (WBS), where the aggregate activities might be: startup, week-1, week-2, midterm, etc.
    c. Assign some likely resource usages for each detailed activity and for each aggregate activity. Make sure they add up.
    d. Which activities are concrete and which are rather fuzzy?

2. Ideally, a detailed WBS element should not cross functional lines, in order to make lines of responsibility clear and simplify accounting. How do you suppose this situation is handled in practice? Back up your claim with one or two hypothetical or actual industrial situations.

Network Tools.

3. Suppose that the tasks in changing a flat tire are as follows:

Task	Predecessors
A Remove flat tire from car	—
B Repair the tire	A
C Get spare tire from fixture in trunk	—
D Put spare on wheel	A, C
E Place repaired tire on fixture in trunk	B, C

The Whatmeworry Engineering Consulting firm comes up with an AOA diagram (Figure 1-11) for this situation:

    a. Find an error that Whatmeworry has committed.
    b. Draw a correct AOA network diagram for the flat tire problem.
    c. Draw a correct AON network diagram for this problem.

4. Consider the following set of precedence restrictions among six activities: A < B, A < C, B < E, C < E, D < F, C < F.

    a. Draw the AOA network if more than one arc is allowed between two nodes.
    b. Draw the appropriate AOA network is only one arc is allowed.
    c. Draw the appropriate AON network for this problem.

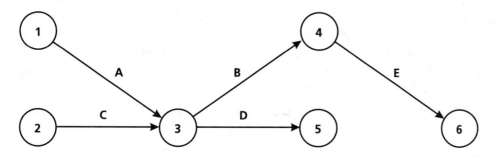

Figure 1-11

AOA Diagram for Changing a Flat Tire

d. Add some processing times to the problem and draw the time-scaled AON network for this problem.

5. Consider the following logical precedence relationships: D < A, E < A, F < C, E < B, F < B. Your boss's nephew came up with the AOA diagram in Figure 1-12.

   a. Identify an error in the nephew's network. (But don't tell your boss!)
   b. Construct a correct AOA network for the project.
   c. Construct a correct AON network diagram for this project.

6. Turn the WBS you constructed in problem 1 into a project network in the following ways:

   a. Classic AOA network
   b. Classic AON network
   c. Time-scaled AON network
   d. Precedence diagram

7. A contractor has won a bid to do part of an office building. The tasks consist of putting up a wall skeleton, doing the electrical work in those walls, putting sheet board on the walls and, finally, painting them. She has chosen crew sizes such that each activity will take 12 days.

   a. If the tasks are to be done sequentially, draw a time-scaled AON network and find the time to finish the project.
   b. If, instead, the tasks may be carried out in parallel, with a one-day lag between starting one activity and starting the next, draw a time-scaled AON network and find the reduced time to finish the project.
   c. Repeat part (b) using a precedence diagram. Which is easier?

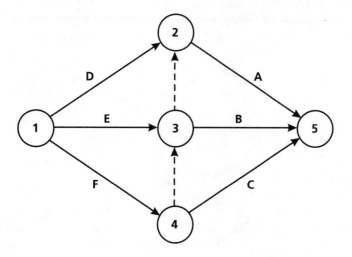

Figure 1-12

Faulty AOA Diagram

8. Now repeat problem 7 with the times for the crews being 12, 12, 6, and 12 days and the further assumption that:

   a. The sheet board activity can be split into two activities separated in time.
   b. The sheet board activity cannot be split but it may be lengthened by paying that crew for any idle time.

   What do you conclude about the importance of balancing the crews if they are to be used in parallel?

Aggregating Networks.

9. Using solutions to problem 1:

   a. Draw the detailed AON (or precedence diagram) network corresponding to your project of taking a course.
   b. Aggregate your activities in a natural way to produce a higher level network with only a few activities.
   c. Did you find the idea of leads and lags and precedence diagrams useful? Why or why not?

10. In a very large project to engineer, produce, and market an improved microwave oven, all departments were asked to cooperate to produce a multi-level project network. All other departments produced a consistent three-level network; however, marketing produced a network which corresponded to levels one and three of the other departments. Marketing resisted attempts to make it conform, claiming that "the second level just wouldn't come out right."

   a. If you were a super strong project manager and could force marketing to do what you wanted, how could you get a consistent three-level diagram?
   b. If you were a rather meek project manager and wanted to steer clear of offending marketing, how could you get a consistent three-level diagram?

1.4 SUMMARY AND PREVIEW OF THE PROJECT MANAGEMENT MODULE

Project Management Chapter 2 develops the foundations of project scheduling for the simplest case when there are no resource limitations preventing activities from being undertaken at the same time. This is often called the "network" case, because the precedence constraints create a network of activities and the principal task is to find the longest path through the network (the "critical" path) and ways to shorten it in order to meet the deadline for finishing all activities.

In Project Management Chapter 3 we consider project scheduling with limited resources. We consider two major approaches to this problem, resource leveling and dispatch heuristic methods. Finally, in Project Management Chapter 4 we take a look at project design and project execution.

Project Scheduling— Foundations

2.1 INTRODUCTION

Perhaps the most important concept in project scheduling is that of finding the longest path through the activity network (AOA formulation) or through the precedence network (AON formulation). When there are no resource constraints, this longest path (critical path) gives the minimum time in which the project can be finished. This in turn means that each activity on the critical path is especially important. We would like accurate estimates of the processing time of these activities and of the likely errors in these estimates. We would like to know how much it would cost to expedite such a critical activity and how much time we would save for the project. If there are other paths nearly as long, we would like to know if it would help to shorten some of their activities as well. In this chapter, we discuss all these issues.

We develop the special case of project scheduling when there are no resource limitations. (It is sufficient that resources be ample enough not to affect the analysis.) This case is important for itself, and also because other, more general techniques build on the critical path concepts.

In Section 2.2 we introduce a company application scenario, a new small software company called Microdimple Software. In Section 2.3 we develop the usual critical path analysis and associated "float" analysis. We also discuss a number of realistic practical considerations which need to be considered in analyzing actual projects. In Section 2.4 we discuss time/cost tradeoffs. We do a benefit/cost analysis of adding extra resources to different activities on the critical path in order to reduce the length of the critical path and thus, reduce the time to complete the project. In Section 2.5 we go back to the original simple model and add the complication that activity durations are probabilistic. Finally, in Section 2.6 we go back to the Microdimple Software Company application scenario to use our new knowledge to help solve their problem.

2.2 COMPANY APPLICATION SCENARIO— MICRODIMPLE SOFTWARE

2.2.1 Introduction

Microdimple Software is a very new software company located in Cicero, Illinois (an older suburb of Chicago). The partners, Robert Clement and his wife, Sylvia Clement, have risked their life savings to make a go of it in business. Robert has been a Professor of Industrial Engineering at the Illinois Institute of Technology for 29 years and has written 48 research articles in forecasting, scheduling, and project management. He is pleased with his work, but longs to make real applications of his research in terms of computer systems for manufacturing. Sylvia is a senior software engineer, having 25 years experience with an engineering software company. She is very experienced as part of a team developing CAD/CAM software, but would like the chance to head a software team.

Robert feels fortunate in having been able to bring his long-time secretary, Arlene Tracy, to be part of Microdimple. She will be the office manager and handle such chores as editing manuscripts, making professional charts and graphs, and controlling quality of software units (via extensive scientific testing). Sylvia also has hired Ramnath Suresh, a programmer with 12 years experience in C++ and knowledgeable in Windows. Robert and Sylvia have found it necessary to give Arlene and Ramnath three-year contracts in order to protect them from the vicissitudes of a new business. Sylvia also has hired two part-time programmers, Patty French and Tommy Satin, from the University of Illinois Circle Campus, to teach them the necessary skills and have a manpower reserve when the need arises.

Robert has a contract to write an undergraduate manufacturing textbook with extensive software. This has provided Microdimple with some needed cash flow in terms of advances from the publisher, and provides a large project to keep personnel busy when nothing else is happening. However, any major revenues from this project are several years away. Therefore, Microdimple is hungry to land industrial clients. Robert and Arlene coded 6000 names of engineers working in industry and sent out a mailing, offering inexpensive high quality consulting and/or software work. They received back about 50 replies expressing the desire for more information, which eventually boiled down to about 15 decent leads. Robert spent several months trying to follow up these leads by telephone. He became discouraged, but kept at it.

Eventually Robert's patience was rewarded. Brad Bradley, a vice-president of Arc de Triumph, a small mini steel mill, agreed to have Microdimple design, build, and implement a scheduling system for them. Robert and Sylvia made several trips to the mill and learned that the mill process had three stages. In Phase I, the electric arc furnace, scrap steel is melted. In Phase II, molten steel is poured into a continuous caster and turned into slabs. In Phase III, slabs are taken to the rolling mill, where they are made into steel plate or coils.

After a few more weeks of discussion the negotiations were finalized. Brad, Robert, and Sylvia agreed on a one-man-year effort with a 35-week deadline for a system fully tested in the mill.

2.2.2 Planning a Software Project

Robert was not too worried about his one-man-year effort quote. Microdimple billed at 2.4 times direct wages, and Microdimple's expenses were mostly fixed, so there was no way he could not be helped financially by the project. However, Arc de Triumph's insistence on the eight-month deadline was really worrisome. He felt meeting the deadline was possible, but very tight. Furthermore, he had never done a large software project of this kind before. Worse than that, he was well aware that software projects were famous for coming in at twice the time and/or cost budget, or getting bogged down and not finishing at all.

Since Robert felt that it was strategic to do very well with his first client, he decided to do some formal project planning for his own project. (In the following table he abbreviated "arc furnace" as ARC, "continuous caster" as CAST, and "rolling mill" as ROLL.) First he divided the work into manageable chunks or activities and listed them; then to each he added who would be assigned to do it, and a time estimate for its completion, as shown in Table 2-1.

The assignments clearly affected how quickly the project could be finished, how well it would be executed, and how much it would cost. Some of Robert's thoughts on assignments were as follows:

1. At this stage, Robert needed to do all study and design personally; however, Sylvia should train in this aspect as there was time.

Table 2-1

Activities for the Scheduling
System Project

Activity	Assignment	Plan Duration Weeks
A. Study Mill Overall	Rob	2
B. Design Overall	Rob	2
C. Study ARC	Rob	1
D. Study CAST	Rob	1
E. Study ROLL	Rob	1
F. Design ARC	Rob	2
G. Design CAST	Rob	2
H. Design ROLL	Rob	3
I. Code ARC	Patty	3
J. Code CAST	Tom	3
K. Code ROLL	Ram	6
L. Debug ARC	Patty	2
M. Debug CAST	Tom	2
N. Debug ROLL	Ram	2
O. Quality ARC	Arlene	2
P. Quality CAST	Patty/Tom	2
Q. Quality ROLL	Ram	2
R. Design Schedule Shell	Rob	3
S. Code Schedule Shell	Sylvia	3
T. Debug Schedule Shell	All	2
U. Quality Schedule Package	All	3
V. MILL TEST	All (part time)	8

2. Ramnath had enough experience to program with little supervision.

3. Patty and Tom were little more than trainees, and hence supervising them for this first project would probably absorb Sylvia's energies full-time. This would bring them quickly up to speed for future projects.

4. Ramnath should do the rolling mill, since it was the most difficult of the three phases and he was more experienced than the two new programmers.

5. Any of the programmers or Arlene could do quality control, but preferably not on their own code.

6. Since there was no shortage of personnel for the final stages of the project, Robert should design the full scheduling program, Sylvia code it, and everyone be involved with quality control and in the final testing at the mill.

Robert still wasn't sure whether the entire project could be done within eight months (35 weeks), so he decided to draw an AON (activity on node) project diagram. The result is shown in Figure 2-1. As is usual in an AON diagram, the 22 activities are shown in boxes. Precedence relations are shown by arrows. It is important in such a diagram not to let the arrows overwhelm and confuse the diagram. Thus, at the top it is natural to let the arrows branch out from DESIGN OVERALL, rather than having three separate arrows. Similarly, an arrow is needed between CODE ARC and DESIGN SCHED SHELL. Rather than letting the arrow cross other things, we simply only show the start and the end of the arrow; there is no confusion. We connect CODE CAST and CODE ROLL to the same box in the same way. Similarly, QUAL ARC, QUAL CAST, and QUAL ROLL are all predecessors of DEBUG SCHED SHELL and are shown in the same way.

Robert also listed the estimated times for each activity next to the appropriate activity. He was very interested in how long the whole project would take. He knew that if one ignored any conflicts due to people being assigned to two different activities at the same time, this total time could be found by finding the longest path through the network.

Robert did not really need any fancy algorithms to find the longest path ignoring people problems. It clearly went through DESIGN ROLL and CODE ROLL and also, looking at only two choices after that, also went through DESIGN SCHED SHELL and CODE SCHED SHELL. Thus, listing all activities and times on the critical path gave the information shown in Table 2-2.

Figure 2-1

Mill Scheduling Software
Project Diagram

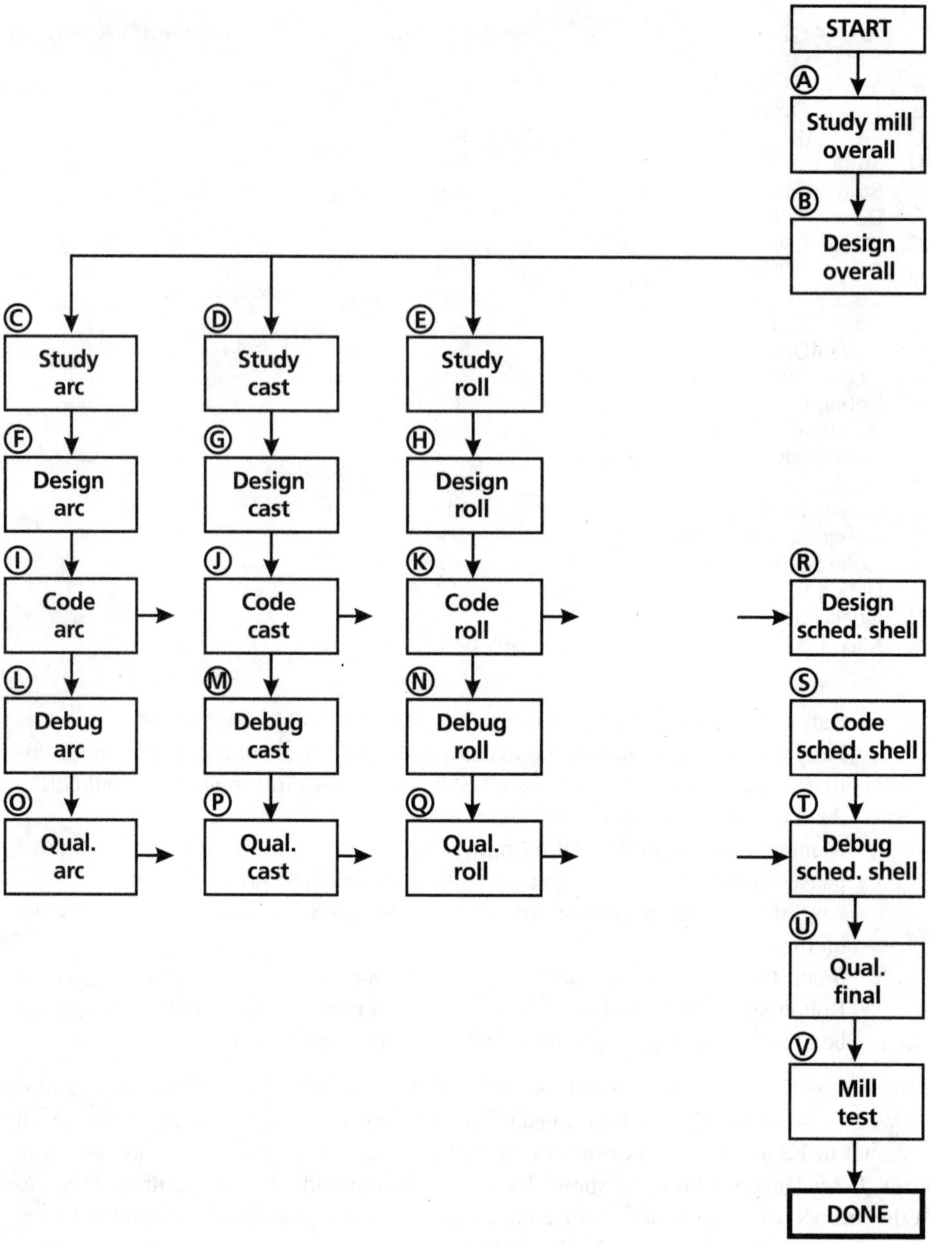

Table 2-2

Critical Path Activities

Activities	Weeks
STUDY MILL OVERALL	2
DESIGN OVERALL	2
STUDY ROLL	1
DESIGN ROLL	3
CODE ROLL	6
DESIGN SCHED SHELL	3
CODE SCHED SHELL	3
DEBUG SCHED SHELL	2
QUALITY FINAL	3
MILL TEST	8
Total Time	33 Weeks

This was within his 35-week deadline, but Robert next had to make sure there were no resource conflicts which would distort this estimate. Sure enough, scheduling everything as early as possible would have him doing activities C, D, and E at the same time. However, there was really no problem. Since E was on the critical path, it should be done first. Thus, if he simply added the constraints E < D and D < C, the critical path was unaffected (and did not shift) and a resource-corrected diagram resulted which still took 33 weeks.

Robert determined he was in pretty good shape. He decided to implement the plan and put pressure on those doing critical activities to "step lively."

How does this schedule get Microdimple into trouble? Can Robert improve his project planning skills enough to save Microdimple? These issues will be discussed in Section 2.5.

2.3 NETWORK ANALYSIS

2.3.1 Overview

In this section we consider a single project that has no resource constraints to complicate our life. (Actually, as in the case of Microdimple, there may be resource constraints, or even resource conflicts, but it is still useful to solve the relaxed no-resource-constraint problem to get insight about the harder one.)

2.3.2 Critical Path Analysis

Proposition 1. Consider a project without resource constraints and all activities available. To minimize any increasing function of project duration, it suffices to minimize the duration itself. Each activity should be started as soon as its predecessors are satisfied. The project's duration will be equal to the longest path through the network, termed the **critical path**.

Next we turn to a procedure to calculate the least possible duration of the project and also determine the critical path which has this duration. First we need some definitions.

For each activity define the following:

1. **Earliest start time (ES)**—The time the activity would start if every predecessor started at its earliest start time (and had no delays).
2. **Earliest finish time (EF)**—ES plus activity processing time.
3. **Latest finish time (LF)**—The latest the activity could finish without delaying the project completion time, assuming no other delays.
4. **Latest start time (LS)**—LF minus activity processing time.

For computational purposes we stylize the network as follows:

1. If there is not a unique starting activity, create a dummy activity with 0 processing time as a predecessor of all activities in the network.
2. Similarly, if there is not a unique finish activity, create a dummy completion activity with 0 processing time as a successor to all activities in the network.
3. Find an activity with no predecessors but activity 1, and label it activity 2.
4. Find an activity with no predecessors but $1, 2, \ldots, k$, and label it activity $k + 1$.
5. Let the last activity be n.

Proposition 2. Early and Late Start Times, Early and Late Finish Times, and the Critical Path may be calculated as follows (Set start time = 0):

A. Calculation of Early Start and Finish Times:

1. ES of activity 1 = 0 (process time = 0); EF of activity 1 = 0.
2. For each activity in turn by increasing number:

   a. The ES is the maximum of the EF of the immediately preceding activities.
   b. The EF is the ES + (activity process time).

3. ES of the finish activity n is the length of the critical path = C.

B. Calculation of Late Start and Finish Times:

1. LF of activity n (dummy) $= C$ (or the project's due date if there is one). LS of activity $n = C$.
2. For each activity in turn by decreasing number:

    a. The LF is the minimum of the LS of the immediately succeeding activities.
    b. The LS is the LF – (activity process time).

C. A chain of activities from beginning to end with ES = LS, when there is no due date (or ES + [Due Date – C] = LS in general) is called the critical path. There may be more than one.

Many texts develop these ideas in terms of AOA networks. It is somewhat easier to do things in terms of AON networks:

1. Proofs are easier.
2. There are no subtle dummies to add in the diagram.
3. More complex precedence ideas require AON.

Thus, if you have had this material before and are used to the arrow being the activity, you should make sure and practice a bit using AON.

Example 2-1. The Zeta Zeta Zeta Fraternity at Polycalpoly wants to build and enter an outstanding float in the annual interfraternity floataway. There are a number of activities required. Activity A is to file the paperwork to get the permit. Activity B is to buy all the float supplies; C is to rent, outfit, and check out a flatbed truck; D is to obtain the permit itself; E is to make thousands of "flowers" from crepe paper; F is to erect chicken wire superstructures on the truck to hold the flowers; and G is to train the driver (and watch his sobriety). Activity H is to attach all the flowers to the chicken wire, and I is final rehearsal. The resulting problem input data is shown in Table 2-3.

We graph (see Figure 2-2) an AON version of the problem. We number the activities according to the numbering method given above. We also write the activity process time above the activity. Above the activity we leave room to write (ES, LS | EF,LF) as they are calculated for the activity.

As we begin to calculate from activity start, we will calculate and write in the ES and EF values on the activities in alphabetical order. For activity start these are 0 and 0; for A these are 0 and 5, and so forth. There are no real calculations until we get to activity H. The early finishes of its three predecessors are 6, 9, and 8. Thus, it cannot start until the maximum of these or until time 9. We finally determine that the early finish for the project is 16. Working backward to find late start and finish values, there are no real calculations until we get to activity C . Since its two successors can start no later than 6 and 4 respectively, activity C can finish no later than the minimum of these or 4.

The longest path in this network is activity C plus activity G plus activity I, which has a total length of $4 + 10 + 2 = 16$, which is the minimum duration for the project. (This corresponds to getting the truck, training the driver, and the final rehearsal. The school

Table 2-3

Float Activity List

Activity	Direct Predec.	Activity Type	Length (hours)
A	—	paperwork	5
B	—	buy supplies	4
C	—	get truck	4
D	A	get permit	1
E	B	make "flowers"	5
F	C	wire superstructure	4
G	C	train driver	10
H	D, E, F	put on flowers	4
I	G, H	rehearsal	2

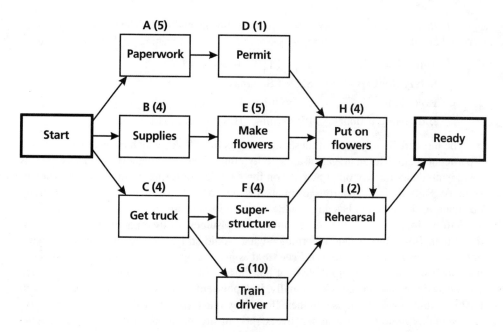

Figure 2-2

AON Network for the
Example

requires an official trainer who is not always available. How much will it help to bribe the trainer?) Critical activities may also be defined as precisely those for which the late start is equal to the early start; that is, the activity can have no leeway without delaying the entire project. For non-critical activities, however, there is some scheduling flexibility. Consider, for example, the scheduling of Activities E and H in Figure 2-3, that is making the flower structure and attaching the flowers. Making the structure can start no earlier than time 4, and the flowers must be on no later than time 14. Since an interval of length 10 is available, and the two activities require only a total duration of 9, there is one unit of spare time to play with. This kind of flexibility is called **float**. Along the critical path there is no float, while along other paths there is some amount of float. There are a variety of ways to quantify this measure of scheduling flexibility with respect to individual activities. (In the following definitions we omit subscripts for activities for simplicity.)

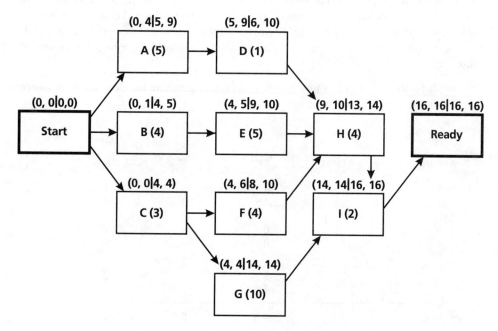

Figure 2-3

Solution of the Example

Definition: Consider an activity with process time p_j, and let $P(j)$ be the set of predecessors and $S(j)$ be the set of the successors. We define $j \varepsilon P$ as meaning j belongs to the set P:

1. **Total float** $TF_j = LF_j - EF_j = LS_j - ES_j$
2. **Safety float** $SF_j = LS_j - \max_{i \varepsilon P}(LF_i)$
3. **Free float** $FF_j = \min_{k \varepsilon S}(ES_k) - EF_j$
4. **Independent float** $IF_j = (\min_{k \varepsilon S}(ES_k) - \max_{i \varepsilon P}(LF_i) - p_j)^+$

The most frequently used of these measures is **total float**, which measures float along a particular path. The manager of an activity could delay that activity by TF_j as long as there is no delay for any other activity on the path before it (upstream) or after it (downstream). Thus, it is a generous estimate of the cushion, since it assumes no activity upstream or downstream has any trouble meeting its schedule.

Safety float is somewhat more cautious; it assumes upstream activities have squandered their float already, and determines what would still be left for this activity (trying not to leave any for downstream). **Free float** is just the opposite. Assuming that all activities downstream will use up their float but those upstream will behave well, how much will be available for this activity? Finally, **independent float** is very conservative. If both upstream and downstream use up their float, how much (if any) will be left for this activity? Note this could actually be negative; delays upstream and downstream might ruin the project even if this activity is on time. By convention we call the float zero in this case. Table 2-4 illustrates the various types of floats for all the activities in our example.

Gantt Charts. A solution to a network problem can be visualized very well by presenting it in bar chart form. Each activity is represented in its own row by a bar starting at its early start time, and ending at its early finish time. A Gantt chart for the Zeta Zeta Zeta Fraternity problem we have been looking at is shown in Figure 2-4.

A Gantt chart may be made even more useful by marking the late finish times on the graph as well (not done in Figure 2-4). Then, if the early finish time and the late finish time are equal, we know the activity is on the critical path; in general we can see directly which activities have leeway and which do not, and which precedences cause the problem.

2.3.3 Realistic Concerns

The known activity time, no-resource-constraints network model that we have solved in Section 2.3.2 is very easy to use, and in fact it is used very widely. Yet a little reflection will show us that there are a number of important ways in which this model is not realistic, some of which were discussed in an intuitive fashion in Section 1.3.3. A few of these are:

1. It is very difficult to think of any real project planning problem where resource limitations may really be ignored!

Table 2-4

Various Floats for Activities in the Example

Activity	TF	SF	FF	IF
A	4	4	0	0
B	1	1	0	0
C	0	0	0	0
D	4	0	3	0
E	1	0	0	0
F	2	2	1	1
G	0	0	0	0
H	1	0	1	0
I	0	0	0	0
Average Slack	1.4	0.8	0.6	0.1

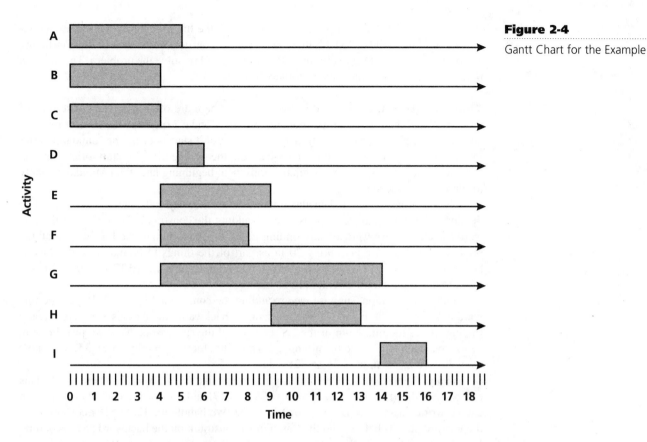

Figure 2-4

Gantt Chart for the Example

2. Time constraints such as: "Don't start C until time 20," or "Finish F by time 33," or "Finish D exactly at time 27" are very common. (See Section 1.3.3.) This is due to such issues as to when a given resource becomes available or when a piece of the project has been promised to be finished.

3. In many cases we must do activity A *or* activity B *or* activity C. But the network model assumes all activities are to be finished; that is, that we have to complete A *and* B *and* C. How can we deal with this?

4. Finally, in point of fact, projects are rarely well known in advance. Long time-span problems are almost always highly uncertain in duration times; often we don't even know which activities will actually occur.

5. Miscellaneous other issues exist.

We will address some of these issues here, some in later parts of this chapter, some in Project Management Chapter 3.

Resource Limitations. One way in which a planner may make use of a simple network model with no resource constraints is to add a number of judgmental constraints to make sure that the actual resource constraints will not cause problems. For example, suppose that in building an apartment house there is only one cement mixer, but two independent activities both require it, for example, "pouring the foundation" and "pouring the curbs and sidewalks." The scheduler may know intuitively that the foundation is more critical to the product, and thus, may simply add a constraint that pouring the foundation *must* come before pouring the curbs and sidewalks. This is a judgmental constraint rather than a logical constraint. Experienced schedulers are often very good at this. However, a difficulty in doing a more sophisticated analysis is that the scheduler may not bother to state which are judgmental constraints and which are real logical constraints. In fact, he/she may not even understand the issue very well. Further, if it is not clear what judgmental constraints to add, the scheduler will probably follow rules of thumb from industry or long personal experience. Here, use of a resource-constrained scheduling package would probably be superior.

A somewhat different approach would be to solve the problem without adding constraints, find the points at which there are resource conflicts, move one of the conflicting activities later (or earlier) to eliminate the conflict, and re-solve the problem. This method is called resource leveling, and is studied in Section 3.3.

Time Constraints. As noted in Section 1.3.3 there are often practical constraints of the form "don't start pouring the foundation until Monday" (perhaps the cement mixer is busy with a different project until that point), or "don't start pouring the foundation after Friday" (perhaps to avoid time-and-a-half on the weekend), or "start brickwork on Monday" (the bricklayer is not available until then; beginning later than Monday is likely to run into the weekend).

These are easily handled in the forward and backward calculations we learned in Section 2.3.3. For example, suppose we are adding the constraint $ES_j >= 20$. In the forward calculations we were already finding ES_j as the maximum of the LS times of all the predecessors. Now we just throw 20 in as part of the things to be maximized. Thus, if before $ES_j = \max (10,17,12) = 17$, now we will have $ES_j = \max (10,17,12, 20) = 20$, and we continue the forward calculations as before.

In a similar fashion, suppose we are adding the constraint $LF_k <= 32$. We do the forward calculations, as before. In the subsequent backward calculations we were already finding LF_k as the minimum of the LS times of all the successors. Now we just throw in 32 as a part of the things to be minimized. Thus, if before $LF_k = \min (38,36,35) = 35$, now we will have $LF_k = \min(38,36,35,32) = 32$.

Finally, suppose we have an equality constraint like $ES_i = LS_j = 17$, where $p_i = 5$. This can be considered to be two constraints, $ES_i >= 17$, and $LS_i <= 17$. The latter constraint can be written as $LF_i <= ES_i + p_i$, or $LF_i <= 22$. We handle the Early Start constraint on the forward pass as before, and the Late Finish constraint on the backward pass as before. It is also possible to handle more complicated time constraints in a similar fashion, but we do not consider this here.

"Or" Constraints. The logic of the network itself is too simplified and limited for many real situations. The network diagrams we have seen have no flexibility at all as to which activities must be performed. In the logic we have studied, all predecessors must be accomplished before doing a given activity. These are called **and** constraints.

For example, if we have a flat tire, then "remove flat tire" and "get spare tire" must both precede "put spare on wheel." But in many real-life examples we have some choices among the predecessors, which are then called **or** predecessors. For example, if we have a flat tire, we could "remove flat tire" or we could "drive on the flat to the service station" before "remove flat tire."

In AOA notation, we may show alternate precedence constraints with a circular connection between those activities, as displayed in Figure 2-5.

For a network without resource constraints, mixtures of "ands" and "ors" are not too difficult to handle within the forward/backward calculations. If the incoming activities are all "and" we determine early start as the maximum of the early finishes of the predecessors, as before. If they are all "or," we take the minimum early finish times of these activities. We create enough dummy activity events so that there will not be a mixture of "ands" and "ors" as predecessors of a given activity.

2.3.4 Network Exercises

Critical Path Analysis.

1. For the project shown in Figure 2-7:
   a. Show the same project in AOA format.
   b. Determine the critical path and its length.
   c. Calculate ES, EF, LS, and LF and the total float for each activity.

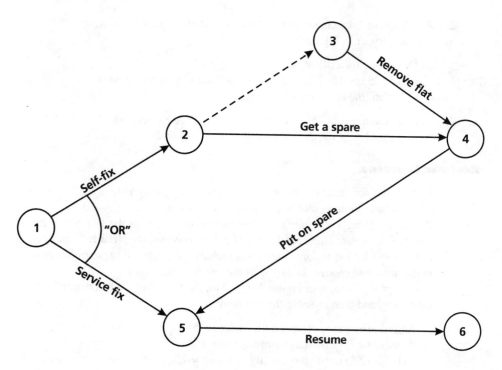

Figure 2-5

Illustration of "Or"
Constraints for an AOA
Network

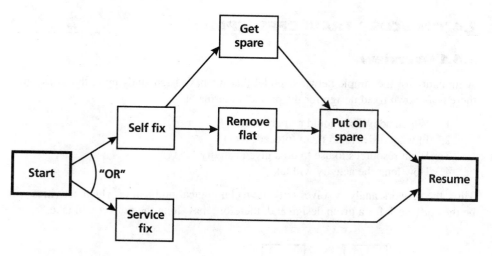

Figure 2-6

Same "Or" Constraints for
AON Version

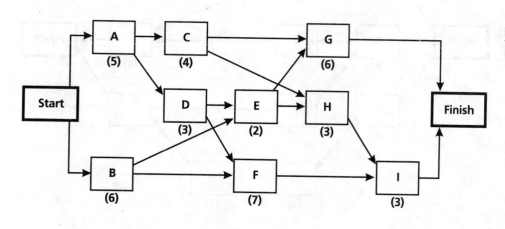

Figure 2-7

Figure for Problem 1

2. For Problem 1, calculate all four types of floats for each activity.
3. For the project in Figure 2-8:

   a. Determine the critical path and its length.
   b. Calculate ES, EF, LS, and LF for each activity in the network.
   c. Calculate the total slack for each activity.

4. Convert the network shown in Figure 2-9 to an AON network.
5. Repeat Problem 3 for the network shown in Figure 2-9.

Realistic Concerns.

6. Repeat Problem 5, assuming that activities coming into node 6 are "or" related, and activities coming into node 10 are "or" related.
7. Repeat Problem 3, assuming that the two predecessors of the finish activity use the same unique resource, and cannot be done concurrently. (**Hint:** *It must be that either* I < J *or* J < I. *Solve the two possible problems with the extra precedence constraint, and choose the one with the smaller duration.*)
8. For the project shown in Figure 2-9, add all the following time constraints simultaneously, and then re-solve the problem:

   a. Activity (6,8) cannot start until time $t = 15$.
   b. Activity (4,7) must start before time $t = 6$.
   c. Activity (2,5) must start exactly at time $t = 7$.

2.4 TIME/COST TRADEOFFS (CPM)

2.4.1 Overview

A limitation of the simple network model that we have been studying is that it assumes there is a known fixed design for the project in terms of:

1. Which activities should be performed
2. In what order to do them (precedences)
3. What resources to use to do a given activity
4. How long the activity will take

Thus, the network analysis solves only the technological problem of which activities will be the bottleneck for a given design and, therefore, how long the project will take.

Figure 2-8

Figure for Problem 3

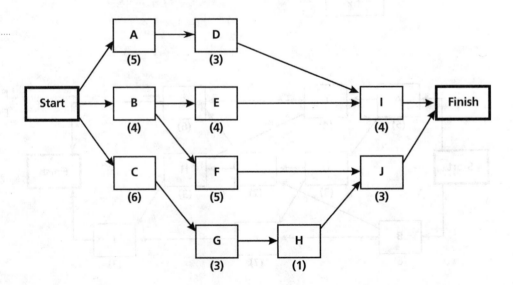

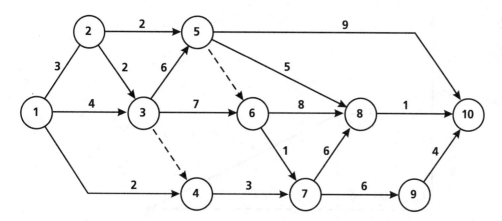

Figure 2-9

Figure for Problems 4, 5, and 8

The design issues we have just mentioned are very often the most important part of project management. But design is such a complex issue, it is hard to quantify the process in a simple way. Perhaps we could be less ambitious and look at the following restricted design question.

Suppose we could express the duration of an activity as a function of how much resources we are willing to expend doing it. To put it even more simply, suppose the durations of activities on the critical path depend on how much money we spend on them, and that it is worth money to finish the project faster. Which activities should we "crash" (expedite) and by how much to achieve an optimal tradeoff between project length and expediting money spent? This question is discussed in the following section.

2.4.2 Basic Analysis

We study here the classic CPM model.

CPM Assumptions.

1. Each activity's duration is a decreasing linear function of the cost expended.
2. Allowable durations are bounded by a maximum and a minimum.
3. There is a linear reward for each day the project duration is reduced.

Definition of Terms. (j subscript suppressed)

m	Minimum possible duration
M	Maximum allowed duration
t	Actual activity duration
C_o	Total activity cost at duration m
c	Cost per unit of expediting activity time
K	Total cost of activity at actual duration t
d	Reward for each day project duration is reduced

Figure 2-10 shows a schematic of the time/cost tradeoff for a given activity.

First we will present an example, to show that small problems can be solved optimally by a simple marginal procedure, which might be called a benefit/cost method. Then we will present a linear programming formulation for solving larger problems.

Example 2-2. Lucky Luke, the CEO of Lucky Luke's Lovely Lamps (LLLL), wishes to create a new lamp and make a splash at the Lamp Exposition, which is 12 months away. He figures it will take the company three months to design the lamp. Once this is finished, it will take him four months to turn out the prototype, and five months for testing, quality control, and final changes. Marketing needs seven months after the lamp is designed to

Figure 2-10

Activity Time/Cost Tradeoff

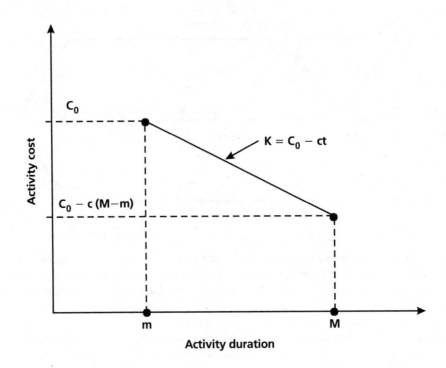

adequately market to potential customers before the Expo. Lucky would rather finish the lamp in less than 12 months. Each month that he can cut off that time he feels to be worth $45,000. He has the capability for shortening each activity by expending extra money, as shown in Tables 2-5 and 2-6.

We start with all activities scheduled at their maximum (original) length. Table 2-5 gives the problem input, and Table 2-6 shows a breakdown of the initial cost of the project. By inspecting our project, we see that the critical path of the initial network is A-B-D, but that C will also become critical by the time two months are taken off the duration of either B or D. Among the critical activities, D is the least expensive to expedite. A two-month reduction in its time costs $40,000 and saves $90,000 in project duration costs. Thus, total costs are reduced to $840K + $40K − $90K = $790K. But at this point C also

Table 2-5

Small Time/Cost Example (time in months, money in thousands of dollars)

Activity	Pred.	M_j	m_j	c_j	C_{oj}
A (design)	—	3	1	$40	$140
B (prototype)	A	4	2	40	180
C (market)	A	7	3	10	110
D (test)	B	5	2	20	130

d = cost per month of project duration = $45

Table 2-6

Cost of Initial Maximum Time (12) Solution

Activity	Duration	Cost (1000s)
Project	12	$540
A	3	60
B	4	100
C	7	70
D	5	70
Total Cost		$840

becomes critical so that the A-C path and the A-B-D path must be reduced simultaneously for further savings. The alternatives for further reduction are:

1. Expedite A at a cost of $40K a month, saving 45K – 40K = $5K a month.
2. Expedite B and C at a combined cost of $50K a month, saving 45K – 50K = –$5K a month.
3. Expedite C and D at a combined cost of $30K a month, saving 45K – 30K = $15K a month.

Thus, expediting C and D looks best. But we can only reduce D one more month before hitting its minimum. Thus, total costs are reduced to $790K – 15K = $775K, and D cannot be further reduced.

We can still reduce A by two months, saving $10K. Thus, total costs are reduced to $775K – $10 K = $765K. Now the only way to further shorten the critical path is to simultaneously reduce activities C and B, but this will *increase* the cost of the project. Therefore, the cost of $765,000 is optimal.

For larger projects, this solution method will not be very practical because as we shorten the project length, more and more paths become critical simultaneously. Therefore solutions to large-scale time/cost problems rely on computerized techniques. When the costs are linear, or piece-wise linear, the problem is easily solved by linear programming. We present the linear programming (LP) formulation for the linear case we have been working with here.

Proposition 3. Given the time/cost definitions presented earlier, and using AON notation, j represents an activity, $S(j)$ all its successor activities, ES_j represents early start time, and N is the finish activity. The problem of minimizing total project time/cost may be solved as:

$$\min (D)(ES_N) - \Sigma c_j p_j \quad \text{(up to a constant)}$$

Subject to:

$$ES_1 = 0$$
$$ES_j + p_j <= ES_k \text{ for all } j \text{ and all } k \; \varepsilon \; S(j)$$
$$m_j <= p_j <= M_j$$

This linear programming formulation is important for several reasons:

1. It is necessary for solving large problems.
2. It gives a very simple direct way of starting the problem solution.
3. It allows many variations to be solved simply by adding other constraints.
4. It is easily generalized to the (convex) piece-wise linear case.

2.4.3 Adding Realism

Practical Issues. One important consideration in looking at time/cost tradeoffs is that crashing one activity can drastically change the cost of crashing another, due to setup costs. For example, suppose the completion of the basement of a building is on the critical path and we bring in a second cement mixer for a couple of days to crash the time required to pour the basement. But this will not only provide extra pouring capacity for the basement; it will also make it quite cheap to do the driveway and walks as well, since a good part of those costs were the setup costs involved in getting the equipment in place.

Doing time/cost tradeoffs for networks with leads and lags involves relatively little change to the LP, since the problem remains convex. On the other hand, adding "or" precedences will often destroy the convex nature of the problem, and so linear programming cannot be used with any safety. Since project planning is a very large economic activity, and since most large projects involve extensive design choices (involving "or"), designing effective heuristics for this case seems challenging.

Newer Ideas. It is not always possible to vary an activity duration smoothly and efficiently simply by spending a little more money on it. Cement mixers do not come in 1.78
sizes. We can usually assign only 0, 1, 2, and so on. However, in some cases we can achieve,
for example, 1.5 by having one mixer shared by two activities which are conveniently
placed. In some cases it is possible to make several different designs for an activity, with various amounts of resources, various amounts of cash outlay, and various amounts of time.

If we have the choice of four such activity designs for an activity on the critical path
we might show the situation as shown in Figure 2-11. Notice that while before we had to
mark an activity only as to time required t, we must now mark the amount of each resource
required R.

In the next chapter we will learn methods for dealing with such resource constrained
problems when there are only "and" constraints. Since in our current example, the network
will have both "and" and "or" constraints, a somewhat more complicated method would be
needed. Suppose that we had a method for dealing with just "and" constraints, as we will
in the next chapter. We could then find a reasonable solution to our problem as follows.

Possible Iterative Method.

1. Make an initial guess as to which activity to pick for each "or" activity set.
2. The problem now has only "and" constraints; solve by methods discussed in
   Project Management Chapter 3.
3. Pick a likely "or" activity to be varied.
4. Solve the problem for each value of the "or" activity.
5. Reset the pick for that activity to whichever choice did the best.
6. Terminate when there is no activity that can be improved by itself.

2.4.4 Time/Cost Exercises

Basic Analysis.

1. A small renovation project consists of the activities listed in Table 2-7. With each
   job is listed its normal or maximum time and its minimum or crash time.

Figure 2-11

Time/Resource Alternatives
on the Critical Path

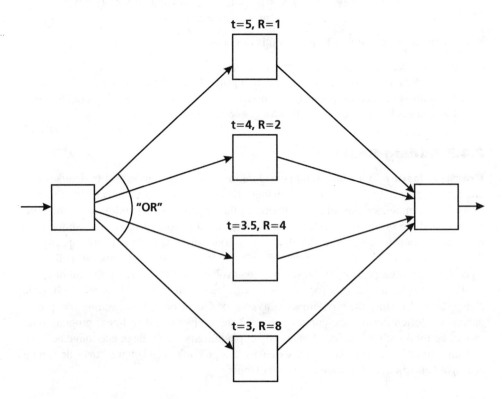

t=5, R=1

t=4, R=2

"OR"

t=3.5, R=4

t=3, R=8

Activity	Predec.	Normal Time(days)	Crash Time(days)	Expediting Cost/Day
A	——	9	6	$30
B	——	8	5	35
C	——	15	10	40
D	A	5	3	20
E	B	10	6	25
F	D, E	2	1	50

Table 2-7

Table for Problem 1

   a. What is the normal project length, and what is the fully crashed project length?

   b. Find the minimum cost of shortening the schedule one day, two days, three days, and so forth.

   c. Project duration penalty costs are $55 a day. What is the optimal length schedule?

   d. What are the scheduled durations for activity in the solution in (c)?

2. Solve Problem 1 using a linear programming code.
3. Change the inputs in Problem 1, so that after an activity is shortened by a day, the cost of expediting goes up $5 a day, and that after shortening another day, the cost of expediting goes up another $5 a day for further expediting. Otherwise, the problem is unchanged. Explain a way to change this into an equivalent problem using the original time/cost methodology. (**Hint:** *Change each activity into three activities in series.*)
4. Formulate the problem in Problem 3 as a linear programming problem.
5. Solve Problem 4 by using a linear programming code.
6. Formulate a linear programming model for a variation of the time/cost problem in which there is no overall penalty cost, but there is a linear penalty cost for any excess (weighted tardiness) if the entire project is not finished by time T.
7. Consider Example 2-1 on page PM-26 (Zeta Zeta Zeta):

   a. Modify it in an interesting way to be a time/cost example.

   b. Solve the example.

Practical Issues/Newer Ideas.

8. Modify Example 2-1 (Zeta Zeta Zeta) to be a time/cost example with both "and's'" and "or's."

   a. Diagram it.

   b. Find a good solution.

   c. Can you argue whether or not it is optimal?

9. Create and discuss an interesting time/cost project where crashing any activity on the critical path affects every other activity on the critical path.

   a. Find a good solution.

   b. Can you suggest a general heuristic procedure for working with such problems?

2.5 UNCERTAIN PROJECTS

2.5.1 Overview

In general, deterministic models are much easier to deal with than probabilistic models. For scheduling problems and project management problems with horizons of less than six months, deterministic models are often adequate, especially if updated from time to time with new information. But project management with horizons of a year, several years, or even decades are a different story. Uncertainties (and even vagueness) dominate the landscape.

The standard assumptions for solving probabilistic models assume that distributions can be estimated for each activity time, and that these are independent of each other. Further, it is assumed that the critical path is considerably longer than other paths. Then a reasonably simple analysis will solve the problem.

This classic model, together with an approximate solution technique, was developed in the 1950s by the Booz Allen consulting company (Baker [1974]). It is known as PERT for Program Evaluation and Review Technique. There are, however, a number of issues in probabilistic models for long-horizon problems for which PERT type analysis is not sufficient. These will also be discussed in this section.

2.5.2 PERT

Using PERT.   The basic PERT model requires three assumptions.

1. The time one activity takes is not affected by any other activity's time.
2. The critical path is "considerably longer" than any other path.
3. The time on the critical path is approximately normally distributed.

Proposition 4. Under the PERT assumptions, the minimum project duration L determined by the critical path q has the following distribution:

1. Mean time = sum of duration mean times on q.
2. Variance of time = sum of variances of times on q.
3. L is approximately normally distributed.

Proof: Equation 1 is true for the *sum* of any random variables.
Equation 2 is true if the variables are, in addition, independent.
Statement 3 is true since the Central Limit Theorem condition is assumed to hold approximately.

Note than in any particular case, with particular actual values for all the activity durations, q may not actually be the critical path ex poste; q is simply the longest path *if all durations happen to take on their average length*. We will return to this point later in this section.

Suppose $\Phi(x)$ is the probability that a cumulative unit normal deviate is less than x. For example, $\Phi(-1) = 0.16$, $\Phi(0) = 0.5$, $\Phi(1) = 0.84$, $\Phi(2) = 0.98$, and so on. A table of the cumulative unit normal distribution is given in Appendix G. Now, suppose the critical path q has mean μ and standard deviation σ, and we want to know the probability of meeting a project deadline of duration d. This would be given by

$$\Phi((d - \mu)/\sigma)$$

For example, if the mean time is 20 days, the standard deviation is 5 days, and we wish to know the probability the project will be finished in fewer than 24 days, the equation would be $\Phi((24 - 20)/5) = \Phi(0.80) = 0.79$. There is then, by the PERT assumptions, a 79 percent chance that we will meet the deadline. The exercises will provide further practice in using the unit normal tables.

PERT provides a decent way to estimate the mean μ_j and the standard deviation σ_j for any activity j. The manager of activity is given a questionnaire or is interviewed, and is asked to provide for activity j an optimistic duration O_j, a most likely duration M_j, and a pessimistic duration P_j. Then the PERT method estimates the mean and standard deviation duration for j as follows:

$$\mu_j = (1/6)O_j + (4/6)M_j + (1/6)P_j$$
$$\sigma_j = (1/6)(P_j - O_j)$$

The formula for the mean is a weighted average of the three estimates, the weights adding to 1.0. We have encountered this idea in the Forecasting Module: it is a foundation for both moving average forecasting and exponential smoothing. Further, it suggests that the manager weights the subjectively most likely value with four times the weight for either endpoint.

The second formula suggests that the difference between the pessimistic and optimistic estimates represents six standard deviations. This is perhaps questionable, since each activity manager is likely to be different in this respect.

Example 2-3. Homestead Hank must buy cattle, fence his land, kill the coyotes, and find a wife in 70 weeks, or else he will lose the homestead to the evil landlord. For the project he has worked out in Table 2-8, what is the probability that it can be finished within 70 weeks?

Solution. Consider the project data, where μ_j and σ_j^2 are first calculated from the optimistic, most likely, and pessimistic estimates O_j, M_j, and P_j. The next step is to construct the AON diagram, and to label each activity j with its mean duration μ_j as shown in Figure 2-12. Solving this diagram by the usual forward and backward calculations, we find that the deterministic critical path is A-D-H.

Activity	Predecessors	O	M	P	μ	σ²
A	——	5	15	25	15	11.11
B	——	5	10	45	15	44.44
C	——	20	25	60	30	44.44
D	A	10	40	40	35	25.00
E	B	5	10	45	15	44.44
F	C	15	15	45	20	25.00
G	C	5	10	15	10	2.68
H	D, G	15	30	45	30	25.00
I	E, F	10	20	60	25	69.44

Table 2-8

PERT Example of Homestead Hank

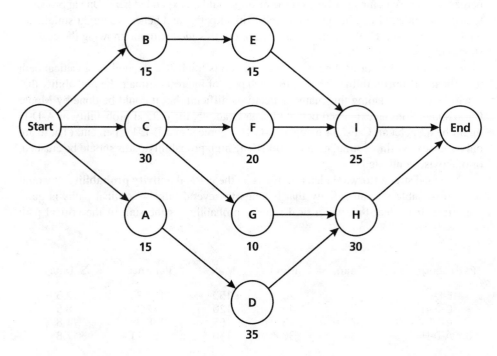

Figure 2-12

AON Network of Homestead Hank

From these calculations, and also using Proposition 4, we can see that the duration of the path A-D-H has a mean of 80 (15 + 35 + 30), and a variance of 61.11 (11.11 + 25.00 + 25.00). The standard deviation is the square root of 61.11, or 7.82. By the PERT method, the probability that path A-D-H will have a length less than or equal to the required 70 is is $\Phi(70 - 80)/(7.82)) = \Phi(-1.28) = 0.10$. Thus, the odds are 9 to 1 against Homestead Hank succeeding honestly. Realizing this, he got the landlord into a crooked poker game and won the day!

Since there is a second almost critical path of length 75, the PERT analysis is actually not very accurate. Even if A-D-H should be as short as 70, the chance that C-F-I will simultaneously be less than 70 is certainly quite a bit less than 0.5. (The true mean for this problem is also somewhat larger than 80, for somewhat the same reason.) We look now briefly at these more theoretical issues.

Theoretical Aspects. A number of different objections have been raised about the PERT model over the years:

1. It looks only at one path; in fact sometimes others will be ex poste critical.
2. Thus, its estimate of the average project duration is too small.
3. It assumes the times to do different activities are independent.
4. It may be difficult to make good estimates of the distribution of activity times.

PERT Path Not Longest?

Example 2-3, Part 2. Look at Table 2-8 and Figure 2-12 of the Homestead Hank example. We see that there are exactly four paths through the network. Table 2-9 gives, for each path, the mean length, the minimum and maximum lengths, and the standard deviation of their lengths. It is quite clear that while A-D-H is the critical path according to PERT, any of the other paths will be sometimes longer than A-D-H. (In fact, it can be shown that C-G-H alone is longer than A-D-H about 36 percent of the time.)

Now suppose that Homestead Hank is allowed to decrease the duration of selected activities by expending extra costs; that is, the CPM assumptions are superimposed on a probabilistic network. Looking at Figure 2-12, PERT would suggest expending all efforts on activities A, D, and H, which are the supposed critical path. However, C-F-I has a 36 percent chance of being critical, so some effort should be expended here. One approach is to note that either H or I lie on all possible critical paths, and hence we might simultaneously shorten I and H. We cannot really check out this idea without knowing the costs of shortening various activities.

One simple idea for dealing with this situation is to change the notion of critical path to **critical path probability**. That is, for each path of interest estimate the probability that it will be critical. (Doing this mathematically is difficult, but it could be done by Monte Carlo simulations as explained below.) In our example, the critical probability of A-D-H might be 62 percent, C-F-I 34 percent, C-G-H 3 percent and B-E-I 1 percent. (These are only guesses; writing a simulation is work!) The high probability paths should be crashed, or otherwise controlled.

A second straightforward idea is to focus on the **critical activity probability**. It would seem reasonable that an activity that belongs to several "likely" critical paths is quite important. It is clear that the critical activity probability is the sum of the critical path

Table 2-9

Comparison of the Paths for
Homestead Hank

Path Length:	Mean	Min	Max	Variance	S. Dev.
B-E-I	55	20	150	158.33	12.5
C-G-H	70	40	120	72.22	8.5
C-F-I	75	45	165	138.88	11.8
A-D-H	80	30	110	61.11	7.8

probabilities for the paths of which the activity is a part. In Homestead Hank's problem, activity H would have a critical activity probability of 62% + 3% = 65%; activity I would have a critical activity probability of 34% + 1% = 35%. (Note, however, that D has 62 percent, so that if it is easier to control than H we may concentrate on D.)

Probably the easiest way to analyze a probabilistic network is by Monte Carlo simulation. The computer can be asked to pick a set of random durations from each activity's distribution, and then analyze the resulting deterministic network. This might be repeated hundreds or thousands of times. It would be especially useful to calculate the average float at each activity. Small average float would be a good indicator of needed attention.

PERT Path Optimistic.

Example 2-3, Part 3. Turning back to Homestead Hank, activity A-D-H has an average length of 80, and only about a 16 percent chance (one standard deviation above the mean) of being over 87.8 (80 + 7.8). Also, C-F-I has an average length of 75 and about a 16% chance of being over 86.8 (75 + 11.8). Thus, without extensive calculations, we are probably safe in estimating the overall average project length is between 80 and 88. Again simulation could pin this down easily. See Baker [1974].

Activities Are Correlated. Activities are not at all independent of each other in an ordinary project. For example, several activities may require the same raw material. If it is late, all these durations will be increased together. Or it may rain off and on for the entire project. This will increase many durations for outside activities; other inside durations may decrease if there are extra personnel now available. A more interesting reason for activity correlation is related to the fact that in many cases, artificial precedence constraints are added to make sure both activities needing a resource do not try to proceed simultaneously. Now if this common resource operates at only partial efficiency (for example, a bank of four generators, one of which is down), then both activities will be delayed. Correlation between activities can be handled quite well in Monte Carlo simulation.

2.5.3 Long Range Projects

The ideas in this section borrow freely from Morton, Sathi, et al. [1984] with the authors' kind permission. There is a large number of serious issues that come up in dealing with major long-range-duration probabilistic projects.

Example 2-4. The Cherrypit Computer Company first came out with the futuristic and highly user-friendly Bingcherry Personal Computer in 1982. This immediately grabbed 25 percent of the rapidly growing PC market. The more conventional PC makers held on to the rest of the market largely because of the expense of shifting to the new system and of transferring software back and forth. CCC countered by increasing the compatibility of the two approaches. The conventional PC makers countered with Win-Doughs, software that allowed the conventional PCs to be much more like the Bingcherry PC.

Seeing their market share slipping, CCC has conceived of the ultimate weapon: Cherrypie. Cherrypie is a futuristic desktop computer. It will:

1. Be a platform for every program in any language in existence
2. Allow high level programming (such as simulations) at no degradation of speed
3. Be trainable to accept natural English spoken commands and dialogue from one or more "owners"
4. Be able to translate natural English commands directly into permanent computer programs
5. Take six years to bring to fruition (Pun intended!)

Given this highly ambitious project, largely based on unproven technology, the management of CCC encountered a number of problems in trying to apply conventional probabilistic project management. Some of these difficulties are discussed in the following sections.

Forecasting the Network Structure. The Cherrypie project depends on the success of a voice recognition technology which is still in early stages. Since this technology will be needed about three years into the development of Cherrypie, it is difficult to even guess the exact network structure of this part of the project, especially if certain anticipated developments fail and alternatives must be developed. These alternatives may be developed in advance using "or" activities, or they may have to be generated "on the run." Or perhaps several alternative ordinary network diagrams could do the job. What are good rolling horizon procedures for updating the network structure and durations without giving up the project planning concept?

Forecasting Activity Durations and Variability. For the Cherrypie project, suppose that the designing, prototyping, testing, and test manufacturing activities number about 800 aggregate activities. The project might involve 15 department heads, each supervising three or four managers, each in charge of perhaps a dozen of the aggregate activities at different points in the future. Getting PERT-type "most likely," "optimistic," and "pessimistic" estimates from the line managers and department heads will probably be quite difficult. Some managers may tend to give high time estimates, so that their goals will be relatively easy to meet. On the other hand, some managers may "lowball" their estimates to get assigned the activities they want. Getting personnel to set "optimistic" and "pessimistic" estimates six standard deviations apart may be extremely delicate. Given the amount of turnover at computer companies, the relevant manager for an activity may not even be available.

Activity Correlation. Two of Cherrypie's goals—trainable to accept natural English commands and translate natural English commands directly into computer programs—both depend on the progress of current natural language technology. Thus, depending on progress, both will be helped or hindered. This leads to correlation between the durations of the two kinds of activities. If this situation can be well-modeled, then a common activity called "theoretical natural language progress" (or several related activities) can be included and good results might be obtained by simulating the resulting network. In general, the activity correlation is often related to common resources or activities used by the activities in question. When they are explicit, we can add these effects directly and simulate. Unfortunately, these effects are often quite subtle.

Probabilistic Branching, Loop Back. At many points in the future progress of the Cherrypie project it will not be clear which of several activities will actually be pursued. An external random event, such as a successful (or a failing) research event, the unexpected introduction of a product by a competitor, or the raising of a tariff barrier, may occur at some point in the project. The resulting diagram is a kind of mix between a decision tree and the usual project diagram. The activity with random branches is shown as an activity (circle) with a cross in it, and the possible branches are marked with their probabilities as shown in Figure 2-13.

The diagram example shows that after the finish of activities A, B, and C, we will know the result of the market probabilistic event. With a probability of 70 percent the activities D, E, and F will be next, or with a probability of 30 percent activity G will be next. (Why do we need the dummies "d"?)

The two branches meet again with an "or" at activity H, concluding with I. How does one find the expected duration of such a probabilistic project? Suppose the prospect containing D, E, and F would have duration 45, and the one containing G would have duration

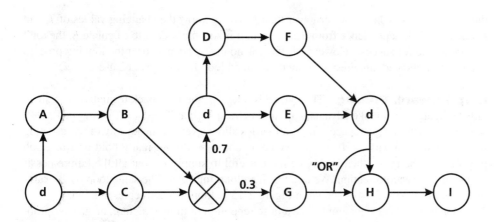

Figure 2-13
....
Random Branching Activities (AON)

35. Then the expected duration is $0.7(45) + 0.3(35) = 31.5 + 10.5 = 42.0$. (One could determine the expected cost of the expected resource usage of the project in much the same way.) Note that random branching is much like the usual "or" except that here we are not allowed to choose the branch. Rather we analyze two problems separately and weigh them together appropriately.

The failure of an activity is shown in special ways using branching. If a test activity shown by a circle with an X in it shows failure, then the most common way to represent this is by **loop back**. If the test indicates that a set of activities has "failed," then the arrow returns back to force these activities to be completed again, as illustrated in Figure 2-14. If the probability of a first failure is 70 percent, it is convenient (but not very realistic) to assume that the probability of a second failure, etc., is also 70 percent.

Then, if the subproject within the loop requires time T each iteration, with probability of failure $Q = 1 - P$ each time, the expected time to successfully complete this part of the project would be

$$E = T[1 + Q + Q^2 + Q^3 + Q^4 + \ldots] = T/(1 - Q) = T/P$$

Thus, with a 30 percent chance of success each time, we would require on the average 3.33 times through for success, a rather intuitive result.

Although this method for treating repeated failure is very common, it is also very inaccurate. Failure, especially in R&D activities such as developing Cherrypie, involves learning. If the learning is of a rather straightforward type, the second expected time T_2 will be probably less than T_1, while the second probability of success P_2 will be higher than P_1. If, on the other hand, failure suggests major redesign, then T_2 may be much, much larger

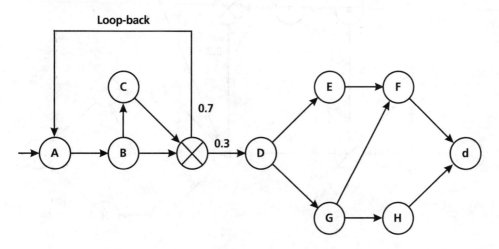

Figure 2-14
....
Simple Loop Back

than T_1 and P_2 may be higher or lower than P_1. If we know the changing values of T_i and P_i and assume independence from trial to trial, it is still fairly easy to calculate E, the total expected time for success. However, if there is no independence, or if the looping process is more complicated, an alternative method called loop forward can be used.

Loop Forward, Pruning. The main advantage of the loop back formulation to show failure situations is to take advantage of symmetries, such as $T_1 = T_2 = T_3 = \ldots$ or $P_1 = P_2 = P_3 = \ldots$, with independence. The symmetries allow a very compact way of representing multiple failure situations. If, as is very common, these do not really hold in a research project like Cherrypie, then it may be more useful to simply lay out all the failure possibilities in a forward direction. We dub this idea **loop forward**. The same loop back example shown in Figure 2-14 is shown in Figure 2-15 in loop forward representation.

Loop forward does not emphasize a false repetition of time, structure, or success probabilities. The main difficulty with loop forward is that far too many branches will have to be represented. A reasonable way out of this difficulty is to remove (prune) branches of less than a certain small probability, and to fudge their consequences roughly into their more important neighbors. We might call this **prunefudge**. Prunefudging is necessarily judgmental in nature. It has the advantage of being similar to the way in which managers actually think about probabilistic events.

Fuzzy Subprojects. Highly accurate recognition of spoken words is an important and highly uncertain subproject in the Cherrypie project. At this early point, it is felt to represent extensive failures, repeats, and activity redesign, without much ability to specify what

Figure 2-15

Loop Forward

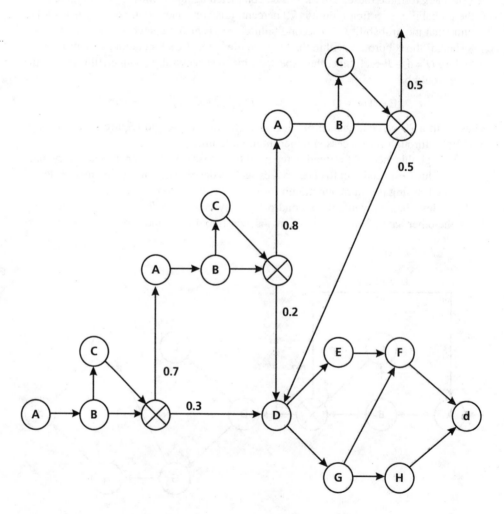

every individual activity will be, where problems will come, and what to do about them. This very fuzzy inner structure does not lend itself well to detailed project structuring, even with failure probabilities. (See Figure 2-16.)

Yet, for such a fuzzy subproject, it is likely to be important to make an initial estimate of this subproject's duration, and subsequently to estimate remaining subproject time with only such indicators as the various resources which have been used to date. A regression analysis of "similar" research subprojects performed in the past might give a way of estimating these durations (Morton, Sathi, et al. [1984]).

2.5.4 Probabilistic Exercises

PERT.

1. Make an estimate (using PERT) of the probability that the following project will be completed in 19 days. Justify whether PERT is a good approximation here.

Activity	Predecessors	O(days)	M(days)	P(days)
A	—	2	5	8
B	—	1	5	9
C	A	4	6	9
D	B	2	2	2
E	A	1	2	9
F	C, D	2	4	5
G	C,D,E	3	8	10
H	F	2	2	3

2. Suppose the duration estimates for activity E in Problem 1 were all low by 10 days. Now what is the PERT estimate of the probability that the project will be finished in 20 days? Justify whether or not the estimate is good.

3. What is the PERT estimate of the probability that the following project will be completed in 19 days? Justify whether or not the estimate is good.

Activity	Predecessors	O	M	P
A	—	3	5	7
B	—	3	6	19
C	A	2	2	2
D	A	4	5	3
E	A	1	2	10
F	B,C	1	6	7
G	B,C	2	5	14
H	D	2	8	8
I	D	1	1	1
J	E,F	1	4	10
K	G	2	3	3

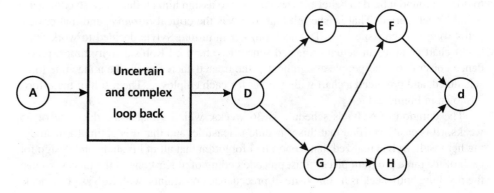

Figure 2-16

Black Box

4. In the project shown, assume all activities have independent distributions with mean and standard deviation given. What is the probability that A-C-E-G will be the longest path in the network? (**Hint:** *The two paths are normally distributed; thus, their difference is also normally distributed.*)

Activity	Predecessors	Mean	St. Dev.
A	—	30	6
B	—	50	15
C	A	40	10
D	B	20	10
E	C	85	30
F	D	60	40
G	E	40	20
H	F	40	10

Long Range Projects.

5. In problem 4, suppose the variation in time for both activities A and B depends primarily on the weather. Thus, the duration of A is always 20 days more than the duration of B. How does this affect the probability that A-C-E-G will be the longest path in the network? Will the *true* standard deviation for the length of the project change?

6. Add a simple loop back to the problem in problem 1. Solve the problem again with this change.

7. In problem 1, suppose there is a 40 percent probability that activity C is unnecessary. Explain how to treat this as a change in the distribution of processing time for activity C. Re-solve problem 1 with this change.

8. Give a loop forward representation in graphical form for problem 6. Explain your pruning strategy.

2.6 MICRODIMPLE SOFTWARE—REPRISE

The scheduling software project agreement with Arc de Triumph specified a completely tested software package in 35 weeks. You will remember that Rob had first computed the critical path ignoring resource constraints (see Figure 2-1 in Section 2.2.2), which had a length of 33 weeks. The critical path consisted of the initial overall study of the mill, studying, designing, and programming the rolling mill, designing, programming, and debugging the integrated shell package, and final testing. To check if resources were a problem, Rob forced some conflicting activities requiring his time to be done separately, and decided the critical path was still 33 weeks.

However, Sylvia was worried. She noted that Rob had been assigned 30 weeks of work to do, and found it hard to believe it was possible to assign him all that work so compactly in a 33 week period. That is, she felt that *Rob* was the critical *resource*, and that critical paths were not the issue here. To check out her intuition, Sylvia decided to work out a Gantt chart creating an actual projected schedule. She used Rob's activity times, precedence constraints, and people assignments. She treated each person like a machine to be scheduled, and produced a chart with one bar for each employee. The result of her efforts is shown in Figure 2-17.

The duration of Sylvia's schedule is 36 weeks, which violates the due date of 35 weeks. (It is easily verified that this schedule is feasible, and that it is optimal.) In studying her result, Sylvia realized that Robert had forgotten that all of his study and design for each of the three program pieces must precede coding of at least one of the pieces, so that the resulting bottleneck is a composite of precedence constraints, with Rob as bottleneck.

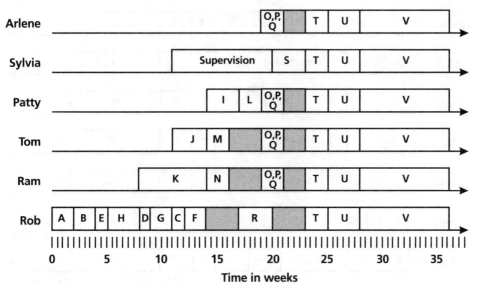

Figure 2-17

A Detailed Schedule for
Steel Mill Software

To Rob's credit, when Sylvia showed him his mistake, he did not get angry, but began to think furiously. "If I am the bottleneck, we must bring in more resources to help me," he muttered to himself. After sleeping on the issue for two or three nights, Rob called an old professor buddy of his, Pent Davidico. He explained the situation to Pent, and asked him as a favor to provide ten weeks of effort over the summer. In return he would pay Pent $30,000. This would make the first project rather unprofitable, but it would be a successful showpiece, which seemed a real must for Microdimple.

Pent pointed out that he was very experienced in software projects, and suggested putting in half time for up to ten weeks; he would charge $1,000 per 20 hour week plus a future return favor to be named later. Rob was overcome with gratitude. After some discussion the two agreed that if they studied the mill and designed the overall concept together, they could save a week, doing the two activities in three weeks. Similarly, while it would take Rob four weeks to study and design the rolling mill program, Pent could probably do study and design for each of the other two in two weeks rather than three weeks. This led to the revised schedule shown in Figure 2-18.

Rob was pleased about several things. First of all, the project duration would now be reduced from 36 weeks, to 32 weeks, leaving a three-week protection against the due date at 35 weeks. Second, this looked to be achieved using Pent for seven weeks at half time, for a cost of $7000. This seemed very reasonable in return for bringing in the project on time.

But after studying the revised schedule, Rob wondered why they couldn't do even better. "Maybe you should help me full time in periods 4 to 7 at an extra $4000, and you work with me designing the rolling mill together," he suggested to Pent. "This might shave another two weeks off the schedule." His friend replied, "I have other uses for the summer besides working for you full time. Besides, you and I would interfere with each other."

Rob saw the point of that. He thought awhile longer, and then said, "Well, here's another harebrained idea. You and I switch. You design the rolling mill and I design the arc furnace and the casting mill. You work full time for two weeks, and finish by week 5. Since coding the rolling mill is on the critical path, this will cut the project from 32 weeks ·to 30 weeks! You'll be working three half-time and two full-time weeks. I'll pay you the $7000 plus $3000 bonus for the two difficult weeks."

"OK, OK!" laughed Pent. "But I get to name that favor to be returned later!"

Are all the problem issues resolved? Or will Microdimple face more problems in its first big software project?

Figure 2-18
....

Relieving the Bottleneck

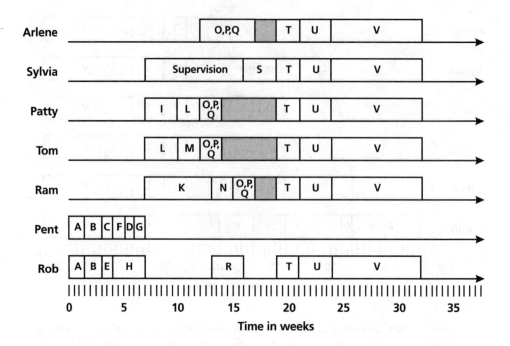

Aftermath

The project came in at 43 weeks, eight weeks behind the due date. Pent's help came in beautifully; in fact, he was called on several times later in the project for emergency help. Tom quit just before his part of the project started, although Sylvia found an excellent replacement, Marsha, through a temporary employment agency. (Marsha is now working half time for the firm.) Patty had not kept backups of her work and lost two weeks of work, which put her on the critical path for awhile.

However, the main problem was Arc de Triumph itself. The vice-president of operations decided in the middle of the project to make major design changes in the requested user interface. The design changes essentially changed the scheduling program into a Decision Support System, so that users could schedule in manual mode, automatic mode, and other intermediate mixed modes. This about doubled the work in designing, coding, and debugging the overall scheduling shell.

Arc de Triumph did not complain very much that the package was late, given the circumstances and the beautiful job that Microdimple had done. In fact, the president suggested that Rob demo the product and discuss it at the next Steel System Symposium of 40 area steel companies the next February. At this conference, Rob made a tentative second sale for a similar system, and many useful contacts. Microdimple could smile freely!

## CHAPTER 3

Project Scheduling— Limited Resources

3.1 INTRODUCTION

The classical way to deal with a large project such as developing the space shuttle is to use a critical path analysis. That is, it is treated as a single project without binding resource constraints (or, more likely, with some resource constraints hidden in the design). But in reality, resource constraints were critical during the time taken to develop it. In addition, the space shuttle shared resources with many other NASA projects that overlapped in time (such as Mariner, Hubble, and new rockets). Thus, the appropriate analysis would be multiple projects sharing common resources. Fortunately, there now exist powerful heuristics for solving large problems of this variety.

We will develop the single project problem with resource constraints rather carefully. While the multiple project case is solvable by the same methods, it is more complicated, and we do not develop it fully. The POMQuest software handles the multiple project case fully.

Simplified network models are still very useful because they always give optimistic lower bounds on the project's duration. Another reason the basic models of Project Management Chapter 2 are useful is that practitioners have grown expert at adding artificial precedence constraints to the relaxed problem to avoid overuse of a scarce resource. For example, if a simplified network solution would involve using a single available crew on two different activities at the same time, a constraint can simply be added that one activity must come before the other. This chapter combines ideas from critical path methods and modern scheduling heuristics to find reasonable solutions to resource constrained problems.

In Section 3.2 we look at Optik, an example of a (multiple) project job shop; that is, a shop in which jobs have a network rather than a serial structure. In Section 3.3 we discuss the resource leveling approach to solving single project scheduling problems. In Section 3.4 we consider dispatch and search methods for solving single-project scheduling problems. Finally, in Section 3.5 we return to Optik for a second look.

3.2 COMPANY APPLICATION SCENARIO—OPTIK

3.2.1 Overview

Optik is a medium-sized manufacturer of all types of large custom optical equipment, located outside of Buffalo, New York. (This scenario is based on a real company. Names and data have been disguised somewhat, for obvious reasons.) Optik manufacturing is done in an integrated shop.

Optik has 225 employees in an engineering group that designs new products to customer request, 160 on the shop floor, and 145 for other functions such as marketing, inventory, shipping, and quality control. It produces such items as large and very large refractive telescopes, reflective telescopes, laser equipment of all sizes, fiber optics in a number of forms, laboratory equipment of a large number of different types, electron microscopes, tunneling microscopes, and holographic equipment. Optik is extremely proud of the variety, quality, and scientific excellence of the custom optical goods it produces.

In a few cases, Optik produces parts for other manufacturing firms to build custom equipment, but the president much prefers to keep creative control. An order may consist of a single large item worth $100,000 to $10 million, but another typical custom order might consist of 50 identical items worth $20,000 each.

In recent years, important customers have been pressuring Optik to shorten lead times, both in engineering and in manufacturing. Meeting fixed deadlines has become increasingly important, and, in addition to payments at the reaching of milestones and at the final completion of the order, there are now often penalties for tardiness written into the contract.

The manufacturing process is complex and varies depending on what is being produced. There is a pretty standard metal fabrication department. There is a lens grinding area. There is a paint shop that has a pair of rooms, one for painting and one for baking. A number of items can be painted the same color or baked at the same time. A paint room batch is transferred as a unit to the bake room with no waiting allowed. There is an assembly shop that is a room with one very large worktable and three smaller ones. Each table has various types of clamps, jigs, and other features to aid in assembly. The large assembly table might be used for one large assembly, or two or more smaller assemblies at the same time.

The workers can be classified as follows:

Class 1 is specialized to a single machine. This includes all workers in the paint shop and all workers in parts of the metal shop.

Class 2 can operate any remaining machine in the metal shop.

Class 3 can operate any lens-grinding machine.

Class 4 represents four different crews, each of which is capable of doing any assembly order.

The production process has the following properties:

1. Some items and subassemblies will be subcontracted.
2. Most will be fabricated on the job floor.
3. All lenses are ground on the premises.
4. Items are painted and baked.
5. There are several stages of assembly, including customized packaging.
6. There are large amounts of delicate WIP on the floor at all times, causing many problems.
7. If a job is preempted by a high priority order for two weeks, it may be hard to subsequently find all the parts, or to find all the parts undamaged.

Optik's management felt that manual scheduling was becoming more and more difficult as the shop became busier and lead times became tighter. They called on an Operations Management professor from a local university, who sent out a group of graduate students to do some preliminary analysis of Optik and suggest a scheduling method.

3.2.2 Preliminary Analysis

Two weeks after making several trips to the shop floor, the students made the preliminary report in Figure 3-1.

Figure 3-1

Optik's Preliminary Analysis
Report

To: Jack Hendrix, CEO
       Optik Co.
From: 45-271 Project Management Class
Subject: Preliminary Analysis of Optik Facilities

Mr. Hendrix, before we go further, we would like to share our initial thoughts about how to model your production facilities, so that we can get feedback from you.

Appropriate Model

Your production process can be analyzed fairly well as a multiple "medium to large" project model. All items in a customer order have a common due date, and therefore count as a single project, whether a single large telescope or twenty laboratory microscopes. If the project is large enough to have milestones, each milestone with all its predecessors is treated as a separate project.

Metal Shop Resources

Machine groups can be aggregated and treated as a single machine. Workers attached to a particular machine are just treated as part of the machine for the purposes of the analysis. That is, machine and operator comprise a single resource. On the other hand, any members of the work force who may be assigned to more than one machine are each treated as a separate resource.

Thus, overall, the metal shop becomes a classic job shop, except that the flexible workers are extra resources that can be shifted to machines as needed. (So far this all fits the multiple large project model with no changes.)

Lens Grinding Shop Resources

All of the machines in the lens grinding shop form one large group of parallel machines. Within this group there are clusters. Each cluster handles just one type of lens. The machines in a cluster can be considered proportional machines to be aggregated into a single composite machine. Operators may be transferred from one cluster to another, and hence are flexible and may each be considered another resource.

Paint and Bake Rooms

The paint room and the bake room both accept items in groups or batches. There are specified group types of compatible items: each group requires a single color, type of paint, baking time, and temperature. Since no waiting can occur between paint and bake, each batch is forced to time its start of painting so that it finishes just as the previous bake batch finishes. Thus, since there is a single queue, the two rooms together really comprise a single resource (although there are two processors).

This composite resource could also be treated as a continuous resource, with special rules about when a batch can start and which items can be processed together.

Assembly Shop Resources

Each table can be considered a separate resource. Small tables are like machines in that they handle only zero or one activity at a time. The large table, however, is a complex resource that can handle several activities, but the number is determined by complex fitting criteria. When several activities are carefully fitted onto the large table, it is not accurate to simply add up the individual areas to see whether they are less than the table area.

For a careful analysis, jigs etc. could be considered separate resources, complicating the analysis somewhat.

3.2.3 Where to Next?

Although the students were of some definite help, they couldn't go much further until they had completed their project management course, which would last two more months. They promised to come back at that point and give a final report.

Will these students be of any further help? Will they be of any help at all? These issues will be addressed in Section 3.5.

3.3 SINGLE PROJECT—RESOURCE LEVELING

3.3.1 Overview

Suppose we are given a resource-constrained project scheduling problem to solve; that is, to get a "good" but not necessarily perfect schedule for it. One way to approach this would be to solve the problem *without* resource constraints (the relaxed solution). Then we could plot out (by hand or by machine) the usage of each resource as it varies over time. These are called the **resource load profiles** for the schedule, and are discussed in Section 3.3.2. If we should be so lucky that none of the resource usages violated their limits, we would be home free. The relaxed network solution would be optimal.

If, on the other hand, the schedule were mostly O.K., but there was one place where some resource constraint was violated, we could jiggle the schedule a little bit to make it feasible. (Move some activity using the resource later in time, perhaps.) This is the idea behind resource leveling heuristics, which are discussed in Section 3.3.3. At the other extreme, the relaxed situation may require four or five times as much of several resources as there are available and therefore violate constraints badly at a number of different times. It is still possible to apply resource leveling to such a heavily constrained problem. However, there is no particular reason to believe that leveling will produce a very good solution. In these circumstances, integer programming (which we do not discuss) can solve very small problems. Large, heavily constrained problems are best solved by the dispatch methods and the search methods to be discussed in Section 3.4.

Single Project Formulation. Let j denote the activities of the project, $1 <= j <= n$, where n is the project completion activity. There are a number of resources for the project k, $1 <= k <= K$. The total amount of resource available for each k is denoted by A_k and is constant over time. When an activity j is in progress, it utilizes a constant amount r_{jk} of the (fixed) resource k. The sum of the r_{jk} at any point for all activities j currently active must not exceed the availability $(RA)_k$. Put more formally: let $x_{jt} = 1$ if j is processing at time t, 0 otherwise. Then the resource constraint for k becomes $\Sigma_{j=1,n} r_{jk} x_{jt} <= (RA)_k$ for all k and t. Activity j cannot begin until all its immediate predecessors in the set of activities $P(j)$ have finished, and in addition until there is enough of each resource it needs available.

3.3.2 Resource Load Profiles

It is easiest to demonstrate how to generate resource load profiles by example.

Example 3-1. Rock-it Sign-tists Co. does final testing of new weather rockets on their single test stand. They currently have a project involving three rockets to be tested for the national weather service and have set up three separate teams for this purpose. The only limiting resource is the testing stand, which can test only one rocket at a time. Figure 3-2 shows the twelve activities involved. The four activities (3, 7, 8, 9) which are marked in the diagram with a black box, all require the test stand. Rock-it Sign-tists Co. would like to know how quickly the project could be finished without the testing stand problem, and what the implied usage of the testing stand would be trying to follow that relaxation.

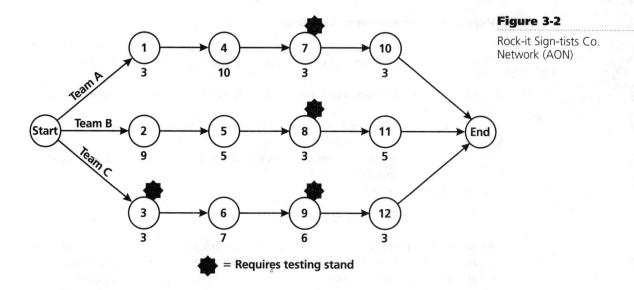

Figure 3-2

Rock-it Sign-tists Co.
Network (AON)

Solution. The network has three paths, of length 19, 22, and 19 respectively. Thus, without the testing stand constraint, Team B would be on the critical path, taking 22 days. In the unconstrained solution, activity 7 would use the test stand from day 14 to day 16 (early start time to early finish time), activity 8 from day 15 to day 17, activity 3 for days 1 to 3, and activity 9 for days 11 to 16. If we plot total utilization of the test stand over time, we would find the picture shown in Figure 3-3 (starting each job at its early start time).

There is over-utilization of the test stand planned in periods 14, 15, and 16 by activities 7, 8, and 9. It is fairly obvious that adding precedence constraints to enforce no more than one of these activities to occur at one time would produce an optimal solution if the right ordering of the three activities were enforced. Since there are only six possible orderings of three activities, we could try all six solutions and pick the best one. In a larger problem, however, there could be thousands, or perhaps millions, of such orderings overall. We will discuss a more orderly way to proceed in the next section on resource leveling.

3.3.3 Resource Leveling Heuristics

There are many ways to do resource leveling in a problem like Example 3-1, but a fairly typical method is listed below.

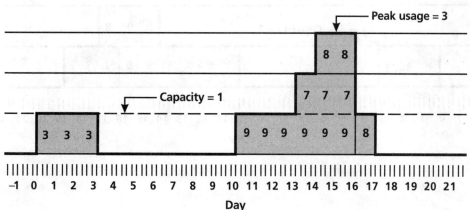

Figure 3-3

Rock-it Sign-tists Resource
Usage Profiles

Procedure for Resource Leveling.

1. Locate a resource and a time period where the resource is heavily overloaded in the network version of the problem. If there are none, there is no need to go further.
2. Pick two activities that contribute heavily to the overload at this point; call them A and B.
3. In turn add the constraint A < B or B < A to the problem to eliminate their overlapping contribution to the overload.
4. Keep the additional constraint which produces the best augmented network solution permanently.
5. Return to Step 1.

We continue with Example 3-1 to illustrate this procedure.

Example 3-1, Part 2. Figure 3-3 makes it clear that periods 14, 15, and 16 are overloaded, and that periods 15 and 16 are the most overloaded. Activities 7 and 9 have three periods of conflict, while activity 8 has only two periods of conflict with either 7 or 9. Thus we consider adding either 7 < 9 or 9 < 7 to the original network problem. (We still ignore resource constraints and solve by standard CPM methods.)

1. Activity 7 comes before activity 9. In this case, Team A and Team B are not delayed, but activity 9 is delayed from starting in period 11 to starting in period 17. Thus Team C's path increases from length 19 to length 25, and the overall project length increases from 22 to 25.
2. Activity 9 comes before activity 7. In this case, Team B and Team C are not delayed, but activity 7 is delayed from starting in period 14 to starting in 17. Thus Team A's path increases from length 19 to 22, and the overall project length does not increase.

Thus, in round one we permanently add 9 < 7. Figure 3-4 shows the situation after the first round of resource leveling. There is now conflict in periods 15, 16, and 17. We choose to force either 8 < 9 or 9 < 8.

1. Activity 8 comes before activity 9. In this case Team B finishes at 22, Team A finishes at 29, and Team C finishes at 26. Thus the overall project length increases from 22 to 29.

Figure 3-4

Situation After First Round of Leveling

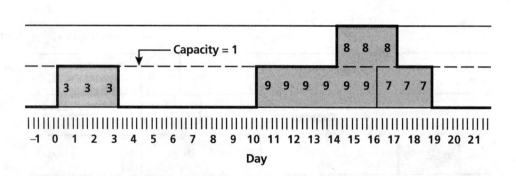

2. Activity 9 comes before activity 8. Team C is not delayed at all and finishes at 19, Team A finishes at 22, and Team B finishes at 24. Thus the overall project length increases to 24.

Thus, after two rounds, we have added permanently 9 < 7 and 9 < 8.

There still remains a conflict between activities 7 and 8 in periods 17, 18, and 19. You can verify that adding 7 < 8 produces a project length of 27, while adding 8 < 7 produces a project length of 25.

Thus, after three rounds, we have added permanently 9 < 8 < 7, with a project length of 25. There are no more resource conflicts, so we have found heuristically a solution with length 25.

It is easily verified, by trying all six permutations of ordering for activities 7, 8, and 9, that this solution is, in fact, optimal. This is left as an exercise. Of course, for larger problems optimality is not easy to verify or there would be no need for heuristics!

Notice that, in general, the idea is to use the resource usage profile to locate the difficult peak resources and time periods. Next use some type of heuristics to move activities earlier/later to spread the peak out over a longer time interval, and eventually to reduce the peak to within allowable resource limits, while delaying the project as little as possible. Note, in particular, that activities with positive total float in the network solution can be moved from their early start back to as far as their late start with no effect on project duration.

Actually, human schedulers (with a little practice) are very good at suggesting ways to spread out the peak. This suggests an interactive system for resource leveling.

Interactive System for Resource Leveling.

1. User enters the problem input.
2. Computer displays (relaxed) network solution.
3. Computer gives the current resource usage profiles.
4. If done, computer displays/prints the best *n* feasible solutions.
5. Computer prompts the user to add/subtract new precedence constraints.
6. User goes back to step 2.

3.3.4 Practical Considerations

One extremely important practical issue in resource leveling is the possibility of preemption. It may very well happen, for example, that one would want to interrupt a long electrical wiring activity in a house, for example, to do a shorter electrical activity, such as wiring the furnace, which is just available, and which is on the critical path. In some cases such interruption may be essentially free; in other cases it may involve some extra cost (we call this **complex preemption**). In still other cases it may be impossible without ruining the longer job. The extra costs in the intermediate complex preemption case may also take a number of forms, such as degradation of quality or wastage.

In real problems there are other methods for accomplishing resource leveling which are often used instead of simply moving activities to a later date. For example, it may be possible to add extra resources to the peak by renting equipment, working overtime, working faster, or recruiting supervisors to help out. In some cases there are alternate ways of doing a peak activity that require less of the critical activity, perhaps by spreading out the use over a longer time. Speeding up the activity by deliberately accepting a slightly lower quality may be possible in some circumstances. (For example, running a tooling machine at faster than the optimal speed.) Creative overlapping of activities is often also employed.

3.3.5 Resource Leveling Exercises

1. Develop a resource load profile for the problem presented in Figure 3-5 with one critical resource of amount 1.0. Activities using the critical resource are marked with black boxes and use amount 1.0.
2. Develop a resource load profile for the problem presented in Figure 3-6. (**Hint:** *Figure 3-5 is part of Figure 3-6.*)
3. Heuristically resource-level the problem given in problem 1.
4. Heuristically resource-level the project scheduling problem given in problem 2.
5. By trial and error find a schedule with shorter project duration than the one given in problem 3 or argue that the solution there is already optimal.
6. Repeat problem 5 for the example in problem 4.

Figure 3-5

Diagram for Problem 1

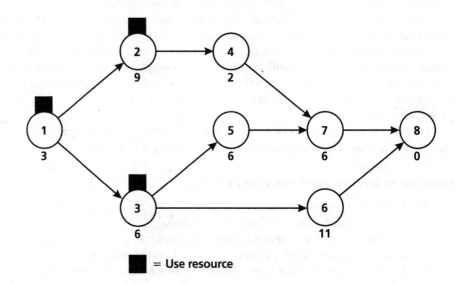

Figure 3-6

Diagram for Problem 2

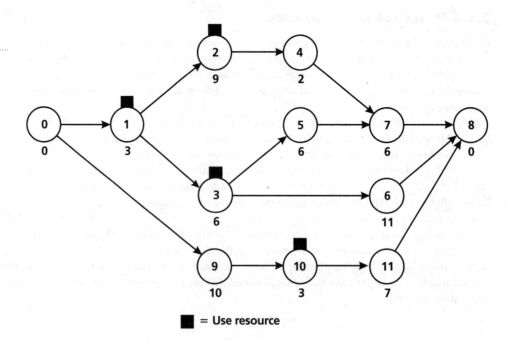

3.4 SINGLE PROJECT—DISPATCH AND SEARCH METHODS

3.4.1 Overview

Problems involving a single project are easier than multiple-project problems in several ways. First, since there are not competing goals, we may simply minimize project duration. Second, heuristics such as bottleneck dynamics, which we shall develop, are somewhat simpler.

While resource leveling is usually a good procedure when the resource profiles only mildly violate the given resource constraints, it seems much less likely to be effective when resource constraints are a severe restriction. For example, if the unconstrained solution to a construction project is 20 days but the single available cement mixer will in itself be busy for 50 days, many iterations of leveling will probably be required, and early leveling may well adversely affect later leveling. Since most projects are likely to be too large for integer programming to solve, we turn to dispatch methods and modern search methods.

Both classic and modern dispatch methods, as well as many search methods, are based on simulation; we discuss this next.

3.4.2 The Dispatch Simulation Process

We sketch an event-based simulation procedure for the single project case. An event is defined as the finishing of an activity, or the new availability of an activity to be processed.

1. Keep an event clock.
2. Increment the clock.
3. If the simulation is finished, terminate.
4. Find the set of all activities that are available and have predecessors satisfied for which there would be enough resources to start.
5. If the set is not empty, choose the activity with highest priority by the heuristic being used and schedule it. If it is empty, go to step 2.
6. Decrement resource availabilities. Add the activity finish to the event clock list.
7. Return to step 4.

Note that for a project, instead of there being a queue of waiting activities in front of each machine, there is a single queue of available activities for the entire shop.

3.4.3 Classic Heuristics

All simple dispatch methods for the single-project case estimate such slack-related variables as slack, operation due date, early start time, or early finish time by solving the relaxed version using the critical path method and obtaining the corresponding values for the relaxed problem. The hope is that these will approximate the corresponding variables for the constrained problem fairly well. Note again that this procedure will not work as well for a highly constrained project.

Example 3-2. The Qwik and Durtie remodeling company has a large job to do requiring primarily carpenters and painters. There are eight activities in the project, with the precedence diagram shown in Figure 3-7.

There are five painters and ten carpenters available. The times and resource requirements for the activities are given in the following table.

Figure 3-7

Qwik and Durtie Project
Network

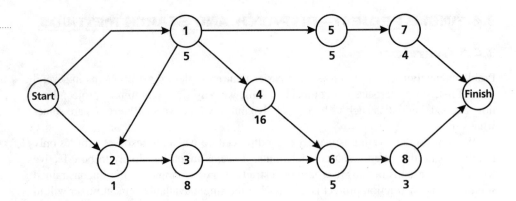

Activity	Duration	# Painters	# Carpenters
1	5 days	3	10
2	1	3	10
3	8	3	3
4	16	1	1
5	5	1	5
6	5	2	4
7	4	1	5
8	3	5	3

When Qwik and Durtie solved the relaxed version of their project, they obtained the slack-related estimates shown in Table 3-1. (We use the terms "float" and "slack" more or less interchangeably.)

The relaxed problem has a project duration of 29 days and a critical path of 1-4-6-8. We will return to the full problem as soon as we introduce and explain some of the standard dispatch heuristics for solving it.

Priority Rule. There are a great number of simple priority rules that have been proposed in the course of the last 30 or 40 years. We discuss some of these here. Others are discussed by Lawrence and Morton [1993]. In the following table, let LS_j be the late start time of activity j in the relaxation, LF_j be the late finish time, t be the current time in the simulation, p_j the activity processing time, and $\#_j$ the number of total successors to j in the network.

Classic Project Dispatch Heuristics.

FCFS	First available, first served	
SLK	Minimum operation slack	$SLK_j = LS_j - t$
SPT	Shortest processing time	p_j
MTS	Most total successors	n_j
LFT	Minimum late finish time (ODD)	LF_j
LFS	Least float per successor	$(SLK_j)/(n_j)$

Table 3-1

Qwik and Durtie Relaxed
Problem Values

Activity	ES	LS	EF	LF	SLK
1	0	0	5	5	0
2	5	12	6	13	7
3	6	13	14	21	7
4	5	5	21	21	0
5	5	20	10	25	15
6	21	21	26	26	0
7	10	25	14	29	15
8	26	26	29	29	0

(It is important to note that SLK_j, as used in a dispatch heuristic, has a slightly different definition than in the critical path calculation. The calculation $SLK_j = LS_j - ES_j$ was made before the project started. In the middle of the simulation, when we wish to calculate an activity's priority to start, we will know the actual starting time, AS_j, updated by any activity problems so far, resource constraints, and so forth. Thus estimating by $SLK_j = LS_j - AS_j$ will give a considerable improvement.)

Note that the late finish time (LF) is the estimated time at which the operation must be finished in order to not delay the project. Hence, it is the same as the operation due date (ODD). Remember also that ODD is the rule for minimizing maximum lateness. It is, therefore, of special interest in a project where completion times of the various branches of a project must be coordinated. Thus it is the myopic heuristic. In the scheduling module we learned that the myopic heuristic is generally the best of the classic heuristics. This turns out to be true here also.

Example 3-2, Part 2. Qwik Jr., the accountant at Qwik and Durtie, decides to work out the SLK heuristic solution to their project. "After all, activities without much leeway should certainly come first." He constructs Table 3-2 by hand, showing the situation, including resource availability, at the finish of each activity. (He did not bother to fill out the decision table after there was only a single chain of activities left, and hence no more decisions to make.) Note that the SLK solution gives a project duration of 38 days, considerably longer than the 29 days possible had resources been in better supply.

Qwik Jr. was not too happy with this solution. In particular, there seemed to be a lot of excess painters and carpenters on various activities; at the same time, the project was taking nine extra days. Then a friend, S. Marty, at a local business school, suggested that SLK tends to unfortunately give preference to very long activities. Marty suggested that Jr. try to schedule by earliest due date, which in this case translated to LFT.

Qwik Jr. gave LFT a shot; he soon was very happy. (See Table 3-3.) Although he still had excess carpenters and painters at some times during the planned project, the new heuristic had reduced the project duration from 38 days to 30 days, very little more than the relaxed solution of 29 days.

But another thought occurred to him. He called up S. Marty to ask if some other heuristic could do even better. S. Marty told him that, due to the very simple nature of the network, the choice of the second activity really completely determined the solution. Thus, one of these two solutions would result from any dispatch heuristic whatever.

3.4.4 Iterated Myopic Dispatch

Remember that bottleneck dynamics for sequencing problems consists fundamentally of two ideas:

Time	Activity Finish	Painters Available	Carpenters Available	Feasible Activities	Selection (min LS)
0	—	5	10	1	1
5	1	5	10	2,4,5	4
5	—	4	9	5	5
10	5	4	9	7	7
14	7	4	9	—	—
21	4	5	10	2	2
22	2				
30	3				
35	6				
38	8				

Table 3-2

Qwik and Durtie—MINSLK Solution

Table 3-3

Qwik and Durtie—LFT
Solution

Time	Activity Finish	Painters Available	Carpenters Available	Feasible Activities	Selection
0	—	5	10	1	1
5	1	5	10	2,4,5	2
6	2	5	10	3,4,5	3
6	—	2	7	4,5	4
6	—	1	6	5	5
11	5	1	6	7	7
14	3	3	4	—	—
22	4	4	5	6	6
15	7	3	6	—	—
27	6				
30	8				

1. A priority for job j of

$$\{\text{Job weight}\}\{\text{Slack factor}\}/\{\text{Total \$ of remaining resources}\}$$

2. Iterative estimation of the slack factors and resource prices

But in a single project, there is only one job, the project. So all activities have the same job weight. Also, all competing activities at a decision point in a project have the same total amount of remaining resources until the project (job) is finished.

Thus, the only element of bottleneck dynamics that can be applied to single project sequencing is improved estimation of the *slack factor*. If we combine lead time iteration with the myopic SLK policy, we have an excellent heuristic for the single project problem.

Lead Time Iteration for Projects. Our simple dispatch procedure developed to date estimates lead times (and thus slacks) by relaxing all constraints and solving the resulting critical path problem to compute early and late start times for the activity, and thus the slack. This is not particularly good; we are basically assuming that there is no waiting on any resource.

An apparently better method would be to assume that the total time in queue waiting for all needed resources (not waiting for predecessors) is a fixed multiple of processing time. Then processing times for each activity could be temporarily increased, and critical path calculations could be made with these adjusted processing times. This approach sometimes works fairly well and is, in fact, the manner in which MRP estimates lead times. The problem is that bottleneck machines will typically have long lines, while low utilization machines will have short ones. Thus, using the same factor for each distorts the problem. Lawrence and Morton [1993] modify the lead time iteration procedure of Vepsalainen and Morton [1987] for projects and project shops.

Definition: The $(n-1)$**th waiting time** $(q_j)^{n-1}$ of activity j on the $(n-1)$th iteration of lead time iteration is the time from when all predecessors of the activity have been satisfied until the time the activity actually starts $[(q_j)^0 = 0]$.

Definition: The **nth forecast waiting time** $(Q_j)^n$ is smoothed from iteration to iteration:

$$(Q_j)^n = (Q_j)^{n-1} + \alpha[(q_j)^{n-1} - (Q_j)^{n-1}]$$

$0 < \alpha <= 1.0$ is the smoothing parameter. A particularly simple result is obtained if we choose $\alpha = 1.0$:

$$(Q_j)^n = (q_j)^{n-1}$$

That is to say, the forecast waiting time for the next iteration is just the actual waiting time for the last iteration.

Definition: The **nth augmented processing time** $(P_j)^n$ is simply the actual processing time plus the nth forecast waiting time:

$$(P_j)^n = p_j + (Q_j)^n$$

Basically, the myopic dispatch policy uses LFT but improves estimates of the latest finish times by adding the times that activities wait for resources into their process times. These waiting times are improved iteratively.

Iterated Myopic Dispatch Procedure ($\alpha = 1.0$).

1. Set $n = 1$, the initial waiting times $(q_j)_o = 0$.
2. $(P_j)^n = p_j + (q_j)^{n-1}$.
3. Use $(P_j)^n$ to construct a network with processing times inflated by waiting times.
4. Calculate LF_j from this inflated network.
5. Schedule the original network using these $(LF_j)^n$, as LFT.
6. Calculate the waiting times $(q_j)^n$. (Time activity available until started.)
7. Enough iterations? If yes, exit; else go to step 2.

Example 3-3. Castin Con Creet (CCC) runs a small cement mixing business. He owns two large mixer-trucks. He has nine separate tasks to do for a customer, Mixtup Ideas. Mixtup would like to get these nine jobs all completed as fast as possible to allow later stages of construction by other contractors to begin. These nine activities have different requirements for the trucks, different times to complete in days, and some cannot be started until others are finished. (The problem is shown in Figure 3-8. The activity number is in the circle, truck requirement above the circle and denoted "R," and process time below and denoted "p.")

Solution. In each iteration, we first solve the relaxed problem (first for real process times, and then in later iterations by process times increased by expected waiting). The iteration figures are shown in Tables 3-4, 3-5, and 3-6.

We can now work out in retrospect what waiting times were for each activity.

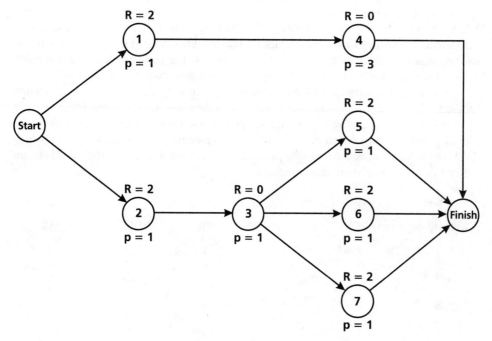

Figure 3-8

A Concrete Problem

Table 3-4

CCC Relaxed Problem
Values—Iteration 1

Activity	ES	LS	EF	LF	SLK
1	0	0	1	1	0
2	0	1	1	2	1
3	1	2	2	3	1
4	1	1	4	4	0
5,6,7	2	3	3	4	1
Finish	4	4	4	4	0

Table 3-5

CCC LFT Schedule—
Iteration 1

Time	Activity Finish	Trucks Available	Feasible Activities	Selection
0	—	2	1,2	1
1	1	2	2,4	2
2	2	2	3,4	3
2	—	2	4	4
3	3	2	5,6,7	5
4	5	2	6,7	6
5	4, 6	2	7	7
6	7	2	Finished	

Table 3-6

CCC Waiting Time
Analysis—Iteration 1

Activity	Available	Started	Wait	Process	Total Time
1	0	0	0	1	1
2	0	1	1	1	2
3	2	2	0	1	1
4	1	2	1	3	4
5	3	3	0	1	1
6	3	4	1	1	2
7	3	5	2	1	3

Notice, after our first iteration, that the classic LFT rule gives a project duration of 6. You may easily verify that the classic SLK rule gives a project duration of 6 also; in fact the schedule would be identical.

We turn next to the second iteration, first looking at the solution to the relaxed problem adding the waiting times from iteration 1 into the processing times. These revised processing times are given by the p^* values in Figure 3-9. The early and late start and finish times, and slacks for the relaxed solution with these times are given in Table 3-7.

(Notice that the inflation of the process time affects only Table 3-7 in the calculation of the LFT. The original process times are used in the simulation in Table 3-8.)

Due to lack of space we do not give iteration 3 (see the exercises) in detail. However the LFT rankings turn out to be (lowest to highest): activities 2, 1, 3, (4, 5, 6, 7), which leads to the identical schedule being produced by iteration 3 as by iteration 2. There are several things to note about this situation.

Table 3-7

CCC Relaxed Problem
Values—Iteration 2

Activity	ES	LS	EF	LF	SLK
1	0	1	1	2	1
2	0	0	2	2	0
3	2	2	3	3	0
4	1	2	5	6	1
5	3	5	4	6	2
6	3	4	5	6	1
7	3	3	6	6	

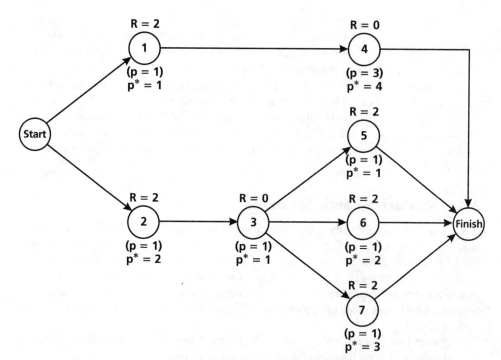

Figure 3-9

A Concrete Problem—
Iteration 2

Table 3-8

CCC LFT Schedule—
Iteration 2

Time	Activity Finish	Trucks Feasible	Activities	Selection
0	—	2	1,2	2
1	2	2	1,3	1
1	—	0	3	3
2	1,3	2	4,5,6,7	4
2	—	2	5,6,7	5
3	5	2	6,7	6
4	6	2	7	7
5	7,4	2	Finished	—

Table 3-9

CCC Waiting Time
Analysis—Iteration 2

Activity	Available	Started	Wait	Process	Total Time
1	0	1	1	1	2
2	0	0	0	1	1
3	1	1	0	1	1
4	2	2	0	3	3
5	2	2	0	1	1
6	2	3	1	1	2
7	2	4	2	1	3

- First, without iteration, any slack-based heuristic is bound to pick activity 1 to go first. It has the smallest slack (0) and the smallest LFT (1). However, resource constraints force 5, 6, and 7 to be carried out sequentially rather than in parallel. This makes the resource constrained critical path go through them rather than 1. This is only revealed in actual simulation of the problem, which shows that the waiting time forced on 7 creates a new critical path.

- Second, notice in this case that lead time iteration reduced the project duration from six days to five days. A 10 to 20 percent savings is typical of lead time iteration.
- Third, notice that since the schedule solution repeated from iteration 2 to iteration 3, it must go on repeating indefinitely. (Why?)
- Fourth, a repeating schedule does not guarantee optimality, or even that the schedule is "very good," although extensive testing has shown that it often is. The procedure is to simply pick the best of the results for, say, the first five iterations, and declare it our heuristic solution. In the current problem our iterated solution is, in fact, optimal. To solve larger problems, you will probably wish to use the POMQuest computer software.

3.4.5 Modern Search Methods

It is not difficult conceptually to use such modern search methods as neighborhood search, tabu search, and simulated annealing on single-resource constrained projects. Consider our LFT heuristic from the last section (either plain or iterated). Basically we are giving an ordering of the jobs in order of priorities. The priority sequence (2 1 3 4 5 6 7) in our example happened to produce the optimal solution. The mechanism was that the simulation halted whenever faced with a choice, and chose the next activity by reference to this priority.

Adjacent pairwise interchange as a neighborhood search method could permute any two activities and get a new solution. As an example of this:

(2 1 3 4 5 6 7) 5 days

(1 2 3 4 5 6 7) simulate to give 6 days,
(2 3 1 4 5 6 7) simulate to give 5 days,
(2 1 4 3 5 6 7) simulate to give 5 days,
(2 1 3 5 4 6 7) simulate to give 5 days,
(2 1 3 4 6 5 7) simulate to give 5 days,
(2 1 3 4 5 7 6) simulate to give 5 days.

(It happens for this problem that all sequences starting with 2 have a 5-day solution and all sequences starting with 1 have a 6-day solution! The computer would probably not be smart enough to figure this out.)

Thus, in this simple problem, one iteration of neighborhood search turns out to be enough to guarantee that we have a local optimum. It is quite easy to extend these ideas to tabu search and simulated annealing. However, search methods use too much computer time for larger problems. Suppose a problem has 100 activities, and three resources. Then a simulation which, at every one of 100 steps, checks all remaining activities for feasibility, including both whether enough of the three resources is available and all predecessors have been completed, will take a long time. After each simulation we must evaluate maybe 100 pairwise interchanges (perhaps with a longest path algorithm). And this is just for one iteration. We must next do, perhaps, 200 iterations from an initial good solution to get to the local minimum. This is a very large calculation. It may be possible to be much more clever, and teach the computer to recognize when a given simulation will give the same answer as the last and terminate the process. This is a research question at this point.

3.4.6 Extension to Multiple Projects

General Discussion. Why can't a multiple set of projects just be treated as one large project and be solved by one-project methods? This is a good question. If our objective is to finish all projects as soon as possible, then this is exactly right. However, some short project might be much more important than a long one. Minimizing the overall duration of both might be costly to the short project. Suppose your projects were to get in your tax returns, which are due tomorrow, and to finish driving lessons. Postponing your tax returns to be done on a weekend two weeks from now would get both done a day quicker perhaps, but might cost you a lot of money!

Multi-project dispatch heuristics. Let j denote project j, and ij denote activity i within project j. Let w_j be a weight giving the relative importance of project j, d_j represent the due date of project j, and p_{ij} represent the processing time of activity ij. All simple dispatch heuristics estimate the slack of activity ij by $\text{SLK}_{ij} = \text{LST}_{ij} - t$, where LST_{ij} is the late start time of ij in a simple critical path analysis of project j. That is to say, the slack is estimated by the slack the activity would have in the project if simple critical path analysis were used. Table 3-10 lists some common simple heuristics.

One would generally expect a good heuristic to consider both the importance w_j of a project, and its due date d_j. EDD, for example, always schedules the activity from the project with the earliest due date first, while MAXPEN and WSPT consider project importance, but ignore project urgency. The last four attempt to consider both factors. They perform the best of the simple heuristics.

Example 3-4. The Miller family owns a single family car (a 1979 De Soto) and are constantly in conflict about who needs it the most. One evening at dinner, Jack Miller reported he wanted to take the car at 8 a.m. to drive to the city, which would take one hour, collect a number of legal papers, which would take one hour, and get back home by noon when an important client would meet him to sign the papers. His customer would probably wait for a little while, but Jack estimates the cost to himself at about $200 an hour for being late. His daughter Janey exploded; she had planned a slumber party. She needs the car for about nine hours to pick up various friends who live at various directions in a 50 mile radius. Her mother, Maggie, will need about five hours to prepare this party, for which she does not need the car. After Maggie has finished preparation and the guests arrive, she will require about an hour for last-minute decorations and making dessert. The party is scheduled for 7 p.m. After talking to Maggie, Janey is willing to estimate the cost of the party being tardy at $10 an hour. Who should get the car? What should the schedule for the day look like?

Solution. Clearly Jack and Janey represent separate projects; say Jack is project 1 and Janey is project 2. Both have weighted tardiness objectives. Jack's project has a weight of $200 per hour and a due date of four hours (noon). His sole activity, labeled 11, has a processing time of three hours. Janey's project has a weight of $10 per hour and a due date

	Heuristic	Formula
FCFS	First available, first served	
SLK	Minimum operation slack	$\text{SLK}_{ij} = \text{LST}_{ij} - t$
SPT	Shortest process time	p_{ij}
MTS	Most total successors (activity)	n_{ij}
LFT	Late finish time (ODD) (min)	LF_{ij}
LFS	Least float per successor	$(\text{SLK}_{ij})/(n_{ij})$
EDD	Earliest project due date	d_i
MAXPEN	Maximum weight (penalty)	w_i
WSPT	Weighted SPT (max)	w_j/p_{ij}
R&M	Slack corrected WSPT(max)	$(w_j/p_{ij})*\exp[-\text{SLK}_{ij}{}^+/kp_{av}]$
WEDD	Weighted EDD(max)	$w_j/(d_i - t^*)$
WLFT	Weighted LFT (max)	$w_j/(\text{LF}_{ij} - t^*)$
WMINSLK	Weighted MINSLK(max)	$w_j/(\text{LS}_{ij} - t^*)$

Table 3-10
....
Simple Multiple Project Dispatch Heuristics

(Here t^* is a fixed earlier reference time.)

of 11 hours (7 p.m.). Her project has three activities. Activity 21 is last minute activities and has a processing time of one hour. Activity 22 is picking up the guests. It has a processing time of nine hours, and precedes 21. Activity 23, cleaning and cooking, has a processing time of five hours and also precedes 21.

Figure 3-10 shows the network diagram for the two projects with the common "car" resource constraint. (Double circles show project completions.) The relaxed problem has both projects completed by time 11. Neither project is tardy, so there is an objective value of zero. We do not bother to show the resource usage profile, since it is clear that two cars are required from time 0 to time 3, one car from time 3 to time 10, and 0 thereafter. Thus the conflict is between activities 11 and 22 (Dad traveling to the city and Janey picking up friends).

We form two augmented problems, one in which Jack gets first dibs, and one in which Janey does. The two augmented problems are shown in Figure 3-11. It is not necessary to solve these new relaxed problems formally, we can see the answers in such a small problem. In both augmented problems we have eliminated the resource conflict. When Dad has dibs, he finishes on time, but Janey's party is two hours late (9 p.m.). Thus the total cost is $20 (0(200) + 2(10)). On the other hand, if we let Janey go first, her party will be on time, but dad won't get home until 8 p.m. Thus the total cost of the second solution is $1600 (8(200) + 0(10)). Thus the best solution is to let Jack have the car first. (Now why doesn't this surprise us?)

Example 3-4, Part 2. How would our simple heuristics compare as to results on the family car problem? That is to say, would Jack or Janey get the car first?

1. **FCFS**—Since both are ready to take the car, it is random depending on which has the lower tie breaker. In Figure 3-10 Dad has the lower number and might get chosen.
2. **SLK**—Both have a slack of one hour, so again it would depend on some tie-breaker rule.
3. **SPT**—Dad is the clear winner, 3 hours versus 10.

Figure 3-10

The Family Car Problem

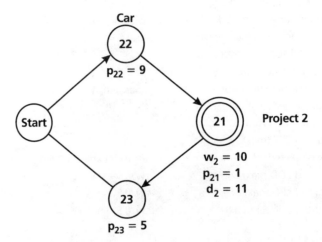

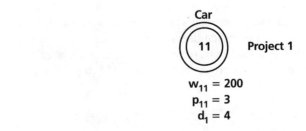

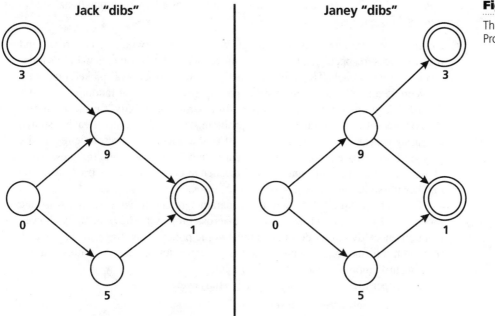

Figure 3-11

The Augmented Family Car Problem

4. **MTS**—Janey is the clear winner, 1 versus 0.
5. **LFT**—Dad wins with an LFT of 4; Janey has an LFT of 10.
6. **LFS**—Janey wins, 1/1 versus 1/0.
7. **EDD**—Dad wins with a due date of 4 versus Janey with 11.
8. **MAXPEN**—Dad wins with importance of 200 versus Janey with 10.
9. **WSPT**—Dad wins with 200/3 versus Janey with 10/9.
10. **R&M**—No details, similar to WSPT here; Dad wins big again.
11. **WEDD**—Dad wins with 200/4 versus Janey with 10/11.
12. **WLFT**—Dad wins with 200/4 versus Janey with 10/9.
13. **WMINSLK**—Dad wins with 200/1 versus Janey with 10/1.

Many computer project management software packages would simply unify the two projects and minimize total project duration. It is clear that such a procedure would let Janey go first, so that everyone would be done by time $t = 13$ (9 p.m. for Dad) while letting Jack go first would have everyone finished by time $t = 14$ (10 p.m. for Janey). Thus such a procedure is poor at dealing with realistic problems.

Iterated Myopic Dispatch / Bottleneck Dynamics.

Two-Stage Dispatch Procedure. Lawrence and Morton [1993] noticed the following things about the way activities compete to be next in a dispatch simulation process:

1. Candidate activities within the same project cannot be distinguished on the basis of relative importance since both are trying to accomplish the same thing.
2. They also cannot be distinguished on the basis of resource usage, since neither is effective until the entire project is completed, which uses the same resources in both cases.
3. Hence, *within* a project we want to minimize maximum lateness by using LFT, which is the best slack-based rule to coordinate completion times as much as possible.
4. In choosing between activities in two different projects, use R&M or bottleneck dynamics.
5. Iterated dispatch uses the R&M heuristic for priorities, while bottleneck dynamics uses somewhat more complex pricing and priority rules.

Computational Study. We give here a brief summary of a large computational study carried out by Lawrence and Morton [1993].

Experimental Design. Four problem sets were generated, with one, two, three, and five resources, respectively. Each problem set included 40 problems with five independent projects each. The number of activities in a project was picked randomly between 25 and 50; the weights of the projects were picked at random between 1 and 10. The number of resources needed for a particular activity was picked at random between 1 and the number in the problem. The total amount of each resource was assigned randomly between 0.3 and 1.0; the fraction of a resource required k was uniform between 0.5 and 1.0. Three levels of due date tightness were assigned: loose, medium, and tight. Precedence constraints as a fraction of the number possible ranged from 0.05 to 0.15.

The authors did a pilot study to set parameters and to validate the two-stage procedure (LFT within project, heuristic across projects). The pilot study showed that bottleneck dynamics dominated the myopic policy. This suggests that, indeed, important information is contained in the prices of downstream activities that can significantly improve scheduling performance.

The experimental factors of the main study were:

number of resources—4 levels
due date tightness—3 levels
scheduling rules—30 policies
replications for each factor set—40

which gave a total of 14,400 scheduling problems for the main study.

Experimental Results. Lead time iteration throughout the study reduced the weighted tardiness of slack-based rules by an average of 18 percent, and found its best schedule on average after 3.8 iterations. Thus LTI proved highly effective in this study. Across all problems the new rules WEDD, WLFT, and WMINSLK yielded the lowest total average weighted tardiness among the 20 simple dispatch rules considered, but did not do as well as bottleneck dynamics, with or without LTI. Table 3-11 gives a summary of the best performers, for loose, medium, and tight due date.

In terms of ranking, bottleneck dynamics with iterated lead time and iterated prices (BD-ITER) was a clear first, at a computational cost about four times a simple policy. A composite policy which ran all 20 simple dispatch policies for each problem and took the best answer (BEST/20) was about 12 percent off the pace, at a computational cost of about 20 times that of a simple policy. The seven best simple policies, at a computational time of 1.0, were WEDD (30%), WLFT (38%), WMNSLK (40%), EDD (51%), LFT (57%), MINSLK (60%), and MAXPEN (107%).

Table 3-11

Multiple Project Weighted
Tardiness Schedule

(Result = % Above
Best Policy)

Policy	Due Dates			Total	Time
	Loose	Medium	Tight		
BD-Iteration	0.0	0.0	0.0	0.0	4
BEST/20	11.3	12.2	11.6	11.7	20
BD-No Iteration	24.9	26.4	19.4	22.4	1
WEDD	47.0	34.3	22.0	30.0	1
WLFT	55.1	42.5	29.0	37.5	1
WMNSLK	56.0	45.2	32.2	40.2	1
EDD	50.1	52.1	50.7	51.0	1
LFT	56.0	56.9	57.4	57.0	1
MINSLK	56.9	59.4	60.7	59.8	1
MAXPEN	206.5	124.0	62.3	106.6	1

Note that the improvements of the weighted simple dispatch heuristics over their unweighted versions increase with due date tightness, as would be expected. Note that BEST/20 is only about 12 percent worse than bottleneck dynamics with lead time iteration. However, the former involves running 20 dispatch simulations, the latter only about 4.

3.4.7 Dispatch and Search Exercises

Classic Dispatch Heuristics.

1. In the Qwik and Durtie problem:

    a. Verify that any dispatch heuristic must produce one of two schedules, depending only on the choice of the second activity to start.
    b. Using (a) to save work, find the schedules that would be produced by FCFS, SPT, MTS, and LFS.

2. In the Qwik and Durtie problem:

    a. Add a precedence constraint from activity 4 to activity 7, and solve the resulting problem with the SLK heuristic.
    b. Solve it for the LFT heuristic.
    c. Compare the two results.

3. In the Qwik and Durtie problem:

    a. Change activity 5 into 10 activities in series, each with process time 10 percent of the original activity process time. Solve the resulting problem by the MTS heuristic.
    b. Compare to the MTS solution for the original problem.
    c. What do you conclude about types of difficulties that might be encountered?

4. Solve the Castin Con Creet (CCC) problem by the MTS heuristic.

Iterated Myopic Dispatch.

5. Solve the Castin Con Creet problem by lead time iteration using:

    a. The MTS heuristic
    b. The SLK heuristic

6. "The Castin Con Creet problem could just as well have been simplified by aggregating activities 5, 6, and 7 into one activity with process time 3." Is this statement true or false? In either case, explain with examples or counter-examples.

7. Modify the Castin Con Creet example by changing the process time on activity 2 to 2, and adding a precedence constraint from activity 4 to activity 5.

    a. Solve the modified problem by iterated myopic dispatch.
    b. Argue whether or not the solution is optimal.

Modern Search Methods.

8. Write down a random permutation of the numbers from 1 to 7. You may use the random number table in Appendix H.

    a. Use this as a set of priorities to schedule the Castin Con Creet problem. Use this as your starting solution for neighborhood search.
    b. Interchange the first two numbers in your priority and re-solve.
    c. Do this also for second and third, third and fourth, and so on.
    d. Were you able to improve your initial solution?
    e. Would it be possible in this case to get a second improvement by repeating (b) and (c)?

3.5 CUSTOM OPTICAL EQUIPMENT—REPRISE

The students came back after 14 weeks to present their final report to Optik's CEO, the gist of which is presented in Figure 3-12.

Figure 3-12

Students' Final Report

General Solution Strategy. Your shop is essentially a multiple-project scheduling problem, except for a few difficulties:

1. The paint and bake rooms are batch.
2. No delay is allowed between paint and bake.
3. There are routing decisions in the assembly shop.

We think that a reasonable strategy would be to:

1. Make approximations to fit these features to the standard multiple-project scheduling model.
2. Solve the resulting problem by the bottleneck dynamics method we have learned, in order to estimate resource prices and lead times.
3. Create a full simulation model with details restored, making any necessary modifications to the assembly and paint shop area.
4. Make a single pass by bottleneck dynamics.

Approximating the Paint/Bake Shop

1. Each item is assumed to require a simple lag time equal to the paint time, followed by a small bake time equal to the actual bake time times the percentage of the bake shop used, plus a final lag equal to the rest of bake time.
2. This is not to make total processing time add up properly, but to show fractional use of bake shop.

Approximating the Assembly Shop

1. Approximate the assembly shop as one resource.
2. Simply add up all table space, and let any activity require a certain fraction of this resource and one crew.
3. The main inaccuracy here is that larger projects will be allowed to use several tables.

Solving the Simplified Model

1. With the simplified Paint/Bake and Assembly Shops, the model is exactly a standard multiple projects formulation.
2. Note that the fixed leads and lags are activities using no resources.
3. The bake shop will have a price; the paint shop price is zero.
4. All tables receive the same price per square foot; this may not be too accurate.

Full Scheduling Procedure

1. The full scheduling procedure must add back an accurate representation of the paint/bake shop.
2. This is also true for the assembly shop.

Paint/Bake Shop Scheduling Design

1. As activities arrive in front of the paint shop they are accumulated into compatible batches and prioritized.
2. The start time is chosen so that the previous bake batch will finish at the same time.
3. Work will start with the highest priority batch.
4. The highest priority batch depends on prices and lead times from the earlier simplified solutions.

Figure 3-12

Students' Final Report
(continued)

Assembly Scheduling Shop Design

1. On small tables choose the highest priority fitting item; the large table is more difficult.
2. You must consider both priority and best fitting factors for table wastage.
3. You may wish to save space for "hot" jobs.
4. You need either fitting heuristics or a DSS system.

The CEO's Reply. Overall, the CEO was very pleased with the students' report, with the caveat that it looked awfully ambitious. He asked for them to come back in two weeks so that he could think it over.

They all came back in two weeks, and the president said to go ahead and build the system, but in stages:

R&D PLAN.

1. Build the simplified simulation and test it.
2. Present the findings to the CEO.
3. Get approval or not to continue.
4. Create a test model of the full scheduling system and test it.
5. Present the findings to the CEO.
6. Get approval or not to continue.
7. Run the system in parallel with the real shop.
8. If it is successful, implement the system.

He asked the students for time and cost estimates. After some huddling, they offered a fixed price of a $10,000 contribution to the university and an average estimated two months calendar time for step 1. They were unwilling to make estimates further into the future. The CEO agreed—they could start as soon as a simple contract was drawn up.

Project Design and Control

4.1 INTRODUCTION

The project methods we have presented are rich and complex; nevertheless they are very limited in some respects:

1. They assume that activities, process times, resource needs and availabilities, rewards, and precedence structures are simply given at the start of the analysis and are accurate as far as necessary into the future.
2. They assume perfect communication and cooperation between different groups within the company and different subcontractors on larger projects.

In this chapter we discuss methods for obtaining these inputs somewhat more accurately, and we also discuss ways to help management use the project scheduling software. Nevertheless, these basic limitations can only be reduced somewhat, never eliminated completely. This means that project-scheduling techniques can only be tools to be used in the broader context of project management. This chapter makes free use of the ideas in Morton et al. [1984] with the authors' kind permission.

In Section 4.2 we meet two subproject managers, Marcy and Phil, who manage parts of the Alpha Centauri Endeavor (ACE) project of Corporal Motors. ACE's ambitious goal is to build and commercialize the first electric automobile with a range of 400 miles, and a cost 80 percent of that of gas-powered cars. In Section 4.3 we discuss some issues in project design. In Section 4.4 we discuss the actual execution (control) of the project after the plan (schedule) has been made. Finally, in Section 4.5, we finish our discussion of the Alpha Centauri Endeavor.

4.2 APPLICATION SCENARIO—
ALPHA CENTAURI ENDEAVOR (ACE)

4.2.1 Overview

Whit Whitestone, a software engineer from Communal Mentat University (CMU,) is trying to build a next-generation project management system. He wonders what issues are important to deal with outside the traditional project planning, scheduling, and control arena. He asks for help from an old friend, Jack King, at Corporal Motors, who introduces him to two subproject managers, Marcy and Phil. They manage parts of the Alpha Centauri Endeavor project (ACE). This is a five-year multi-billion dollar project to build the first truly competitive electric car. It is planned to have a 400 mile range between re-charging and to sell at 80 percent of the price of gas-powered cars. Its success depends largely upon commercializing a recent revolutionary breakthrough in battery technology in the laboratory. There is expected to be considerable risk and difficulty in implementing the new technology on a mass scale.

Jack arranges separate interviews with Marcy and Phil, who have each agreed to give a half hour or so from their busy schedules, partly as a favor to Jack, and partly in hope of learning some academic tricks to help them in their work.

4.2.2 The Interview with Marcy

Marcy found a few minutes to spend with Whit first. He told her the interview would be taped to make sure he didn't miss anything. He planned it to be in four parts (not rigid):

1. He would tell her a little bit about his background, and the nature of the project he was working on.
2. She would tell him a little bit about her background.
3. She would verbally ask him a number of important questions she thought a good project management software program should be able to answer.
4. They could have some general discussion, including whether she would like him to come back in a couple of weeks with feedback on what he thought a good project management system *could* do.

Whit's Background and Current Work. Whit spoke first: "I have a Master's Degree in Industrial Engineering specializing in Operations Management and Manufacturing. My doctorate is in Software Engineering. I have a joint appointment with the Business School and the Computer Science Department. I have been at CMU for 22 years, 14 of them as a full professor. For the past ten years I have been developing fast and accurate algorithms for standard job shop scheduling and project management models. I have built laboratory systems and demonstrated, through extensive simulation experimentation, that my methods work well. This work has been widely published in journals. However, I find that my ideas are not being implemented by anyone.

"My ultimate goal has always been for my ideas to really be used, of course. I guess it's just a case of 'If you want something done right, do it yourself.' But when I started to look at real-world problems, I was shocked to discover that academic project management models aren't anywhere nearly adequate to build a useful commercial system! I've got to go to the source and find out what the real problems are. The worst real problems are probably in projects like yours (and mine!) which over five years or more try to commercialize a hot new laboratory technology. So here I am to learn from you. If you get any help from me in return, so much the better."

Marcy's Background and Current Work. Marcy's turn: "Before I start, let me say I am glad to help you and, perhaps, myself, with only the requirement that Phil and I are allowed final control over written material arising from these conversations, to protect company proprietary material. Typically you can use or publish anything you want as long as sensitive material is disguised." Whit answered that he understood this condition and agreed.

Marcy continued, "I have a Master's Degree in Chemical Engineering and a later Master's Degree in Electrical Engineering. I have been involved with battery technology for 31 years, and have been project manager for battery technology development at the Corporal Motors Research Laboratories for 15 years. I headed the project which three years ago produced the battery breakthrough which led to project Alpha Centauri Endeavor. I now head the subproject in ACE which is expected to reduce the size of the batteries required to power the new car from the 2000 pounds achieved by our last project, to 800 pounds, and to preserve the 400-mile range. The price of the last project batteries would be $15,000 per car even with mass production. Our specs are to reduce the material costs to $2000, with a total cost of $4000 per car given mass production. We are considering using a new 'wonder material' now in lab testing in Germany to achieve these results. (I cannot tell you anything about this material except that it is potentially much cheaper and much lighter than what we have.)

"I am to produce the prototype of the final battery. Although the overall car cannot succeed without my project succeeding, neither can it succeed if that battery cannot be successfully mass produced. Nor will it succeed unless a car can be designed that the consumer will find as comfortable, practical, and glamorous as a conventional car. So we are all under the gun. We must absolutely meet deadlines and deliver what is expected to make it all work."

Marcy's Questions. Whit said he was delighted with the interview thus far. Next he wanted to know what questions Marcy thought a good project management software system should be able to answer. She asked the following questions extemporaneously. (These are the actual questions asked by a real R&D project manager in the same type of interview.)

1. How much will this cost?"
2. In what parts of the project are the risks highest?
3. How long will it take?
4. What is the expected completion date?
5. How much variation is there in that estimate?
6. What items contribute most of the risk?
7. What are the critical tasks?
8. What critical skills are required? Where?
9. What do the resource needs over time look like?
10. What is the potential for loop back (rework) for this milestone?
11. What is the impact on the project if we loop?
12. Where are you relative to where you planned to be?
13. Are we still on track overall?
14. No? Then who is performing well?
15. No? Then who needs help and what kind?
16. No? Then what tasks have become critical?
17. No? Then what critical activities were missed during planning?
18. No? Was there a systematic error in the plan?
19. No? What is the revised date for the project?

4.2.3 The Interview with Phil

Marcy suggested they postpone the final discussion until after the interview with Phil, so that all three of them could talk together and decide on the next move. Whit agreed that this was a good idea.

Phil's Background and Current Work. "Let me say, first of all, that although Marcy and I are officially heading independent subprojects, in actuality Marcy is much senior to me, and this is the first time I am not actually working for her. In many ways I still treat her as my mentor and general advisor. In addition, I am responsible for a great deal of input on the prototype battery to make sure it will be manufacturable, and she is responsible for telling me during prototype manufacturing which manufacturing methods are likely to fail, and so on. Her difficulties will likely become my difficulties; and her breakthroughs will reduce my problems.

"I have a Master's in Manufacturing Management from an engineering school, with a minor in Chemical Engineering. I have 18 years experience in manufacturing, and was hired by Marcy 15 years ago when she came to Corporal Motors. For the last 10 years I have been Assistant Project Manager under Marcy; this is my first relatively independent managerial position. It is extremely exciting, but a little scary."

Next they turned to the questions Phil thought a software package should be able to answer.

Phil's Questions.

1. What changes have occurred since I last reviewed the project, in terms of:

    a. schedule
    b. context
    c. things
    d. people
    e. places

2. What do these changes mean?
3. Which are really critical?
4. Are these changes to be expected?
5. If unexpected, are they symptoms or causes?
6. What other similar elements can help identify causes?
7. What predictors or indicators can help to:

    a. improve performance
    b. identify planning flaws
    c. provide early warning of future problems

8. Where should I put my management attention most:

    a. people
    b. schedule
    c. things
    d. concepts
    e. planning

9. What are this period's top five areas to concentrate on?
10. What have we learned from past experience about this problem?
11. Who is responsible for those things that have changed?
12. What adjustments have been made to catch up to schedule?
13. In order to catch up, which activities can be:

    a. done in parallel
    b. delayed
    c. deleted

14. How can histories of actual progress versus planning be used to help our current planning?
15. What are the assumptions behind this activity?
16. Who should be notified of this change . . . and when?
17. Why can't the computer give exception reports that are tailored to my needs instead of masses of output?
18. What small events have big importances?
19. How do I find non-apparent dependencies between activities?
20. How do we plan loop back (rework) and other exception paths into the main network flow diagram?
21. How does a reporting system deal with project norms, versus project predictions, versus project reality?
22. How does one deal with external events over which one has little control, which nevertheless are part of the network flow diagram?
23. What would be a good system with high-level planning blocks for high-level planning and major contingency planning?

24. How does one fine-tune fuzzy constraints as more becomes known about them?
25. How does one talk about "confidence levels" for the completion time (or resource usage) of a project milestone?
26. How does one deal with families of projects?
27. How does one replan and control projects which have had major extensions to them in mid-life by top management?
28. How does one make good estimates of cost/resource/duration tradeoffs without studying hundreds of possibilities?

4.2.4 The Following Discussion

Whit Whitestone was overwhelmed by the diversity and meaty difficulty of these questions. At first blush he felt that perhaps 25 percent of these questions could be addressed by current project management systems and another 25 percent could be handled by carefully designed new systems, but that maybe 50 percent of the questions could probably only be handled by human experts in the foreseeable future.

Marcy and Phil were not too surprised, but somewhat disappointed by Whit's assessment. Before jumping into an effort to design new project management features to deal with some of their questions, they asked him to spend two or three weeks, and give short answers to the questions. (It could be as simple as saying "these three are handled now," etc., or more completely if possible.)

Whit accepted the assignment, but still went home a bit overwhelmed.

Can Whit deal with a large, non-mathematical verbal task? Will he write a program? Will he return with many answers to the questions? Answers to these and other questions will be discussed in Section 4.5, Alpha Centauri Endeavor—reprise.

4.3 PROJECT DESIGN

4.3.1 Overview

To develop a Level 4 schedule for the project requires that the project first be specified in detail. For this, in turn, a number of different things must be accomplished:

1. Define the work to be done (work breakdown structure).
2. Cost out the activities individually and in groups.
3. Similarly estimate the other resources needed by activity and in groups.
4. Negotiate corresponding budget (authorization) with the financial authorities, both in terms of costs and resources.
5. Estimate activity durations and constraints.

In designing a project, these five activities cannot really be done independently and in parallel. The person designing the work breakdown structure (WBS) must clearly have some idea about costing and the maximum the budget will allow. Otherwise, if that person comes in five times over budget, the corrective redesign will be so radical that a great deal of time will be lost.

Thus the design will typically be somewhat in parallel among the five functions, but with a lot of communication among the groups, to forecast that the results will be somewhat compatible. Inevitably, the five groups will have major or minor disagreements anyway. When this happens some decision will be reached as to which group(s) must redesign, and an iterative process will begin until the five groups have consistent results.

Many times a number of complete designs will be created to allow for major uncertainties (such as how the CEO will react). This process is very much an art. Here we shall concentrate more or less on the individual functions.

4.3.2 Work Breakdown Structure

A work breakdown structure (WBS) in its simplest form is a hierarchical breakdown of a project into subprojects, subprojects into major activities, major activities into subactivities, etc., without consideration of precedence constraints, start and finish constraints, or activity durations. Typically, a WBS employs a hierarchical, or Dewey-Decimal-type, nomenclature, where the first digit identifies the project, the second digit the subproject, the third digit the major activity, and so on. Figure 4-1 illustrates the skeleton for a work breakdown structure for the Alpha Centauri project. (Most of the details are omitted.) The bottom level work elements of the tree are often called **work packages**. Each of the work packages must be analyzed carefully to establish a detailed set of task definitions. The WBS clearly facilitates summarization and reporting; it provides a list of tasks, which is an important input for costing, resource planning, and scheduling. Once the detailed multi-level work structure has been defined, similar multi-level costing structure and resource usage are added. The resulting hybrid structure is also often called a WBS. Other popular names are tree diagram, hierarchical chart, and gozinto chart. (This is also called top-down planning or bottom-up planning; see the following paragraphs.)

Strategies for Building the WBS. Three popular strategies for building the WBS are top-down planning, bottom-up planning, and mixed-mode planning.

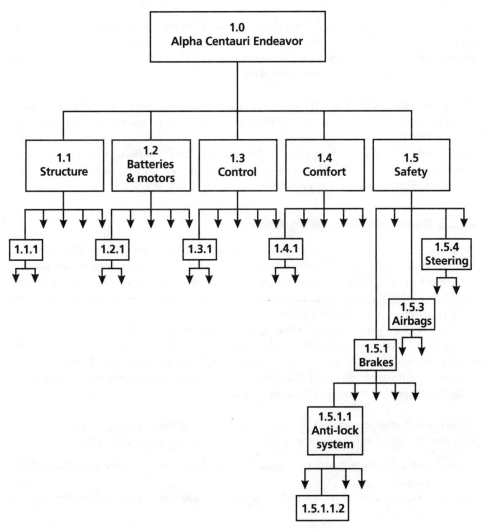

Figure 4-1

WBS Skeleton for Alpha Centauri Project

Top-down Planning. If the details of the project are not well known at the outset when a WBS is required, a top-down approach is generally employed. In this strategy, the entire project as an objective is placed at the top level. Then non-overlapping and exhaustive subproject objectives are placed at the next level. (For example, in Figure 4-1 the entire automobile represents the whole project, while structure, batteries/motors, control, comfort, and safety represent the subprojects.) Each of these segments is then discussed until people can decide how to break this into smaller parts, etc.

The strength of the top-down procedure is that it forces initial strategic thinking about the whole picture. The weakness here is that rather hazy decisions made at Levels 2 and 3 may cause great problems at the detailed activity level. Some activities may end up being duplicated, while others may not be feasible or may be very expensive in the structure forced on them.

Bottom-up Planning. The bottom-up strategy is exactly the opposite. If one knows a great deal about the details of a project, one might start by describing the detailed activities, and then figure out how to combine them in larger groups of "major activities," then to combine them into subprojects, and so on. The strength of bottom-up is that it forces an initial good understanding of the details of the projects and allows individual work packages to be well designed. It also avoids unnecessary duplication. Its weakness, of course, is that one does not see the overall picture very well and may combine elements in a way that does not make sense from the big picture.

Mixed-Mode Planning. In practice it is often useful to employ both top-down and bottom-up separately until the respective procedures run out of steam. Then the two procedures can be matched up and modified to produce a fuller WBS. Missing difficult pieces may still require conferences and serious thinking.

Computer Capabilities. While most software packages allow hierarchical numbering of activities, and can be sorted and summarized using them, most do not automatically enforce the full hierarchical structure implied by that coding. Exceptions include ViewPoint™ and Harvard Total Project Manager II™. Viewpoint also allows plans developed for each piece of the WBS to be saved in a library, which then may be accessed so that pieces of it can be used again when constructing a new WBS.

4.3.3 Resources/Costing/Budget

Resource usages need to be developed for each level of the WBS. This in itself can be a bottom-up or a top-down activity. With bottom-up, one states the resources needed and adds them up to get the total resources required. With top-down one starts with the resources available (initial budget) and allocates them among activities at the second level (subproject budgets), and then the third level, etc.

Once resources are allocated, a manager can cost them using prices where the resource has an explicit price, or an internal transfer price set by the company if that is available, or else she may have to determine an implicit price in the fashion that bottleneck dynamics does. The manager also needs the firm's cost of capital (implicit interest rate) to determine the net present value (NPV) of these costs.

Resource Assignment. At the greatest level of detail being managed in a project, the manager may use combinations of the following resource assignment methods:

1. Estimate roughly the resources likely to be in short supply, by phase of the project.
2. Estimate critical activities heavily using resources at times when they are the bottleneck.

3. Define the resources that would be required for a critical task, possibly at several levels of resource intensity, or for several different task designs.
4. Do some kinds of implicit resource leveling:

    a. Reschedule so an individual works on one activity at a time

    b. Reschedule to reduce resource conflicts

    c. Redefine tasks to use different resources

Of course, using resource leveling in this informal way before doing resource-constrained project scheduling is duplicating some of the work of the computer. If the informal leveling is "obvious," it may reduce the workload of the computer, or even improve the schedule. A good procedure, perhaps, is to run a schedule leveled by only the computer, and compare the results.

Costing. In one sense, costing is automatic after establishing the tasks, the resources for each task, the duration of the tasks, the cost rate for each resource, and the other fixed costs. This becomes largely an interesting information systems and accounting problem, which we will not address here. However, this is basically a bottom-up approach and may deliver total costs that are inconsistent with the total budget being set at the top.

4.3.4 Planning Activity Durations

Here we may distinguish between *elemental activities* and *aggregated activities*. Elemental activities are those activities that are at the bottom of the WBS hierarchy. They can be combined to form higher order activities, but cannot be decomposed into subactivities. (This is just for the purpose of the analysis.) Elemental activities almost always have an inner structure, but it is not considered worth capturing explicitly. To put it another way, the manager of an elemental activity is assumed capable of managing it without interacting formally with the system. The methods for estimating durations of elemental activities and aggregated activities are somewhat different.

Planning Elemental Activity Durations. We have already studied the best-known method for estimating elemental activity durations—PERT. Recall that the activity manager is asked to estimate most likely, optimistic, and pessimistic values for the task duration. Then a distributional form is estimated, and the mean and standard deviation of the project duration is estimated.

If the manager is not comfortable about making these estimates, but data is available from similar activities in past projects, direct statistical estimation of the activity may be possible. If there are a number of past situations similar to the current one, one might simply take the mean and standard deviation of these data points, and apply them to the current situation. If, however, there are several differing aspects, such as size, resource availability, etc., one could build a simple regression model to estimate a fit on past project data in order to predict the current situation.

Planning Aggregated Activity Durations. The planning duration of an aggregated activity, whether project, subproject, or major activity, refers to the scheduled time from start to end. Once we have elemental activity durations, precedence constraints, timing constraints, and resource constraints, we may then apply resource leveling, dispatch, or search methods to produce a master resource-constrained schedule for the entire project. This is a detailed schedule, but we may also determine ES for the start of an aggregate activity or EF for its finish, for example, by simply finding the start and the end of the aggregate activity in the detailed schedule. On the other hand, if we assume allocations of resources for the aggregate activity, we may consider it as a subproject, and simply produce a schedule for this piece of the problem, thus determining the aggregate activity length.

4.4 PROJECT EXECUTION

4.4.1 Overview

For both shop scheduling and project scheduling, we have previously set out a five-level hierarchy:

1. Long range planning
2. Medium range planning
3. Short range planning
4. Scheduling
5. Control (reactive scheduling, execution)

Project scheduling, which has occupied our attention for most of the Project Management Module, is primarily concerned with Levels 3 and 4. We turn very briefly to Level 5.

The sequence of events in project control progresses generally as follows:

a. Track the actual progress of the work, resource usage, and cost accumulation.
b. Compare the actual progress of work and resource/cost needs with those expected from the current (Level 4) schedule.
c. Update the forecasted activity durations and resource/cost needs for the remainder of the project.
d. Revise the Level 4 schedule based on these forecasts, and pinpoint problem areas.
e. Exercise control: change resource availabilities, activity priorities, project design, etc. to produce an improved revised project schedule.
f. Repeat c, d, and e, until the revised project schedule is satisfactory.
g. Proceed with the new schedule until the next scheduled review, or until new problems crop up.
h. Repeat the entire process from a.

Remember that we suggested using a rolling horizon approach both in inventory control and in shop scheduling. In project scheduling the dollars at stake are typically higher, and the time frame somewhat longer, so that we can afford to do many full revisions of the schedule if necessary. We now look at the rolling horizon, interactive project control process in more detail.

Suppose now that we have created and saved a complete project schedule. (Alternatively, we are in the middle of the project, and our created and saved project schedule is our last revised schedule.) We proceed pretty much according to this schedule until one of two things happen:

1. It is time for a regular periodic review and revision of the schedule.
2. Sufficient problems have surfaced to require a special review and schedule revision.

In either case, it is important to copy the schedule and then revise the copy. This allows a sequence of schedules to be saved and stored for possible later post mortems. In the following subsections, we go through the sequence of project control that we have just previously outlined.

In Section 4.4.2 we discuss tracking the actual progress of the work, tracking the resource usage, and the cost accumulation. Then we look at comparing these actual results with those expected from the current schedule. In Section 4.4.3 we talk about updating the forecasts for remaining activity durations and resource/cost requirements for the remainder of the project, and we discuss revising the project based on these updated forecasts. In Section 4.4.4 we address management control based on comparing the new schedule to management goals. We also discuss a possible iterative process to bring the new schedule and management goals into confluence.

4.4.2 Actual Versus Expected

There are three types of usage of concern to management: time usage (work progress), resource usage, and accumulated costs.

Tracking the Work Progress. In tracking the work progress, a great deal depends on the quality of the data that is collected from the developing project. Almost all systems will record the actual start time and finish time for each activity (call them t_{jsa} and t_{jfa}) in addition to the scheduled times t_{js} and t_{jf}. (Note the latter are not necessarily from the original schedule, but from the latest revised schedule.) In addition, it is important to report some measure or measures of the status of in-progress activities. In tracking the work progress, we are primarily interested in estimating the remaining duration of the activity, as estimated from the current time t. Call this estimate $(p_j)_t$.

The simplest such estimate, which requires no further information, is just to subtract the time the activity has actually been processed to date from the time originally planned.

$$(p_j)_t = p_j - (t - t_{jsa})$$

While this estimate requires no sophisticated information, it also may not give very good answers. Suppose this estimate is negative, and yet we have received no notice of completion, t_{jfa}. Setting the estimate to zero in this case gives us some improvement. But certainly the manager of the activity can give us some better estimate than zero since the activity is not finished. Types of information we might hope the manager would supply would include one of the following:

Time remaining in activity
Percentage remaining in activity
Percentage completed in activity
Revised estimate of total activity duration

While the availability of any of these would solve our problem, unfortunately the manager is often unable or unwilling to supply accurate answers about this process. The manager, for example, may say early on that the activity is 80 percent complete to avoid hassle from the project manager, and then never estimate above 90 percent complete for a long time!

Sometimes it makes sense to use formal forecasting models. For example, we might keep track of the rate at which the project is being completed, and use exponential smoothing to forecast the average future rate. Or we might use regression on past similar activities, using their completion times from various partial completion stages to forecast our completion time from our partial completion stage.

One other variable to consider is how to deal with **out-of sequence activity progress**. It must be understood that the activity precedence logic established in the original schedule was only a rough best guess at how the work would actually be done. Remember that project management techniques are often used for work that is unique in nature, so that we have less benefit from hindsight. Thus actual durations will vary considerably from planned, and some of the planned logical constraints will be ignored.

Software programs treat this issue in a number of different ways. One of the best is called "logic override": simply proceed with this activity and its successors as if all predecessors had already been processed.

Tracking Actual Resource Usage. The process of tracking resource usage is quite similar to the process of tracking duration times discussed previously, except that we need to keep track of each separate resource used by the task. Thus we address the actual use of each resource in such quantified terms as actual units used, estimated units remaining and/or percent remaining, with similar types of choices of computational forecasting.

Some software packages do not have the capability of showing resource usage. That is, they fully support resource planning in obtaining the original schedule, but do not track them during execution. They do allow showing the effect of resource usage by entering the *cost* of the actual resource use. This allows analysis of overall project cost performance to date, and may be satisfactory for many purposes. Some of the difficulties with this are that:

1. You have to figure out the costs to enter them, using planned usage rates.
2. If actual usage rates differ, these are poor estimates.
3. It is difficult to measure resource productivity.

Many programs, however, allow entering actual resource utilization experience and forecasting resource needs to complete an activity independently of time needs.

Tracking Actual Costs. It is especially important to track actual costs carefully, since top management is often most concerned with this summary of all resource usage. Ledgers are needed for both the commitment of costs (purchase orders) and for actual (invoiced) costs. Measuring committed costs against the budget allows early recognition of cost overruns. Unfortunately, most systems track only actual costs, which does not allow enough reaction time for good remedial control.

In this tracking and analysis phase, we will be interested in how our actual costs compare with planned costs for each activity. We may also want to summarize and evaluate cost performance by resource, cost account, or work breakdown structure.

Updating Activity/Resource Forecasts. So far we have discussed updating duration, resource, and cost estimates for the remainder of current activities. However, suppose labor costs have consistently been averaging 15 percent higher per hour than our plan allows for. We probably should make some adjustment to estimated labor resource costs for the rest of the project. We may not want to increase them a full 15 percent, but perhaps 10 percent. Or we may be using exponential smoothing to update, and we would simply use that to make our forecast.

Similarly, suppose the new technology has been more difficult to develop than thought, and that activities to date have consistently required 25 to 50 percent more time than previously estimated. We may want to correct future estimates for this fact.

Most commonly, managers are somewhat afraid to make negative adjustments for fear of "buying trouble." (Let sleeping dogs lie?) They don't like to make positive adjustments either, since that takes away from the slack they privately hope they can keep. Reluctance to make accurate forecasts of the future as things change is probably one of the most costly problems in project management.

4.4.3 Project Revision

Once the proper revisions have been made to show the actual project results to date, and forecasts have been made for future activity durations and resource usage, it is a straightforward process to rerun the full resource-constrained project scheduling machinery and get revised estimates of the start and finish times for future activities, project completion, activity costs, and project costs.

Management will also be interested in a change report. If the changes in start and finish times are fairly small, and resources and costs have not changed greatly, then management will probably suppress the change in schedule, since frequent small changes cause confusion to activity managers without improving the schedule much. (This is called "schedule nervousness.") On the other hand, if there are larger changes, more serious management attention is called for.

4.4.4 Management Attention

When upper management looks at a new proposed schedule, although there may be one or two noticeable changes, the schedule may look quite reasonable overall. In this case, management may simply allow the new schedule to become the standard without interfering.

Pinpointing Problem Areas. When management allows the new schedule to become standard, they may instead anticipate serious problem areas. There are two aggregate problems that will first concern them: projected project completion overrun and projected cost overrun. Then they will turn their attention to individual areas of the project. They will be especially interested in **trends**, or smoothed production rates, or cost rates over several periods. A dip in the production rate or a spike in costs, at a single point in time may well be random and thus unimportant. But to ignore such signals if they persist would be folly.

Exercising Control. Management has a number of ways to exercise control when it becomes needed. They can speed up the project completion by using extra resources at strategic points in the project. Unfortunately this will also increase costs. Similarly, of course, they can decrease costs, often by stretching out the project somewhat. In general, management will have to have a rough cost/time tradeoff in mind in making such decisions.

It may be possible to change the project design somewhat, or change an activity method. It may be possible to change managers on a critical activity. However, all such major interventions run the risk of lowering morale and further damaging the project.

Iterating the Procedure. If management has made major changes, it will be necessary to reforecast the remainder of the project, run the resource-constrained project scheduling procedure again, pinpoint any remaining problem areas, and take any further needed management action. In difficult cases this may need to be repeated.

4.5 ALPHA CENTAURI ENDEAVOR—REPRISE

Whit returned to Marcy and Phil in two weeks with the following report, which he suggested they scan and then provide feedback in an hour or so. (Marcy's questions are designated by the letter "M" and question number, Phil's by the letter "P" and question number.)

Figure 4-2

Whit's Report

Current project management systems do allow making resource-constrained schedules and revising them during execution on a rolling horizon basis. Thus they literally answer updated questions like, "How much does it cost?" and "How long will it take?"; that is, questions like M1, M3, M4, M9, M12, M13, and M19. A weakness in current systems, however, is revising the forecast as to how long current and future activities will take. I have some ideas for this listed later in this report. In general, this is a very hard question.

Current project management systems handle risk poorly or not at all. I envision a system with PERT-like estimates, which are revised as the project goes along, and which take into account dependencies between activities. My ideas would make a good start on M2, M5, M6, M10, M11, P19, P20, P24, and P25. This system would start with a regular deterministic schedule, but then do a distribution of time required across longest paths. It would depend on activity managers to revise the activity estimates.

Critical activities in the simple sense can be found by looking for those with low resource-corrected slack. In the profound sense, these can be found only through

Figure 4-2

Whit's Report, continued

> human experience. Thus questions M7, M8, M17, M18, P2, P3, P4, P5, P8, P9, P11, P12, P13, P15, P16, and P18 have some easy answers in the sense of slacks and implicit resource prices, but are probably asking much deeper questions that are beyond computer systems at this point.
>
> I have good methods for handling multiple projects, and am working on including hierarchical systems, doing regression estimates of times from past similar activities, and so on. These include questions P6, P7, P10, P13, P14, P17, P19, P21, P22, P23, P26, P27, and P28.
>
> I obviously don't have time to develop all these topics in detail at this time, but would be glad to talk to you on a few of special interest.

Marcy and Phil's Response. Marcy and Phil were extremely interested in Whit's forthcoming project management system, and asked if they could have more details of the design. They thought it quite possible that Corporal Motors might provide some research funding through CMU for Whit to help create a system they might be able to use. Whit thought this a great idea, but said it would take him three months to whip a design into shape. They agreed to meet again when the design was ready.

BIBLIOGRAPHY

General/Book

Archibald, R. D. (1977). *Managing High-Technology Programs and Projects.* New York: John Wiley.

Baker, K. R. (1974). *Introduction to Sequencing and Scheduling.* New York: John Wiley.

Carlson, R. D. and J. A. Lewis (1980). *The Systems Analysis Workbook: A Complete Guide to Project Implementation and Control.* New Jersey: Hall.

Cleland, D. I. and W. R. King (1969). *Systems, Organizations, Analyses, Management: A Book of Readings.* New York: McGraw-Hill.

Cleland, D. I. and W. R. King (1975). *Systems Analysis and Project Management.* New York: McGraw-Hill.

Cleland, D. I. and W. R. King (1988). *Project Management Handbook* (2nd Edition). New York: Van Nostrand Reinhold.

Moder, J. J., C. R. Phillips, and E. W. Davis (1983). *Project Management with CPM, PERT and Precedence Diagramming* (3rd. edition). New York: Van Nostrand Reinhold.

Morton, T. E. and D. W. Pentico (1993). *Heuristic Scheduling Systems—With Applications of Production Systems and Project Management.* New York: John Wiley and Sons.

Wiest, J. D. and F. K. Levy (1977). *A Management Guide to PERT/CPM.* Englewood Cliffs, NJ: Prentice-Hall.

Strategic Issues

Archibald, R. D. (1986). "Implementing Business Strategies through Projects," in *Strategic Planning and Management Handbook* (2nd edition). Eds. King, W. R. and D. I. Cleland, New York: Van Nostrand Reinhold.

Baker, N. R. and J. Freland (1975). "Recent Advances in R&D Benefit Measurement and Project Selection Methods," *Management Science* 21, 1164–1175.

Cleland, D. I. and W. R. King (1988). "Life-Cycle Management," Ch. 9 in *Project Management Handbook*. Eds. Cleland, D. I. and W. R. King (2nd edition). New York: Van Nostrand Reinhold, 191–205.

Horwitch, M. (1979). "Designing and Managing Large-Scale, Public-Private Technological Enterprises: A State of the Art Review," *Technology in Society* 1, 179–192.

Horwitch, M. (1984). "The Convergence Factor for Successful Large-Scale Programs: The American Synfuels Experience as a Case in Point," in *Matrix Management Systems Handbook*. Ed. D. I. Cleland. New York: Van Nostrand Reinhold.

King, W. R. (1988). "The Role of Projects in the Implementation of Business Strategy" Chapter 6 in *Project Management Handbook* (2nd edition). Eds. Cleland, D. I. and W. R. King, New York: Van Nostrand Reinhold, 129–139.

Moolin, F. P. and F. McCoy (1980). "The Organization and Management of the Trans Alaskan Pipeline: The Significance of Organization Structure and Organization Change," in *Proceedings of the Project Management Institute Conference, Atlanta, 1980*. Drexel Hill, PA: Project Management Institute.

Morris, P. W. G. (1988). "Managing Project Interfaces—Key Points for Project Success" Ch. 2 in *Project Management Handbook* (2nd edition). Eds. Cleland, D. I. and W. R. King, New York: Van Nostrand Reinhold, 16-55.

Seamans, R. and Ordway, F. I. (1977). "The Apollo Tradition: An Object Lesson for the Management of Large Scale Technological Endeavors," *Interdisciplinary Review* 2, 270–304.

Souder, W. E. and T. Mandakovic (1986). "R&D Project Selection Models: The Dawn of a New Era," *Research Management* 24, 36–41.

Stuckenbruck, Linn C. (1984). "Interface Management—Or Making the Matrix Work," in *Matrix Management Systems Handbook*. Ed. Cleland, D. I. New York: Van Nostrand Reinhold, 330–343.

Youker, R. (1977). "Organizational Alternatives for Project Management," *Project Management Quarterly* 8, 18–24.

Project Scheduling—Foundations

Adamiecki, K. (1931). "Harmonygraph," *Polish Journal of Organizational Review*.

Crandall, K. C. (1973). "Project Planning with Precedence Lead/Lag Factors," *Project Management Quarterly* 6, 18–27.

Elmaghraby, S. E. (1967). "On the Expected Duration of PERT Type Networks," *Management Science* 13, 299-306.

Hartley, H. O., and A. W. Worthman (1966). "A Statistical Theory for PERT Critical Path Analysis," *Management Science* 12, B469–B481.

Kelly, J. F. and M. Walker (1959). "Critical-path Planning and Scheduling," in *Proceedings of the Eastern Joint Computer Conference*.

Malcolm, D. G. et al. (1959). "Applications of a Technique for R&D Program Evaluation (PERT)," *Operations Research* 7, 646–669.

Ringer, L. J. (1971). "A Statistical Theory for PERT in which Completion Times of Activities are Interdependent," *Management Science* 17, 717–723.

Swanson, L. A. and H. L. Pazer (1971). "Implication of the Underlying Assumptions of PERT," *Decision Sciences* 2, 461–480.

Wiest, J. D. (1981). "Precedence Diagramming Methods: Some Unusual Characteristics and Their Implications for Project Managers," *Journal of Operations Management* 1, 121–130.

Project Scheduling—Limited Resources

Calica, A. (1965). "Fabrication and Assembly Operations," *IBM Systems Journal* 4, 94–104.

Cleland, D. I. (1969). "Project Management," in *Systems, Organizations, Analyses, Management: A Book of Readings*. Eds D. I. Cleland and W .R. King. New York: McGraw-Hill, 281–290.

Cleland, D. I. and W. R. King (1975). *Systems Analysis and Project Management*. New York: McGraw-Hill.

Cooper, D. F. (1976). "Heuristics for Scheduling Resource-Constrained Projects: An Experimental Investigation," *Management Science* 22, 1186–1194.

Davis, E. W. (1973). "Project Scheduling under Resource Constraints—Historical Review and Categorization of Procedures," *AIIE Transactions* 5, 297–313.

Davis, E. W. and J. H. Patterson (1975). "A Comparison of Heuristic and Optimum Solutions in Resource-Constrained Project Scheduling," *Management Science* 21, 944–955.

Kurtulus, I. and E. W. Davis (1982). "Multi-Project Scheduling: Categorization of Heuristic Rules Performance," *Management Science* 18, 161–172.

Lawrence, S. and T. E. Morton (1993). "Resource-Constrained Multiproject Scheduling with Tardy Costs: Comparing Myopic, Bottleneck, and Resource Pricing Heuristics," *European Journal of Operational Research* 64, 168-187.

Morton, T. E., S. Kekre, S. Lawrence, and S. Rajagopalan (1988). "SCHED-STAR: A Price-Based Shop Scheduling Module," *Journal of Manufacturing and Operations Management* 1, 131–181.

Patterson, J. H. (1982). *Exact and Heuristic Solution Procedures for the Constrained Resource Project Scheduling Problem, Vols. I-IV,* Monograph, Department of Operations Management, Indiana University, Bloomington, Indiana.

Talbot, F. B. (1982). "Resource-Constrained Project Scheduling with Time-Resource Trade-offs: The Nonpreemptive Case," *Management Science* 28, 1197–1210.

Thesen, A. (1976). "Heuristic Scheduling of Activities Under Precedence Restrictions," *Management Science* 23, 412–422.

Thomas, E. and D. Coveleski (1973). "Planning Nuclear Equipment Manufacturing," *Interfaces* 3, 18–29.

Vepsalainen, A. and T. E. Morton (1987). "Priority Rules and Leadtime Estimation for Job Shop Scheduling with Weighted Tardiness Costs," *Management Science* 33, 1036–1047.

Wiest, J. D. (1967). "A Heuristic Model for Scheduling Large Projects with Limited Resources," *Management Science* 13, B359–B377.

Project Design

Emmons, M. W. (1988). "Contracts Development—Keystone in Project Management," Chapter 18 in *Project Management Handbook* (2nd edition). Eds. Cleland, D. I. and W. R. King. New York: Van Nostrand Reinhold.

Guyton, R. et al. (1983). *Prerequisites for Winning Government R&D Contracts,* Universal Technology Corporation.

Kerzner, H. (1988). "Pricing out the Work," Chapter 17 in *Project Management Handbook* (2nd edition). Eds. Cleland, D. I. and W.R. King. New York: Van Nostrand Reinhold.

Lavold, G. D. (1988). "Developing and Using the Work Breakdown Structure," Chapter 14 in *Project Management Handbook* (2nd edition). Eds. Cleland, D. I. and W. R. King. New York: Van Nostrand Reinhold.

Morton, T. E., A. Sathi, et al. (1984). "Activity Management—a Study of Needs," Intelligent Systems Laboratory, Pittsburgh, PA: Carnegie-Mellon University.

Thamhain, H. J. (1982). "Marketing in Project-Oriented Business Environments," *Project Management Quarterly* (December.)

Thamhain, H. J. (1988). "Developing Winning Proposals," Chapter 19, in *Project Management Handbook* (2nd edition). Eds. Cleland, D. I. and W. R. King. New York: Van Nostrand Reinhold.

Project Execution and Control

Bent, J. A. (1988). "Project Control: An Introduction," Chapter 23 in *Project Management Handbook* (2nd edition). Eds. Cleland, D. I. and W. R. King. New York: Van Nostrand Reinhold.

Bent, J. A. (1988). "Project Control: Scope Recognition," Chapter 24 in *Project Management Handbook* (2nd edition). Eds. Cleland, D. I. and W. R. King. New York: Van Nostrand Reinhold.

Chapman, C. H. et al. (1979). "Project Cost Controls for Research, Development and Demonstration Projects," *PMI Proceedings*, 53–63.

Chilstrom, K. O. (1988). "Project Needs and Techniques for Management Audits," Chapter 25 in *Project Management Handbook* (2nd edition). Eds. Cleland, D. I. and W. R. King. New York: Van Nostrand Reinhold.

Clarke, W. (1979). "The Requirements for Project Management Software: A Survey of PMI Members," *PMI Proceedings*, 71–79.

Cullingford, G., et al. (1977). "Design and Implementation of an Integrated Cost and Schedule System for the Construction Industry," *PMI Proceedings*, 390–397.

Kerzner, H. (1988). "Evaluating the Performance of Project Personnel," Chapter 26 in *Project Management Handbook* (2nd edition). Eds. Cleland, D. I. and W. R. King. New York: Van Nostrand Reinhold.

Levine, H. A. (1988). "Computers in Project Management," Chapter 28 in *Project Management Handbook* (2nd edition). Eds. Cleland, D. I. and W. R. King. New York: Van Nostrand Reinhold.

Miller, E. J. (1980). "Project Information Systems and Control," Chapter 9 in *Planning, Engineering, and Construction of Electric Power Generation Facilities*. Eds. Willenbrock, J. H. and H. R. Thomas. New York: John Wiley and Sons.

Morton, T. E., A. Sathi, et al. (1984). "Activity Management—A Study of Needs," *Intelligent Systems Laboratory*, Pittsburgh, PA: Carnegie Mellon University.

Niwa, K., et al. (1979). "Development of a 'Risk' Alarm System for Big Construction Projects," *PMI Proceedings*, 221–229.

Ramsaur, W. F. and J. D. Smith (1978). "Project Management Sytems Tailored for Selective Project Management Risk," *PMI Proceedings* IV-A.1–IV-A.7.

Tuman, J. Jr., (1988). "Development and Implementation of Project Management Systems," Chapter 27 in *Project Management Handbook* (2nd edition). Eds. Cleland, D. I. and W. R. King. New York: Van Nostrand Reinhold.

Planning 5

MODULE

Introduction to Planning

1.1 PLAN AHEAD!

1.1.1 Overview

Thirty years ago a great many business people felt that planning activities in operations, whether at the long-term level (strategic planning), the middle-term level (aggregate planning), or at the short-term level (tactical planning) were simply not as important as financial or marketing planning. More recently, however, the Japanese have made the world aware that operations planning issues are absolutely central to survival:

   a. Producing at lower cost
   b. Producing just-in-time (JIT) with near zero inventories
   c. Producing with shorter lead times
   d. Producing with much higher quality

These concerns have now spread to the entire global community. The United States automobile industry, for example, has adopted these concerns very successfully; it is now Japan's turn to scramble.

Planning Levels. Whether a group of assets are to be lumped together as a single resource or not for doing planning depends to some extent on whether the internal lower level decisions are being worked with seriously, or are simply given by some fixed simple rules that need not be explicitly considered. Thus a given plant might be considered to be a number of resources when modeled in detail. If we move up a level, we may only be concerned with what to produce and when. This can be repeated several times, leading to a classification of manufacturing planning and/or scheduling problems at several levels. We present such a scheme with five levels in Table 1-1.

Levels 4 and 5 are discussed in the Scheduling Module. We discuss the first three levels here.

1.1.2 Levels of Planning

Level 1: Strategic Planning. At the five- to ten-year planning horizon, "jobs" are mostly large "projects" and include design, sizing, and location of new capacity (plants, warehouses, assembly lines, foundries and the like) and the expansion, redesign, and layout of current facilities. Activities are any smaller pieces of these projects, such as designing electrical systems or installing walkways. Needed resources include financing, engineering, management, crews, and land. Often several such projects are being carried out at once, with many concurrent and interfering activities, so that sequencing and timing

Level	Examples of Problems	Horizon
1. Strategic Planning	plant expansion plant layout plant design	5–10 years
2. Aggregate Planning	production smoothing logistics	1–2 years
3. Tactical Planning	requirements plan shop bidding due date setting	3–6 months
4. Scheduling	job shop routing assembly line balancing process batch sizing	2–6 weeks
5. Reactive-Scheduling/ Control	hot jobs down machines late material	1–3 days

Table 1-1

Classification of Planning Levels

issues are clearly important. Examples of routing issues include alternate sources of financing and alternate vendors.

However, forecasting dominates the scene much more at Level 1 than at lower levels. Which products will be popular five years from now? How fast will technology move? Will the new assembly line have a chance of being obsolete in four years? Furthermore, as discussed in the Forecasting module, long-range forecasting models are inherently very inaccurate. Methods in use are often quite subjective, such as expert panel methods, the Delphi method, or the scenario approach. Fancier stochastic models have not proven very useful.

Level 2: Aggregate Planning. At the one- to two-year horizon, the issues include production smoothing, logistics and machine replacement. Production smoothing deals with re-configuring resources over time to balance capacity facing highly seasonal demand loads. Types of reconfiguration which are possible include hiring, firing, layoff, subcontracting, overtime, opening and closing lines, and shifting manpower between shops. Sequencing, timing and routing are definitely necessary to produce a production schedule. In the past, production smoothing models were so simplified that the scheduling flavor didn't come through. However, with better heuristics and computational power, it is quite feasible to do a detailed schedule of 18 product lines on 15 resources monthly over a 24-month period.

Logistics is similar to production smoothing, except that it involves an entire network of plants, warehouses, and distribution centers. Balancing the system is necessary not only due to seasonal demands, but also regional differences in demands and productive capacity. Typical decisions include which plants to use to produce how much and when, which distribution routes to use and when, which transportation methods to use, and so forth.

The issues in machine replacement are somewhat similar to those in capacity expansion, except that the horizon is often shorter and the dollar amounts much smaller.

Both deterministic and probabilistic models have been used successfully at Level 2. Although forecasting issues are still very important, issues of grouping, aggregation, and desegregation are probably most central.

Level 3: Tactical Planning. At the three- to six-month time horizon, models of interest include material requirements planning (MRP), shop bidding, setting/negotiating due dates, and order forecasting. MRP uses the production smoothing plan and order forecasting to produce a "master schedule," which is a period-by-period forecast of what needs to be produced by product type. Each piece of the master schedule is then broken down into components, which are moved backward in time to show time-based requirements for inputs. (This is a somewhat simplistic procedure which ignores shop capacity and often produces an irregular shop load.)

Shop bidding and due-date setting allow balancing the shop in a different fashion. Higher prices and slower delivery would be negotiated for an overworked shop; lower prices and fast delivery can be used when the shop has slack. In the past these procedures were mostly done subjectively by a skilled negotiator; however, modern scheduling methods can handle these issues more scientifically.

1.1.3 Summary and Preview of the Chapter

In Section 1.2 we give a more detailed discussion of planning decisions, whether at the strategic level, the aggregate level, or the tactical level. In Section 1.3 we present a company application scenario concerning Tectonics International, which is in the business of insuring against earthquakes and is in big trouble. We discuss long term investment strategies in Section 1.4, including basic investment concepts and dealing with risk. Finally, we complete the Tectonics case in Section 1.5.

1.2 ABOUT PLANNING DECISION METHODS

1.2.1 Strategic Decisions

There are three central characteristics of strategic decision making:

1. Strategic decisions affect the very survival of the firm.
2. The effects of a decision last a long time, perhaps five to ten years.
3. The long-range effects of a decision are very hard to forecast.

Actually, the first characteristic is really the *definition* of a strategic decision. The other two characteristics follow from it. If we could correct a bad decision of any size within a year or two, then it would be less likely to harm the firm permanently. And it should be clear that any decision whose effects last for many years will be extremely difficult to forecast.

We discussed the difficulties of long-range forecasting in the Forecasting Module, but we repeat some of the main ideas here:

1. Long-range forecasts are usually *ill-structured*; that is, it is impossible to make a really good mathematical model of what is being forecasted.
2. Forecasting accuracy drops off rapidly as one looks further into the future. This is essentially because unforeseeable changes accumulate as we peer further and further ahead.
3. Forecasts need to mix subjective and objective information, since different kinds of information are being captured.
4. The longer the horizon, the less objective information is available, the worse models will be, and the more we must rely on subjective forecasts.

Given that huge financial stakes are involved and that strategic decisions have a long horizon with poor forecasts available, it is hardly surprising that most Operations Management (OM) texts do not delve deeply into this problem. Many methods which are in practical use are not deeply quantitative, and are, in any event, difficult to describe and justify. Nevertheless, manufacturing executives do not have the luxury of ignoring strategic decision making and must be careful consumers of the best available methods. Long-range decision making methods cannot be taught completely in a textbook, since subjective expertise typically grows through many years of experience. Yet, much of it *can* be taught.

First of all, the best quantitative tools we have at our disposal are deterministic plans or models, although long-range decisions are not even close to being based on known data. How can we reconcile this discrepancy? There are several fairly good ways, and we shall review one of these here. You may recall from the Forecasting Module that the **scenario approach** involves:

1. Choosing decision alternatives to evaluate
2. Creating perhaps 10 to 20 alternative complete forecasts of the future (These alternatives should be representative of a number of types of good, average, and bad cases.)
3. Evaluating, for each scenario, the cost or profit of each decision alternative
4. Weighing carefully the good outcomes, medium outcomes, and bad outcomes
5. Making the final decision.

One strength of the scenario approach is that a number of possible outcomes of a decision may be investigated without a formal probabilistic model of the future (which is unlikely to be very good). Another strength is a very careful formal interaction between objective and subjective decision making. One weakness of the scenario approach is that not all bad future outcomes can be considered in only a few scenarios. Those which are left out tend to be ignored entirely. Another weakness is that there is very little objective or mathematical help in making the final decision.

1.2.2 Aggregate Decisions

There are four central characteristics of aggregate planning decision making:

1. Aggregate decisions affect the balance, rather than the survival, of the firm.
2. The effect of a decision lasts an intermediate time, typically one or two years.
3. Forecasting is of intermediate difficulty, but still must be a mixture of objective and subjective factors.
4. Seasonality of demand and/or production is likely to be an important issue.

What kinds of aggregate planning decisions affect the balance of the firm? Production smoothing is an important example. Over a one-year time span the firm may very well face seasonal demand, such as for air conditioners or snowmobiles. Producing Just-in-Time is desirable in the abstract, but huge seasonal surges in production will very likely destroy the balance of the firm. Some compromises must be made between hiring and firing, overtime, carrying seasonal inventories, subcontracting, and so on.

Another important example is logistics, which considers the overall problem of how to choose among multiple sources of raw materials, multiple plants in which to produce, multiple places to store seasonal inventories, and routes to ship to final customers

Forecasting over a one- or two-year horizon is typically done using econometric methods, most commonly linear regression with various special factors treated with dummy variables. It is also possible to make estimates of the forecast errors, the best way being by analysis of actual forecasting errors in the past.

The models we typically employ are again deterministic, but often include some simple provision for safety stock correction after considering historical errors. Thus we are really assuming some econometric models have been used, and the results filtered before using the model for decision purposes.

There is much less reliance on scenarios for aggregate decision making, since, with the shorter horizon, risks are considerably less. One might develop a production smoothing model with three scenarios, for example, with low, medium, or high levels of overall demand. On the other hand, one would be equally likely to simply run a single "high" case, chosen to produce enough extra to protect against likely uncertainties in demand. By analogy with simple inventory theory, this is known as introducing a "safety stock" into the model.

The modeling technique used most commonly for production smoothing is linear programming, although many other techniques have also been used. Linear programming has the advantage of being fast, versatile, and easy to use. There are situations where it is important to round results to whole numbers, which will be briefly discussed. There are also very nonlinear situations, such as large setup costs on major machines. The models needed for these situations lie outside our scope.

1.2.3 Tactical Decisions

There are three central characteristics of tactical decision making:

1. No single decision is crucial to the firm.
2. Decisions must be made repeatedly, perhaps weekly, with effects of from three to six months.
3. Forecasting demand is a mixture of orders already received, and those being forecast.

A typical example of a tactical decision making procedure is MRP. MRP assumes a forecast has been made of demand for each product for each week out to perhaps 13 weeks into the future. This demand is then "exploded" (disassembled into components) and assigned to rough production times on the shop floor. No individual decision here is critical; however, given the thousands of decisions which must be made, a smoothly running and accurate MRP system is actually a must.

Methods used at the tactical level are quite varied and eclectic. MRP uses a mixture of database management, linear explosion methods, economic lot sizing, and human consultation. Order planning employs a number of different methods, including stochastic bidding models and game theory bidding models among others. Assembly line balancing models have employed integer programming models, heuristic models, and simulation.

1.3 COMPANY APPLICATION SCENARIO—TECTONICS INTERNATIONAL

N. O. Fault, president and chief executive officer of Tectonics International, sat dejectedly on a plane bound from Los Angeles to Tokyo, trying to do some spreadsheets to estimate the effects of the great 1995 Kobe earthquake disaster on Tectonic's bottom line. With a sigh he gave up trying to concentrate on his laptop and concentrated on his gin and tonic instead.

"It's funny," he mused to himself, "our company is built on a foundation of predicting earthquakes, protecting against earthquakes, and certifying clients with insurance companies for a certain class of earthquake coverage. Earthquakes make people more aware of the possibility of further earthquakes, and always bring in more customers. How could one large earthquake, while producing new business, also threaten us with catastrophic losses?"

Actually, he thought he knew the answer to that, but the answer had possibly painful implications for Tectonics. Back in the early days of the company, Shay King, the founder of Tectonics, had carefully maintained the position that the company was a consultant only, and did not guarantee any of its services. They kept up with the latest earthquake prediction methods and even advanced some of them. But the contract always stated clearly that the forecasts were advisory only, and that Tectonics assumed no responsibility for anything that nature might deal. Other services, such as advice on where to locate a plant near a fault, or whether to purchase insurance, or whether to diversify operations, or how much to spend on what technology in quake-proofing a building, were also tied to such disclaimers. In particular, Shay King made it clear that in no way could the company afford the risk of getting involved with insuring enterprises against earthquakes.

But Shay King eventually died, and N. O. Fault became the next president and CEO of Tectonics, which at that time had 112 employees and gross profits of a little over $12 million a year. Fault had ambitions to grow. So when Lloyds of London and Prudential approached him with a lucrative proposition, he listened closely. They didn't want Tectonics to directly insure clients against earthquakes. But they would pay handsomely for Tectonics to investigate potential clients thoroughly, and then to issue warranties and/or guarantees about the class of earthquake risk that the client represented. Fault saw the chance for growth and, within ten years, Tectonics had 952 employees with gross profits of $145 million a year.

But now, with the Kobe disaster, the insurance companies dealing with Tectonics were out hundreds of millions of dollars, and they in turn were trying to say that the certification by Tectonics was careless. The charges were not fair, but, at best, Tectonics could expect to lose many millions of dollars in court costs. At worst they might be bankrupt.

The strategic decision facing Tectonics (assuming they survive the court battles) is whether or not to continue offering warranties and guarantees to insurance companies. If they were to simply stop this practice, they would lose perhaps two-thirds of their revenues. They would have to downsize drastically, and the company might have a tough time healing after the surgery. Perhaps there was some middle strategy, but he didn't see it very clearly yet.

The middle-horizon decision facing Tectonics was basically how to devote a great deal of energy to the several court cases against them, while maintaining normal business not affected by the case. The short-horizon decision was how to deal with all the excess activity which would be caused by Kobe over the next six months to a year, in terms of new business, settling smaller claims, and so on.

One Year Later. After the dust settled from the Kobe earthquake, it became clear that Tectonics would lose between five and ten million dollars from the catastrophe, but could probably survive by a mixture of drawing down capital reserves, borrowing, and issuing stock. However, Tectonic could not survive a second loss of this magnitude. Thus the real question was how to reposition the company for the future.

Following endless discussions with the board of directors and the executive committee, it became clear that no one thought it viable to continue issuing warranties and guarantees as in the past. The base case of simply withdrawing from this business was feasible, but painful. It was estimated to be five years before the shock wave of downsizing would dissipate and revenues return to some kind of normalcy.

A software consultant, Phil Grates, offered the suggestion that the problem lay not in the methods Tectonics used to evaluate the riskiness of insurance projects, but in the fact that Tectonics was simply not large enough financially to bear these risks. Perhaps Tectonics should put all their evaluation techniques into a decision support software system, together with educational materials and extensive training. This would allow the insurance companies themselves to evaluate the risks. Since Tectonics had a strong reputation, it could charge an insurance company perhaps $500,000 for this software support.

N. O. Fault thought this a very interesting idea. Compared with the base case, he decided the project would cost $10 million in the current year, but return $2 million in year 1, $2 million in year 2, $3 million in year 3, $3 million in year 4, $4 million in year 5, and $4 million in year 6. He was unwilling to project revenues past that point, since there might be competitive products entering the scene. Fault considers his cost of obtaining capital is about 10 percent.

Will the banks or other investors go for this scheme? How safe an investment is it? What reasonable ways are there to analyze this investment? We will discuss these questions in Section 1.5, after we study investment strategies.

1.4 RISK AND INVESTMENT STRATEGIES

1.4.1 Overview

Many planning decisions can be cast as investments: they require cash in an initial period, and then yield a stream of cash inflows over a following longer period. In a typical strategic planning problem, such as presented previously for Tectonics, there is a large initial investment for perhaps a year or two, followed by a stream of returns for five or sometimes even ten years. The information available in deciding whether to make such an investment is complex and, many times, highly uncertain. What good objective methods are there for help in making such a decision? What subjective factors must also be taken into account?

In looking at this question, two main issues come up immediately. First there is the time value of money. A thousand dollars received six years from now is not as good as a thousand dollars right now. Without looking at the deeper reasons for this, it is obvious that a thousand dollars now could be invested at compound interest, and hence will be worth considerably more in six years. On the other hand, interest is not the whole answer here. We will look at this issue briefly in Section 1.4.2, as well as review the formulas for compound interest, present value, and annuities.

The other serious question is risk. How much will the project really cost? What is the chance of failure? How soon will the income stream begin? How large will it really be? What event could make the income stop prematurely? The problem of risk is overwhelming in long term investment. There are a number of techniques to deal with it. One method we have already met is to work out a number of different scenarios. Another is to ignore revenues further than, say, five years in the future. Another is to put formal probabilities on everything and average over all the probabilities. We will look at this issue briefly also in Section 1.4.3.

Next we look at specific techniques that are used in evaluating investments in Section 1.4.4. The simplest and most widely used methods are payback and ROI (return on investment). These methods have some important strengths and weaknesses. However, the best theoretical methods, which are becoming much more widely used, are net present value and the internal rate of return. We discuss these and several other methods in this section.

1.4.2 The Time Value of Money

The Cost of Capital. A common definition of a firm's "cost of capital" (which it uses in any investment calculations) is the interest rate at which it can borrow from the bank. This is commonly stated as a percentage above the prime rate. If our firm borrows at "1% above prime" and prime is currently 7%, then we would be able to borrow at 8% and might call 8% our cost of capital.

Unfortunately, we cannot borrow all we desire at 8% even if we have a good investment. Banks are reluctant to lend large amounts to small companies, due to the risk it involves to them. Thus, borrowing has the hidden cost of increasing the rate charged for further borrowing. This hidden cost might be worth another 5% or 10% on the rate, depending on the circumstances. A different way to estimate the cost of capital by the firm is to look at the least rate of return for existing investments which are considered to be good ones. If this is 20%, then we would consider our cost of capital to be 20%.

The cost of capital is also sometimes adjusted for risk or inflation. We do not consider these issues here. In any case, once the cost of capital is estimated, it is used in investment analysis exactly as if it were the effective rate of interest to the firm. Thus we turn now to briefly reviewing concepts in compound interest and annuities.

Compound Interest. Tables for compound interest calculations are given in the Appendix I, Financial Tables. Table I.1, called Future Value, gives the future value of an investment compounded for a certain number of periods. Table I.2, called Present Value, shows how much would have to be invested today to have a certain amount after compounding for a certain number of periods. We also will review the formulas by which these calculations are derived.

Why do we bother to learn formulas when financial pocket calculators are now cheap and do everything so easily? For one thing, it is good to know more than one method of doing something; to be more versatile. For another thing, if you can approximate the answer in your head, you have a good method of protecting yourself against unreasonable answers when you make a mistake on the calculator.

Future Value. In the following calculations, let F be defined as the accumulated future value of the investment, P be the original (one shot) investment today, r be the cost of capital (compound interest rate per period), and n be the number of periods.

Also in our example, we shall assume compounding yearly. However, if compounding were quarterly, we would simply use the smaller quarterly interest rate, with four times as many periods. To compute future value, simply multiply the present value by $(1 + r)$ for each year: $F = P(1 + r)(1 + r)(1 + r) \ldots (1 + r)$ or

$$F = P(1 + r)^n \tag{1}$$

This formula is tabulated in Appendix Table I.1 for various interest rates and numbers of periods. Let us see how to use it. Think about Tectonics' investment problem. If they simply borrowed the $10 million and paid it back at the end of the six years, at 10% interest, how much would they owe? (This is called a "balloon" payment; there are no annual payments, and suddenly the whole thing becomes due, like a balloon popping up.)

Looking in Table I.1, using the column for 10% and the row for 6 years, we find the number 1.77156. This means we owe the principal plus 77.2% interest at that point. That is, $F = (10)(1.772) = 17.72$ million dollars. Since simple interest would have meant we owed 60% in interest, the extra 17.2% represents the compounding of the interest.

Suppose we didn't have to pay back for 20 years. In this case we see we would owe $67,275,000 or $57,275,000 in interest. Since simple interest would mean we owed only 200% in interest or $20 million, the extra $37 million is all compound interest! This illustrates that compound interest is only a medium-sized correction for five or six years, but becomes very important for longer periods.

Present Value. Now let us consider the reverse problem. Tectonics' potential investment is expected to produce $4 million in year 6. How much would this be worth today? That is, how much money, received today and compounded at 10% per year would give a future value of $4 million in year 6? This is called the **present value** of $4 million in six years at 10%. The formula for present value is simply given by solving formula (1) for P. Present value is tabulated in Appendix Table I.2 for various interest rates and numbers of periods. Let us practice using it. What is the present value of Tectonics' expected net cash receipts of $4 million in year 6? Looking down the column for 10% to the row for six periods, we find the number 0.56447, which means that $1 received in six years is worth $0.56 today. Thus the present value of $4 million is ($4 million)(0.56447) = $2.258 million.

What would the value be of $4 million not received until year 9? We have that value as ($4 million)(0.42410) = $1.696 million. This is about 30% less than the figure for six years, which is to be expected since interest is 10% per year and there is little compounding in three years.

Annuities in Arrears. In many situations, such as the net present value method and the internal rate of return methods that we shall study, we need to add up the present value or the future value of a number of sequential cash amounts. This is easy using a calculator, but a bit of a pain by hand. One case that can be done quite easily using tables is when the amounts are all equal. A number of equal payments (either received or given) is technically called an **annuity**. Tables usually assume the payments come at the end of each period. This is called an **annuity in arrears**.

Future Value, Annuity in Arrears. Appendix Table I.3 gives the future value of n payments, each given at the end of the period. The formula for future value of an annuity in arrears is given by:

$$F = P[((1 + r)^n - 1)/r] \qquad (2)$$

Let us do an example. Suppose a client promises to pay Tectonics $10,000 a quarter for five years, beginning at the end of the quarter. If this accrues at 4% compound interest quarterly, how much will Tectonics have at the end of the five years?

There will be $5 \times 4 = 20$ payments. Look in Table I.3 in the 4% column and the 20 payment row. The factor listed is 29.78. So the future value of this annuity is ($10,000)(29.78) = $297,800. The payments themselves total $200,000. The average value outstanding of the loan is about one-half of $200,000 or $100,000. Thus total simple interest would be about ($100,000)(.04)(20) or $80,000. Thus the remaining $17,800 represents compound interest, or about a 22% increase over simple interest.

Present Value, Annuity in Arrears. Suppose a second client wants to borrow some money from Tectonics, and promises to repay it at $10,000 a quarter for five years, beginning at the end of the first quarter. How much should they loan the client, if interest is 4% a quarter compounded?

Now we need to know the present value rather than the future value of the same annuity we looked at before. So we just solve equation (2) for P. More easily, we look up the appropriate factor in Appendix Table I.4. The factor is now 13.59 so that the present value of the annuity is (13.59)($10,000) = $135,900.

Other Annuity Calculations. We will illustrate some variations on the theme, to show how versatile annuities are. If, on Tectonics' main investment we talked about, they expected to receive $4 million in each of years 5, 6, 7, 8, 9, what is the total present value?

As viewed from year 4, we could look up a 10% annuity for five years in Appendix Table I.4, to obtain (4 million)(3.791) = 15.164 million. But from Table I.2, 15.164 million in year 4 is worth the four-period present value of that now, or (15.164)(.6209) = 9.415 or $9,415,000 dollars .

Sometimes we are interested in determining the size of the payment rather than the amount. Suppose Tectonics wanted to know how big the yearly return from year 4 to year 9 would have to be so that the present value would be $20 million.

Now we simply reverse the calculations. $20 million now would be worth (20)(1.6106) = 32.212 million in year 4. Since a five-year annuity is worth 3.791 payments, each payment must be worth (32.212/3.791) = 8.497. Thus the needed yearly return in years 5 to 9 is $8,497,000.

1.4.3 Risk

The longer the time horizon in a problem, the more the solution is dominated by uncertainty. This is especially pronounced, of course, in strategic and aggregate planning problems. For these long-horizon problems we face a paradox:

1. The models which are robust, easy to understand, and therefore widely used—namely, interest and present value—are **deterministic models**.
2. The problem can simply not be adequately described by such models. There are several good methods which have evolved to try to make use of deterministic models to deal with highly uncertain outcomes. These include:

   a. The scenario method

  b. Safety stock adjustments
  c. Expected profit
  d. Interest rate adjustments

We compare them very briefly.

The Scenario Method. We sketched this method in Section 1.2.2. If we describe a set number (10 to 20) of complete alternatives for the future and compute a discounted present value analysis for each, then we have embodied some understanding of the risk of the problem and can make a better choice. However, there are two weaknesses of this method. First, not all bad future outcomes can be considered in a few scenarios. Second, the method makes no attempt to say which scenarios are more likely than others. But this method has the great advantage of being well understood and easily calculated. It is available in the POMQuest forecasting software associated with this book.

Safety Stock Adjustments. One way to avoid creating a large number of worst case scenarios is to create a single "bad case" scenario that is not the worst possible, but is worse than is likely to happen. For example, in the Tectonics example, we expect the investment to be $10 million, and perhaps the worst possible would be $15 million. However, we may be "90 percent sure" that the investment will not exceed $12 million. Instead of producing one full scenario at $10 million and another full scenario at $15 million, we might save effort by creating a single rather pessimistic scenario at $12 million. Here the extra $2 million over the expected $10 million is called the **safety stock**. We have added $2 million to our investment for "safety."

  Really, however, this produces a reduction in the number of scenarios to look at, but no real "safety." For this compromise scenario may tell us not to invest, when really we should believe the $10 million dollar scenario which says we should, for example. However, if there are a number of factors we might vary in the scenarios, our reduction in effort in using safety stocks may be overwhelming. The method is never safe, but often is very convenient.

Expected Profits. A very popular method among theoreticians is to estimate probability distributions for the amount of investment, for the demand in each year, for the cost in each year, and so on. For any particular decision and corresponding particular values of all these random variables, one may then compute a net present value (NPV) of the investment. Then this is averaged probabilistically over all the distributions to get the *expected NPV*. The decision which yields the highest value of the expected net present value should then be chosen.

  The strength of the NPV method is that it yields a cohesive unified method for making decisions. It has a number of defects, however. First, the probabilities are not known and usually must be very crudely estimated. Second, there is no particular reason we care only about our average monetary return. We may be interested in the risk of bankruptcy, for example. Third, the method is a little too powerful. It leaves perhaps not enough room to incorporate the experience and expertise of the human manager.

Interest Rate Adjustments. Quite often one has a lower belief in the cash returns shown in the further future of a scenario. The reason is that many things may happen by this time, such as competing new products. If one adds a safety stock to the interest rate, for example, increasing 10 percent for Tectonics to 12 percent, then the value of future returns will go down in an appropriate fashion. The defect here is that the method is rather crude and hides distrust of the estimates in the interest rate, which tends to confuse the analysis.

1.4.4 Decision Methods

Payback. The payback method is extremely simple and intuitive, and is still widely used by top managers who want a quick understanding of how interesting an investment is. Basically, one simply calculates the number of years it takes for revenues from the investment to pay off the investment, with no interest considered. Formally:

1. Find the cumulative cash flow for increasing numbers of years.
2. The payback is the number of years until the cumulative cash flow goes from negative to positive.
3. Interpolate to get the answer to a fraction of a year.
4. Shortest payback projects have the highest priority.

In our Tectonics Example: (millions)

Year	0	1	2	3	4	5	6
Cash Flow	−10	2	2	3	3	4	4
Cumulative	−10	−8	−6	−3	0	4	8

Thus the payback is exactly 4.0 years.

One advantage of the method is that we don't have to trust the accuracy of revenues after four years. Another is that no interest rate calculations are needed. Finally (1.0/Payback) gives us a rough idea of the rate of return of the project for at least the first four years.

Ignoring interest is also a major disadvantage, since we must pay off not only the investment but interest on the investment to break even. Similarly, ignoring payoffs after four years may mean that large strategic projects with slow payoffs are ignored.

ROI (Return on Investment). The ROI method is also quite simple and easy to use, since it depends on numbers available from the company's accounting records. It tries to estimate a simple rate of return from the project, that is an interest rate paid by the project to the company. It takes simple interest into account and uses the full horizon of the investment.

Formally:

1. ROI = (Average return per year)/(Average investment per year).
2. Average return per year = [Total revenue – Total investment – Total interest]/[horizon in years].
3. Average investment per year = [Total investment]/2.

As a result of these calculations, choose the project with highest ROI. In our same example,

Total revenue = 2 + 2 + 3 + 3 + 4 + 4 = 18
Total investment = 10
Total (simple) interest = 0.5(10)(6)(0.10) = 3.0
Av return per year = (18 – 10 – 3)/6 = 0.833
Average investment = (10)/2 = 5.00
Thus ROI = 0.833/5.00 = 0.167 or 17%

(In spite of the fact that compound interest has been ignored, this is in good agreement with the IRR method to be discussed later, which yielded 13%.)

The advantage of ROI is that it is relatively intuitive and easy for a manager to understand. Its results are often reasonably accurate. The disadvantages are that it ignores compound interest and varying revenues.

NPV (Net Present Value). The NPV method (net present value) is recommended by most theoretical texts in finance. Its greater complexity is less of a problem with the advent of computers, and the method is growing in popularity.

In the Net Present Value method we convert all cash inflows and outflows to present values, and then add them up. Formally:

1. Estimate the cost of capital (interest rate) r.
2. Estimate all future periods' cash inflows and outflows (including investment.)
3. Discount each period's total cost back to the present.
4. Add together to get NPV.
5. Accept all projects with NPV greater than zero.

We illustrate the calculations with our same example:

Year	0	1	2	3	4	5	6
Cash Flow	−10	2	2	3	3	4	4
PV	−10	1.82	1.65	2.25	2.05	2.48	2.26
CUMPV	−10	−8.18	−6.53	−4.28	−2.23	0.26	2.52

Notice we have added the present values together one at a time in the last row to show the NPV for a one-period project, a two-period project, and so on. The NPV we want is the last entry of 2.52, so the NPV for the problem is NPV = $2,520,000. Thus the project should be accepted, irrespective of what the other projects may be.

The NPV method has many theoretical advantages. It takes full account of compound interest and varying revenues. It has the ability to treat multiple projects easily. Nevertheless, the model has some major weaknesses. It makes three very strong assumptions:

1. The cost of capital is known.
2. There can be unlimited borrowing or lending at that rate.
3. Far future cash flows are known pretty well.

How accurate are these assumptions?

First, the cost of capital is notoriously poorly known, especially for a number of years out into the future. Analysts using NPV can try to fix this by sensitivity analysis. Do a complete analysis using several different scenarios with different costs of capital. See how much difference the interest rate really makes.

Second, no individual or company can borrow unlimited amounts of cash at the same rate of interest. (Ask Donald Trump or Lee Iacocca about this one!) (Very pure NPV theorists are adamant about the ability of companies to borrow unlimited amounts at the same rate of interest, however, using complicated arguments.)

Third, the manager pushing the investment tends to put in big returns far out into the future, where they cannot be verified or challenged effectively. The CEO tends to mistrust NPV analysis (or other analyses with a long horizon) for this reason. Again, analysts using NPV can try to fix this by sensitivity analysis. Do a complete analysis using several different scenarios for far distant revenues. See how much difference the far future really makes.

But these ways of fixing NPV have their disadvantages also. Sensitivity analysis produces large numbers of scenarios to analyze. This is both time consuming and often confusing to the decision maker, who tends to prefer a simpler, more intuitive answer. This is not because the CEO is stupid, but because other less quantitative information must be incorporated to make a good decision; such a mixture of information is best accomplished if the situation is not deliberately made more complicated.

Methods such as Payback and IRR (Internal Rate of Return) elegantly fix some of these problems, but have their own shortcomings. We consider IRR next.

IRR (Internal Rate of Return). The internal rate of return method solves the problem of not knowing the rate of capital by directly giving a range of interest rates for which the project should be accepted and a range of interest rates for which it would be rejected. A typical result might be: "accept the project if the cost of capital is less than 16 percent, reject otherwise." It solves the problem of the amount of capital available being finite, by ranking the projects in order of their rate of return, and suggesting taking projects in order until funds are exhausted.

Following is a summary of the IRR method:

1. Use the NPV machinery.
2. Solve for the interest rate at which NPV = 0, which

   a. Can be done graphically, or
   b. Can be done by interpolation on the computer.

3. Call this the internal rate of return (IRR).
4. Sort projects by decreasing IRR.
5. Accept projects in order of priority until the budget is exhausted.

Example 1-1. In the Tectonics example, we saw that for $r = 10\%$, NPV = 2,515,000. If we guess 15% we find NPV = $-1,316,000$. Using linear interpolation, we estimate NPV = 0 at about $r = 13\%$. That is, we estimate IRR = 13%.

Example 1-2. Now consider a second investment as follows. You are required to put up $1 trillion to make an investment which will pay $1.1 trillion in one year. This has an NPV at 10% of exactly zero. As an added inducement you receive another payment at the beginning of $2,515,000. The NPV method, using a 10% interest rate, would say that the Tectonics investment, and this investment are equally worthy since they both have NPV = $2,515,000!!! But the IRR method says the first has IRR = 13%, while the second clearly has an IRR with 10% < IRR < 10.01%. (You may verify this using simple interest.) Thus IRR would strongly prefer the first, and find the second one very marginal, since the 10% figure for cost of capital is shaky in the first place.

ROI and IRR are really quite similar. They both have the important advantage of being *normalized*; that is, they express the return per year as a fraction of the investment. This makes them less sensitive to errors in measuring the cost of capital, and takes into account the limitations in the amount of capital available. IRR is superior to ROI in that it takes compound interest and revenue timing into account in its calculations. IRR has a problem in that it is possible to cook up oddball examples where NPV = 0 for more than one interest rate. This happens due to the presence of large negative cash flows far in the future. (This problem, although rare, can be avoided as follows. Plot NPV as a function of the interest rate. Define the IRR as the first place where the curve crosses zero from plus to minus.)

1.4.5 Investment Exercises

Decision Methods.

1. The manager of manufacturing for an assembly shop is considering an investment with the following cash flows (revenue less costs):

Year	0	1	2	3	4	5	6	7	8	9	10
Flow	−500	0	50	100	200	600	1000	1000	1000	800	600

   The firm accepts only projects that pay back within three years. Should he accept or reject the investment? What, if any, shortcomings of the payback approach does this example illustrate?

2. Consider again the investment profile of problem 1.

   a. What is the NPV given a cost of capital of 15%?
   b. What is the IRR?

3 Consider the following problem where the cost of capital is 10%. ($ millions)

Year	0	1	2	3	4	5	6	7	8	9	10
Flow	-60	10	15	20	20	20	25	20	15	10	5

a. What is the NPV?

b. What is the Payback?

c. What is the IRR?

4. Suppose the Tectonics example is modified to go out to year 12, with revenues (in millions) 2, 2, 3, 3, 4, 4, 5, 5, 6, 6, 7, 7.

a. Calculate Payback, NPV, and IRR for this modified problem.

b. Calculate ROI for this problem.

c. Which measures changed significantly from the six-period problem; which did not? Discuss the significance.

d. In what kinds of situations might you prefer payback to NPV or IRR with this data?

5. Projects Alpha and Beta are currently being reviewed by the investment executive committee of Ironwill, Inc. Each has a capital cost of $9 million, and only one can be chosen. The following is the expected stream of revenues less expenses:

Year	0	1	2	3	4	5	6
Alpha	-9	1	2	3	4	6	8
Beta	-9	6	3	3	3	3	3

a. For each project, graph the NPV versus the interest rate, using a common graph.

b. What is the internal rate of return for each project? Relative ranking?

c. Which project would you select?

6. Microtech, a computer software house, is considering a software product that requires an initial investment of $400,000 and subsequent investments of $200,000 and $100,000 at the end of the first and second years. Microtech expects this project to yield annual after-tax cash inflows for seven more years: $150,000 for the third through eighth years. (Annuity tables are useful here.) What is the NPV if the cost of capital is 10%? 20%?

7. The Millwright Company is considering the purchase of one of two milling machines for their metalworking shop. For machine 1 the capital cost would be $26,000, while for machine 2 it would be $19,000. Both have an expected life of ten years. Maintenance costs would differ for the two machines. For machine 1 the maintenance cost would be $1100 a year, while for 2 it would be $600 the first year and increase by $200 each year thereafter. The salvage value for machine 1 at the end of the ten years would be $7000, while for machine 2 it would be $2000. If the cost of capital for Millwright is 15 percent, which machine should be purchased?

8. Stan Muse, the director of manufacturing for the Diskreet Manufacturing Company, is interested not only in the profitability of a certain large investment, but also its risk. He prefers not to accept it if there is more than a 5 percent chance that it will yield less than a 12 percent internal rate of return. He estimates that the chance the project will have a life of ten years is 60 percent, a life of nine years is 25 percent, and a life of eight years is 15 percent. He estimates a 40 percent chance the investment cost will be $9000, a 25 percent chance it will be $10,000, a 10 percent chance that is will be $11,000, a 15 percent chance it will be $8000, and a 10 percent chance it will be only $7000. He estimates the yearly

net revenue stream as a 50 percent chance of $3500, a 20 percent chance of $4500, and a 30 percent chance of $2500. Assume that the life probabilities and revenue probabilities are independent of each other.

a. Using a random number table, simulate the IRR 20 times.
b. Should Stan accept the investment?

1.5 TECTONICS INC.—REPRISE

N. O. Fault sat at home utterly exhausted, watching TV. The board of directors had just voted down his new software project. Although Tectonics' cost of capital was 10 percent, and the IRR calculated for the project was 13 percent, the board of directors felt this to be a risky project, and therefore needed to clear a 16 percent hurdle rate. Another way of looking at it was that the project was expected to pay back in four years, but the board felt risky projects should pay back in three. N. O. Fault had tried to point out that there would probably be further revenues after year 6. However, the board was simply not interested in revenues projected in the far future.

But Fault was not the type to give up. He had an ace up his sleeve. He contacted a software house in India, and worked out arrangements to have most of the software produced offshore, using a dedicated communications line to keep supervision current. This reduced his estimated costs for the project from $10 million to $7 million. This would obviously increase his NPV by $3 million for any interest rate.

Thus for 10%, NPV = 2,515,000 + 3,000,000 = 5,515,000, and for 15%, NPV = −1,316,000 + 3,000,000 = 1,684,000.

Extrapolating to estimate the IRR:

$$IRR = 10.0 + [15.0 - 10.0] [5515/(5515 - 1684)] = 10.0 + 7.2 = 17.2\%$$

Thus, with his new scheme, the IRR was above the required 16 percent, and the payback was reduced to the required three years!!!

This was not the end of the board meetings. Several members of the board were concerned that there could not be adequate supervision for software produced halfway around the world, even with a dedicated communications link. However, Fault was ready for this. He showed the board a detailed analysis of several other companies who had used the data link strategy successfully and a complete blueprint for Tectonics to follow. The board was finally convinced and approved the project.

Three Years Later. Fortunately, the project was going to be very successful. There were some initial problems with controlling the software production using the data link. These were solved after a year. The project finally cost $8.2 million rather than $7 million. However, the revenues were $3.5 million in the second year, and $4.7 million in the third year; much better than projected. Tectonics could breathe easy again!

1.6 SUMMARY AND PREVIEW OF THE PLANNING MODULE

Planning Chapter 2 considers strategic planning decisions. We give an overview of operations strategy, including quality issues, Just-In-Time, and time based competition. Then we discuss capacity expansion issues, including the make or buy decision, followed by models for plant and warehouse location and plant layout models with heuristics for their solution. Finally, we give a brief discussion of technological innovation and learning, product and process life cycles, and new directions in strategic planning.

Planning Chapter 3 considers aggregate planning decisions. First we discuss production smoothing, including modeling and cost estimation, simple heuristics, solution by linear programming, interactive heuristics, and disaggregation issues. Next we consider logistics, that is, the entire production and distribution network, beginning with solution by network algorithms, and then methods for adding congestion into the model. After that we look at machine replacement, including fixed horizon models, issues of economic life, and Terborgh's approach.

Planning Chapter 4 considers tactical planning models. First we discuss Material Requirement Planning (MRP), including the basic MRP structure, the explosion calculus, strengths and weaknesses, and MRP II. Next we present order planning, including order release, bidding for orders, and deadline planning. Finally, we discuss assembly line balancing. First we present a simple line balancing model, together with heuristics for solving it. Then we present more realistic models and heuristics.

Strategic Planning Decisions

2.1 OVERVIEW

Many critics charge that American companies have placed more emphasis on marketing and financial strategies than on production and operations strategy. It is a fact, for example, that engineers and manufacturing managers are much more likely to become the CEOs of companies in Japan than in the United States. There is little question that careful manufacturing strategies are critical to a firm's success. For example, an auto firm may locate an engine assembly plant in Brazil because labor costs are low there. But this can cause many less obvious problems. Large inventories of engines may be necessary at the U.S. assembly plant to protect against long and variable leadtimes in ocean shipping. Upper level communication may become more difficult. Local politics could cause problems.

Some argue that we are simply changing over into a service economy and that manufacturing does not really matter. Consider, however, that the United States has historically been a leader in innovation. If new products are abandoned after they are developed in the United States to be manufactured on foreign soil, then the major returns for innovation will be captured elsewhere. Furthermore, innovation very often comes during the manufacturing process. The news is not all bad. The United States still does more manufacturing than any other country in the world. We may be slipping a bit, but we are far from down. It is time for us to return to the basics.

There are a number of basic dimensions to strategy to become and remain world-class in manufacturing. Products must be produced at low cost, they must be of very high quality, they must be developed and produced in a timely fashion, and they must be developed and produced in a flexible way to match changing customer needs.

Cost. A very fundamental manufacturing strategy is to produce a good, simple product at a lower cost than the competition, and to sell it at a lower price. This philosophy has been alternately embraced and discarded by American industry. When Henry Ford developed the moving assembly line for the Model T, he revolutionized automobile manufacturing. However, over the years, auto manufacturers became more interested in fancier, high-priced cars, and strove to sell the customer on a fancier product. After World War II, the Volkswagen beetle, Honda, and Toyota reestablished the importance of sound, inexpensive transportation, and steadily eroded American car manufacturers' market share. Japanese auto makers for many years could deliver an automobile to the United States (including shipping) for $1500 less than the cost of producing it here. Now the U.S. auto manufacturers have closed the gap again to within several hundred dollars.

Quality. Although cost is an important strategic consideration in manufacturing, low cost is not enough. Fifty years ago, the Japanese had an image as low cost, low quality imitators. They were no threat to the United States at that point. Deming is given credit for popularizing quality control in Japan in the early 1950s. Today he is a national hero in that country, and has seen Japan move into the forefront of quality and low cost.

The quality issue has since moved into the forefront in the United States in recent years. Many American industries are fighting for their lives against the onslaught of global competition (Japan, Europe, Asia.) There are many consulting companies that specialize in providing quality training to companies, including the Juran Institute and Philip Crosby Associates. There is a fair amount of evidence that American firms are serious about catching up in quality, as evidenced in the auto industry, the machine tool industry, and many others.

We will discuss quality in much more detail in the Total Quality Management (TQM) module.

Time-based Competition. Many people speculate that America has caught up to the Japanese in such areas as cost and quality, and that the next big fighting area will be **time-based competition**. There are really two types of time-based competition:

   a. **Time to market**—How long is the cycle from the time the new product is conceived until it is designed, produced, and brought to market?
   b. **Cycle time**—How long does it take from the time a customer orders a particular item until the item is actually delivered?

Early introduction of new features and innovative design tends to determine which new cars will be the winners in the automobile industry. This is even more true in the computer industry, where the first company with a new feature often dominates the market until the next large breakthrough.

Just-In-Time. Just-In-Time (JIT) means literally to produce something exactly when it is needed, not earlier (producing inventories) or later (producing stockouts). This is a Japanese philosophy toward manufacturing which was made famous by Toyota's Kanban system, which was a powerful way of implementing JIT. Since Kanbans work best for uniform repetitive manufacturing, part of the challenge is to redesign processes to be repetitive.

Actually, JIT is a strategic philosophy which is concerned not with inventory levels per se, but with promoting an environment in which the way of producing goods can keep improving over time. Drastic inventory reductions are only one tool to this end. The Japanese noted that if inventories are low then it will not be possible to hide badly produced units in the floor inventory. Similarly, if there is little inventory between two departments, then they will be forced to coordinate their scheduling instead of depending on the buffer to fix things. Also, under JIT, the customer will be able to receive more things made to order, rather than having to accept something in the inventory which doesn't match his needs exactly.

Variety. Consumers are increasingly demanding individualized products, and shifting preferences rapidly, so that new products must be produced imaginatively and quickly to remain at the center of the market. Note that time-based competition and JIT speak directly to this issue.

2.2 COMPANY APPLICATION SCENARIO—EXPONENTIAL ENTERPRISES INC.

"Slugging" Jim Samuels, the boyish president of Exponential Enterprises, has been spending many hours recently in conference with the rest of the expansion committee. This small group, consisting of Jim, Jan Bierdon—the Vice-President of Strategy, and Pete Garfield—the Vice-President of Finance, is charged with the rather pleasant task of expanding capacity to meet the tremendous growth in demand that the firm has been experiencing for its compact disk player line. The current factory has a capacity of 800,000 units per year. Using the current year as year 0, demand (in 1000s of units) is projected for future years as follows:

Year	0	1	2	3	4	5	6	7	8	9
Demand	700	750	800	880	980	1080	1240	1400	1600	1900
Increase		50	50	80	100	100	160	160	200	300

Thus, the new plant must be ready by the beginning of year 3. This is a reasonable time allowance, since in their experience it takes two to three years to plan, construct, and implement a new facility. The committee has already decided that the new plant should be located in South Carolina, which has good availability of a trained labor force and has offered the company a favorable tax situation. Pete Garfield estimates that the cost of the new plant in millions of dollars can be adequately estimated by

$$C(x) = 40.0 + 0.4x$$

where x is the chosen capacity of the new plant in 1000s of units. Pete uses 15 percent as the firm's cost of capital.

The expansion committee realizes there is a tradeoff between economies of scale in building the new plant and reductions in excess capacity cost in building smaller new plants more often. How big a plant should Exponential Enterprises build?

Pete Garfield is commissioned to develop a net present value analysis (NPV) to determine how big a plant should be built. At the same time, Jim worries about a number of simplifying assumptions that have been made so far in the analysis. Should the new plant come on line right when the old plant is at full capacity? Perhaps demand might grow faster than expected in the next three years and cause shortages. A similar issue would be that perhaps planning for minor capacity shortages (backlogging) just before expansion would allow postponing the major capital outlays and thus be worthwhile.

A related problem is that EE's current logistics system involves distributing from the Buffalo plant to five major warehouses across the country. With the opening of the new plant in South Carolina, the distribution pattern will become unbalanced. How many warehouses will be needed now? Should any of the current warehouses be closed? Finally, there is the whole question of how the new facility should be laid out in terms of departments to allow efficient transportation and communication within the factory. They agree to ask Jim Brown, Vice-President of Manufacturing, to look into this facility layout question.

2.3 CAPACITY EXPANSION

2.3.1 Overview

The capacity of a plant is often defined as the number of units that the plant can produce in a given time. It is important to have a simple concept such as this, but it is also important to recognize that this definition is somewhat slippery. How are the different kinds of units being made to be aggregated together? Do we include overtime? Inferior lines? Do we deduct for downtime and work stoppages? The important thing is to have a fairly standard definition. Perhaps the definition might be 80 percent utilization without overtime, or downtime, for a standard mix of products, for example.

One important motive for capacity expansion is the decision to make a component in-house which previously had been purchased from a vendor. Another very important motive for capacity expansion is to meet increasing demand for the product.

2.3.2 Make Versus Buy

Simple Break-Even Analysis. In the classic version of the make versus buy problem, the firm can purchase the product from a supplier at a cost c per unit or produce it internally for a lower cost of d per unit. However, the product may not be produced internally without investing $K to create the appropriate new capacity. Which strategy should the firm follow?

Remember that in the full capacity expansion problem the essential tradeoff is between economies of scale and excess capacity. Here we are simply trading off the initial investment against volume savings. The total cost of the firm to produce X units is $K + dX$, or an average cost of $(K/X) + d$. Thus, as X increases, the average cost gradually decreases to d, which is lower than c. If we graph the total costs of internal and external purchasing, we can find the point where the two costs are equal. This is known as the break-even point, or the break-even quantity. The break-even analysis is shown in Figure 2-1.

The break-even quantity is the solution to the equation $K + dX = cX$, which yields $X = K/(c - d)$.

Example 2-1. The E. Z. Over mattress company has been subcontracting the packaging of their luxury mattresses. The contractor charges $45 to package the standard $1200 mattress. E. Z. estimates that this could be done internally for $20 per mattress. However, the necessary plant expansion and purchasing of the new packaging equipment would cost about $6 million. Should they undertake the expansion?

Solution. The break-even quantity is $X = 6,000,000/(45 - 20) = 240,000$. Thus, E. Z. would have to sell 240,000 of the luxury mattresses just to cover the initial investment, without any consideration as to how fast the investment would pay off.

Simple break-even analyses such as this have precisely the advantage that they are easy, and give a quick estimate of the desirability of a capacity function. But this simple analysis is always over-optimistic. Management doesn't simply want to know that the investment will eventually be paid back; instead they are urgently concerned with *how quickly*. That is, they are concerned with the time value of money. We turn next to a somewhat more sophisticated analysis of this problem.

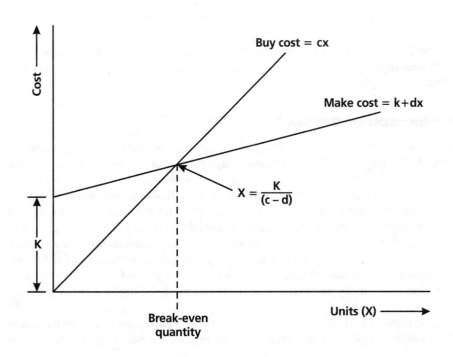

Figure 2-1

Break-Even Analysis

Payback. In order to take into account the time value of money, we must have some idea of the rate at which our investment will be paid off. Suppose that we can estimate the rate of sales per year D.

We may calculate the payback period by

$$T^* = K/[(c - d)D]$$

Example 2-1, Part 2. Management estimates that luxury mattress sales will be 65,000 a year. They further estimate that the investment will have an economic life of about six years. The CEO uses a payback of 3.5 years as her cutoff for new investment. Should E. Z. expand into packaging?

Solution. Since total sales are estimated at $65,000(6) = 390,000$ the investment should certainly break even eventually. The payback on the investment would be $T^* = (6,000,000)/((25)(65,000)) = 3.7$ years. Since the first cut at the payback is only slightly worse than the CEO's usual standard of 3.5 years, the president asks for further study.

Internal Rate of Return. Suppose that we use the internal rate of return method to evaluate our make versus buy problem. We pay out K for the initial investment. Our return is an annuity which pays $(c - d)D$ per year for T years. Call the value of $1 paid for T years discounted at $r\%$ to the present $A(r,T)$. We wish to find the appropriate rate of interest so that the present value of the annuity is just K. That is, we wish to solve $K/[(c - d)D] = A(r,T)$ for the appropriate r.

Example 2-1, Part 3. The vice-president for finance of E. Z. Over decides that it might be interesting to calculate the internal rate of return for the proposed packaging investment. He calculates

$$6,000,000/[(25)(65,000)] = 3.69 = A(r, 6)$$

Looking in an annuity table, he finds that $A(15\%, 6) = 3.78$ while $A(20\%, 6) = 3.33$. By linearly interpolating between these, he estimates the internal rate of return by:

$$r^* = 15.00 + 5(3.78 - 3.69)/(3.78 - 3.33) = 16.00\%$$

The president knows of other projects in the firm which are waiting to be funded with internal rates of return of 20 percent or more, and decides not to make the investment at this time.

2.3.3 Increasing Demand

A very common reason to build new plant capacity is to meet increasing consumer demand. Here there is a tradeoff. Building a large plant with enough added capacity for, say, the next seven years of growth provides good economies of scale in construction, but causes large excess capacity for much of the seven years. Building two smaller plants, perhaps for four years and then for three more years, provides less economies of scale, but also much smaller excess capacity. This is illustrated in Figure 2-2. Figure 2-2(a) illustrates the traditional plot of capacity versus demand when demand increases at a constant rate of D per year, and a new plant is built every x years with added capacity of xD. Figure 2-2(b) presents, for the same assumptions, a plot of excess demand over time. It becomes obvious that this is really an inventory lot sizing model. (See Chapter 2 of the Inventory Module.)

Excess capacity plays the part of inventory, and the construction cost plays the part of the lot production cost. We could even charge interest on the excess capacity to play the

Figure 2-2

Capacity Planning with
Constant Demand Increase

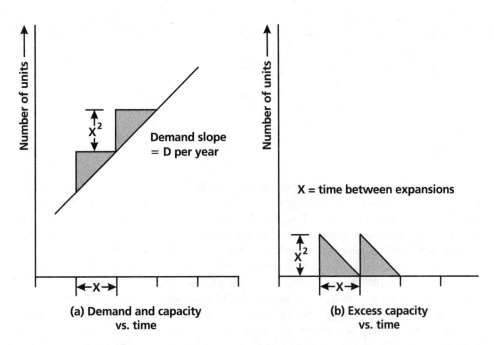

Demand slope = D per year

X = time between expansions

(a) Demand and capacity vs. time

(b) Excess capacity vs. time

part of holding costs. However, we will achieve somewhat more accurate results by working through a net present value (NPV) analysis. The more general case of varying demand increases can be handled by a Silver-Meal-type heuristic (see Chapter 2 of the Inventory Module). We do not discuss it here.

We look at a discrete version of a model developed by Manne [1967]. Let

D	=	Annual increase in demand
T	=	Number of years between successive expansions
r	=	Cost of capital
f(X)	=	f(DT) = Cost of constructing a plant of capacity X
TC(T)	=	Total discounted cost of all expansions over the future (to be minimized over T)

(Manne considered the case where $f(X) = KX^a$ where $a < 1.0$. We shall look mainly at the case where $f(X) = K + MX$; that is, there is a setup cost for any size facility of K, plus M per unit of capacity built. However, our method does not depend on the form of $f(X)$ assumed.)

Let $PV(r,T) = (1+ r)^{-T}$ = the present value of \$1 received T periods in the future. Now $TC(T)$ is the cost of expanding now, plus the discounted cost of expanding again in T years, plus the twice discounted cost of expanding again in $2T$ years, and so on. Thus

$$TC(T) = f(DT) + PV(r,T) [f(DT) + PV(r,T) [f(DT) + \ldots \text{ or}$$
$$TC(T) = f(DT) + PV(r,T)TC(T) \text{ or}$$
$$TC(T) = f(DT)/[1 - PV(r,T)]$$

We can minimize this cost easily by computing $TC(T)$ for increasing values of T until it begins to increase again.

Example 2-2. Sounders, Inc. makes a very popular type of portable CD player. Building a plant costs \$55 million minimum, plus \$5 million for every million units of capacity added. Demand is increasing 5 million units per year. Sounders cost of capital is 20 percent per year. How large a plant should be built?

We build Table 2-1, shown on page 24, increasing in T.

Thus, a plant should be built for four years, with a capacity of 20 million units. (Note that the result is not too sensitive; choices of three to six years give no more than a 3 percent error. Thus, other factors may be taken into consideration as well.)

Table 2-1

Sounders Problem:
Constant Demand

T	DT	f(DT)	1.0 – PV(0.2,T)	TC(T)
1	5	80	0.1667	479.9
2	10	105	0.3056	343.6
3	15	130	0.4213	308.6
4	20	155	0.5177	299.4**
5	25	180	0.5981	301.0
6	30	205	0.6651	308.2

** is optimum

The Case of Dynamic Increases in Demand. The case when demand increases irregularly is also rather easily handled by a modification of the Silver-Meal heuristic, which we discussed in Chapter 2 of the Inventory Module. Suppose now that the only change in the model is that demand in successive years increases by $D_1, D_2, D_3, \ldots$. Then if we build a plant for T years, its total capacity will need to be $X(T) = D_1 + D_2 + D_1 + \ldots + D_T$.

Remember that in the dynamic lot sizing model in the Inventory Module we faced a similar problem with unequal demands and unequal lots. Here also, we could solve the problem exactly by a version of the Wagner-Whitin algorithm. However, remember in that case that the Silver-Meal heuristic was much easier and very accurate. The Silver-Meal heuristic said basically to calculate the average cost per period for a one-period lot, then for a two-period lot, and so on, until a minimum is achieved. If $C(1,t)$ represents the cost of a lot lasting for t periods, then we would compute successively: $A(1) = C(1,1)/1$; $A(2) = C(1,2)/2$; $A(3) = C(1,3)/3$; and so on, looking for the smallest average costs.

We can use the same idea here, except that instead of dividing by the number of periods, we make each future period worth less by its discount factor. That is, for $A(T)$ we would have

$$A(T) = f(X(T))/[(1 + r)^{-1} + (1 + r)^{-2} \ldots + (1 + r)^{-T}]$$

Now the denominator can be simplified to:

$$(1 + r)^{-1}[1 + \ldots + (1 + r)^{-T+1}] = (1/r)(1 - PV(r,T))$$

Thus, $A(T) = f(X(T))/(1 - PV(r,T))$ up to a constant factor $(1/r,)$ just as for the constant demand case!

Example 2-2, Part 2. Now reconsider the Sounders example, with the only change that demand increases are not constant over time. Suppose demand increases year by year are forecasted as: 1, 1, 1, 2, 2, 3, 4, 5, 5, 5, 5, 5 respectively. How large a plant should be built? When would we expect to build a second time, and how big should that plant be? We build Table 2-2 increasing in T.

The plant should be built for a five-year capacity of 7 million units. It would cost about 3 percent extra to build for four years, and 5 percent to build for six years. Other choices would be prohibitively expensive.

The second plant should be built in year 6. To find its size, we simply move the reference point so that year 6 becomes year 1, as shown in Table 2-3.

Table 2-2

Sounders Problem:
Dynamic Demand

T	X(T)	f(X(T))	1.0 – PV(0.2,T)	0.2A(t)
1	1	60	0.1667	359.9
2	2	65	0.3056	212.7
3	3	70	0.4213	166.2
4	5	80	0.5177	154.5
5	7	90	0.5981	150.5**
6	10	105	0.6651	157.9
7	14	125	0.7209	173.4

** is optimum

T	X(T)	f(X(T))	1.0 – PV(0.2,T)	0.2A(t)
6	4	75	0.1667	449.9
7	9	100	0.3056	327.2
8	14	125	0.4213	296.7
9	19	150	0.5177	271.9**
10	24	175	0.5981	292.6

Table 2-3

Sounders Problem:
Dynamic Demand, Second
Plant

** is optimum

Thus, the second plant would be built in year 9 with a four-year capacity of 19 million units. Note that we can avoid inflation problems by expressing everything in constant dollars, and using real interest rates rather than nominal ones.

2.3.4 Expansion Exercises

Make Versus Buy.

1. A software company, Hope Springs, Inc., has a great new computer software game called Wizard Wraith on the drawing boards. The president, Mort Sol, estimates that it will cost $125,000 to write the software, debug it, test it, and bring it to market. Each unit will cost him $3 to produce, and will sell for $30.

   a. How many Wizard Wraith copies must be sold in order for Hope Springs to recover its investment?
   b. If Hope Springs can expect to sell 1900 copies a year for a lifetime of five years, what is the payback period of the project?
   c. What is the internal rate of return?
   d. What is the NPV at a 15 percent cost of capital?

2. In problem 1, modify the problem by assuming first-year sales will be 1000 copies a year, and then increase 40 percent a year for four years, after which the game will be replaced by another product.

   a. Now what is the payback period for the project?
   b. What is the internal rate of return?
   c. What is the NPV at 15 percent?

3. Discuss the pros and cons of letting an outside supplier manufacture critical components for a proprietary product.
4. Discuss the pros and cons of a simple break-even analysis versus a more complicated financial analysis of a make versus buy decision.

Increasing Demand.

5. Based on past experience, a plastics firm estimates that the cost to add new capacity obeys the law $f(X) = 20.0 + 2.5X$ where $f(X)$ is in millions of dollars, and X is in 1000s of tons. (X represents the growth in capacity for an integral number of years.) Demand is growing 3000 tons per year, and finance gives the firm's cost of capital as 15 percent.

   a. How many years should separate each plant expansion?
   b. What is the size and cost of each addition?
   c. What is the total discounted cost of additions over the indefinite future, assuming an addition is about to be made?
   d. What is the total discounted cost of the next five additions?

6. Solve problem 5 again if the cost to add new capacity is given by $f(X) = 15.0X^{0.5}$.

7. Solve problem 5 if the cost to add new capacity is given by $f(X) = 20.00 + 2.5X - 0.25X^2$.

8. Consider the Sounders, Inc. problem of Example 2-2 in the text, with demand increases modified to be 1, 1, 1, 2, 2, 3, 4, 5, 5, 5, 5, ...

    a. Re-solve the example if the minimum cost for a plant is increased to $110 million.

    b. Re-solve the example if the minimum cost for a plant is decreased to $27.5 million.

    c. Re-solve the example if the demand increases are modified to be 5, 0, 0, 1, 1, 1, 8, 8, 8, 8, 8, ...

2.4 FACILITY LAYOUT

2.4.1 Overview

Both manufacturing and service industries are faced with the strategic problem of how to physically organize a given new facility. An important aspect of this question is the size, shape, and relative location of the different departments within the facility; this is called the **facility layout** problem. It has been estimated that over $250 billion is spent annually on constructing new facilities and modifying existing facilities. For layout problems, the most common objective used in formal modelling is to minimize the cost of material handling. While not perfect, this objective provides us a good introduction to the subject.

One of the difficulties in determining good layouts by algorithms is that departments may come in many sizes and shapes. Different layouts with the same departments may use entirely different shapes, which nevertheless must fit properly into the overall floor plan. For this reason, it is worthwhile to first study the simpler case in which each department is identical to every other. We will study simple layouts first, and later show several ways to extend that methodology to the more realistic complex layout case. We call the these simple layouts and complex layouts, respectively. These layouts are illustrated in Figure 2-3.

A simple layout problem can always be formulated as an **assignment problem**. In an assignment problem, there are n departments (or machines or people) to be assigned to n locations. Most often we consider either the linear assignment or the quadratic assignment problem.

In the linear assignment problem, there is a cost of assigning a particular department to a particular location, which does not depend on any other assignment. In the quadratic assignment problem, there is a cost assigned between every *pair* of departments. The cost of the flow between two departments is the product of the average number of units of flow per unit time, and the cost per unit of flow.

2.4.2 Layouts—Simple Linear Case

The linear assignment case can be solved exactly by a special fast form of linear programming. However, there are several hand methods for approximately solving large problems quickly. It is easiest to illustrate the assignment problem and the solution methods by means of an example.

Example 2-3. Mr. Jones, the dean of a very small business school, must assign the four faculty members to the four assigned business school offices in the new building. Knowing which faculty will work most with which faculty, he tries to give a cost for assigning any faculty member to any location. The faculty members are Dean Jones and Professors Gibbs, James, and Finkelstein. The office numbers are 101, 102, 103, and 206. Dean Jones refuses to be assigned to 102, which is a small office. Professor Gibbs cannot

Figure 2-3

Simple and Complex Layouts

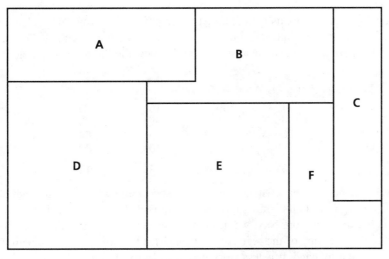

A	B	C	D
E	F	G	H
I	J	K	L
M	N	O	P
Q	R	S	T

(a) Simple Layout

(b) Complex Layout

be assigned to 206, because there is no elevator, and he is in a wheelchair. Dean Jones finally arrives at the following assignment matrix, where 9999 represents an infeasible assignment.

| | LOCATION | | | |
Faculty/Room	101	102	103	206
Dean Jones	13	9999	19	79
Prof. Gibbs	65	19	95	9999
Prof. James	64	12	25	64
Prof. Finkelstein	75	85	16	80

In developing heuristics to solve problems like this, it is important to use common sense. But at the same time it is dangerous not to educate the common sense as much as possible. For example, the easiest and most obvious heuristic for this problem would be the *myopic* one; that is, choose the cheapest assignment, then the cheapest remaining assignment, and so on. If we constructed the myopic solution to this problem, we would first assign Professor James to room 102, at a cost of 12 Now we eliminate the third row and the second column. The next cheapest assignment is to assign Dean

Jones to 101 at a cost of 13. The next cheapest assignment is to assign Ms. Finkelstein to room 103 at a cost of 16. Unfortunately this assigns Mr. Gibbs to go up the stairs in his wheelchair, at a cost of 9999! Thus, this assignment is not even feasible, let alone optimal! (The optimal solution has a total cost of 112. Can you find this solution by inspection?)

Vogel's Approximation. The myopic approach thinks only one step ahead. For many types of problems this is good enough. However, for the assignment problem, as we have seen, this is not enough. We now illustrate what would happen if we think *two steps* ahead. The principle is called **maximum regret**, and the result of using maximum regret for the assignment problem is called **Vogel's approximation**.

Look back at the problem. We picked "12" because it was the cheapest cost in the matrix. And yet if we added 20 to every cost in column 102, it would no longer be the cheapest in the matrix, however the optimal solution would not be changed, since after all we must pick *something* from column 102. We are really more interested in how much better 12 is than the other choices in column 102. The difference between the cheapest choice and the second cheapest choice in a column or a row is called the **regret** of not choosing the cheapest.

The first step in Vogel's method is to list the regret for each row and each column at the bottom and at the right side. Next we choose the row or column with the largest regret for not being chosen, and make that assignment, as shown in the following table.

	101	102	103	206	Regret
Jones	13	9999	19	79	6
Gibbs	65	19	95	9999	46
James	64	12	25	64	13
Finkelstein	75	85	16	80	59
Regret	51	7	3	15	

We choose "16" because Finkelstein will be at least 59 more unhappy if it is not chosen, and this is the highest of all eight regrets. We assign Finkelstein to room 103.

This is the first iteration. Next we delete the Finkelstein row, and the room 103 column, and recalculate any of the regrets that change for the now 3 by 3 problem. (When solving a problem by hand, it is less work just to put a line through the row and column being deleted. Regrets which get modified can be crossed out also, and the new regret written further right or below.)

	101	102	206	Regret
Jones	13	9999	79	66
Gibbs	65	19	9999	46
James	64	12	64	52
Regret	51	7	15	

In the 3 by 3 problem the highest regret is for not assigning Jones to 101, with a regret of 66. So we make this assignment, and delete that row and column leaving us the following 2 by 2 problem.

	102	206	Regret
Gibbs	19	9999	9999
James	12	64	52
Regret	7	9999	

In the 2 by 2 problem we see the regret is very very high for not assigning Gibbs to 102. (Or James to 206, for that matter.) Thus, our final solution is:

Finkelstein to 103	cost 16
Jones to 101	cost 13
Gibbs to 102	cost 19
James to 206	cost 64
Total cost	112

You will be asked in the exercises to argue that this is, in fact, the optimal solution to this particular problem. Another exercise will show that even two steps ahead methods can occasionally get in trouble.

The assignment problem can also be used if there are more departments than locations, or more locations than departments. We simply add extra "dummy" rows or columns with appropriate costs. If there are extra locations, we probably assign a 0 cost to assigning them a dummy department. If there are more faculty than offices, however, we may need to assign quite a high cost to receiving a dummy office (especially for the dean)!

Example 2-4. Smitty Smith, the owner of a small manufacturing firm in Knoxville, Tennessee, has decided to expand production. He is adding a new wing to the plant with room for five machines. He actually has four machines to be located: a grinder, a lathe, a welding machine, and a punch press. He estimates costs for locating each machine in each location as shown below.

Machine/Location	A	B	C	D	E
1	62	19	84	96	24
2	75	88	18	80	16
3	11	9999	81	21	45
4	94	13	62	71	82

His complete worksheet for the problem (all on one worksheet!) is shown below:

Mach/Loc	A	B	C	D	E	Regrets				
1	62	19	84	96	24	5	38	out		
2	75	88	18	80	16	2		57	out	
3	11	9999	81	21	45	10				out
4	94	13	62	71	82	49	out			
dummy	0	0	0	0	0	0				
Regrets	11	13	18	21	16					
		out								
					out					
			out							
				out						

(Smitty actually crossed out rows and columns as he went, but simply updated regrets by writing a new number by the old one as shown.)

Thus, his minimize regret strategy in order of selection is illustrated below.

B-4	cost 13
E-16	cost 16
C-2	cost 18
D-3	cost 21
A-dummy	cost 0
Total cost	68

It is readily verified for this problem, that the myopic solution would have cost 124. It can also be verified that Vogel's method has again produced the optimal solution to the problem.

2.4.3 Layouts—Simple Quadratic Case

More commonly, there are major transportation costs for goods and/or information which flow between departments, costs that depend on both locations. We can easily give a model which combines both kinds of assumptions:

a. Departments have costs depending on where they are assigned.

b. There are flow costs between every pair of departments.

For these calculations, label departments to be located as $i, j, \ldots$ and locations as $q, r, \ldots$.

Let the distance traveled in feet between location q and location r be given by a distance table d_{qr}. (Note that for various reasons the distance from q to r need not be the same as from r to q. We may also weight the distance by how difficult the travel is.) Such a distance matrix is shown in Table 2-4. (Sometimes this table is labeled cost per trip, etc. This does not change things very much.)

In a similar fashion, let the total yearly cost of the flow between department i and department j per foot distance between them be given by f_{ij}. This cost/distance matrix is given in Table 2-5. In general, the flow from department i to j is very different than the flow from department j to department i.

A fair amount can be learned by studying the distance matrix. For example, location D tends to be far from other locations.

Even more can be learned by studying this flow matrix, also called the "cost per unit distance" matrix. The heaviest flows are from department 1 to department 2, from department 2 to department 3, from department 3 to both 4 and 5, and from department 4 to department 5. This sounds very much like a flowshop, with department 5 being perhaps packaging and shipping.

Any particular assignment solution will assign every department to one location, and every location will be assigned exactly one department, as before. Suppose, in particular, that some department i is assigned to location $A(i)$ and that department j is assigned location $A(j)$. The flow between i and j is $f(i,j)$, and the distance between $A(i)$ and $A(j)$ is $d(A(i), A(j))$. Thus, the cost of the flow from department i to department j is

$$f(i,j)d(A(k), A(j))$$

But if there are n such departments or locations, then there are n^2 of these cost which must be added up. (Self flows are considered to have zero costs.) Thus, the total cost of any assignment solution A is given by

$$\text{Cost(A)} = \sum_{j=1,n} \sum_{j=1,n} f(i,j)d(A(i), A(j))$$

If there are 10 departments, for example, there will be $(10)(10) = 100$ terms in the sum for a single assignment solution. Unfortunately there will be $10! = 3,628,800$ possible solutions, so it would not be practical to simply evaluate them all. The problem can be formulated as an integer programming problem, but it is far too large to solve exactly for realistic sized problems, even on super computers.

Table 2-4

Distance d_{qr} Between Locations

From/To	A	B	C	D	E
A	—	17	3	35	16
B	15	—	4	32	18
C	5	4	—	25	10
D	30	30	22	—	6
E	16	18	12	5	—

Table 2-5

Flow f_{ij} Between Departments

From/To	1	2	3	4	5
1	—	350	3	14	60
2	56	—	560	121	50
3	13	35	—	656	400
4	48	96	150	—	750
5	15	25	24	39	—

Manual Heuristics. Let us try to find a simple, commonsense heuristic for the quadratic assignment problem represented in Tables 2-4 and 2-5. We noticed heavy flows from department 1 to 2, 2 to 3, 3 to 4, and 4 to 5. This suggests we might try to put these departments in locations which are sequentially close to each other. After staring at Table 2-4 for a bit, we see that A is close to C, C is close to B, B is close to E, and E is close to D. This suggests the assignment A-1, C-2, B-3, E-4, and D-5. One way to calculate the cost of this assignment in an orderly manner is to write down the distance matrix, leaving room after each entry to multiply by the resulting flow for each pair of locations.

Cost (Solution 1).

	A(1)	B(3)	C(2)	D(5)	E(4)
A(1)	+(0)(0)	+(17)(3)	+(3)(350)	+(35)(60)	+(16)(14)
B(3)	+(15)(13)	+(0)(0)	+(4)(35)	+(32)(400)	+(18)(656)
C(2)	+(5)(56)	+(4)(560)	+(0)(0)	+(25)(50)	+(10)(121)
D(5)	+(30)(15)	+(30)(24)	+(22)(25)	+(0)(0)	+(6)(39)
E(4)	+(16)(48)	+(18)(150)	+(12)(96)	+(5)(750)	+(0)(0)

	A(1)	B(3)	C(2)	D(5)	E(4)
A(1)	+0	+51	+1050	+2100	+224
B(3)	+195	+0	+140	+12800	+11808
C(2)	+280	+2240	+0	+1250	+1210
D(5)	+450	+720	+550	+0	+234
E(4)	+768	+2700	+1152	+3750	+0
Col. Total	+1693	+5711	+2892	+19900	+13476

Which simplifies to a total cost of 43,672, when the column totals are added together.

This seems to be a reasonable heuristic. But what could we do to improve on it? We see that well over half of the total cost is from location B to locations D and E; that is, from department 3 to departments 4 and 5. Perhaps we can reassign to shorten these distances so that these two flow costs would be greatly reduced? Other costs would, of course, be increased in the process. So we would have to check whether the overall solution really improved.

After some thought, we come up with the solution D-1, E-2, C-3, A-4, and B-5, which moves departments 4 and 5 closer to department 3.

Next we cost our new assignment out.

Cost (Solution 2).

	A(4)	B(5)	C(3)	D(1)	E(2)
A(4)	+(0)(0)	+(17)(750)	+(3)(150)	+(35)(48)	+(16)(96)
B(5)	+(15)(39)	+(0)(0)	+(4)(24)	+(32)(15)	+(18)(25)
C(3)	+(5)(656)	+(4)(400)	+(0)(0)	+(25)(13)	+(10)(35)
D(1)	+(30)(14)	+(30)(60)	+(22)(3)	+(0)(0)	+(6)(350)
E(2)	+(16)(121)	+(18)(50)	+(12)(560)	+(5)(56)	+(0)(0)

	A(4)	B(5)	C(3)	D(1)	E(2)
A(4)	+0	+12750	+450	+1680	+1536
B(5)	+585	+0	+96	+480	+450
C(3)	+3280	+1600	+0	+325	+350
D(1)	+420	+1800	+66	+0	+2100
E(2)	+1936	+900	+6720	+280	+0
Col. total	+6221	+17050	+7332	+2765	+4436

Which simplifies to a total cost of 37,804.

Thus, our second attempt at a heuristic solution for the problem yields an answer that is 13 percent cheaper than that for our first try.

Computer Help. We went to a lot of work to get a decent solution to the problem. Furthermore, the effort in evaluating an assignment is about four times as great for a 10 by 10 problem as for a 5 by 5. Thus, it makes sense to look to the computer for help.

A simple and useful approach is to allow the human planner to make trial assignments, and for the computer to evaluate them and perhaps suggest new ones. This has the advantage that the human expertise is fully utilized, and that many solutions may be evaluated visually as well as mathematically.

More automatic computer methods, such as neighborhood search and tabu search, can also be powerful allies in a situation like this. The computer can look at all possible small changes to our existing best solution, and choose that new possible solution which helps the most. When no small change gives an improvement, the method stops. The small change which is usually used is a **pairwise interchange**. For example, our second solution was D-1, E-2, C-3, A-4, and B-5. One pairwise interchange would be to switch C and B, giving D-1, E-2, B-3, A-4, C-5.

Neighborhood Search.

1. Choose any desired starting solution as the "base case."
2. Calculate the costs of the new solutions for every possible pairwise interchange.
3. Note the new solution with the lowest cost.
4. If it is higher than the current best solution, stop.
5. Install the improved solution as the new base case.
6. Go to step 2.

A problem with neighborhood search is that just because there are no nearby solutions better than the base case does not guarantee that there are not any better solutions further away.

Tabu Search. The tabu search is a modification to the neighborhood search which attempts to deal with the problem of a greater range of solutions. If there is no better solution nearby, this method saves the best solution to date, and chooses as the new base case the new solution which hurts the least. It then typically tries a great many moves, with certain restrictions on moves to try to avoid duplicating the same moves over and over.

2.4.4 Heuristics for Complex Layouts

In our discussion of the simple assignment problem, we have been restricted to the assumption that all departments are rectangular and have the same size and shape, so that they may be easily interchanged. There are a number of computer programs to do job shop layout which allow the departments to be different sizes, and for their shapes to be changed as they are moved about in the layout in the search for improved solutions. These programs include CRAFT, COFAD, ALDEP, and CORELAP, and are relatively similar. We shall describe CRAFT as a representative method.

CRAFT (Computerized Relative Allocation of Facilities Technique) uses the standard quadratic assignment method of evaluating a layout. Departments are assumed to have a rectangular shape, or else to be composed of several rectangles. For purposes of calculating the distance between departments, the departments are treated as if they are located at their center of gravity, or centroid. We omit discussion of exactly how to calculate the center of gravity. (The assumption that the department may be replaced by its center of gravity is not perfectly accurate.)

CRAFT requires a good initial solution to begin with. Figure 2-4 illustrates a four department layout. The flows between departments must be input into CRAFT. However, the centroids are calculated from the current layout. In our case:

$(x_A, y_A) = (60, 80)$ $(x_B, y_B) = (160, 80)$

$(x_C, y_C) = (50, 30)$ $(x_D, y_D) = (150, 30)$

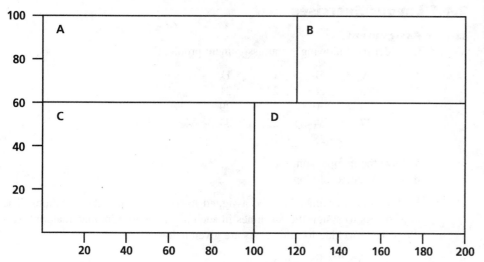

Figure 2-4

Initial CRAFT Layout

CRAFT approximates the distance between departments by the rectilinear distance between the centroids. That is to say, the distance between A and C is $(60 - 50) + (80 - 30) = 60$. Other distances are calculated in the same way. Note that CRAFT assumes the distance from A to B is the same as the distance from B to A.

CRAFT considers the pairwise interchange of every pair of departments that either have the same area or are currently touching each other. The interchange works as follows: An area in the larger department is marked off equal to the area of the smaller department. The two equal areas are interchanged, and the remainder stays unchanged. Figure 2-5 illustrates the interchange of departments A and C.

CRAFT uses neighborhood search. That is, all allowable pairwise interchanges are tried and costed out. The one with the greatest savings becomes the new standard. (When no pairwise interchanges can save anything, CRAFT tries three-way interchanges. We do not discuss this here.)

The strengths of CRAFT are that it is reasonably fast, and allows treating departments with reasonable shapes. The main weakness is that it can sometimes create departments of unreasonable shape so that the results are not always very useful.

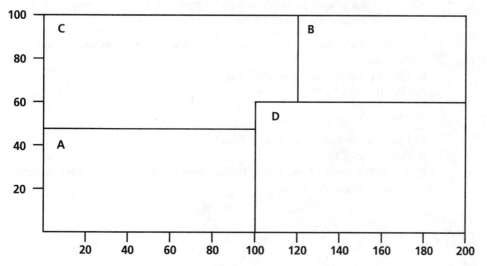

Figure 2-5

Interchange of Departments
A and C

2.4.5 Layout Exercises

Linear Assignment.

1. Consider the following linear assignment problem:

	A	B	C	D
1	23	26	24	21
2	29	30	27	29
3	27	34	25	24
4	25	28	26	28

   a. Give the myopic solution.
   b. Give Vogel's solution.

2. Each of four machines is to be assigned to one of six possible locations. The objective is to assign the machines in such a way as to minimize material handling. The machine-location costs are given below:

	A	B	C	D	E	F
1	25	21	22	20	26	31
2	26	40	33	31	35	29
3	25	16	23	18	15	999
4	999	30	33	34	31	50

   a. Find the myopic solution.
   b. Solve the problem by Vogel's approximation.
   c. Argue whether or not Vogel's solution is optimal.

3 In problem 1

   a. Change the problem slightly so the myopic solution would be optimal.
   b. Change the problem just sufficiently so that Vogel's approximation would not give a good answer.

4. Prove for the linear assignment problem that if the same constant C is subtracted from an entire row or column, that the optimal assignment is unchanged, but that the original problem has a cost C greater than the revised problem. Use this idea repeatedly to establish a minimum possible cost in problems 1, 2, and 3.

Quadratic Assignment.

5. Consider the quadratic assignment problem given by Tables 2-4 and Table 2-5. Suppose it has already been decided that department D is to be assigned to location 4, and department E is to be assigned to location 5.

   a. Specify the resulting three-department, three-location quadratic assignment problem.
   b. Find a good heuristic solution by inspection.
   c. Give the cost for this solution.

6. In problem 5

   a. Find a second good heuristic solution.
   b. Give the cost for this solution.
   c. Argue that one of these two solutions must be optimal, and therefore determine the optimal solution.

2.5 FACILITY LOCATION

2.5.1 Overview

Suppose we need to find the best location for a new plant or a warehouse which is part of a national production and distribution logistics network. We will want to place it where costs are low, but also where total distribution costs to customers can be significantly reduced. Typically, for this type of problem, we will first evaluate perhaps 10 or 20 locations as to cost, and then evaluate the cost of the total logistics network for each possible choice and pick the lowest cost possibility. Special versions of linear programming are very useful for this task.

Sometimes we wish to locate several new plants or several new warehouses at the same time. This can easily be formulated as an integer programming problem, which unfortunately is not computationally feasible for most realistic-sized problems. In the following section we present a tabu search heuristic which can handle larger problems.

2.5.2 Single Facility

We use real cost data for building a site, and real distance and transportation costs, rather than using Euclidean distances or the like. This is for several reasons:

a. It is important to investigate possible sites in advance to check on taxes, rent, labor laws, etc. This work can only be done for perhaps 10 to 20 locations. Thus, having a location picked at random is not very useful.
b. Distances depend on actual rail miles, road miles, and hauling rates. This information needs to be individualized for each possible route.

It is easiest to explain our approach with an example.

Example 2-5. The Perry Air Company is a producer of high quality sparkling water. They currently maintain two production facilities, one in Cincinnati and one in Omaha. From these plants they ship to regional warehouses located in Newark, St. Louis, and Los Angeles. Recently demand has been increasing, and they have decided to build another plant. After an exhaustive search they have found two likely sites: one in Seattle and the other in Atlanta.

The warehouse requirements, production capacities, per unit variable production costs of the existing and proposed facilities, and the building and equipment costs are listed below.

a. **Warehouse demand**

Newark	110
St. Louis	130
Los Angeles	210
TOTAL	450

b. **Capacity and Costs of Existing Plant**

Plant	Capacity	Unit cost
Cincinnati	95	400
Omaha	160	450
TOTAL	255	

SHORTAGE $450 - 255 = 195$

c. **Estimated Fixed (Yearly) and Variable Costs for New Plants**

Plant	Fixed Cost	Unit cost
Seattle	$135,000	600
Atlanta	$132,000	650

d. **Transportation Costs per 1000 Units**

To From	Newark	St. Louis	Los Angeles
Cincinnati	40	60	125
Omaha	70	50	60
Seattle	130	70	50
Atlanta	50	75	100

Our strategy is to first consider adding Seattle to the network to produce exactly the shortage amount of 195, and cost out the entire system. Then we will do the same thing for Atlanta. Finally, we simply pick the cheaper of the two.

To find out what the total cost would be of adding Seattle to the network, we must first determine what the total transportation cost would be. But it is not at first clear which plant should ship to what warehouse. We must determine the cheapest assignments of production to warehouse needs. In Table 2-6 the transportation costs between the plants and warehouses are entered in the appropriate cells. The demand generated by each warehouse is given along the bottom row and the capacity of each plant is given in the last column. The capacity of the Seattle plant is chosen to match exactly the needed capacity.

As a result, the total supply equals the total demand. The problem is to assign shipping numbers to each plant-warehouse shipping choice such that each warehouse receives its total demand, each plant produces its total capacity, and the total transportation cost is minimized.

This is called the transportation algorithm, and there are several fast ways to solve it exactly on the computer. However, Vogel's method, which we have already met in Section 2.4.2, produces very fast and accurate manual solutions for this type of problem. The maximum regret is 30 for not filling Newark out of Cincinnati. So we mark 95, the most possible, in the Cincinnati to Newark box. Then we cross out the Cincinnati row, and mark Newark's remaining demand to 15. Now the highest regret is not to ship to Newark from Omaha, so we ship them their remaining 15 units, and close down Newark as a destination, decreasing Omaha's capacity by 15 units. In the remaining 2 by 2 problem the highest regret of 20 is not to ship from Omaha to St. Louis, so we ship 130 on this route, and so forth. The final solution is shown in Table 2-7.

Solution of the Seattle Alternative. The optimal strategy for the Seattle alternative is, therefore, to ship according to the following plan.

Cincinnati to Newark	95	@$40	$3800
Omaha to Newark	15	@$70	1050
Omaha to St. Louis	130	@$50	6500
Omaha to Los Angeles	15	@$60	900
Seattle to Los Angeles	195	@$60	11,700
Total Seattle alternative transportation cost			$23,950

Table 2-6

Seattle Alternative in
Transportation Format

	Warehouse			
	Newark	St. Louis	Los Angeles	Capacity
Plant				
Cincinnati	40	60	125	95
Omaha	70	50	60	160
Seattle	130	70	60	195
DEMAND	110	130	210	450

	Warehouse			
	Newark	**St. Louis**	**Los Angeles**	**Capacity**
Plant				
Cincinnati	95 40	0 60	0 125	95
Omaha	15 70	130 50	15 60	160
Seattle	0 130	0 70	195 60	195
DEMAND	110	130	210	450

Table 2-7

Final Solution Seattle
Alternative

Solution of the Atlanta Alternative. We present the Atlanta solution without going through the procedure in Table 2-8.

The optimal strategy for the Atlanta alternative is, therefore, to ship according to the following plan:

Cincinnati to St. Louis	95	@ $60	$5700
Omaha to Los Angeles	160	@ $60	9600
Atlanta to Newark	110	@ $50	5500
Atlanta to St. Louis	35	@ $75	2625
Atlanta to Los Angeles	50	@$100	5000
Total Atlanta alternative transportation cost			$28,425

Comparison of Alternatives. Now we can compute the sum of the building, production, and shipping costs for each of the two strategies. Since the Cincinnati and Omaha plants will operate at full capacity regardless of the alternatives chosen, we therefore have:

Total Seattle alternative costs:

Building and equipment	$135,000
Variable Production 600×195	117,000
Transportation	23,950
TOTAL SEATTLE COSTS	$275,950

Total Atlanta alternative costs:

Building and equipment	$132,000
Variable Production 650×195	126,750
Transportation	28,425
TOTAL ATLANTA COSTS	$287,175

Thus, locating in Seattle is the better choice by $11,225.

2.5.3 Multiple Facilities—Logistics Networks

The General Problem. Consider a group of plants serving the entire market for a product. (It could be a product mix. The model can be generalized to the multiple product case also.) In the previous section, the concern was with the location of one additional plant. In many cases a more realistic set of questions is: How many plants should be

		Warehouse			
Plant	**Newark**	**St. Louis**	**Los Angeles**	**Capacity**
Plant				
Cincinnati	0 40	95 60	0 125	95
Omaha	0 70	0 50	160 60	160
Atlanta	110 50	35 75	50 100	195
DEMAND	110	130	210	450

Table 2-8

Final Solution Atlanta
Alternative

added, and where should they be located? Once this extra dimension is added to the problem, it becomes necessary to consider the yearly building and equipment costs for a location as a fixed cost explicitly appearing in the location model. The tradeoff is between increased overhead costs from more plants and reduced transportation costs. The problem can be solved with a mixed-integer programming formulation, which can be found in many texts. Since the formulation is not particularly practical, we do not present it here, but turn to a high accuracy heuristic.

Tabu Search. For a given choice of which plants are to be opened, and which are not, the above problem has no fixed costs which are not sunk costs. Thus, it can be solved by the transportation algorithm, which is a special very fast version of linear programming. (Actually it can be solved by network algorithms which are very fast versions of the transportation algorithm.) Due to this speed, the problem can be solved many many times for different attempts at specifying which warehouses are to be opened.

In order to use tabu search, we need an analog of pairwise interchange. Let O be the set of plants currently open, and S be the set of plants currently shut. We define three types of open plant changes.

Types of Open Plant Changes.

1. Close a plant currently open and open a plant currently closed.
2. Open a plant currently closed.
3. Close a plant currently opened.

Tabu Search for Plant Location.

1. Choose an initial solution to be the current problem.
2. Evaluate the cost of the current problem using a network algorithm.
3. Make all possible open plant changes from the current problem and evaluate their costs using a network algorithm.
4. Choose the cheapest new solution not previously explored (not tabu), which becomes the current problem designate.
5. Save the least cost solution to date, in case the current problem designate is not the least cost.
6. Is the termination criterion met? If the answer is yes, exit. If it is no go back to step 3.

Tabu search is an accurate and quite general method for solving these and similar problems.

2.5.4 Location Exercises

Single Facility—Logistics Networks.

1. Plant 1 can ship to warehouses A, B, and C at costs of 7, 3, and 5 respectively; it has a capacity of 90. Plant 2 can ship at costs of 4, 6, and 5 respectively; it has a capacity of 110. Plant 3 can ship at costs of 9, 6, and 7; it has a capacity of 150. A has a demand of 70, B of 160, and C of 100. Solve the resulting transportation problem by Vogel's approximation. (*Hint: Add a dummy warehouse marked "unused capacity" with transportation costs all 0.*)
2. A large manufacturer currently maintains three factories and three regional warehouses. The demand from the warehouses, however, exceeds the productive capacity of the factories. (Please see the following figures.) Management would like to add a factory to bring productive capacity in line with demand. Two locations are under consideration. Determine the optimal strategy.

Plant	Capacity	Warehouse	Demand
1	250	A	290
2	130	B	210
3	180	C	160

The fixed and variable costs for the two plants under consideration are as follows:

Plant	Fixed Cost	Variable Cost
4	21,000	110
5	17,500	140

The transportation costs from the five warehouse locations to the three warehouses are as follows:

	Transportation Costs		
To	A	B	C
From 1	7	9	6
From 2	4	5	11
From 3	9	4	3
From 4	8	6	5
From 5	7	6	2

Multiple Facilities.

3. Show in detail how tabu search would solve problem 2.
4. Consider a logistics network problem where both several plant locations and several regional warehouse locations are to be determined to deliver goods to existing local warehouses in a number of cities. Explain how to use tabu search to solve this problem.

2.6 STRATEGIC PRODUCT/PROCESS ISSUES

2.6.1 Overview

We have mostly dealt with products and the processes for making them as being static over time. This view may be reasonable for many purposes for situations with short time horizons. However, it does not capture the flavor of strategic issues for products and processes.

Learning and Experience Curves. The skill of an individual worker increases in making a particular product as experience is gained. In a similar fashion, the production of a particular product by an industry becomes more efficient as the companies gain more experience. Operations management strategists have made progress in quantifying the relationship that describes how efficiency increases as the cumulative number of units that have been produced increases. The hope is to accurately predict the eventual capacity of existing shops and the future unit costs of production.

Early studies of the aircraft industry made more than a half century ago showed that the direct labor hours (and thus the cost) to produce a unit of final output declined as the total cumulated number of units produced increased. The term "learning curve" was given to this effect. It has also been observed in many situations that variable production costs also decline as the cumulative number of units produced is increased, which is called the "experience curve."

Product Life Cycle and Process Life Cycle. A new product faces different phases in its life, much like an individual. A typical life cycle consists of start-up, exponential growth, maturity, and decline. A manufacturing method or process undergoes similar phases. Abernathy and Townsend [1975] call these phases: early, middle, mature.

2.6.2 Learning Curves and Experience Curves

Learning Curves. The most common relationship which has been observed for the learning curve is of the form: "Each time the total cumulative production of the item is doubled, the labor cost of the last item goes down by a constant percentage."

More precisely, let $M(X)$ be the number of labor hours required to produce the Xth unit. Then $M(X)$ often approximates the form

$$M(X) = AX^{-b}$$

where A is the cost of producing the first unit and b is a measure of the rate at which costs decrease with cumulative production. Learning curves are usually described by the percentage decline of labor hours (and thus labor costs) required to produce item $2N$ compared with item N. The formula above makes it clear that this percentage is independent of N. If the time to produce unit $2N$ is, say, 80 percent of the time to produce unit N for any value of N, then we term it an "80 percent learning curve." Typical learning curves in many industries are 70 to 80 percent learning curves.

Now for a 75 percent learning curve $M(2X)/M(X) = [A(2X)^{-b}]/[A(X)^{-b}] = 2^{-b} = 0.75$, thus $-b \log_{10}(2) = \log_{10}(.75)$ or $b = -\log_{10}(.75)/\log_{10}(2) = 0.415$.

Figure 2-6 shows an ideal 75 percent learning curve. It is actually quite informative to plot learning curve data on log-log paper, since the learning curve should be roughly a straight line if the functional relationship is indeed quite accurate. We can see this linear relationship by taking logarithms of both sides of the learning curve equation:

$$\log(M(X)) = \log(A) - b \log(X)$$

Thus, $\log(M(X))$ is a linear function of $\log(X)$ with intercept of the constant $\log(A)$ and slope of $-b$.

Example 2-6. Microsphere has kept records of the exact number of labor hours required to produce one of its innovative new products, a circuit board used in very large screen television sets. The Table 2-9 is a sample from their records. (We list logarithms based 10 for the data, for convenience in graphing.)

We plot log units versus log hours in Figure 2-7. It is evident that a linear fit works quite well for cumulative units between 10 and 1000. A quick visual fit here (on the good linear fit between X = 10 and X = 1000) gives

$$\log M(X) = 2.21 - 0.78 \log(X)$$

Since $\log(L) = -b\log(2)$, we deduce that in this region $\log(L) = -0.235$ so that $L = 0.6$ (roughly). However, for volumes between 1000 and 25,000, the rate of learning appears to have slowed dramatically. The cost value for 25,000 seems especially to destroy

Table 2-9

Microsphere Production Data

Cumulative Units Produced	Log$_{10}$ Units	Hours Needed for Last Unit	Log$_{10}$ Hours
10	1.000	50.22	1.701
25	1.398	16.34	1.213
100	2.000	8.50	0.929
250	2.398	2.44	0.387
500	2.699	1.70	0.230
1000	3.000	1.03	0.013
5000	3.699	0.60	−0.222
10000	4.000	0.50	−0.301
25000	4.398	0.48	−0.319

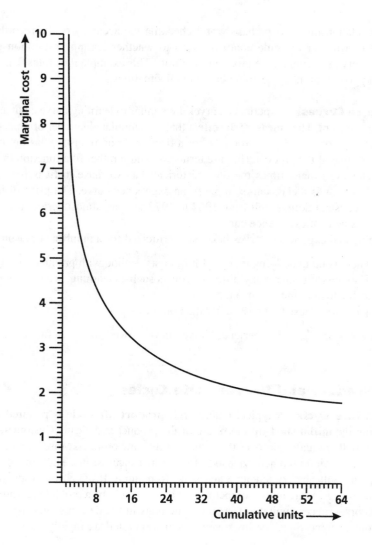

Figure 2-6

A 75 Percent Learning Curve

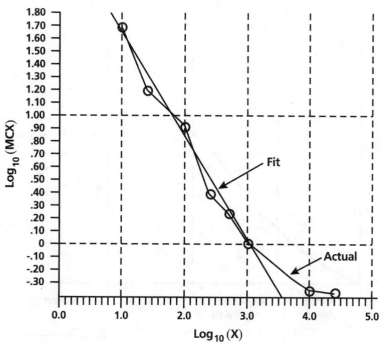

Figure 2-7

Microsphere Learning Curve

the linear relationship. It is perhaps worth checking the accuracy of the records for this value. (It is a matter of some controversy as to whether learning saturation generally occurs for very high cumulative production or not.) This example illustrates that it may be quite tricky to extrapolate a learning curve in all situations.

Experience Curves.   Experience curves are similar to learning curves, but are a more aggregated concept. They measure the effect that the cumulated number of units produced of a product (or of a family of products, for a firm or for an industry) has on the overall cost and/or price of the product. (In pure terms we would rather fit a function to the over-all cost. However, many times the only historical data we have to fit is for the price.) Integrated circuits is a classical example of an experience curve. The price of integrated circuits (in constant dollars) fell from 1964 to 1972 with an almost perfect log-log linear fit, with a 72 percent experience curve.

Learning and experience curves have been criticized for a number of reasons:

a. There is no underlying model of how costs decline with production.
b. They mix together many different effects such as learning, scale economies, and technological improvement.
c. They are focused on cost rather than on profit.

However, learning and experience curves have proved to be useful when carefully applied.

2.6.3 Product and Process Life Cycles

Product Life Cycle. A typical (successful) **product life cycle** is pictured in Figure 2-8. During the **initial start-up** the future of the product is delicate. Customers who are innovators will gradually discover the virtues of the new product. More cautious imitator customers will wait until others have used the product successfully. Thus, the initial ramp-up in demand will be very tentative and slow. Remaining R&D costs, production costs, and distribution costs are high. Competition will not usually be a problem (competitors are also imitators—success imitators). At this time bugs in the design should be ironed out, and customer suggestions for improvements incorporated as rapidly as possible. One

Figure 2-8

A Typical Product Life Cycle

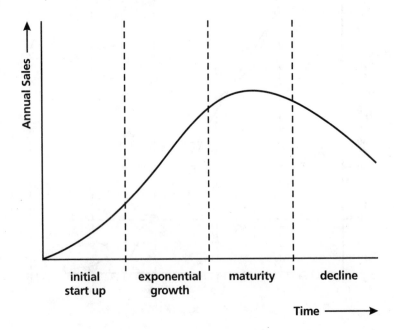

strategic concern is to apply experiences gained in marketing and the R&D and/or manufacturing process to improve the product, its production, and its marketing. Since cash flow is still negative, another strategic concern is often to keep the product afloat financially.

The period of **exponential growth** is much less delicate but just as stressful. Imitators are out in force, buying the product, beginning to make competing products, and offering financial help. Management should be on the lookout for improved products that the competition may be developing, and should already be developing its own improved product ideas. They should consider standard marketing tools such as pricing differentiation and brand loyalty advertising. As cumulative volume increases, the manufacturing process should be improved and standardized to produce learning curve effects. Keeping manufacturing flexible and modularized may well be desirable at this state.

During the **maturity** phase the product becomes a "cash cow," generating a great deal of excess cash to pay back investors and finance the next product. There is now a real danger that the competition will introduce improved products; the company's own next product should be near prototype form. Competitive pricing and heavy advertising are needed. The manufacturing process should continue to be improved and standardized. Listening and responding to customer complaints and desires are critical in maintaining market share.

During the **decline** phase the product may continue to be a cash cow for some time given good maintenance. Both the company and competition have already introduced improved products. The price will gradually be lowered to maintain existing customers. Any media advertising and improvements in the manufacturing process will also be focused on this residual market. Customers will be gradually encouraged to move to the new products with incentives of various kinds. The timing of the decision to discontinue the old product will be largely contingent on the ease of moving existing customers to the new product.

The Product Life Cycle concept should be used very carefully. For example, if customers do not really like the next product all that much, attempts to wean them and discontinue the old product may be disastrous. Think about Coca Cola's abortive attempt to introduce "New Coke" and discontinue the old formula. Generalized abstract models are useful in general thinking about the product or products, but there is no substitute for careful understanding of the actual current situation.

Process Life Cycle. As we previously stated, the three stages of the process life cycle have been called early, middle, and mature by Abernathy and Townsend [1975]. They do not necessarily coincide with the phases of the product life cycle, although they are at least correlated. In the *early* phase, the manufacturing process is much like a job shop. There will be a rather varied mix of rather low-volume orders to process simultaneously. The types and the quality of the raw materials will vary, and the firm has rather little control over suppliers.

In the *middle* phase, the manufacturing process is more like a batch process shop, or possibly a simple assembly line. There will be a less varied mix of medium- to high- volume orders to process. Unit production costs decline. The firm begins to exercise control over suppliers.

In the *mature* phase, the manufacturing process is more like a high speed transfer line. Most of the major operations are fully automated, the production process is standardized, and major further changes are rare. The firm may treat its suppliers as satellites in some cases.

This evolutionary picture is not at all appropriate for all types of new products. Some kinds of products will continue to be job shop items indefinitely, for example. The process life cycle only makes sense for new products that eventually mature into high-volume items.

2.6.4 Product/Process Exercises

Learning and Experience Curves.

1. What are some of the difficulties in getting the input for learning curves and experience curves to predict costs? What are some of the pitfalls of using such curves to predict future costs?

2. Consider Example 2-6 with a rough fit of the data as Log $M(X) = 2.21 - 0.78$.

   a. Give this formula in other than logarithmic terms.
   b. What does the formula predict for $X = 25,000$? How accurate was this?
   c. What does the formula predict for $X = 1,000,000$?
   d. How much do you trust this prediction?

3. A marketing analyst predicts that a 75 percent experience curve should be a predictor of the cost of producing a new product. Suppose the cost of the 10th unit is $800. What would she predict is the cost of producing the

   a. 640th unit?
   b. 10,240th unit?

Product and Process Life Cycles.

4. Give an example of a product which has undergone the four phases of the product life cycle and has

   a. Died a natural death
   b. Stabilized and continued indefinitely

5. Write a short two- or three-page scenario of a new product from birth to death, illustrating some of the characteristics of the product life cycle and the process life cycle for it.

6. A firm has kept careful records of the cost required to manufacture its product, an innovative instrument for measuring concrete strength as it hardens.

Cum. Units Produced	Last Unit Cost
50	3.4
100	2.3
400	1.0
1000	0.49
10,000	0.19

   a. Compute the logarithms (base 10) of the numbers in each column.
   b. Graph log (hours) vs. log (units) and eyeball a straight line fit. Use this fit to estimate an experience curve formula.
   c. Using the results of part (b) estimate the time required to produce the first unit, and the appropriate percentage learning curve for this fit.

7. Repeat problem 6 but use an exact least squares fit of the data rather than eyeballing it. Make a comparison of the two methods.

2.7 EXPONENTIAL ENTERPRISES—REPRISE

Pete Garfield worked hard on his analysis of the proper size for the capacity expansion and brought his work back to show Slugging Jim about three weeks later. He used the Silver-Meal approximation applied to capacity expansion; that is, figured the average cost to be

$$A(T) = f(X(T))/[1 - PV(r,T)]$$

where T is the number of years of expansion to plan for (taking year 2 as the base instead of year 0, since the new plant will be built then), $X(T)$ is the total growth in demand over

T	X(T)	f(X(T))	1.0 – PV(r,T)	Cost(t)
3	80	72	0.1667	431.9
4	180	122	0.3056	399.2
5	280	152	0.4213	360.8**
6	440	216	0.5177	417.2
7	600	280	0.5981	468.1
8	800	360	0.6651	541.3
9	1100	480	0.7209	667.2

** is optimum

T years, $f(X(T))$ is the cost to build a plant of this size, and $PV(r,T)$ is the present value of $1 received T years in the future at interest rate r.

Pete concluded that a plant should be built large enough to cover increasing demand for three years. Two-year or four-year alternatives give costs at least 10 percent higher. As far as building the plant a little earlier, Pete estimates that there is only a one-in-four chance that demand will reach the 880 annual rate three months early. Thus, he recommends expediting the building a bit, and bringing it on line three months before the end of year 2. Jim Brown said he was unable to answer the question of how many warehouses would be needed and where immediately. Analysts would have to pick some possible warehouse locations, do some costing analysis at each, and finally do a full warehouse location analysis. This was not hard in principle, but would probably take nine months.

Aggregate Planning Models

3.1 INTRODUCTION

Remember that we have defined aggregate planning issues to be issues affecting the whole firm, but having a shorter horizon than strategic decisions. There are five main characteristics of aggregate planning issues:

1. The time horizon is about one or two years.
2. Decisions are made about aggregates of products and aggregates of resources.
3. Decisions tend to affect the balance of the firm more than its survival.
4. (Discounted) regression might be a typical forecasting method.
5. Seasonality of demand and/or production is likely to be an important issue. For logistics, regionality of supply and demand will be an important added issue.

Typical aggregate planning issues, which we will address in this chapter, include production smoothing, logistics, and machine replacement.

Often, in a production smoothing model, all of the products produced in a plant are averaged or aggregated into a single product. The single product model is much easier to solve and to understand intuitively. However, there are two difficulties with this:

1. The decisions must be eventually broken down (disaggregated) into decisions for each product; it may not be clear how to do this wisely.
2. Lumping the products together may lose valuable information, so that the aggregate solution may be less useful.

This is a rich and important issue, which we can't discuss completely here. However, with much better complex heuristics and the vastly increased computational power that is available, it is quite feasible to both solve an aggregate problem and, in a coordinated manner, create a detailed schedule of, for example, 18 product lines on 15 different machines monthly over an 18-month period. Thus, in some cases, it is less necessary to solve simplified models.

In Sections 3.2 and 3.6 we present a company application scenario. We discuss production smoothing in Section 3.3. Logistic systems simultaneously consider production, transportation, and inventory control in large production/distribution systems; we examine them in Section 3.4. We discuss machine replacement in Section 3.5.

3.2 COMPANY APPLICATION SCENARIO—CLIMATE MASTER

Kool Kuke, president and CEO of Climate Master, Incorporated, sat at dinner with his wife Katie Kuke in the solarium of their John Hancock penthouse, staring out at the view of Chicago and thinking furiously. His production costs were way too high. The Knoxville plant, which produces air conditioners, seemed to run up astronomical bills for overtime, hiring and firing costs, and subcontracting, especially just before the peak period in July and August. The Skokie plant, on the other hand, which produces electric heating units, seemed to carry enormous inventories, especially in the off-season months of April to September. Due to minor changes in the units being manufactured, the inventory often had to be modified before it could be sold, leading to additional expenses.

On top of these production cost problems, Kool was aware that electric heating unit demand had increased in recent years. His strategy VP was proposing building a new plant for electric heating units in Harrisburg, Pennsylvania. Should a new plant be built, allowing all new technology, or would it be better to expand one of the old plants?

On the next Monday, Kuke called Jesse James at the Lazy Bar O Consulting firm to investigate these questions. Jesse was to look into the questions and in six weeks recommend:

1. A better production strategy for each of the existing plants.
2. A capacity expansion strategy for the new heat pump capacity.

3.3 PRODUCTION SMOOTHING

3.3.1 Overview

Production smoothing is aggregate planning applied to the single plant level. (Some texts equate the terms production smoothing and aggregate planning, but we use the latter more generally.) The time horizon is typically exactly one year, so that the full effects of seasonal demand may be modeled, while keeping the model as simple as possible. Decisions are typically made about the total level of aggregate plant production month by month. Resources are commonly aggregated into regular time, overtime and subcontracting, although more detailed classifications are sometimes used.

Production smoothing is very important. To what extent should we produce in advance of seasonal peaks, and thus use inventories to absorb the fluctuations? Why not have the same effect by simply producing more or less as necessary, either through overtime or hiring and firing workers temporarily? Why not keep production rates stable, on the other hand, and let the subcontractors have the problem of our fluctuating demand? Would some mixed strategy be better?

Problems in Aggregating Production. When the types of items produced are similar, an aggregate production unit can be thought of as an "average" item. On the other hand, if there are many different kinds of items being produced, it may be more convenient to use some common measure such as weight (tons of copper products), volume (barrels of oil products), amount of work invested (man-months of computer programming), or dollar value ($1000s of production). It is not always obvious what the aggregation scheme should be, and sometimes it will necessarily be rather arbitrary.

Example 3-1. The Louisville plant of the Freezingaire Company makes five varieties of miniature refrigerators. The characteristics of these refrigerators in terms of worker hours to produce them and selling price are:

Item Code	Worker Hours	Selling Price
5A12	2.1	$125
5A14	2.2	155
6B1	2.6	210
6B3	2.7	215
9G	3.0	290

One possible aggregation scheme is to define the aggregate unit as $100 of output. Unfortunately, the selling prices of the various miniature refrigerators are not consistent with the number of worker hours required to produce them. Selling price per working hour is $60 for 5A12 and $97 for 9G. On the other hand, the manager notices that the sales mix of these items has been quite constant: 33, 20, 18, 19, and 10 percent respectively. He decides to use, as his unit of aggregate production, a fictitious unit which is an appropriate weighted mix of the five products. The fictitious product requires $(.33)(2.1) + (.20)(2.2) + (.18)(2.6) + (.19)(2.7) + (.10)(3.0) = 2.41$ hours of labor time. The fictitious unit then costs $(.33)(125) + (.20)(155) + (.18)(210) + (.19)(215) + (.10)(290) = \$179.90$. The sales forecast for these fictitious aggregate units may be obtained in the same way by multiplying the forecast for each refrigerator by the appropriate fraction and adding them up. Here our situation was relatively easy, because the units being aggregated were basically quite similar. However, aggregating at a higher level over a broader mix of products is more difficult. A natural tendency is to use dollar sales as the aggregate unit. Our example shows that this is far from perfect, but it will generally provide an adequate approximation.

3.3.2 Formulating the Problem

Types of Cost. The goal of production smoothing models is to minimize cost. Therefore, it is important to identify, understand, and quantify those costs that are affected by the production smoothing decisions.

Hiring and Firing Costs. Hiring and firing costs are incurred by changing the size of the work force from one period to the next. Hiring, or increasing the work force, requires costs in terms of advertising for employees, interviewing them, and training them. Firing, or decreasing the size of the work force, may be temporary (layoff) or permanent. This may involve severance pay or increases in unemployment compensation payments. Other indirect (and hard to measure) costs of firing include the decrease in morale of the remaining workers, and a bad reputation in the community resulting in future hiring problems.

Most of the models used in production smoothing assume that the costs of hiring and firing are proportional. That is, there is one cost per employee hired and a second cost per employee fired. This being an aggregate model, we allow fractions, and round at the end. We shall use the notation c_H for the cost of hiring a worker and c_F for the cost of firing a worker. This relationship is shown in the solid line function in Figure 3-1.

While the simplicity of this assumption is appealing, and makes the model easy to use, it is not all that accurate. In the first place, a certain number of workers can be "fired" for free, simply by not hiring to replace workers who quit. This **attrition** is rather constant for a large company on the average, and means that there are firing costs only on the excess above attrition, hiring costs for those hired above attrition. In addition, if the employer tries to hire, or fire larger numbers of workers in a period, the cost per worker will go up. Thus, the true hire/fire cost function is probably like the dashed line in Figure 3-1. Nevertheless, the simpler solid line function is the one usually used. (We shall develop an attrition model in the exercises.)

Holding and Shortage Costs. There are several kinds of inventories a firm may have. Lot-sizing inventories come from producing in economical batches. Safety stocks come from

Figure 3-1..................................

Hiring and Firing Costs

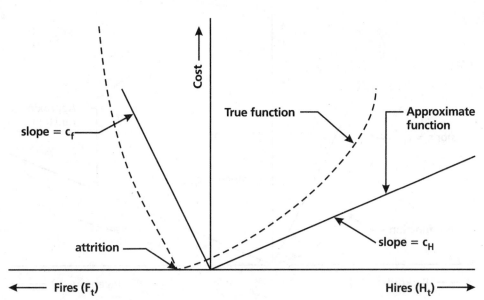

having extra stocks for unexpectedly high demands. Holding costs are the costs that come from carrying inventory. (See Chapter 1 in the Inventory Module.) In particular, holding costs include the interest on the capital tied up in the inventory, obsolescence, and storage costs.

Here we are interested in costing "seasonal" inventory, which is held from low-demand periods for use in high-demand periods, and we define "seasonal inventory" ("inventory" for short) to be inventories only in excess of lot-sizing and safety stock inventories. It is usually assumed that holding costs are also linear, and are expressed in terms of dollars per unit held per period, and that holding costs are charged against inventory on hand at the *end* of the period rather than the more accurate average amount on hand. This does not cause much inaccuracy and is easier to use.

Holding costs are charged on positive inventory. Negative inventory represents orders which have been recorded to be filled in a future period (backlogging). (The case in which demand is simply lost must be treated separately. We shall treat only the backlogging case here.) Backlogging costs are also typically assumed to be linear. We shall use the notation c_I for the cost of inventory and c_B for the cost of backlogging. This is represented by the solid line function in Figure 3-2.

Again, if we wished to be more realistic, we would note that small amounts of inventory above the ideal still have some value occasionally in reducing stockouts and should cost us at a lower rate. Similarly, small amounts of inventory below ideal, although representing inventories smaller than that needed for lot sizes and safety stocks, still give us some protection, and therefore will not cost us the full backlogging cost. This more realistic function is shown by the dotted line function in Figure 3-2.

Regular Time, Overtime, and Subcontracting Costs. Regular time, overtime, and subcontracting are different methods of producing a unit. We add up both direct and indirect costs to estimate a cost per unit for each.

Regular time costs are the total costs of producing one unit of output during regular working hours. They include the actual payroll costs of regular employees working on regular time; they also include direct costs of materials, and various overhead costs. We will call regular time costs c_R. Overtime involves all regular time costs, plus a premium on wages (typically 50 percent). There may also be other extra overhead costs. We will call overtime cost c_O. A vendor who produces on the outside (subcontracting) is typically assumed to sell us units at a fixed cost per unit, at a higher rate than the regular time

Figure 3-2

Holding and Backlogging
Costs

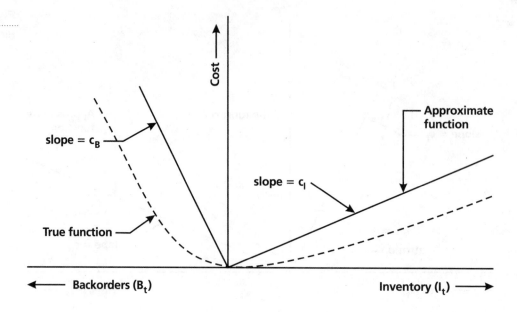

change. It is very much like a separate category of overtime. We will call the subcontracting cost c_S.

Example 3-2. Snowizard produces a line of snow equipment, such as snow blowers, snowmobiles, snow plows, ice huts, augers, and so on. Their heavy demand season is in the late autumn and winter months. They want to plan their work force and production levels for their next budget year, which runs from July 1 of the current calendar year to June 30 of the next calendar year. Their plant is located in Toronto. They plan with a two-month planning period (to reduce their computational effort). They have a standard composite production unit, which translates roughly as the amount of production one worker can produce in two months. The bimonthly demand forecasts over the next budget year are forecasted as shown in the following list.

July/August	2100
Sept/October	2500
Nov/December	4500
Jan/February	5100
March/April	3200
May/June	2200

There are currently (at the end of June) 2605 workers employed in the plant. Ending inventory at the end of the current June is expected to be 1040, and the ending inventory for the end of next June is desired to be 950. The desired ending work force at that time is 3050. (Here inventories mean inventories in excess of safety stocks and lot inventories; that is, there are 1040 units available to meet the winter seasonal peak.)

The simplest way to incorporate starting and ending inventories is just to modify the values of the forecast demand. Predicted net demand in the first period is simply demand minus the initial inventory. (What would you do if the initial inventory were greater than the predicted demand?) The desired ending inventory should simply be added into the demand in the last period. Thus the beginning net predicted demand is 2100 − 1040 = 1060, and the ending net predicted demand is 2200 + 950 = 3150. (However, since the final ending inventory will now be artificially shown as 0 rather than 950, we will have to add the one-period storage costs for 950 units to make our results comparable with other methods.)

Snowizard figures it costs about $500 to hire a worker and about $1000 to fire a worker. A unit of production (two man-months) costs about $8000 to produce. The cost of holding is figured at 3 percent per month or 6 percent for two months, or about $(0.06)(8000) = \$480$. The cost of lost sales is figured at 40 percent of item cost or $(0.4)(8000) = \$3200$. Hiring and firing are considered instantaneous. Because hiring and firing are relatively easy, Snowizard does not usually utilize overtime. The plant manager is interested in learning about a wide variety of possible methods, starting with very simple ones.

3.3.3 Simple Heuristics

Chase Strategy. The "chase" strategy is so called because we chase demand in each period, producing as much or as little as is needed. Thus this might better be called the "zero inventory" plan; we stick with the classic term.

Example 3-2, Part 2. Since the manager's analyst chose the units so that one unit of production can be produced in one time period, calculation of the zero inventory aggregate plan is very simple, as shown in Table 3-1.

Thus the cost of the zero inventory plan in terms of hiring, firing, and inventory costs is $(4040)(\$500) + (3595)(\$1000) + (0)(\$240) = \$5,615,000$. But as we have said, we must add in $(\$480)(950)$ for the fact that we actually have 950 final units of inventory, so that the total cost becomes $\$5,615,000 + \$456,000 = \$6,071,000$. Note that we have achieved zero inventory costs only at the expense of very high hiring and firing costs as our work force "chased" the demand up and down.

Constant Work Force Strategy. At the other extreme, the manager wished to know the cost of the plan resulting from hiring and firing as little as possible, and leaving the work force constant. We note that the average net demand over the year is: $(1060 + 2500 + 4500 + 5100 + 3200 + 3150)/6 = 3252$. If we immediately raise the work force to 3252 and leave it there at the end before lowering it to 3050, the work plan shown in Table 3-2 will result. Hence the total cost of the constant work force plan is $(647)(\$500) + (202)(\$1000) + (7038)(\$480) + (152)(\$3200) + \$456,000 = \$4,846,140$.

Other Strategies. The plant manager noticed that the constant work force strategy cost only $4.8 million, compared with $6.1 million for the chase strategy. But she thought perhaps a better strategy would be to apply a constant work force strategy at a bit higher level set to just run out at the end of the peak period in January/February, and then to chase demand downward at the end of the year. She called this the "peak period strategy."

The analyst worked through the peak period strategy, as shown in Table 3-3. The total cost of this strategy is $(685)(\$500) + (240)(\$1000) + (7060)(\$480) + \$456,000 = \$4,427,300$.

Table 3-1

Zero Inventory Aggregate Plan for Snowizard

Month	Demand	Work force	N. Hired	N. Fired	Inventory
Start		2605		1545	
July/Aug.	1060		1440		0
Sept./Oct.	2500		2000		0
Nov./Dec.	4500		600		0
Jan./Feb.	5100			1900	0
Mar./April	3200			50	0
May/June	3150			100	0
End		3050			
Totals	19,510		4040	3595	0

Table 3-2

Constant Work Force
Aggregate Plan for
Snowizard

Month	Demand	Work force	N. Hired	N. Fired	Invent.	L. Sales
Start		2605	647			
July/Aug.	1060	3252			2192	
Sept./Oct.	2500	3252			2944	
Nov./Dec.	4500	3252			1696	
Jan./Feb.	5100	3252			0	152
Mar./April	3200	3252			52	
May/June	3150	3252		202	154	
End		3050				
Totals	19,510		647	202	7038	152

The peak period approach has slightly higher inventory, hiring, and firing costs as the constant work force method, but saves almost $500,000 in lost sales. Thus overall it is more than $400,000 cheaper. Finally, it occurred to the analyst that delaying hiring for one period and still planning to meet peak demand exactly might be even cheaper. (You will be asked to investigate this strategy in the exercises.)

3.3.4 Transportation Algorithm—Johnson's Algorithm

In Example 3-2, Snowizard's plant manager was able to find a relatively good production planning solution to her problem; a "peak period" solution. This was possible because the number of variables to control was small. She was able to trade off only hiring and firing with carrying seasonal inventory. There is a rather different special case in which we can find good solutions easily. Suppose we are not allowed to hire or fire workers. Instead, we can trade off overtime and subcontracting to meet the peak period versus carrying seasonal inventory. The resulting simplified problem may be solved relatively easily by a series of network algorithms called **Johnson's Algorithm**, which is a special case of the Transportation Algorithm.

The case where no hiring or firing is allowed is especially easy to solve with Johnson's Algorithm, which is explained in Part 3 of Example 3-2.

Example 3-2, Part 3. The plant manager of Snowizard is very concerned. There is heavy union pressure to make it very difficult to fire workers, so that the hiring/firing strategy would become impossible. In spite of the fact that she had not authorized overtime and subcontracting in the past, she wished now to find the best production smoothing policy which prohibits hiring and firing, but allows overtime and subcontracting. She decides to raise the work force from 2620 to 3050, and then plan to leave it there permanently.

It costs $8000 to produce a unit by regular time, $1600 of which is wages. It costs $8800 to produce a unit by overtime, $2400 of which is wages. The overtime amount is limited to 850 units per period. (To make the results comparable with earlier work, the analyst considers the regular cost of producing a unit to be sunk, and therefore treats regular production as $0 cost and overtime production as $800 cost.) The analyst turns this

Table 3-3

Peak Period Aggregate Plan
for Snowizard

Month	Demand	Work force	N. Hired	N. Fired	Inventory
Start		2605	685		
July/Aug.	1060	3290			2230
Sept./Oct.	2500	3290			3020
Nov./Dec.	4500	3290			1810
Jan./Feb.	5100	3290		90	0
Mar./April	3200	3200		50	0
May/June	3150	3150		100	0
End		3050			
Totals	19,510		685	240	7060

into a Johnson's Algorithm format by pretending that each type of production (regular, overtime, subcontracting) in each period is a separate source of production, and that the demand in each period is a separate destination. He comes up with the diagram in Table 3-4. This diagram is a standard transportation tableau, such as was introduced in Section 2.5.2. However, this is a special case, with an exact solution much easier to arrive at. The rows represent ways to produce units. That is, July at regular time with a capacity of 3050 is one source; July at overtime with a capacity of 850 is another source; September at regular time with a capacity of 3050 is another source, and so on. The columns show the ways units are consumed. That is, 1060 units are needed in July, 2500 in September, etc.

There is a cell for each combination of source and destination. The initial number in each cell gives the per unit cost of shipping from that source to that destination. For example, using July regular production to meet July demand costs 0 (we consider normal production costs as "sunk"). Using July regular production to meet September demand has, in addition storage costs of $480; to meet November demands costs $0 + 2($480) = $960 and so on. Using July overtime production to meet July demand costs $800 overtime cost; using it to meet September demand costs $800 + 480 = $1280 and so on.

Note that we have no entries for the possibility of using September regular production to meet the previous July's demand. This would mean that we were backlogging demand for a period, which in this particular case is not being allowed. Almost half of the matrix would involve backlogging, and hence is omitted.

Johnson's Algorithm is intuitive. We work forward and satisfy July demand first, then September and so on. We simply pick the cheapest available source first. Thus we assign all 1060 July demand to be produced by July regular production, which costs 0 per unit. Moving on to September, we assign all 2500 September units to be produced by September regular production, which again costs 0 per unit.

Table 3-4

Johnson's Algorithm for Snowizard

Capacity	Demand	July 1060	Sept. 2500	Nov. 4500	Jan. 5100	Mar. 3200	May 3150
July R	3050	0 **1060**	480	960 **50**	1440 **1200**	1920	2400
July O	850	800	1280	1760	2240	2720	3200
Sept. R	3050	0	480 **2500**	960 **550**	1440	1920	
Sept. O	850		800	1280	1760	2240	2720
Nov. R	3050			0 **3050**	480	960	1440
Nov. O	850			800 **850**	1280	1760	2240
Jan. R	3050				0 **3050**	480	960
Jan. O	850				800 **850**	1280	1760
Mar. R	3050				0	480 **3050**	
Mar. O	850				800	1280 **150**	
May R	3050						0 **3050**
May O	850						800 **100**

Meeting November demand is somewhat more interesting. We can meet only 3050 units of the 4500 needed from November regular at a cost of 0 per unit. The next cheapest is to meet as much as possible from September regular at a cost of $480 per unit, but there are only 550 units left of this production, so we still have 900 more to meet. The next cheapest production is November overtime time at a cost of $800 per unit; we can meet all 850 units there. We produce the final 50 units in July regular time. Meeting the January demand of 5100 is next. We use January regular time first, followed by January overtime, and finally November overtime. Finally, both March and May demands are filled from regular time and overtime in their own months, since no earlier inexpensive time is available.

What is the cost of this solution? We stored 550 units for one period at a total cost of $264,000; 50 units for two periods at $48,000 and 1200 units for three periods at a cost of $1,728,000. There were 1950 overtime units used in the same period at a cost of $1,560,000. Finally, 430 workers were hired at the start at $500 each at a cost of $215,000, and we must add our usual final inventory correction of $456,000. Thus the total cost of the overtime solution is $4,223,000 which is about $200,000 better than the peak period solution of $4,427,300. One serious question remains though: the whole analysis depended on the initial choice of 3050 as the initial workforce. Might 2950 have been a better choice? Or perhaps 3150?

Extensions. Johnson's Algorithm can easily be extended to cases in which there are several types of production possible in each period. There might be a choice of two different shops, or subcontracting, or several types of overtime. For each type for each period, a separate row must then be entered, with the maximum amount of production of each type available. The algorithm can easily be extended to the case of lost sales simply by adding a single row to the entire matrix with the source marked "Lost Sales." The cost entry in each cell will be the opportunity cost of a lost sale. The diagram can also be easily modified for backlogging, such as when it costs 0 to produce in November, and a customer will wait from September at a backlogging cost of $1000 per period. Although Johnson's Algorithm is not exactly optimal for the backlogging problem, it is very accurate when used as a heuristic. Using the same basic tableau as input to the Transportation Algorithm will provide an optimal solution, however.

3.3.5 Linear Programming

Standard Formulation. We have been looking at various special cases of production smoothing problems with linear costs. First we looked at the problem with just hiring, firing, and inventory costs. We costed out various simple solutions such as the chase strategy, the constant work force strategy, and peak strategies. We also learned how to solve similar problems without hiring and firing costs, but with inventory, overtime, backlogging, and lost sales, by using Johnson's Algorithm. Here we had to try several values of the long term work force level, comparing their total costs.

Linear programming provides a way of efficiently handling *all* of these variables in the same formulation, obtaining the optimal answer easily and quickly by use of a standard linear programming package. Optimal solutions can be obtained for very large problems. One minor problem should be mentioned: linear programming may give a fractional answer for such variables as work force or production. Sometimes these values must be rounded to give useful answers. However, this is rarely a problem. We are dealing with an *aggregate* model which typically involves other assumptions (such as linearity) which are more serious.

Initially Given Costs and Other Information. There are many possible linear programming formulations for the production smoothing problem. We present one general enough to deal with the Snowizard situation.

Let: c_H = Cost of hiring one worker

      c_F = Cost of firing one worker

      c_I = Cost of holding one unit of stock for one period

      c_B = Cost of backlogging one unit of stock for one period

      c_L = Cost of a lost sale

      c_O = Incremental cost of overtime

      c_U = Opportunity cost of undertime (idle workers)

      c_S = Cost to subcontract one unit of production

      K = Number of units produced by one worker in one period

      I_0 = Initial inventory at the start of the problem

      W_0 = Initial work force at the start of the problem

      I_T = Final inventory at the end of the problem

      W_T = Final work force at the end of the problem

      D_t = Forecast of demand for period t

Problem Variables. The program will choose the values of the following variables in order to minimize costs. Note that if there are T periods in the problem, then there are $10T$ variables.

      W_T = Work force in period t

      P_t = Production level in period t

      I_t = Inventory level in period t (positive)

      L_t = Sales lost in period t

      B_t = Units backlogged in period t

      H_t = Number of workers hired in period t

      F_t = Number of workers fired in period t

      O_t = Overtime production in units in t

      U_t = Undertime units in t (idle workers)

      S_t = Subcontracted units in period t

The Linear Programming Model. We first present the linear programming objective function and constraints. Next we will explain each term:

(1) Minimize $\sum_{t=1,T}(c_H H_t + c_F F_t + c_I I_t + c_L L_t + c_B B_t + c_O O_t + c_U U_t + c_S S_t)$

    subject to:

(2) $W_t = W_{t-1} + H_t - F_t$ for each t

(3) $P_t = KW_t + O_t - U_t$ for each t

(4) $I_t = I_{t-1} + P_t + S_t + B_t + L_t - D_t$ for each t

(5) I_0, I_T, W_0, W_T have given values

(6) $H_t, F_t, I_t, L_t, B_t, O_t, U_t, S_t, P_t >= 0$ for each t

The explanation of this linear programming formulation is as follows. Expression (1) says that in each period we add up the costs of hiring, firing, inventory, lost sales, backlogging, overtime, undertime, and subcontracting. Then we add up these costs over all T periods. Our desire is to minimize this overall total cost. The program will do this by choosing the best values each period of hiring, firing, overtime, undertime, subcontracting, backlogging, and lost sales.

Expression (2) says that the work force in any given period is the work force in the immediately preceding period plus any hiring, less any firing. Expression (3) says that production in a period will be K units for each worker plus any overtime units produced less any undertime units not produced. (Note that we are expressing undertime, that is workers paid but not producing, in units rather than workers. Thus the cost of undertime is $1/K$ times the wage of a worker for a period.)

Expression (4) says that the inventory at the end of a period is just the inventory from the previous period, plus any additional units from current production, plus any units from current subcontracting, plus any units that are backlogged (borrowed from the future), plus any lost demand (which therefore does not come out of inventory) less the demand for the period. Expression (5) says that the initial inventory and work force are specified as inputs, as well as final inventory and work force levels. Finally, expression (6) says that none of the variables (hiring, firing, inventory lost sales, backlogging, overtime, under-time, subcontracting, production) can be negative in any period.

We may occasionally need short names for each of the expressions. Expression (1) is called the objective function; expression (2) is the workforce balance equation. Expression (3) is the production equation, and Expression (4) is the inventory balance equation. Expression (5) is the initial and ending conditions (boundary conditions). Expression (6) is the non-negativity constraints.

Example 3-2, Part 4. The analyst noted that neither the simple strategies that had been tried, trading hiring and firing versus inventory, nor the Johnson Algorithm, which traded off regular time, overtime, and inventory, used all the possible control variables of hiring, firing, overtime, undertime, backlogging, lost sales, and subcontracting. He decided to make a full linear programming formulation, which should provide the "opti-mal" answer to the full problem. The formulation is presented below.

$$\text{Minimize } (500\sum_{t=1,6}H_t + 1000\sum_{t=1,6}F_t + 480\sum_{t=1,6}I_t + 3200\sum_{t=1,6}L_t + 1000\sum_{t=1,6}B_t + 800\sum_{t=1,6}O_t + 1600\sum_{t=1,6}U_t)$$

W_0					$= 2605$	
W_1	$-W_0$	$-H_1$	$+F_1$		$= 0$	
W_2	$-W_1$	$-H_2$	$+F_2$		$= 0$	
W_3	$-W_2$	$-H_3$	$+F_3$		$= 0$	workforce balance
W_4	$-W_3$	$-H_4$	$+F_4$		$= 0$	
W_5	$-W_4$	$-H_5$	$+F_5$		$= 0$	
W_6	$-W_5$	$-H_6$	$+F_6$		$= 0$	
W_6					$= 3050$	
P_1	$-W_1$	$-O_1$	$+U_1$		$= 0$	
P_2	$-W_2$	$-O_2$	$+U_2$		$= 0$	
P_3	$-W_3$	$-O_3$	$+U_3$		$= 0$	production
P_4	$-W_4$	$-O_4$	$+U_4$		$= 0$	
P_5	$-W_5$	$-O_5$	$+U_5$		$= 0$	
P_6	$-W_6$	$-O_6$	$+U_6$		$= 0$	
I_0					$= 1040$	
I_1	$-I_0$	$-P_1$	$-B_1$	$-L_1$	$= -2100$	
I_2	$-I_1$	$-P_2$	$-B_2$	$-L_2$	$= -2500$	
I_3	$-I_2$	$-P_3$	$-B_3$	$-L_3$	$= -4500$	inventory balance
I_4	$-I_3$	$-P_4$	$-B_4$	$-L_4$	$= -5100$	
I_5	$-I_4$	$-P_5$	$-B_5$	$-L_5$	$= -3200$	
I_6	$-I_5$	$-P_6$	$-B_6$	$-L_6$	$= -2200$	
I_6					$= 950$	
O_1		$<=$	850			
O_2		$<=$	850			
O_3		$<=$	850			limitation on overtime
O_4		$<=$	850			
O_5		$<=$	850			
O_6		$<=$	850			

First he wrote down the linear programming problem in the exact form required to solve his problem, using the costs that affected Snowizard. We have solved this model using the LINDO package developed by Schrage [1984]. The output is shown in Table 3-5. (Some of the exercises involve using linear programming. You may omit these if you are not familiar with using an LP package, without much loss of continuity.) Note that linear programming achieves a cost of $4,011,100, which is about 10 percent cheaper than any of the other methods Snowizard has tried. Notice also that the linear programming method produced sort of a combination of a delayed peak period method, and limited overtime, to reduce the size of the peak somewhat, reducing inventory carrying costs considerably.

Extensions. Linear programming can also be used to solve many other versions of the production smoothing problem. We have just seen how easy it is to add limits on the amount of overtime. We could just as easily have added constraints on total production capacity, or limited hiring to some fraction of the current work force, and so on, or considered multiple facilities, or multiple demand locations.

3.3.6 Other Approaches

Linear Decision Rule. Holt, Modigliani, Muth, and Simon [1960] suggested a very creative approach for solving the production smoothing problem. In those days computers were slow and had small memories, so that linear programming was not a very practical

Table 3-5

Linear Programming Solution of Snowizard Problem

(LINDO Output)

LP optimum found at step 26
Objective function value: 4011100

Variable	Value	Reduced Cost	Variable	Value	Reduced Cost
H1	0.000	480.000	O1	0.000	1,280.000
H2	500.000	0.000	O2	0.000	800.000
H3	195.000	0.000	O3	0.000	320.000
H4	0.000	480.000	O4	850.000	0.000
H5	0.000	1,440.000	O5	0.000	740.000
H6	0.000	1,500.000	O6	0.000	260.000
F1	0.000	1,020.000	U1	0.000	1,120.000
F2	0.000	1,500.000	U2	0.000	1,600.000
F3	0.000	1,500.000	U3	0.000	2,080.000
F4	0.000	1,020.000	U4	0.000	2,560.000
F5	0.000	60.000	U5	0.000	1,660.000
F6	250.000	0.000	U6	0.000	2,140.000
L1	0.000	3,680.000	W0	2,605.000	0.000
L2	0.000	3,200.000	W1	2,605.000	0.000
L3	0.000	2,720.000	W2	3,105.000	0.000
L4	0.000	2,240.000	W3	3,300.000	0.000
L5	0.000	3,140.000	W4	3,300.000	0.000
L6	0.000	2,660.000	W5	3,300.000	0.000
I1	1,545.000	0.000	W6	3,050.000	0.000
I2	2,150.000	0.000	P1	2,605.000	0.000
I3	950.000	0.000	P2	3,105.000	0.000
I4	0.000	1,380.000	P3	3,300.000	0.000
I5	100.000	0.000	P4	4,150.000	0.000
I6	950.000	0.000	P5	3,300.000	0.000
B1	0.000	1,480.000	P6	3,050.000	0.000
B2	0.000	1,000.000	I0	1,040.000	0.000
B3	0.000	520.000			
B4	0.000	40.000			
B5	0.000	940.000			
B6	0.000	460.000			

method for companies to use. HMMS basically approximated the costs of hiring/firing, inventory/backlogging, overtime/undertime by quadratic functions. The first two are shown in Figure 3-3.

This created a rather straightforward calculus problem. Minimize a quadratic function subject to linear constraints:

$$\min \textstyle\sum_{t=1,T}[a_1W_t + a_2(W_t - W_{t-1})^2 + a_3(P_t - KW_t)^2 + a_4(I_t - a_5)^2]$$

subject to

$$I_t = I_{t-1} + P_t - D_t \text{ for } 1 <= t <= T$$

(Here we have simplified the model to omit backlogging, lost sales, and subcontracting.)

The best values of the constants a_1, a_2, ... a_5 are fitted to the cost data for a particular company. One way to find a_2, for example, would be to fit the best quadratic to the V-shaped curve in Figure 3-3(a). The optimal solution to this calculus problem will occur

Figure 3-3

Linear Decision Rule
Approximations

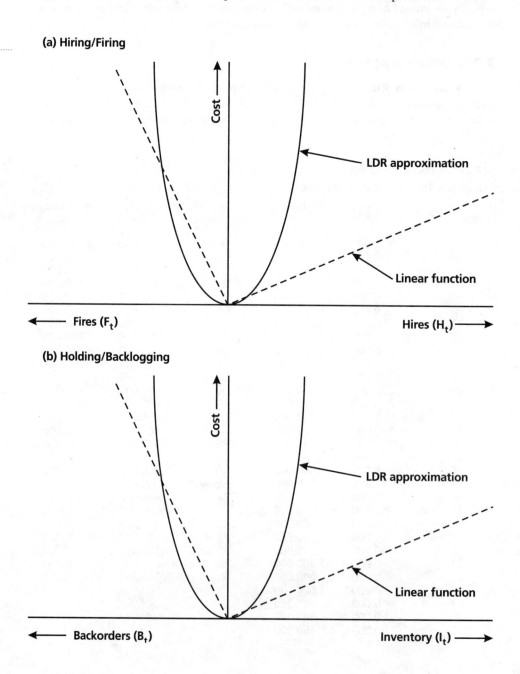

where the first partial derivative with respect to each problem variable is zero. Since the derivative of a quadratic function is linear, this will yield a system of linear equations, which is quite easy to solve.

The main advantage of the linear decision rule is that it yields a very simple policy which does not require a computer to implement. There are several difficulties, however. First of all, the quadratic functions are symmetric, but the cost of firing is much higher than the cost of hiring, for example, so that symmetric curves can simply not fit well. Secondly, the linear decision rule suggests that small amounts of hiring and firing are very cheap, and so it tends to suggest hiring and firing a few people every period. Because linear programming gives a much more accurate answer to the problem, and because linear programming is very practical on today's powerful personal computers, linear programming is now to be preferred to the LDR.

This all does not change the fact that the text by Holt, Modigliani, Muth and Simon was a revolution in its day. They developed a solution method that results in a set of formulas that are easy to implement, and they actually implemented the method for many companies.

Modeling Management Behavior. There are several serious problems with the type of aggregate planning procedures we have been discussing to this point:

1. It is difficult to assess how accurate the assumptions (such as linearity of costs) are.
2. It is hard to determine the input values of all the cost parameters required by the model.
3. No use is being made of the very real expertise of the manager. Bowman [1963] developed an approach called **management coefficients**, which circumvents some of these problems. The idea is to construct a sensible model for controlling production levels, and then to estimate the parameters of the model by econometrically fitting past decisions of the manager in question.

The investigators have compared the actual experiences of several companies with the experiences that they would have had using their approaches, and found that in most cases there would have been a substantial reduction in costs. Since the fitted model is really just trying to duplicate management behavior, why should it result in reduced costs? The idea is that the fitted model reflects the typical rational behavior of the manager. However, the model does not overreact as the manager might when unusual events happen, such as breakdowns or demand spikes. Hence, the use of a simple but consistent model for making decisions would stabilize management. Although the basic idea is appealing, there are few reports on actual implementations in the literature to date.

3.3.7 Smoothing Exercises

Formulating the Problem.

1. A local software company employs 30 workers, who have a variety of different skills. The company does some large projects for companies, but also accepts a number of small one-time orders. Discuss some of the difficulties in using production smoothing models in this context.
2. A company personnel officer states that there is about a 2 percent quit rate from the company each month (attrition). He therefore argues that firing costs are not needed in the production smoothing formulation.

   a. Discuss the personnel officer's point of view.
   b. Show an analogue to Figure 3-1 for this case.

3. Discuss the "more realistic" dotted line holding/backlogging cost function shown in Figure 3-2.

Simple Heuristics.

4. Suppose, in the Snowizard example, that a special order causes November/December demand to increase to 5250. Evaluate the new cost of the chase plan. (Do not completely recalculate the problem.)

5. In the Snowizard example, evaluate the cost of a peak period strategy with hiring delayed for:

   a. One period
   b. Two periods

6. In the Snowizard example, evaluate the cost of a constant work force strategy if the initial inventory is increased by 200 units.

Johnson's Algorithm.

7. In the Johnson's Algorithm version of the Snowizard example, solve the problem with the initial workforce changed to:

   a. 2950
   b. 3150

8. In the Johnson's Algorithm version of the Snowizard example, solve the problem approximately if backlogging is available at a cost of $550 per unit per period backlogged.

9. In the Johnson's Algorithm version of the Snowizard example, suppose that the first 500 units of overtime only cost $400 more than regular time per unit produced. Solve the resulting problem.

Linear Programming.

10. Solve the Snowizard problem using a linear programming package for the original problem (you should agree with Table 3-5).

11. Modify the Snowizard problem and solve using linear programming for the following changes:

    a. Every worker makes two units per period.
    b. Every worker makes 0.5 units per period.

12. Solve the original Snowizard problem, with the added constraint that regular production in any period may not exceed:

    a. 2500
    b. 2000
    c. Explain the strange result in (b).

3.4 LOGISTICS

3.4.1 Overview

Logistics plans the entire procurement, manufacturing, storage, and distribution of products. There may be several different plants, a number of intermediate and final warehouses, and final demand points (often cities). There will be various transportation methods to choose from. Demand (or sometimes production) will often be seasonal, so that the dimension of time must be considered as well. This is a type of aggregate planning analysis. In fact, the production smoothing work we have done is just a logistics system with a single plant, a single destination, no transportation costs or limitations, and both production and demands distinguished in terms of time periods.

3.4.2 Solution by Network Algorithms

Transportation Algorithm. The earliest mathematical logistics model is probably the transportation model. Look at Figure 3-4. There are three normal resources—plants 1, 2, and 3—each with some capacity and cost of production (not shown). There are four negative resources or demands—cities A, B, C, and D—each with some negative capacity (need) and negative cost of consumption (revenue). The arrows show routing: we must choose good (and feasible) amounts to route across each. We have already met this particular transportation logistics model in Sections 2.5.2 and 2.5.3, where we studied simple problems in the location of facilities. Each way of locating facilities led to a transportation problem of the type shown in Figure 3-4. We also just met a different logistics problem in Section 3.3.4. Here there were twelve sources, namely the same plant with regular or overtime production at different points in time. In our diagram we could tag them: Plant-1-regular-November, Plant-1-overtime-January, and so forth. In a similar fashion, there were six destinations, namely the same demand need at different points in time. We could tag them: Demand-November, Demand-January, and so on.

The arrows in Figure 3-4 show routing choices, the circles show resources. In this sense, there are 12 missing resources in the figure: the transportation resource on each route. (To be complete, we would add a circle on top of the middle of each route, with the original arc becoming two arcs: one going into the transportation resource, and one coming out.) These also have costs of production (transportation). The early transportation algorithm assumed no limitation on the amount shipped on each route and no change in the unit cost for shipping very large amounts on a route. This probably means a single resource (such as a truck) was being considered. In our further analysis we shall always specify transportation resources as specific resources. This is important since a rail line may have limited capacity, congestion slowdowns, and certainly differing lead times for delivery.

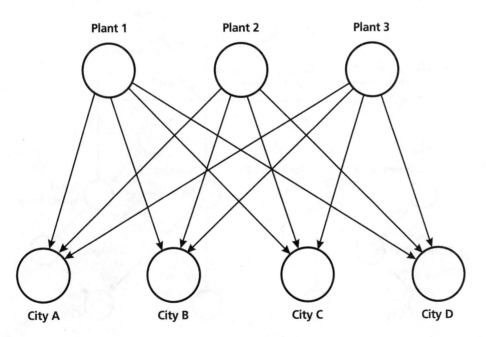

Figure 3-4

Simple Logistics Network (Transportation Algorithm)

Full Network. More complex logistics networks, such as the one-period network shown in Figure 3-5, can still be solved by standard linear programming codes, but not efficiently. In the 1970s powerful network codes, specialized transportation algorithms, were developed that are hundreds or thousands of times as fast for large networks. This allows us to deal with a much more realistic logistic network: raw material suppliers, vendors, manufacturing plants, warehouses, customers, and various types of transportation. Thus we may model just about any aggregate resource needed for aggregate planning purposes. Resources can have capacities and even increasing marginal costs. Resources can have conversion factors, wastage, and other losses.

It is even possible to add the time dimension to networks, at the expense of multiplying the size. If we want to show each of 10 two-week periods separately in Figure 3-5, we simply make 10 copies and label them period 1, period 2, and so on. If we want the choice to store in plant 1 from week 1 to week 2, we simply put an arrow from it in week 1 to it

Figure 3-5

More Complex Logistics
Network (Single Period)

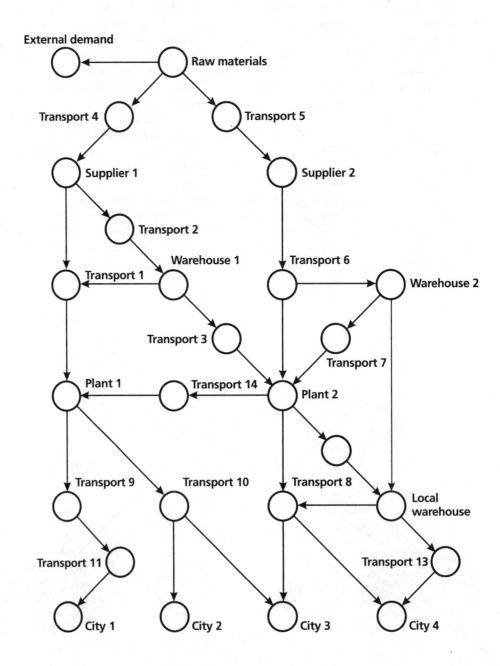

in week 2. Of course, we do not show storage possibilities where they do not exist. Also if we want to show storage quantity limitations, we would put an explicit circle between marked plant storage, with limitations shown.

Another kind of richness these algorithms allow is to add multiple products. To do this, we would simply make a full multi-time-period diagram for each product. If several products are produced in plant 2 in period 5, for example, the total production in that period must not exceed the capacity of the plant, giving a cross constraint between the products involved in that plant and that period. This is no longer a pure network model; however, it can still be solved exactly by linear programming.

3.4.3 Logistic Exercises

Networks.

1. Invent a one-period logistics network with three final demands (cities), two plants, three suppliers, and both truck and rail transportation. Include necessary issues of capacity, demands, and cost in your diagram.
2. Find a reasonable solution (amounts to ship on each resource) manually in problem 1.

3.5 MACHINE REPLACEMENT

3.5.1 Overview

Machine replacement decisions are more common than new investment decisions and have somewhat shorter horizons. Replacement decisions may be made as often as every two years, or as seldom as every five to ten years. Thus, it is not clear whether to consider machine replacement a strategic issue or an aggregate planning issue. Replacing a machine is often a more routine decision than major capital investment, so we have taken the latter point of view here.

All machines suffer from some kind of physical aging with combinations of usage and time, which brings higher maintenance costs. Also, newer machines with lower operating costs are continually being introduced. Why then aren't machines being replaced every 3–6 months? For one thing, frequent replacement would mean high capital expenditures. Thus a complete statement is that replacement should occur when operating costs and capital costs of the current machine increase above those of the next generation machine.

All machines are really candidates for replacement at every instance in time. Adequately modeling machine replacement is quite difficult, because one would need to consider purchases of all future generation machines at distant points in time. This is impractical, both because the far future is not known, and because computational requirements for a very long-horizon scheme are exorbitant. Most companies use **coterminated** models, in which all machines are assumed sold at the end of some fixed horizon, which we will consider first. Then we will present a model developed by Terborgh. His model is superior because he treats the future more realistically than coterminated models do. However, fixed horizon models are still the most widely used in practice.

We assume that the profitability of the overall project of which a given machine is a part is considered as a separate issue. We assume further that the task is to determine a replacement strategy for a particular machine, such that we maximize the productivity of the available capital. Since we are only comparing which of two machines to use to accomplish a job, we will simply analyze the savings if the new machine were in operation instead of the current one. For convenience the new machine under consideration will be called the **candidate** and the current machine will be called the **incumbent**.

3.5.2 Coterminated Models

Consider a simple example, which will allow us to see some of the problems in using typical coterminated models for machine replacement. Consider an incumbent with an estimated economic life of four years, and a candidate with an economic life of eight years. The purchase price of the candidate is $17,500 while the current resale price of the incumbent is $4500. The cost of capital is taken as 10 percent. The operating expenses for the incumbent are $8400 a year for four years. The operating expenses for the candidate would be $4400 a year for eight years. We choose the benefit/cost ratio of the investment as our criterion. Others could be used, but this is the simplest normalized measure and is thus good for illustrative purposes.

The additional cost if we choose the candidate is simply $17,500 – $4500 = $13,000. The problem comes in trying to determine the benefit stream. One choice is over eight years; the other choice is over four years. In coterminated methods we must somehow choose a common horizon. There are three common ways to do this:

Method 1. Compare the equipment over the shortest life (here, four years).
Method 2. Compare the equipment over the shortest life, and include the estimated salvage or resale value of the longer life equipment.
Method 3. Find a common denominator for all investments (in this case, eight years).

Method 1: We compare the difference in operating costs over four years. The candidate saves $4000 a year for four years at 10 percent. The present value of a four-year annuity of $1 at 10 percent is $3.1699. So the benefit stream is worth ($4,000)(3.16999) = $12,680. Thus the benefit cost ratio of the investment is 12,680/13,000 = 0.98. Remember that if a number of investments are to be compared, the highest benefit/cost ratios above 1.00 will be chosen within some budget. A ratio of 0.98 will not be chosen.

On the other hand, it is patently unfair to assume that the challenger will have no value to us at the end of four years, which leads to Method 2.

Method 2: If we estimate that the candidate will have a salvage value of $5500 at the end of the fourth year, then the present worth of the savings would be 12,680 + (5500)(0.6830) = 16,437 and the benefit/cost ratio would increase to 16,437/13,000 = 1.26.

The second method seems much more reasonable; the problem here is that estimating a salvage value four years into the future may be quite difficult.

Method 3: In the third method, we compare over an eight-year horizon. The incumbent's facts and figures are repeated twice, the candidate's are considered once. (It is as though we make the decision all over again to keep the defender at year 5 with its current value.) Thus we assume that the capital costs of the candidate versus the defendant are $17,500 – $4500 – $4500(0.6830) = $9927. As far as the benefit stream goes, there is now $4000 difference a year over eight years. The factor for an eight-year annuity at 10 percent is 5.335, and (5.335)(4,000) = $21,340. The benefit/cost ratio is now 21,340/9927 = 2.15.

3.5.3 Economic Life

We have generated cost benefit/cost ratios for the three methods of 0.98, 1.26, and 2.15. Which is correct? Certainly 0.98 is much too low, because Method 1 treats the candidate as worthless after four years. On the other hand Method 3, yielding 2.15, is certainly much too high. Even if we keep the incumbent for four years, why should we force ourselves to keep it a second four years, when much better alternatives are likely to be available? If we keep the incumbent, we certainly want to make the best decisions in the future.

It is difficult to say whether Method 2 gives an answer that is too low or too high, since we simply pulled a salvage value out of the air. In some sense, the whole question is to find a scientific way to estimate salvage values, not simply to guess. In considering keeping the incumbent, it would be much more realistic to introduce the cost and expense stream of the best available candidate into our computations starting at the beginning of year 5 (although the best available candidate may also be hard to determine). For example, this candidate might have a capital cost of $20,000, an operating cost per year of $3500, and an economic life of 10 years. But now we are running the incumbent's analysis out to year 14, and we need to do the same for the original challenger! There may never be a point where both sides run out in the same number of years. This makes the process of comparison very cumbersome. We will find that Terborgh (discussed in the next section) offers us a way out of this dilemma.

To this point we have assumed that an economic life n was simply given for each possible machine. However, the best n^* is difficult to determine, and we must consider methods for finding it. If there were no technological progress, economic life would simply be the number of years for which the sum of discounted capital and operating costs are at a minimum. However, since in actuality machines are continually being improved, we must consider a factor called obsolescence, which will tend to encourage earlier replacement, thereby reducing economic life.

It should be clear that a knowledge of the future does affect the replacement decision. As an example, consider that a new machine substantially better than anything available now will be on the market in three years. Not only is it expected to produce a product of higher quality, but its operating costs will be much lower than all current machines. It might very well be that our best strategy is to wait for three years to buy this new machine. If, however, we compared a currently available candidate to the current incumbent, replacement might be strongly indicated. In summary, we cannot determine economic life without considering the future; comparison of existing current choices is insufficient.

3.5.4 Terborgh's Approach

Terborgh [1949] was able to make an analysis of the replacement problem by making assumptions about the way obsolescence and deterioration will develop in the future.

Deterioration, Obsolescence and the Inferiority Gradient. Deterioration is the increase in operating costs each year that a machine has been in operation, due basically to wear and tear on the machine. The behavior of this cost is shown in Figure 3-6. The solid line represents the operating cost of a given machine and is shown rising as a result of increasing maintenance costs. When replacement takes place, the line drops down to the heavy dashed line, which represents the operating cost of a new machine with current technology.

Obsolescence is the decrease in operating cost of each generation of new machine over the cost of the last generation, in both cases when the machines are new. Obsolescence comes from technological improvement. Graphically, obsolescence can be seen in Figure 3-6. The inferiority gradient is defined by:

Inferiority gradient = Deterioration + Obsolescence

The inferiority gradient basically tells us the total opportunity cost in terms of extra operating costs for each additional year we keep a machine.

Determining Economic Life. Terborgh's basic assumptions about the future may be presented in the following three statements:

1. Operating inferiority is accumulated, past and future, at a relatively constant rate.
2. Operating inferiority is similar in incumbent and candidates.
3. The far future doesn't matter very much.

Figure 3-6

Operating Cost

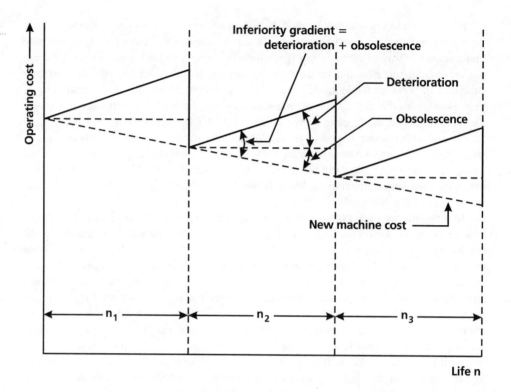

Given these assumptions, we can estimate roughly the average cost per year of keeping a new candidate machine for n years, with a yearly inferiority gradient of g, a capital cost of C and a salvage value at the end of S.

First, the average age of the machine in its life was $n/2$, and thus its average operating cost penalty compared to a new machine is $gn/2$.

Second, the capital cost over n years is $(C - S)$, so that the average capital cost per year is $(C - S)/n$.

Third, the capital cost is incurred at the beginning, so that we pay interest on it for about $n/2$ years, at a cost of $iCn/2$, or $iC/2$ per year.

Fourth, the salvage is not obtained until the end, so that we lose interest on it for about $n/2$ years, at a cost of $iSn/2$, or $iS/2$ per year.

Fifth, we ignore compound interest.

This leads to an average cost per year (in operating inferiority and capital) of **average cost for a candidate**, which can be expressed in the following formula:

$$AC(n) = gn/2 + (C - S)/n + i(C + S)/2$$

Note that this is just an economic lot size model, except that S is a function of n. If we approximate salvage as 0, take the derivative, set it equal to 0, and solve for the economic life we obtain, the **economic life for a candidate**, which is

$$n^* = [2C/g]^{0.5}$$

What about the average cost and economic life for the incumbent? It usually happens that the defender has been in service for many years N before the replacement is being considered. Terborgh argues that a reasonable assumption is that the average cost for the incumbent is already increasing, and we should approximate the average cost for the incumbent as if the life were only one more year. This **average cost for incumbent** would be expressed as

$$AC(N + 1) = (N + 0.5)g + (C - S) + i(C + S)/2$$

(In this case C is the salvage value at time N, and S is the salvage value at $(N + 1)$.)

Example 3-3. Fred Fleming is considering replacing the main line in the hot strip mill portion of his mini steel mill. The current line's operating costs are estimated at $11.5 million a year. The new line he is thinking of investing in would have a capital cost of $22 million, and an initial operating cost of $4.5 million a year. The current line is ten years old. If the current line is salvaged now, it will bring $4 million. After one year it might be worth $2 million dollars, after two years $1 million, and nothing after three years. The interest rate Fred uses is 10 percent. Should Fred invest now in the new machine?

Solution. Since the old machine has accumulated an operating inferiority of $7 million over ten years, we linearize this to $0.7 million per year for both machines. We conservatively estimate no salvage for the new machine. The optimal life and average cost for the new machine are estimated as:

$$n^* = [2(22)/(0.7)]^{0.5} = 8 \text{ years}$$

$$AC(8) = (8)(0.7)/2 + (22 - 0)/8 + (0.1)(22 + 0) = \$7.75 \text{ million}$$

The average cost for the defender is taken as:

$$AC(11) = 10.5(0.7) + (4 - 2) + (.1)(4 + 2) = \$9.95 \text{ million}$$

Thus, even assuming no salvage for the new rolling line, Fred should replace the current line now.

3.5.5 Replacement Exercises

Terborgh's Approach.

1. You are considering the replacement of an 11-year-old machine with one which is under programmed control. The new machine costs $650,000 and will save you the following costs:

Repairs	$32,000
Downtime	55,000
Rejects	33,000
Power	9,000

   The old machine has a salvage value currently of $110,000, but that will decline to $80,000 next year and $60,000 the year after. Should the new machine be purchased if your cost of capital is 12 percent?

2. A job shop is considering the purchase of a new lathe to replace a 15-year-old machine of the same kind. The new machine will cost $155,000. The present machine is worth $75,000 now and will be worth $62,000 in one year. There are several advantages associated with the new machine. First, there will be a direct labor savings of $32,000 per year. Then, because the machine produces a product of higher quality, there will also be an $11,000 per year direct labor savings on subsequent operations. The maintenance that will be saved next year is estimated to be $3100; and since the machine takes less floor space than its predecessor, there will be an additional $1500 per year saving. The cost of capital is 10 percent a year. What is the appropriate course of action?

3. The city of Great Falls, Montana is considering the purchase of a new snowplow to replace a 10-year-old unit. The new machine, however, is much more versatile and productive. It can accomplish 25 percent more work than the old one in the same period of time. This would mean the city would save $51,000 yearly in payments to contractors who plow snow for the city. In addition, the new unit will save about $10,000 next year in maintenance costs.

The cost of the new unit is $95,200, and the resale value of the old unit is $11,000 now and will drop to $5000 next year. If the city's cost of capital is 15 percent, should they make the trade?

3.6 CLIMATE MASTER—REPRISE

Jesse James returned in two weeks to ask for more detailed demand data and cost data for the Skokie and the Knoxville plants, as well as demand projections for the proposed new electric heating plant. It took Kool Kuke's people longer than expected to gather this data, and so it was 11 weeks before Jesse came back to make his report. This is what he had to say:

"First of all, I have analyzed the production smoothing strategies of both Skokie and Knoxville, and I feel that the managers are doing a pretty good job already, although I have some refinements suggested in an appendix to this report. The Skokie plant has relatively high costs of hiring and firing and of overtime, and hence tends to follow a constant inventory plan, producing extra units in April to September for the peak winter months. The Knoxville plant, on the other hand, has somewhat lower costs of hiring and firing and of overtime, and follows more of a chase strategy, with hiring and overtime at the peak, followed by layoffs afterward.

"Possible strategies for the new electric heating production capacity are quite interesting. There are really three strategies, although you didn't mention the third one initially:

a. Add to Skokie's electric heating capacity.
b. Build a new plant in Harrisburg.
c. Diversify the Knoxville plant to both heating and air conditioning.

"To understand the point behind the diversification strategy, I have prepared an exhibit superimposing the seasonal patterns for the two types of products on a common graph.

"The dotted line shows the composite seasonal pattern if the new heating capacity is built. The point is, if the new electric heating capacity is obtained by expanding the air-conditioning plant, and workers are trained to be able to operate either the air conditioning line or the heating line, then aggregate demand will be much less seasonal over the course of the year. This will reduce the need for seasonal inventories and all but eliminate overtime and subcontracting."

Figure 3-7

Seasonal Patterns of Heating and Air Conditioning

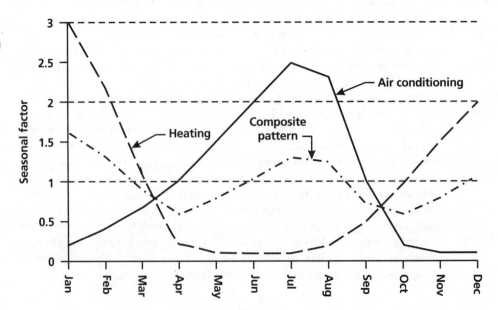

"The correct choice among the three alternatives is really not all that obvious, therefore:

a. If we add to Skokie's electric heating capacity, we have relatively low startup costs, since we already have experienced heating personnel there. Also we get some economies of scale in having a very large electric heating facility.

b. If we build a new plant in Harrisburg, we have all the advantages of building a completely new plant with the latest technology.

c. If we diversify the Knoxville plant to both heating and air conditioning, and pay the costs of double-training the labor force, then we create a non-seasonal plant with attendant reductions in inventories, hiring and firing, overtime, and subcontracting.

"I have done some preliminary calculations which suggest that adding capacity to Skokie would produce units costing \$366; building the new plant at Harrisburg would produce units at \$320, and diversifying the Knoxville plant would produce units at \$318. I suggest a larger costing study to be carried out by your accounting department to refine the costs of the Harrisburg and Knoxville options, and to choose between them."

After some further discussion, Kool Kuke agreed and assigned the cost accounting department to do a more detailed study of the situation.

Tactical Planning Models

4.1 INTRODUCTION

Tactical (short range) planning issues are one level down and more detailed than aggregate planning issues. Whereas aggregate planning issues affect the whole firm and have a horizon of one to two years, tactical planning affects individual products within a single shop, and has a horizon of three to six months. The main characteristics of tactical planning are:

1. The time horizon is three to six months.
2. Decisions are made about large numbers of individual products.
3. The shop is modeled down to the level of work centers.
4. Forecasting is a mixture of known and statistically estimated orders.

Typical tactical planning issues, which we will address in this chapter, include material requirements planning (MRP), planning of orders, and assembly line balancing.

4.2 Company Application Scenario— Artful Assemblers, Inc.

Carl Wrigley, production manager for Artful Assemblers, Inc., was beginning to feel that AAI's rapid growth was more of a curse than a blessing. And since the new riding mower had been added to their line, things were going from bad to worse! For one thing, component inventories were hopeless. They were carrying way too much of some items, and yet it seemed they were always out of stock on at least one or two components of anything they wanted to make. This led them to do a lot of emergency ordering, which was very expensive, and still made production late. AAI was using a standard exponential smoothing procedure for estimating the demand and safety stock necessary for each raw material and component kept in inventory. Surely there must be a better way!

Mr. Wrigley was also having problems with extreme variations with how long it took to get an order from order release until shipping. A related problem was that Work-In-Process on the floor was always very high and, periodically, certain assembly stations would get very congested, with work piled everywhere.

Finally Mr. Wrigley called in a consultant, Terry Tranh, who specialized in problems in assembly shops like theirs. After a week or two of discussions, Terry said that he saw two basic types of problems. First of all, AAI was treating each raw material and component as a separate forecasting and inventory problem. That is, demands were being treated as independent. However, as soon as there was an order for, say, ten riding mowers, each of which have 957 parts, then new demands for a total of $957 \times 10 = 9570$ parts was known. That is, demands are really dependent on each other. More precisely, demand for components can be calculated by knowing demands for the final products and extrapolating down to sub-assembly and sub-sub-assembly needs. Improved procedures for estimating amounts and timing of future final orders come under the heading of master scheduling, while extrapolating from these final demands down to individual component demands is the job of computer software called material requirements planning (MRP). Terry said that he would be happy to study such systems and recommend the best one for Artful Assemblers.

As for the extreme variability in floor leadtimes and periodic bottleneck areas on the floor, Terry said that these were job shop scheduling problems. He felt that it was important to get the master scheduling and MRP improved first, so that a major attack on scheduling problems should be deferred.

4.3 MATERIAL REQUIREMENTS PLANNING (MRP)

4.3.1 Overview

A production plan may be broken down into three major parts:

1. The master production schedule (MPS)
2. The material requirements planning system (MRP)
3. The detailed shop schedule

Each of these three parts is often complex. Remember that the aggregate planning level aggregates both products and resources. MPS and MRP are at the one lower tactical planning level: resources remain aggregated, but products are dealt with at the individual product level. MRP aggregates resources by simply assuming any product can be produced by waiting a given lead time. The detailed shop schedule takes the schedule proposed by MRP and produces from it a more realistic schedule that considers actual machine availability. Customer orders basically drive the MPS, which in turn drives MRP, which orders raw materials and production of various stages and quantities in order to meet demand in a timely fashion.

Thus, the control of the production system has three parts, each of which uses as input the output of the previous part:

- **Part A**—Collect and integrate the information required to develop the master production schedule.
- **Part B**—Determine the planned order releases using MRP.
- **Part C**—Determine detailed shop floor schedules and resource requirements.

4.3.2 The MRP Calculus

Master Production Schedule. Suppose that the shop plans for order deliveries needed for up to 13 weeks in the future and plans on a weekly basis. Then the Master Production Schedule for any given product, such as a riding mower, is a statement of the number of units needed to be produced each week into the future for the next 13 weeks. Making this schedule is a complex issue; there will be firm and pending customer orders, past sales, and shop load and production smoothing issues to consider. Somehow these needs must be melded together.

More specifically, at any point in time the shop will have information from a large variety of resources, such as:

- past demands
- firm future orders
- future orders in negotiation
- past experience of cancellation probabilities
- shop load and other problems
- production smoothing issues

What often happens is that the shop makes two kinds of forecasts and then tries to reconcile them with each other. One kind of forecast is based on the past demand for the product and involves formal forecasting techniques, such as exponential smoothing or regression analysis. The other source is from the management information system, which has records of firm (and possibly likely) future orders, both in terms of size and when they are expected. The human forecaster cannot simply add these two forecasts together to get the final forecast, because they often have a high overlap. More typically, the manager looks at the two forecasts carefully, and then comes up with a third composite forecast, which uses all the information, as well as the manager's expertise and judgment. It seems reasonable that a good decision support system (DSS) could help the manager in performing this complex task.

The MRP Explosion Calculus. At the heart of MRP is the **bill of materials** for each product and the associated **product explosion**, which takes place in the MRP bookkeeping. The bill of materials or product structure gives the system of subassemblies, sub-subassemblies, down to individual components, and the estimated lead time for producing each item. It is most often used in a tabular form, but a graphical presentation is given for clarity in Figure 4-1. Producing one unit of the end item requires one unit of A, two of B, and ten of C. Production (assembly) of A requires 3 weeks, B two weeks, and C one week. A, B, and C are first level "children" of the end product. In order to produce one unit of A, two units of D and three units of E are required. In order to produce one unit of B, one unit of F is required. D, E, and F require one week, two weeks, and three weeks lead time respectively. The respective lead times (ordering or production) for obtaining the items also appear on the bill of materials diagram. Bills of material can be very complex with hundreds of components and 15 or 20 levels. We review the explosion bookkeeping in MRP by working through an example.

Example 4-1. The Greener Garden Products Company produces a variety of garden tools at its plant in Augusta Georgia. The company uses MRP to try to plan and coordinate its production.

One of the tools Greener produces is the model 6A manual hedge trimmer. The hedge trimmer is a premium product and has been rather successful, even at its $75 price. Based

Figure 4-1

Typical Graphical Bill of Materials

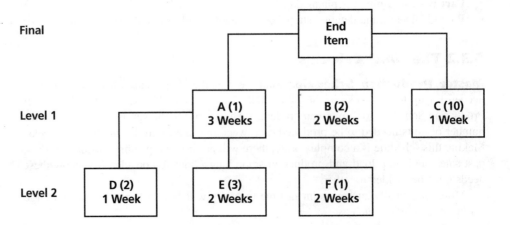

on orders from hardware chains and gardening outlets around the country, the production manager makes fairly firm forecasts of demand about three months into the future.

Figure 4-2 shows the hedge trimmer and its various subassemblies. Figure 4-3 gives the product structure diagram for the construction of the hedge trimmer. The left-hand and right-hand cutters are bolted together in final assembly, using one bolt, two lock washers, and one hex nut. A common wood handle was previously fitted and cemented to the left-hand and right-hand cutter forgings. Due to lot sizing and other considerations, the two cutter forgings require three weeks to make. The wood handles require two weeks to make. Cementing the wood handles to the forgings requires one week. The bolt, lock washers, and hex nut all require four weeks. The final assembly requires one week. (Most of the time for doing an operation involves waiting for the necessary machines to be available.)

The hedge trimmer assembly problem is a three-level MRP system. Level 0 corresponds to the end item, which is the salable hedge trimmer. Level 1, the child level relative to the trimmer, corresponds to the left- and right- hand cutters, and the bolt, washers, and nut. Level 2 corresponds to the wood handle and casting assemblies, for both left- and right-hand cutters.

In practice the information in the bill of materials is represented in an indented list called the indented bill of materials (BOM). The indented bill of materials in our case is:

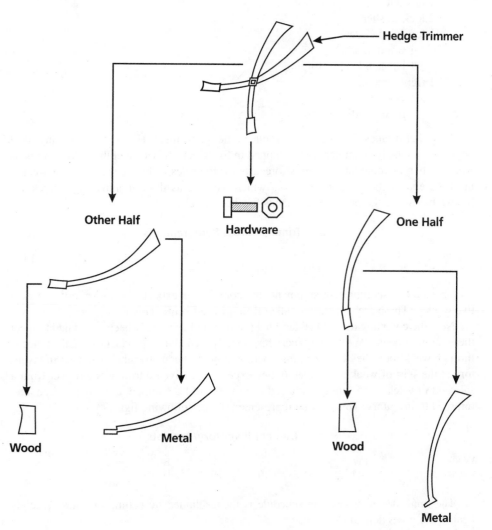

Hedge Trimmer

Other Half

Hardware

One Half

Wood

Metal

Wood

Metal

Figure 4-2

Hedge Trimmer and Subassemblies

Figure 4-3

Graphical Bill of Materials
for Hedge Trimmer

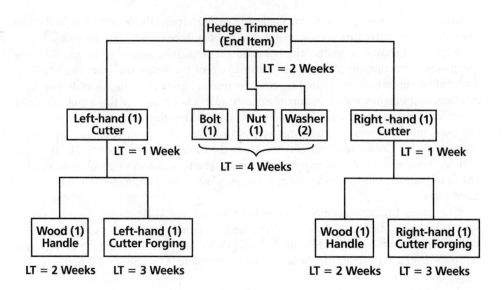

1 Hedge Trimmer
  1 bolt
  1 hex nut
  2 lock washers
  1 left-hand cutter
    1 wood handle
    1 left-hand cutter forging
  1 right-hand cutter
    1 wood handle
    1 right-hand cutter forging

Note that it takes five weeks to produce a hedge trimmer. Hence, the company must begin now on hedge trimmers to be shipped in five weeks. If we label the current week as week 1, then the company requires forecasts for the sales of hedge trimmers for week 5 until the end of the planning horizon, which we take as three months, or to week 13. Shown below are the predicted demands for those weeks.

Hedge Trimmer Gross Requirements

Week	5	6	7	8	9	10	11	12	13
Demand	75	0	110	30	0	0	135	101	23

These forecasts represent shipments the company is expected to make in the respective weeks. (These are sometimes called **time-phased requirements**.)

Next the company must consider what production has already been scheduled to meet these requirements. When they net this already scheduled production against needs through week four, they calculate that there will be 41 hedge trimmers on hand in inventory at the start of week 5. In week 6 they expect to receive 30 trimmers left over from a sale and in week 7, 15 mildly damaged trimmers will be returned, quickly repaired, and returned to inventory. This may be represented by the following figures.

Hedge Trimmer Inventory/Receipts

Week	Inv.	5	6	7	8
Inv./Receipts	41	0	30	15	0

The final master production schedule is then obtained by netting out these receipts against the gross demand.

Net Hedge Trimmer Time-Phased Requirements
(Master Schedule)

Week	5	6	7	8	9	10	11	12	13
Net Demand	34	0	65	30	0	0	135	101	23

This is the final adjusted Master Production Schedule. It gives us the final time-phased requirements for the final assembly of the hedge trimmer. Next we translate it into requirements for the components at the next level of the bill of materials. These are the left-hand cutter, the right-hand cutter, bolt, nut, and lock washers. The two cutters, bolt and nut will have the same requirement moved one week back, while the washer will have twice the requirement one week back. We will illustrate developing time-phased requirements for the left-hand cutter; the others are similar.

Because one left-hand cutter goes into each hedge trimmer and the final assembly lead time is one week, the Gross Requirements are just the final requirements shifted back one week. Then we adjust for on-hand inventory (say, 22) to obtain the net requirements. Based on the cutter's lead time, we shift back one week to see when the cutter must be started. Finally, we apply the simple EOQ rule to get the final time-phased requirements. Assume for this stage a setup cost of 75 and a holding cost per period of 1. Averaging the phased requirements over periods 4 to 12 gives $366/9 = 40.7$. Then we estimate $Q^* = [2(75)(40.7)/(1)]^{0.5} = 78.1$, rounded to 78. The requirements 4, 5, and 6 add to 77; 4, 5, 6, and 7 add to 107, so we round to three periods, and so forth.

Net Left-Handed Cutter Phased Requirements

Week	4	5	6	7	8	9	10	11	12
Gross Req'ments	34	0	65	30	0	0	135	101	23
Net Req'ments	12	0	65	30	0	0	135	101	23
Phased Req'ments	12	0	65	30	0	0	135	101	23
Order Release 77	0	0	30	0	0	135	101	?	—

Now the order release for left-hand cutters becomes the final requirements for the Level 2 components, namely the wood handle and the left-hand cutter forging. As an example, we show the calculations for the left-hand cutter forging, which are similar to those just done, except that the lead time is three weeks rather than one week.

For this problem, we also determine lot sizes by the simple EOQ method. Assume a setup cost of 121 and holding cost of 0.8 per period. Here average requirements are $(77 + 30 + 135 + 101)/8 = 42.9$. Thus, $Q^* = [2(121)(42.9)/(0.8)]^{0.5} = 114.0$.

Net Left Handed Cutter Forging Time-Phased Requirements

Week	1	2	3	4	5	6	7	8	9
Gross Req'ments				77	0	0	30	0	0
Net Req'ments				77	0	0	30	0	0
Phased Req'ments	77	0	0	30	0	0	135	101	?
Order Release	1070	0	0	0	0	135	?	?	—

(We round in the last row, using our Q^* of 114.0.)

Notice that the Wood Handle Phased Requirements, which we did not calculate, would have two sources of gross requirements, from left-hand cutters and right-hand cutters. When there are multiple entries to be made, one simply adds all the gross requirement from all sources to make the cumulative gross requirement, and then proceeds to net out any available inventory, followed by time phasing and lot sizing.

We have used a rather casual lot sizing rule here, because our point was to illustrate the bookkeeping. More exact lot sizing becomes complex rather quickly. We deal with this topic in Chapter 2 of the Inventory Module.

4.3.3 MRP II

Strengths of MRP. MRP has a number of important strengths:

1. The explosion calculus handles dependent demand properly. Correct forecasts of final demands will produce good forecasts for individual components.
2. It provides good database support, and is well oriented for interacting well in a decision support system (DSS) mode.
3. It represents the product structure adequately, and deals with intermediate and final inventories well.
4. It is relatively easy to understand.

Weaknesses of MRP.

1. MRP ignores capacity constraints and assumes fixed lead times for production stages irrespective of how heavily the shop is loaded.
2. It produces no feasible aggregate schedules. Without even a minimal simulation, there is no real way to estimate capacity violations as a function of time.
3. In practice, it almost always inflates lead times to provide safety stocks of materials on the shop floor. This in turn makes the shop look even more loaded, destabilizing the associated Capacity Requirements Module.
4. It makes no real attempt to interface with scheduling on the shop floor.
5. It cannot give any guidance as to which orders can be met on time and which cannot.
6. Its use of a fixed yield factor, without safety stocks, to estimate production losses is inadequate.

MRP II. As we have seen, MRP is a stand-alone production planning system that takes a time-phased final demand forecast (Master Production Schedule), and explodes and offsets it to produce planned order releases. Manufacturing Resource Planning (MRP II) is an extended version of MRP that tries to incorporate the financial, accounting, and marketing functions of the firm into the operations function. To show some of the difference between MRP and MRP II, consider the way the MPS is treated in the two systems. In MRP, the MPS is basically considered as input to MRP. In MRP II, on the other hand, it is an integral part of the planning system and changes in it would be considered legitimate decisions. For example, the manufacturing manager and the marketing manager could negotiate compromises based on what marketing would like to see produced and what production feels it can produce.

4.3.4 MRP Exercises

The Master Production Schedule.

1. The Blare Trumpet Company makes a premium trumpet, the Blaster. They have one large rather regular customer who tends to order in advance, and a number of very small customers who expect immediate delivery when they order. Ordering records week by week reveal only the total trumpets ordered, not the customers. The demands recorded for weeks 20 to 30 are 27, 65, 29, 23, 71, 19, 31, 56, 28, 24, 62. It is now week 30, and a forecast is desired for weeks 31 to 43. So far the large customer has ordered 45 to be delivered in week 33, and 40 to be delivered in week 36.

   a. Make a naive forecast for weeks 31 to 43 based simply on exponentially smoothing past demand.
   b. Make a naive forecast based simply on the apparent behavior of the large customer only.
   c. Make a naive forecast by adding together the forecasts in (a) and (b).

2. In problem 1:

   a. Develop a combined method which uses exponential smoothing for the small customers only and actual orders for the large customer only (when available), adding these together.
   b. Make a forecast for weeks 31 to 43.

3. The forecasting manager has been analyzing sales records for the Blare mainline series trumpet. He finds that 30 percent of customers order with no warning (0 lead time), 70 percent with less than or equal to one week lead time, 90 percent with less than or equal two weeks lead time, and 100 percent with less than or equal to three weeks. He is considering creating a forecasting system in which the three classes of customers are tracked and forecast separately.

   a. Lay out such a system using exponential smoothing for each class of customers.
   b. What are the advantages and disadvantages of such a system?

4. Standard Furniture Co. assembles desks from components. It imports the Formica top from Canada, but gets the metal drawers and drawer supports from its plant in Arkansas. The top of each desk is supported by drawer units on the left and the right, which are identical. Each drawer unit is made of a support casing and three drawers, which are also identical. The product structure diagram for the desk is given in Figure 4-4 (a).

   Suppose that the forecasted demands for the desk for weeks 6 to 13 are 200, 50, 235, 158, 120, 85, 140, 210. The starting inventory of assembled desks in week 6 will be 94. The production manager anticipates returns of 35 in week 8 and 6 in week 9.

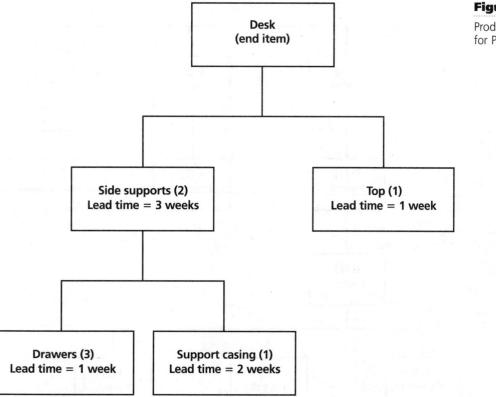

Figure 4-4(a)

Product Structure Diagrams for Problem 4

a. Determine the appropriate master production schedule.
b. Determine the planned order release for the drawer units assuming no lot sizing is used.
c. Determine the schedule of outside orders for the desk tops.

5. For the previous problem, suppose that Standard Furniture has 1550 drawers currently on hand in inventory. It has an incoming order in week 3 of another 1840 drawers. (Vendor problems caused this particular order to be delayed.) The vendor requires a minimum order of 1000 drawers. If Standard buys as few drawers as possible at a time, what orders should it be placing and when should it place them to cover the eight weeks of demand?

6. An end item has the product structure diagram given in Figure 4-4 (b).

a. Write this diagram as an indented bill-of-materials list.
b. Suppose that the master schedule for the end item is

Week	35	36	37	38	39	40	41	42
Demand	150	250	0	125	450	325	175	225

c. If no provisions are made for lot sizing, find the planned order release for component E.
d. Find the planned order release for component G.
e. Find the planned order release for component J.

Figure 4-4(b)

Product Structure Diagrams
for Problem 6

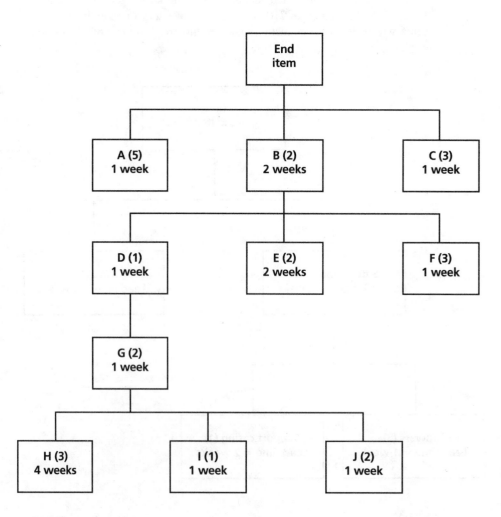

4.4 ORDER PLANNING

4.4.1 Overview

Order planning is a Tactical Planning (Level 3) function which covers getting the orders, forecasting the amount and timing of the orders, using the explosion calculus to translate final orders into time-phased ordering from vendors and into time-phased order release of jobs to the floor, setting due dates for new jobs released to the floor, and following the progress of jobs on the floor when there are problems. Order scheduling is a Scheduling (Level 4) function which covers the detailed scheduling of the order through the shop, taking into account detailed capacity restrictions. There are three order planning topics not covered well by MRP: the process of bidding for orders, finite capacity order release, and due-date planning.

4.4.2 Bidding for Orders

Much of a firm's time, whether large or small, is spent in trying to obtain new orders by a variety of marketing methods, which fall basically into two categories: giving information (advertising), and negotiating terms (pricing, etc.).

Although these topics might seem more appropriate to a marketing text, the second topic, negotiation, is a complex function which is often shared jointly by marketing, production, and the CEO. Indeed, in a small job shop, most negotiation is done by the shop manager, who may easily spend 20 to 30 percent of her time soliciting orders.

Negotiating for an order may involve price, quantity, delivery date, quality specs, guarantees, and liability. We look only at setting price and due dates. We also restrict our attention to the closed bidding situation. The customer announces an order to be bid on and solicits secret bids in writing. The lowest bid receives the order.

The classic operations management approach is to estimate a distribution of what the low bid from the others will be. Then, using standard decision theory and ignoring any effect of this bid on future bids, the optimal bid is determined. We explain the approach, and discuss its strengths and weaknesses.

In the classic approach we make several simplifying assumptions:

1. The bid is a one-shot affair; it does not affect future bids or future business in any way.
2. The true short-term cost (variable cost) of making the item is known; the price minus variable cost gives the contribution margin per unit of item in the bid.
3. The probability of winning the bid for each bid of interest is either known or can be estimated accurately.

These are indeed rather strong assumptions, but in the following example we will compute an optimal bid.

Example 4-2. The Electricks Company is a jobber, making a variety of consumer appliances to customer specifications. They do not put their own brand name on the product. Their output supplies excess demand for a number of different customers, who attach their own brand name to the product. The air conditioner group within Electricks is lean and hungry and is looking for any order that will cover direct variable costs, with any coverage of overhead or profit being a plus.

Frozenaire, a potential customer, has put out a bid for 1000 large window air conditioners. The manager of the air conditioning group in Electricks feels that the Frozenaire order is a fluke, because Frozenaire does not usually subcontract this model of air conditioner. Thus, the bid will have little or no effect on future business. It costs Electricks $200 in out-of-pocket costs to make a unit (with nothing allowed for overhead or profits). After extensive discussions with marketing, the CEO, and a few friends at other companies,

Sheez Brite, the group manager, feels that bidding $250 will give her a 75 percent chance of winning the bid, bidding $300 will give a 60 percent of winning, bidding $350 will give a 35 percent of winning, bidding $400 will give a 15 percent of winning, and bidding $450 will lose the bid. By a simple decision analysis:

Bidding Analysis at 0 percent Overhead

Bid 250	worth (250 − 200)(1000)(0.75) =	$37,500
Bid 300	worth (300 − 200)(1000)(0.60) =	60,000 *best*
Bid 350	worth (350 − 200)(1000)(0.35) =	52,500
Bid 400	worth (400 − 200)(1000)(0.15) =	30,000
Bid 450	worth (450 − 200)(1000)(0.00) =	0

Sheez Brite submitted a report to the CEO recommending that the firm bid $300,000 for the contract, or $300 per unit. This would represent a $100,000 contribution margin for Electricks, or $100 per unit. With an estimated 60 percent chance of winning the bid, this would net Electricks an expected value of $60,000 on the bid.

The CEO reviewed the recommended bid for a week, and then called Sheez Brite to his office. "I'm concerned that we've been winning too many bids with no allowance for overhead," he explained. "In the long run we have to cover our overhead and some profit to stay in business. This super sharp pencil is all right once in awhile, but I want you to repeat the bidding process, with a sensitivity analysis on the amount allowed for overhead. We've already done 0 allowed overhead; let's try 25 percent and 50 percent as well."

Sheez Brite carried out the required sensitivity analysis that very evening; her results are shown below:

Bidding Analysis at 25 Percent Overhead

Bid 250	worth (250 − 250)(1000)(0.75) =	$0
Bid 300	worth (300 − 250)(1000)(0.60) =	30,000
Bid 350	worth (350 − 250)(1000)(0.35) =	35,000 *best*
Bid 400	worth (400 − 250)(1000)(0.15) =	22,500
Bid 450	worth (450 − 250)(1000)(0.00) =	0

Bidding Analysis at 50 Percent Overhead

Bid 250	worth (250 − 300)(1000)(0.75) =	−$37,500
Bid 300	worth (300 − 300)(1000)(0.60) =	0
Bid 350	worth (350 − 300)(1000)(0.35) =	17,500 *best*
Bid 400	worth (400 − 300)(1000)(0.15) =	15,000
Bid 450	worth (450 − 300)(1000)(0.00) =	0

The CEO looked at the new sensitivity analysis report that Sheez Brite gave him with satisfaction. "Just as I thought. We will bid $350, not $300 as you originally suggested. Even if the proper overhead rate is 0 percent, it comes close to the best expected contribution margin ($52,500 versus $60,000), while it gives the best expected contribution margin at either 25 percent or 50 percent. If no one gives me any reason to change my mind in the next three or four days, I'm going to send in a bid of $350."

Formal Statement of the Classical Model. In general, let x be the final bid per unit to be determined, and m be the minimum per unit bid at which the firm would just break even. Let $F(x)$ be the probability of winning the bid if we bid x. Then, our problem is to choose the bid x to maximize the expected contribution margin which is given by $\max_x (x - m)F(x)$.

If $F(x)$ is a discrete distribution, we do a spreadsheet for different values of x, and choose the maximum. If $F(x)$ is continuous, we may approximate it as discrete. There is a better procedure for the normal distribution, but we omit it here.

Determining the Distribution of Low Bid. One of two methods is most commonly used in estimating the distribution of the low bid:

   a. Expert judgment
   b. Regression analysis of bidding history

Expert judgment may or may not be good, depending on how good the expert is. It is not particularly clear whether estimating the probability distribution of low bids is easier or more difficult for the expert than simply guessing the correct bid directly.

A typical regression procedure would be as follows.

   1. Gather results of a great many past bids on this item and similar items.
   2. Build a regression model with independent variables including such items as item type, volume of contract, number of bidders, bidders with especially low costs, item retail price, etc.
   3. Predict the low bid in normalized terms in excess of the company's break-even cost for the dependent variable.
   4. Take the residual errors from the regression to represent the distribution of the low bid.
   5. In a particular new bidding situation, insert the estimated values of the independent variables to give a forecast of normalized low bid above our break-even, and the standard deviation of that.

Problems with the Classical Approach. One problem with the classical approach is that it assumes our bid has no effect on the future, when obviously smart analysts from other companies will be analyzing *our* bid. Furthermore, if the other smart analysts know our bidding procedures, they can make sure our distributions are wrong by bidding in a different way than they know we expect!

The true typical bidding situation probably lies somewhere between the extremes of the classical assumptions and the high knowledge assumptions. In practice, the bidder should be aware of the classical solution and use it in her strategy, but not be a slave to it.

4.4.3 Order Release and Due Date Planning

The Classic Approach. In the classic MRP approach the master production schedule defines the due date for a particular job, and leaves the process for determining the dates for the master schedule rather fuzzy. The dates are presumed to be requested by the customer. Then the order release time for a job is calculated by allowing a fixed multiple of the processing time for each stage of manufacture and/or assembly and working backward from the due date to the beginning.

Setting Due Dates by Scheduling Simulation. When the order taker and the customer get together to work out a jointly acceptable lead time, there are several things to take into account. First of all, the customer wants a due date that is not too far off. Second, once a due date has been set, the customer will probably prefer that the actual finish of the job be neither early nor tardy. These two kinds of costs are roughly additive for the customer and are similar to the ideas of "long range costs" and "short range costs" in economics. The cost to the customer of setting the due date at a time d in the future might be something like the smooth curve shown in Figure 4-5. The cost of delivery deviating from the given due date might typically be quite sharp, especially for the tardiness side, but less so for the early side, as also shown in Figure 4-5. (We are suggesting that the customer is more concerned about accurate completion time than early completion time.)

Of course, we have no way to directly find out the customer's cost curve. However, we assume a fairly friendly relationship so that neither side will tend to lie. We also assume that each side wishes to minimize total costs.

Figure 4-5

Cost of Setting a Due Date
and Deviating from It

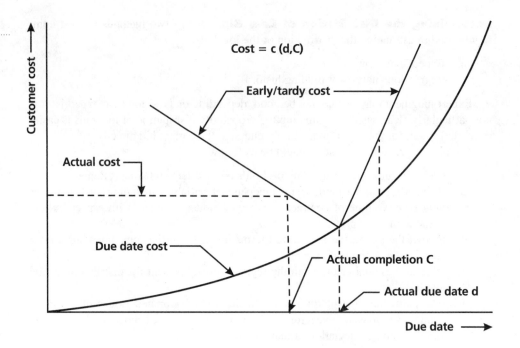

Suppose, for the sake of the discussion, that all shop costs are fixed, and that the shop manager knows the due date for a job and the associated early/tardy cost function (supplied by the customer). The shop manager sets a release time for the job and runs it with all the other jobs already in the shop. (Setting the release time is discussed below.) His objective will be to minimize the sum of early/tardy costs for all customers, including the new one. Thus, given the aggregate cost functions for a customer class, and given the particular due date being tested, one could simulate the shop using good scheduling heuristics and find the total cost for all orders, including the one of interest. To this we could add the due date cost from the customer's cost curve. This could be done for perhaps three different representative due dates, with the cheapest one chosen.

One problem with this scheme is that simulating a full shop with good heuristics several times for each new order and potential due date would be computationally expensive. One possible answer to this would be to group customers into classes by urgency and type, and to estimate appropriate due date allowances by class. These due date allowances might be updated only occasionally. A second problem is that the customer's true due date preferences are not known. Here we simply would have to assume that the order taker has enough skill and experience to make fairly decent guesses.

Setting Release Dates by Scheduling Simulation. A job with a regular objective, such as makespan, flow, or tardiness, will always prefer to be finished as early as possible and thus to be released to the job floor as early as possible. Thus, we are led to consider more general objectives which have a cost for early release. The main motive for release times, in practice, is usually that it is more expensive (in terms of floor space, congestion, etc.) to store work in process on the floor rather than as raw materials in the warehouse. If we assume that the completed job will not be delivered (and paid for) until the due date no matter how early it is finished, then finishing it early will simply cause the job to be stored longer as expensive finished goods. It is possible to create such a model, and create good heuristics for it using bottleneck dynamics. This is beyond our scope here.

4.4.4 Order Planning Exercises

Bidding for Orders.

1. A senior partner in Candid Consultants must bid on a government contract to supervise quality control on a major dam to be built on the Columbia River. He is unwilling to accept less than $500,000 for doing the project. He feels that bidding $550,000 will give him a 90 percent chance of winning, $600,000 a 70 percent chance, $650,000 a 40 percent chance, $700,000 a 20 percent chance, $750,000 a 10 percent chance, and $800,000 no chance. Using classical bidding analysis, what bid should he make?

2. In problem 1, plot the optimal bid as a function of the minimum the firm feels it must have to do the project.

3. Another senior partner at Candid Consultants decided to repeat the analysis using a normal distribution approximation to the winning bid distribution. For the same Candid Consultants maximum of $500,000 for the project, he feels that the mean minimum winning bid is $630,000 with a standard deviation of $110,000. Using classical bidding analysis, what bid should he make?

4. In problem 3 plot the optimum bid as a function of the minimum the firm feels it must have to do the project.

4.5 ASSEMBLY LINE BALANCING

4.5.1 Overview

Assembly line balancing is concerned with readjusting the size and assignment of the work force (balancing) of a high-volume transfer line or assembly line for different desired production rates. The detailed scheduling of individual operations is not necessary for high-volume operations. The line is like one huge machine, and the sequencing is part of its original design. However, there is some flexibility to reassign labor and resources across the line if the production rate is increased or decreased. Thus, when an aggregate plan calls for a change in the labor force level, it is through rebalancing that we can absorb more or less labor on the lines.

There are two basic line balancing models which are usually considered. The first (called Model I) tries to determine the minimum work force to achieve a given desired production rate. The second (called Model II) tries to determine the maximum production rate which can be achieved with a given number of workers. Even the simple classic forms of these problems, however, are difficult to solve exactly. Although they can be formulated as integer programs, they are usually too large to solve.

4.5.2 Simple Line Balancing Models

In the simple classical form of line balancing, the product to be fabricated or assembled can be represented by a network of tasks and associated task times, some of which must be performed in a given sequence in order to meet the product design specs. Such a precedence diagram for the product tasks is shown in Figure 4-6. It is useful visually to show all the tasks with no predecessors (Level 1 tasks) vertically in a column. Then all the tasks with only Level 1 predecessors, called Level 2, are organized vertically in the next column, and so on. The time for an operator (station) to perform each task is shown next to that task. Note that the total work content to build a unit of product is 51 minutes.

Suppose that we desire a production rate such that a unit of product will come off the assembly line every 18 minutes (the cycle time). Then the first station on the line must be assigned no more than the first 18 minutes of work on each unit of product as it comes by.

Figure 4-6

Precedence Diagram for
Tasks

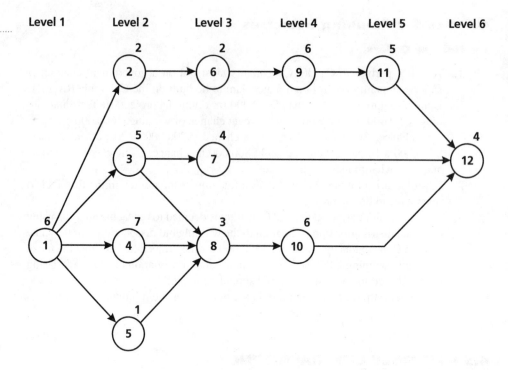

The second operator must be assigned no more than 18 minutes, and so on. Also the first operator must be assigned work which logically comes before the work of later operators on each unit of production, and so on. Since there are 51 minutes of work, and no more than 18 minutes per station, it is clear that the best we could do would be [51/18] = 3 stations (we round up). This does not guarantee there will be a solution with three stations, only that we cannot possibly have fewer. For this small problem, it is indeed possible by inspection of the graph to find a solution with three stations, which is therefore known to be optimal. This solution is represented on the product graph by partitioning the tasks into stations as shown in Figure 4-7. (The total station times are shown in ( ) under the station identifiers.)

This problem, finding the minimum number of stations for a given cycle time, is called Model I. The reverse problem, finding the minimum cycle time for a given number of stations, is called Model II. Classically, the main emphasis in the literature has been on the first problem, since one can always solve problems with the same number of stations, and smaller and smaller cycle times, until no solution can be found. In our problem, for example, what is the smallest cycle time possible with three stations? The solution in Figure 4-7 was for a cycle time of 18. A cycle time of 17 would be the theoretical minimum, since 51/17 = 3 exactly. It certainly seems difficult by inspection to find three stations all of content 17. So we simply say that 18 is the best we could find, with it known that no solution less than 17 is possible.

Problems with as many as 12 stations can often be solved optimally by inspection, but they get rapidly much more difficult as the size increases. Since problems with hundreds of tasks are common in practice, we turn to heuristics to help us find good solutions to large problems.

4.5.3 Heuristics for the Simple Model

There are a number of different major types of heuristics for trying to minimize the number of stations for a given cycle time. We shall look at two major types:

1. Dispatch heuristics
2. Search packing

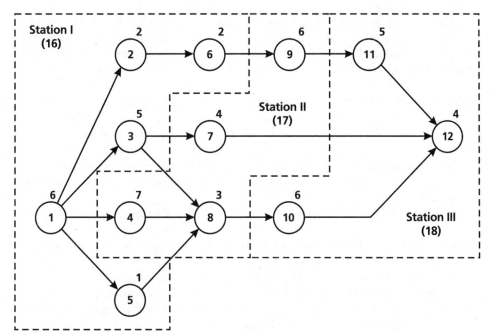

Figure 4-7

A Three Station Solution,
Cycle Time = 18

Dispatch Heuristics. The algorithm for dispatch heuristics is quite simple. First choose a priority rule (we will come back to this). Then compute the numerical priority of every task. Define a "fit" task as one which is currently feasible and doesn't exceed the available remaining time on the station. Assign the highest priority fit task to the current station. Revise which tasks are now fit. Repeat until there is no feasible task which doesn't exceed the remaining available time. Unless all tasks have been assigned, open another station and continue.

There are many priority rules which have been suggested and tried over the years. Two simple and popular rules are "longest processing time" and "ranked positional weight." The longest processing time rule simply chooses the longest fit job first. The idea here is similar to filling a grocery bag: put the biggest items in first when there is lots of room, and use the smaller items to finish up. The ranked positional weight rule, on the other hand, gives priority to tasks which have lots of successors and/or long cycle time successors. The idea is that scheduling such a task gives us many more choices further down the line. Let us try these two rules on our example with cycle time of 18.

Longest Processing Time Rule. As we select tasks, we list them and their processing times, to be sure to stay under 18. This is shown in Table 4-1.

Fit Tasks	Chosen Task	Process Time	Time Remaining
1	1	6	12
2,3,4,5	4	7	5
2,3,5	3	5	0
2,5,7	7	4	14
2,5	2	2	12
5,6	6	2	10
5,9	9	6	4
5	5	1	3
8	8	3	0
10,11	11	5	13
10	10	6	7
12	12	4	3

Table 4-1

Longest Processing Time
Heuristic

Thus, for our example, "longest task first" gets the optimal number of stations.

An interesting point is that the longest task first heuristic (or any other heuristic) can also be run *backward*, which may give different and useful results. To do this simply reverse all the arrows in the diagram, and run the heuristic on the new problem.

Ranked Positional Weight Rule. The positional weight of a task is just the sum of the processing times of the task and all of its successors. Thus, the positional weight of job 1 is 51, just the sum of all times. We first construct a table of positional weights, shown in Table 4-2.

Next we rank the tasks in order of decreasing positional weight. Here the rankings are 1, 3, 4, 2, 6, 9, 5, 8, 10, 11, 7, 4. Using this ranking, our heuristic produces the results shown in Table 4-3.

In this case ranked positional weight method also gets a three-station solution.

Search Packing. Dispatch rules basically try to pack as much as possible in each station. But they make only a single attempt (single pass). Why not make more effort to pack each station in order as perfectly as possible, to get an improved heuristic?

We present our own version. First, prioritize the tasks by some dispatch rule, for example, longest task first. Suppose there are k items in the fit list. Create k separate subproblems where one of the k choices is forced to be chosen, and the entire remainder of the problem is solved by longest task first. Permanently fix the choice into the master solution whose subproblem had the best solution. (Break ties in any way desired.) Now move to the new fit list, keeping all permanent choices to date, and run the appropriate group of subproblems again, and so on. This general approach, called **beam search**, is not suited to hand computation, but it is very fast on the computer, and works well for other types of problems.

4.5.4 More Realistic Models

More Realistic Assembly Lines. There are a number of features which the classical model does not recognize, which are often important in practice. Some heuristic models can be adapted to some of these, others cannot. We simply summarize these issues here.

1. What should be done if a task is larger than the cycle time? Can it be broken up? Can a second person usefully be assigned? Can parallel stations be used, each doing parts of the work?
2. Suppose some tasks must be located in a certain part of the assembly line. (This is called a zoning constraint.) How can the heuristic take this into account?
3. Does time to obtain a tool need to be allowed for, especially for a tool that may be useful for several tasks?

Table 4-2

Positional Weights for the Example

Tasks	Positional Weight
1	51
2	19
3	22
4	20
5	14
6	17
7	8
8	13
9	15
10	10
11	9
12	4

Fit Tasks	Chosen Task	Process Time	Time Remaining
1	1	6	12
2,3,4,5	3	5	7
2,4,5,7	4	7	0
2,5,7	2	2	16
5,6,7	6	2	14
5,7,9	9	2	12
5,7,11	5	1	11
7,8,11	8	3	8
7,10,11	10	6	2
7,11	11	9	9
7	7	4	5
12	12	4	1

Table 4-3

Positional Weight Heuristic

4. What about allowing time for the worker to change positions between tasks?
5. Should tasks be grouped according to skills required? Or expensive equipment? Or to satisfy environmental considerations?
6. Is worker movement between units assembled allowed, and how would this change the solution?
7. Suppose the units have variation: e.g. suppose half the cars have air conditioners to be attached, and half do not. How does this affect the solution?
8. Suppose the time for some tasks is quite variable. Does this change the nature of a good solution?

We do not have room to investigate these issues further here.

More Realistic Objectives. In the larger context, it is not clear that a company should want to minimize costs for a given production rate, or to maximize production rates for a given cost. The firm is likely to have some larger model of profits or costs that needs to be optimized.

For this reason, it would make sense to find the optimal number of stations for a large number of different production rates. The firm could then evaluate a number of different (rate, cost) pairs in the larger model, and then choose the best one.

4.5.5 Balancing Exercises

Simple Line Balancing Models.

1. Consider the assembly line balancing problem represented by Figure 4-8. Using no formal heuristics:

   a. What is the theoretical minimum (lower bound) number of stations for a cycle time of 15?
   b. Of 20?
   c. Find a reasonable balance for cycle time of 15.
   d. Find a reasonable balance for cycle time of 20.

2. Consider the assembly line balancing problem represented by Figure 4-9. Using no formal heuristics:

   a. What is the theoretical minimum number of stations for a cycle time of 35?
   b. Of 12?
   c. Find a reasonable balance for a cycle time of 35.
   d. Find a reasonable balance for a cycle time of 12.

Figure 4-8

Assembly Line Network
(Problem 1)

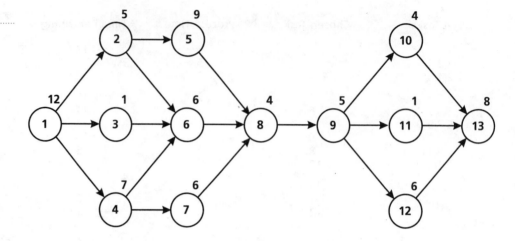

3. For problem 1, determine by trial and error the minimum cycle time for a four-station balance.
4. For problem 2, determine by trial and error the minimum cycle time for a five-station balance

Heuristics for the Simple Model.

5. Solve problem 1 using the longest processing time heuristic.
6. Consider the assembly line network shown in Figure 4-8.

   a. Determine positional weights for each of the activities.
   b. Solve problem 1 again using the ranked positional weight heuristic.

7. Solve problem 2 using the longest processing time heuristic
8. Consider the assembly line network shown in Figure 4-9.

   a. Determine positional weights for each of the activities.
   b. Solve problem 2 using the ranked positional weight heuristic.

Figure 4-9

Assembly Line Network
(Problem 2)

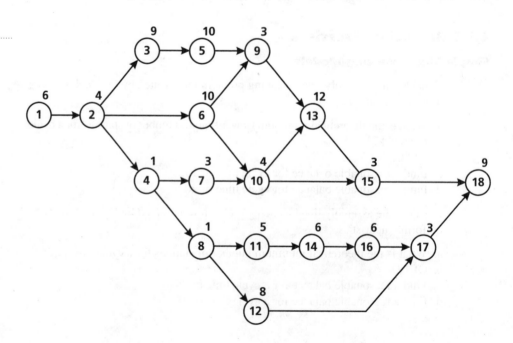

9. Consider the reversal of the assembly line network shown in Figure 4-9. Solve this network by the longest processing time heuristic. Compare your result with that of problem 7.

4.6 ARTFUL ASSEMBLERS—REPRISE

With Terry Tranh's help, Mr. Wrigley chose an MRP system, and Artful Assemblers went through the painful process of implementing it. Bills of materials, lead times, and master production scheduling procedures had to be worked out and verified for every product. The first try at using the new system did not go very well. There were a few bugs.

Once the system seemed to be working, a new problem arose. The system seemed "nervous." That is, there were always demand changes being entered every week which changed the order releases on the floor much too often. The floor managers complained that a more stable system would be preferable.

After about six months, all of these problems were pretty much worked out. The emergency ordering problem seemed to be vastly reduced, since items were being replaced order by order instead of component by component. Variability in stocking levels was also much reduced. These two factors alone seemed to Mr. Wrigley to more than pay for the system.

On the other hand, the shop floor problems of highly variable lead times on the shop floor, excessive WIP on the floor in general, and occasional extreme bottlenecks did not seem to be helped by the new MRP system. Terry Tranh pointed out that MRP is not really designed to answer shop floor problems of this nature. Eventually a finite capacity scheduling system might need to be added, after the MRP system was fully operational.

BIBLIOGRAPHY

General/Books

Apple, J. M. (1977). *Plant Layout and Material Handling* (3rd Edition). New York: John Wiley.

Bell, D. (1976). *The Coming of the Post-Industrial Society: A Venture in Social Forecasting*. New York: Basic Books.

Blackburn, J. D. (1991). *Time-Based Competition: The Next Battleground in American Manufacturing*. Homewood, IL: Business One Irwin.

Brown, R. (1978). *Materials Management Systems*. New York: John Wiley.

Cohen, S. S. and J. Zysman (1987). *Manufacturing Matters: The Myth of the Post-Industrial Economy*. New York: Basic Books.

Freidenfelds, J. (1981). *Capacity Expansion: Analysis of Simple Models with Applications*. New York: Elsevier North Holland.

Hax, A. C. and D. Candea (1984). *Production and Inventory Management*. Englewood Cliffs, NJ: Prentice-Hall.

Holt, C. C., F. Modigliani, J. F. Muth and H. A. Simon (1960). *Planning Production, Inventories, and Workforce*. Englewood Cliffs, NJ: Prentice-Hall.

Manne, A. S. (ed.) (1967). *Investments for Capacity Expansion: Size, Location, and Time Phasing*. Cambridge, MA: The MIT Press.

Nahmias, Steven (1993). *Production and Operations Management, 2nd ed.* Homewood IL: Irwin.

Orlicky, J. (1975). *Materials Requirements Planning*. New York: McGraw-Hill.

Plossl, G. and O. Wight (1967). Production and Inventory Control. Englewood Cliffs, NJ: Prentice-Hall.

Porter, M. E. (1980). *Competitive Strategy: Techniques for Analyzing Industries and Competitors.* New York: The Free Press.

Schmenner, R. W. (1982). *Making Business Location Decisions.* Englewood Cliffs, NJ: Prentice-Hall.

Schrage, L. (1984). *Linear Integer, and Quadratic Programming with LINDO.* Palo Alto, CA: Scientific Press.

Shore, Barry (1973). *Operations Management.* New York: McGraw-Hill.

Silver, E. A. and R. Peterson (1985). *Decision Systems for Inventory Management and Production Planning, 2nd ed.* New York: John Wiley.

Skinner, W. (1978). *Manufacturing in the Corporate Strategy.* New York: John Wiley.

Vollmann, T. E., W. L. Berry and D. C. Whybark (1992). *Manufacturing, Planning, and Control Systems, 3rd ed.* Homewood, IL: Business One Irwin.

Wight, O. (1974). *Production and Inventory Management in the Computer Age.* Boston, MA: Cahners Books.

Strategic Planning

Abernathy, W. J. and P. L. Townsend (1975). "Technology, Productivity, and Process Change," *Technological Forecasting and Social Change* 7, 379–396.

Abernathy, W. J. and K. Wayne (1974). "Limits of the Learning Curve," *Harvard Business Review* 52 (September-October), 109–119.

Block, T. E. (1977). "A Note on Comparison of Computer Algorithms and Visual Based Methods for Plant Layout," by M. Scriabin and R. C. Vergin, *Management Science* 24, 235–237.

Buffa, E. S., G. C. Armour and T. E. Vollmann (1964). "Allocating Facilities with CRAFT," *Harvard Business Review* 42, 136–158.

Cerevent, R. (1980). "An Application of Warehouse Location Techniques to Bloodmobile Operations," *Interfaces* 10, No. 6, 88–94.

Coleman, D. R. (1977). "Plant Layout: Computer versus Humans," *Management Science* 24, 107–112.

Desenroth, M. P. and J. M. Apple (1962). "A Computerized Plant Layout Analysis and Evaluation Technique (PLANET)," *Technical Papers.* Norcross, GA: American Institute of Industrial Engineers.

Devinney, T. M. (1987). "Entry and Learning," *Management Science* 33, 706–724.

Dhalla, N. K. and S. Yuspeh (1976). "Forget About the Product Life Cycle Concept," *Harvard Business Review* 54 (January-February), 102–112.

Drucker, P. F. (1991). "Japan: New Strategies for a New Reality," *The Wall Street Journal,* October 2.

Fine, C. H. and A. C. Hax (1985). "Manufacturing Strategy: A Methodology and an Illustration," *Interfaces* 15, 27–47.

Goldhar, J. P. and M. Jelinek (1983). "Plan for Economies of Scope," *Harvard Business Review* 61, 141–148.

Hayes R. H. and S. Wheelwright (1979). "Link Manufacturing Process and Product Life Cycles," *Harvard Business Review* 57 (January-February), 133–140.

Kuehn, A. and M. Hamburger (1963). "A Heuristic Program for Locating Warehouses," Management Science 9, 643–666.

Love, R., and L. Yeret, (1976). "An Application of a Facilities Location Model in the Prestressed Concrete Industry," *Interfaces* 6, No. 4, 45–49.

Schniederjans, N. Kwak and M. Helmer (1982). "An Application of Goal Programming to Resolve a Site Location Problem," *Interfaces* 12, No. 3, 65–72.

Aggregate Planning

Bitran, C. R., E. A. Haas and A. C. Hax (1981). "Hierarchical Production Planning: A Single Stage System," *Operations Research* 29, 717–743.

Bowman, E. H. (1956). "Production Scheduling by the Transportation Method of Linear Programming," *Operations Research* 4, 100–103.

Bowman, E. H. (1963). "Consistency and Optimality in Managerial Decision Making," *Management Science* 9, 310–321.

Ebert, R. J. (1976). "Aggregate Planning with Learning Curve Productivity," *Management Science* 23, 171–182.

Hansmann, F. and S. W. Hess (1960). "A Linear Programming Approach to Production and Employment Scheduling," *Management Technology* 1, 46–51.

Holt, C. C., F. Modigliani and H. A. Simon (1956). "A Linear Decision Rule for Employment and Production Scheduling," *Management Science* 2, 159–177.

Johnson, S. (1957). "Sequential Planning over time at Minimum Cost," *Management Science* 4, 435–437.

Jones, C. (1967). "Parametric Production Planning," *Management Science* 15, 843–866.

Kunreuther, H. (1971). "Production-Planning Algorithms for the Inventory-Over-Time Tradeoff," *Operations Research* 19, 1717–1729.

Modigliani, F. and F. Hohn (1955). "Production Planning over Time and the Nature of the Planning Horizon," *Econometrica* 23, 46–66.

Silver, E. (1967). "A Tutorial on Production Smoothing and Work Force Balancing," *Operations Research* 15, 985–1010.

Sullivan, G. and K. Fordyce (1990). "IBM Burlington's Logistic Management System," *Interfaces* 20, No. 1, 43–64.

Taubert, W. H. (1968). "A Search Decision Rule for the Aggregate Scheduling Problem," *Management Science* 14, B343–59.

Terborgh, George (1949). "Dynamic Equipment Policy," *Machinery and Allied Products Institute*, Washington, D.C.

Tactical Planning

Anderson, J. C., R. G. Schroeder, S. E. Tupy and E. M. White (1982). "Material Requirements Planning Systems: The State of the Art," *Production and Inventory Management* 23, 51–66.

Arcus, A. L. (1966). "COMSOAL: A Computer Method for Sequencing Operations for Assembly Lines," *International Journal of Production Research* 4, 259–277.

Baker, K. R. (1984). "Sequencing Rules and Due-Date Assignments in a Job Shop," *Management Science* 30, 1093–1104.

Baker, K. R. and J. W. Bertrand (1981). "An Investigation of Due-Date Assignment Rules with Constrained Tightness," *Journal of Operations Management* 1, 109–120.

Bennett, G. B. and J. Byrd (1976). "A Trainable Heuristic Procedure for the Assembly Line Balancing Problem," *American Institute of Industrial Engineers: AIIE Transactions* 8, 195–201.

Carlson, R., and M. Rosenblatt (1985). "Designing a Production Line to Maximize Profit," *IIE Transactions* 17, 117–122.

Foulds, L. R. (1983). "Techniques for Facilities Layout," *Management Science* 29, 1414–1426.

Glassey, C. R. and M. G. C. Resende (1988). "A Scheduling Rule for Job Release in Semiconductor Fabrication," *Operations Research Letters* 7, 213–217.

Held, M., R. M. Karp and R. Shareshian (1963). "Assembly Line Balancing—Dynamic Programming with Precedence Constraints," *Operations Research* 11, 442–459.

Helgeson, W. P. and D. P. Birnie (1961). "Assembly Line Balancing Using the Ranked Positional Weight Technique," *Journal of Industrial Engineering* 12, 394–398.

Ignall, E. J. (1965). "A Review of Assembly Line Balancing," *Journal of Industrial Engineering* 16, 244–254.

Johnson, R. V. (1982). "SPACECRAFT for Multi-Floor Layout Planning," *Management Science* 28, 407–417.

Karmarkar, U. W. (1989). "Capacity Loading and Release Planning with Work-In-Progress (WIP) and Leadtimes," *Journal of Manufacturing and Operations Management* 2, 105–123.

Kilbridge, M. D. and L. Wester (1961). "A Heuristic Method of Line Balancing," *Journal of Industrial Engineering* 12, 292–298.

Krajewski, L. J., et al. (1987). "Kanban, MRP, and Shaping the Manufacturing Environment," *Management Science* 33, 39–57.

Liberatore, M. J. (1979). "Using MRP and EOQ/Safety Stock for Raw Material Inventory Control: Discussion and Case Study," *Interfaces* 98, No. 2, 1–6.

Mahmoodi, F., K. J. Dooley and P. J. Star (1990). "An Evaluation of Order Releasing and Due-Date Assignment Heuristics in a Cellular Manufacturing System," *Journal of Operations Management* 9, 548–573.

Scriabin, M. and R. C. Vergin (1975). "Comparison of Computer Algorithms and Visual Based Methods for Plant Layout," *Management Science* 22, 172–181.

Scriabin, M. and R. C. Vergin (1985). "A Cluster Analytic Approach to Facility Layout," *Management Science* 31, 33–49.

Steele, D. C. (1973). "The Nervous MRP System: How to Do Battle," *Production and Inventory Management* 16, 83–89.

Talbot, F. B., W. V. Gehrlien and J. H. Patterson (1981). "A Comparative Evaluation of Heuristic Line Balancing Techniques," Working Paper #215, GBS, Ann Arbor, MI: University of Michigan.

Wemmerlov, U. (1979). "Design Factors in MRP Systems: A Limited Survey," *Production and Inventory Management* 22, 15–35.

Total Quality Management 6

CHAPTER 1

Total Quality Management (TQM)

1.1 INTRODUCTION

Total Quality Management (TQM) is the strategic coordination and improvement of all parts of the manufacturing/delivery process in order to produce goods and services which give high satisfaction to the customer. The manufacturing/delivery process is very broadly defined to include strategy, marketing, engineering, manufacturing, and so forth. The increased interest in quality in the United States is due largely to the continued erosion of American markets due to competition from Japan, but increasingly also from Europe and the rest of the Pacific Rim. The overall American trade deficit continues to grow, and has done so unremittingly for more than 20 years.

American citizens' opinion of American quality is not particularly rosy. A 1989 study by the American Society for Quality Control found that 74 percent of executives gave American products less than eight on a ten-point scale for quality. In like fashion, a panel of Fortune 500 executives concluded that American products deserved no more than a C+ for quality. In another American Society for Quality Control [1988] study less than one-half of the respondents thought American products deserved high marks for quality.

However, there are some bright spots. There has been a major turnaround in the fortunes of America's automakers, apparently due largely to a general perception of dramatically increased quality. For example, Ford's "Quality Is Job One" campaign may have been a factor in increasing focus on quality. There has also been a rapidly growing interest in the American culture in the last ten years or so in Total Quality Management (TQM).

What Is TQM? There are two rather complementary ways to think about quality. The first way is to define quality directly in terms of customer satisfaction. We may call this the **product approach** (see Feigenbaum [1991], Crosby [1979], and Garvin [1988]).

The second way is to think about quality in terms of the quality of all parts and functions of a company, and also the integration of all functions at all levels. That is, this is a **process approach** (or systems approach.) The overall quality of the entire organization is greater than the sum of its parts. The watchword here is "continuous improvement." These two definitions are clearly complementary. We can't make a quality product without knowing what such a product would be. But we can't also make it without a well-designed and finely tuned process for making it.

History of TQM. A major impetus for more formal quality control came with the industrial revolution. For example, advances in gun manufacturing in the 1800s made it important that parts be manufactured with tolerances such that parts could be interchangeable rather than hand-crafted for each gun.

Over the last 100 years or so, the maturation of the industrial revolution greatly increased the trend toward the division of labor. Workers lost the opportunity to fashion the entire product. They became specialists who were responsible for only a small part of the process. This led to great economies of production. However, it also led to two basic problems:

    a. It became more difficult for workers to maintain the motivation towards high quality work, since they could not directly see the results of their labors.

    b. For the same reasons, it became more difficult for workers to perform their tasks at sufficient speed.

Around the beginning of this century, Frederick Taylor developed a system of scientific management. His system of time and motion study and incentive pay dealt mostly with obtaining more speed from workers, rather than with the quality problem. Taylor was a great pioneer in manufacturing; we owe him much. Nevertheless, the system of work standards turned out to be somewhat perverse, putting an upper bound on productivity expectations and in many cases encouraging low quality.

Shewhart [1931] conceived the idea of the control chart while he was an employee of Bell Telephone Laboratories. Other employees of Bell Labs are given credit for developing acceptance sampling. Industry adopted statistical quality control rather slowly. However, World War II found the military making broad use of acceptance sampling and developing its theoretical foundations more fully. Abraham Wald developed the theory of sequential sampling in the same period.

At about this time Dodge and Romig, also at Bell Labs, were developing a system for the lot-by-lot inspection of work-in-process and finished goods. This **acceptance sampling** procedure was sound statistically. Unfortunately, it led to further emphasis on inspection and defect detection, rather than on broader procedures for improving quality.

During World War II, sampling inspection methods grew in popularity, and in the economically lush years right after the war, acceptance sampling became the norm. This is not to say that Shewhart's control chart methods were not also being used by some companies. However, they did not achieve broad popularity, probably because top management did not understand the total quality message underlying Shewhart's approach.

Following World War II, a number of pioneers began to create a broader theory of quality and to develop practical techniques for improved quality. Deming is the best known of these pioneers. He popularized quality control in Japan in the 1950s, delivering a series of lectures on quality control methods. Deming then became active in the Japanese quality movement and ultimately became a national hero in Japan. Using the royalties from a book based on his lectures, Deming established a national quality prize in Japan. We will discuss his ideas further in the next section.

Shortly after the Second World War, Genichi Taguchi became interested in applying the statistical methods in the design of experiments to improve product design in Japanese industry. In 1949 the Japanese government asked him to improve the efficiency of R&D activities in the Electrical Communications Laboratory. He quickly recognized that most of the work involved the design and performance of costly experiments and set about trying to use existing statistical methods to achieve superior results. From this work, his methods for higher quality product designs emerged.

J. M. Juran was invited to Japan in 1954 to give a series of quality lectures. He introduced such managerial topics as planning, organizing, controlling, and the need for setting goals. His notion of quality more closely fit the point of view of the customer, and he was prepared to quantify such issues and focused on top-down management techniques rather than worker satisfaction. Juran now runs the Juran Institute. His contributions are probably somewhat broader than those of Deming, who is more focused on statistical process control.

A. V. Feigenbaum also achieved recognition through his work with the Japanese, which was much more behavioral and managerial-oriented and might be considered a forerunner of TQM. He believed quality could not be achieved without changing the group culture within the organization. P. B. Crosby stresses motivation and planning rather than statistical techniques. He argues for prevention rather than inspection, zero defects, and quality measured by the cost of poor quality. S. Shiba is a professor at Tsukuba University in Japan who has been actively researching and teaching TQM for many years. He is currently an adjunct professor at MIT and assisted in the foundation of the Center for Quality of Management there.

1.2 CONCEPTS OF QUALITY

1.2.1 Deming's 14 Points

Deming developed a plan, referred to as Deming's 14 points, to help management to achieve improvements in both quality and productivity. These points are discussed briefly here.

1. **Create constancy of purpose for the improvement of product or service.** Deming was especially critical of American management's focus on projects with short paybacks that may affect the quarterly income statement well, but are inimical to the long-term health of the company. He states that management must act as if it will be in business for a long time and care about the future. A strong future, in turn, depends on a strong relationship with the customer which, in turn, depends on developing the types of products and the processes for making them that will continue to build such relationships.

2. **Adopt the new philosophy.** New methods for quality will never succeed without overwhelming support from top management. Since quality is expensive in the short run, any quality movement within the company will always flounder if the CEO is indifferent. The lip service paid to quality in many companies attests to this fact.

3. **Cease dependence on mass inspection for quality control.** In the older-style quality control, the output from the process (or some fraction of it) is inspected. Good product is shipped; defective product is reworked or scrapped. Such an approach can certainly keep what is shipped pretty much defect-free. But the procedure is not a good one for two reasons:

   a. It is very costly in terms of inspection and rework.
   b. The part of the process causing the defects is never fixed.

   Under a process control model for quality control, we concentrate on finding and fixing the underlying causes of the problem in the process. As a result, both quality and productivity can be improved together.

4. **End the practice of awarding business on the basis of price tag.** In much of American industry, the procedure has been to obtain raw materials or other inputs by having several suppliers submit bids and accepting the low bidder. This gave a feeling that the best deal was being obtained and that suppliers were being "kept in line." Unfortunately, this tends to produce an adversarial relationship with the supplier.

5. **Improve constantly and forever the system of production and service to improve quality and productivity, and thus constantly decrease costs.** Deming developed a four-point cycle for constant improvement:

   a. Recognize the opportunity.
   b. Test the theory to achieve the opportunity.
   c. Observe the test results.
   d. Act on the opportunity.

6. **Institute more thorough, better job-related training.** Thorough training is necessary in order to implement higher quality and improved methods in general. Management must also change the way things are done so that people are given the tools to implement their training.

7. **Institute leadership.** Managerial leadership should have the goal of motivating people to work to their peak ability. Too often the supervisor is concerned with managing the product being produced, rather than the people producing it. All too often the management system fosters mediocrity, as the worker negotiates low objectives to avoid being embarrassed.

8. **Drive out fear, so that everyone may work effectively for the company.** Fear of failure, and of being exposed, inhibits our willingness to do the correct difficult thing. Fear causes us to mistrust others in the organization. To reduce fear requires an emphasis on people, rather than on things.

9. **Break down barriers between departments.** It is obvious to many that cliques and groups within an organization· are destructive of common goals. Departmentalization is one of the most common problems of this sort. To break down the barriers, the system must be changed so that it fosters teamwork. Systems which appraise and reward departmental performance tend to set department against department. Alternatives must be sought.

10. **Eliminate slogans, exhortations, and targets for the work force that ask for zero defects and new levels of productivity.** Talk is cheap. It is all to easy to try to pump workers and middle management with slogans and high sounding goals. But exhortations are no substitute for giving training and providing people with the authority and other tools to do the job properly.

11. **Eliminate work standards on the factory floor.** Work standards tend to be either impossible to reach, which destroys their credibility, or else they are too easy and provide the worker with motivation not to try harder. Ideally, with good supervisors and the right tools, workers will be motivated to continually do their very best and to keep improving.

12. **Remove the barriers that rob employees at all levels in the company of their right to pride of workmanship.** In order to get pride of workmanship, we will have to make supervisors emphasize the need for quality, not for high output. Financial incentive systems based on the short-term "bottom line" must be changed. Weekly production reports must be abandoned.

13. **Institute a vigorous program of education and self-improvement.** People must not be treated as disposable items which can be cheaply bought and sold, but as major assets to the company. Workers and management must believe that the company will invest in their future.

14. **Put everybody to work to accomplish the transformation.** Major changes such as these cannot be implemented unless everyone in the organization is on board. But above all, the 14 points are the responsibility of top management.

1.2.2 Taguchi's Definition of Quality

Over the years, the most widely used measure of quality has been "conformance of the product to design specifications." This definition is very limited because it defines quality for a *unit* of product on how well manufacturing has been able to match design specifications, rather than for the product *as a whole* on how well the product, including its design, meets customer needs and expectations.

Taguchi's Approach to Quality Engineering. Taguchi emphasizes reducing variation in the production process and in the final product as the principal way of improving quality. He believes this can be done by designing products which perform in a consistent manner, even under conditions of varying or adverse use. He also believes that one can make this happen at the design stage by appropriate statistical experimental design methods.

He sees quality as avoiding the "loss due to functional variation." This loss will clearly be minimized when the product performs exactly as specified (performance is nominal) and will increase as the performance deviates more and more from nominal. The cost will increase more and more rapidly as the deviation increases, leading to the idea that in many cases a quadratic loss function may be a good approximation. Figure 1-1 illustrates the idea for a specific example of a motor shaft designed to have a 2.250 inch diameter.

Small deviations in motor shaft diameter do not matter too much but larger ones affect the other components assembled to the shaft.

Example 1-1. The Acme Winch company buys large numbers of the AC5-7 motor shaft from two suppliers, OK Guys and Hotshots, for use in its Super-Winch product. The motor shaft is specified at 2.250 inches in diameter with a tolerance of plus or minus 0.010. That is, specifications are that the diameter lie between 2.240 inches and 2.260 inches. The loss function is shown in Figure 1-1. Acme gives an extended warranty with its winches. We may consider this loss to be the warranty cost in terms of future repairs for a shaft with a given diameter of deviation.

OK Guys delivers shafts that almost always lie within tolerance, but whose diameters have a distribution spreading over 90 percent of the tolerance range. Hotshots' shaft diameters have a distribution spreading over 30 percent of the tolerance range. OK Guys charge $300 per hundred shafts, while Hotshots charge $301 per hundred. The deviations from nominal for each are shown in Figure 1-2.

Since both suppliers supply product within specifications, should the cheaper supplier be chosen?

Solution. Superimpose the cost-of-warranty curve (loss function) on top of the distribution of shaft diameters for the two suppliers, as shown in Figure 1-3.

Without making a full quantitative analysis, it should be clear that all of Hotshots' shafts will have low warranty costs, while a significant portion of OK Guys' shafts will have high warranty costs. Thus savings of a penny a shaft are very unlikely to pay the extra warranty costs, not to mention compensating for long-term customer unhappiness.

Taguchi's Seven Points. We now state Taguchi's approach somewhat more precisely. Conventional quality control activities center on final inspection sampling or on

Figure 1-1

Quality Loss Function for a Motor by Diameter

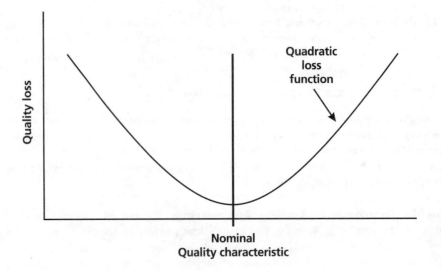

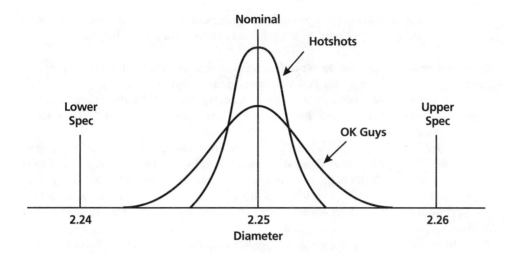

Figure 1-2
....
Shaft Deviations for OK
Guys and Hotshots

control charts and process control. This is called on-line quality control. Taguchi pushed the process upstream to focus on product and process design. This is called off-line quality control.

1. Product quality is measured by the total loss to society created by that product.
2. Continuous quality improvement and cost reduction are necessary to survive in world competition.
3. Quality improvement requires continual and repeated reduction of variation in the product/process performance around the standard nominal values.
4. Quality loss is frequently proportional to the square of the deviation of the performance from the nominal value.
5. Product and process design can have an important impact on a product's quality and cost.
6. Performance variation can be reduced by suitable adjustment of the product's parameters and/or the process parameters.
7. The appropriate parameter settings that reduce variation can be identified with the appropriate statistically designed experiments.

1.2.3 Shiba's Viewpoint

Shiba, Graham, and Walden [1993] distinguish four hierarchical levels of quality, which they call **the four fitnesses**. Shiba says that the history of Japan since World War II is a

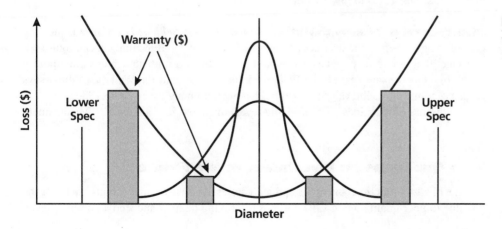

Figure 1-3
....
Warranty Costs for the Two
Suppliers

clear progression to higher levels of quality or fitness. In the late 1940s and early '50s there was no real concept of quality. Japan had a reputation for shoddy merchandise.

Quality Level 1: Fitness to Standard. *Fitness to standard* is the first step up in quality. Quality is doing what the designers have specified that the product is to be and do. The main way to create quality for a product is then a question of statistical sampling and inspection. Deming brought these methods to Japan in the early 1950s; at the time, they were a major improvement.

In modern times, fitness to standard used as the only concept of quality has two major weaknesses. The first is that quality can be maintained by weeding out the worst of the items. This leaves the better of the items produced by a dubious process and does not guarantee good results. The second weakness is that it neglects asking in any depth what the customer wants. The designer issues specs; after that, the process tries to please the designer rather than the customer.

Shiba says that fitness to standard was typical of Japanese companies in the late 1950s.

Quality Level 2: Fitness to Needs. *Fitness to needs* is the second step up in quality. Certainly, after all, we may agree that the product should meet its design specs. But can the product be used as (all) the customers want to use it? At this stage we are still focusing on inspecting the final product, but we inspect it in ways that check whether the product meets its intended use. We may have a consumer laboratory which takes items and tests them extensively in the ways customers will use them, and accepts or rejects lots on this basis.

However, we are still basically allowing a process with high statistical variation, throwing away the "tails" of the distribution. This is expensive. Shiba says that fitness to needs was typical of Japanese companies in the 1960s.

Quality Level 3: Fitness of Cost. *Fitness of cost* is the third level of quality. The only way to maintain the first two levels of quality and get lower costs is to move away from the high costs of "inspecting quality in" and toward "building quality in." That is, we must reduce the variability of the production process, so that all units will lie within the specifications, and none will have to be discarded. (In many cases it will not be worthwhile even to inspect, if control is strong enough.) The goal is 100 percent quality without inspection!!! This requires control, feedback, and correction at each step of the production process.

We will discuss this issue of process improvement in later chapters. Shiba says that this level of quality was attained in Japan in the early 1970s. A weakness still remains, however. Companies that reach this level are producing very reliable, useful products at low cost. However, other companies can adopt the same methods and perhaps achieve lower costs. This leads to the final fitness.

Quality Level 4: Fitness to Hidden Need. *Fitness to hidden need* means meeting the user's needs before the user is even aware of those needs. If a company can figure out a product that would be popular somewhat before others do, it can achieve a temporary monopoly. Good examples are the Polaroid Land camera and the Walkman. Shiba says Japanese companies achieved fitness to hidden need in many cases in the 1980s.

We discuss Shiba's ideas for achieving levels of fitness in Total Quality Management Chapter 2.

1.2.4 Quality as an Investment in the Future

If Taguchi's loss function concept is applied carelessly, then we may simply trade off the loss due to poor quality against the costs of improving quality, and find an optimal level.

This is the old concept of the **Acceptable Quality Level** (AQL), which is basically a static concept; we find the appropriate AQL and stay there. Taguchi and Deming would rather argue for continuous quality improvement over time. The rate at which we choose to improve quality would be determined by balancing quality and quality costs, but we would never choose to stop improving! Here we present the traditional view; in Total Quality Management Chapter 2 we present the modern view.

Traditional Static Analysis—Acceptable Quality Level. For each given level of quality control cost c and tolerance deviation x (perhaps discretized in thousandths of an inch above or below desired) we will have a probability of $f(x,c)$ of having this deviation. Suppose we have a Taguchi loss function cost of Ax^2. Then the total cost of quality if we invest c in quality is the sum of this cost over all deviations, that is $Q(c) = \sum Ax^2 f(x,c)$. The total cost is then $c + Q(c)$. If we plot c, $Q(c)$, and $c + Q(c)$, we find a minimum total cost for some c^*, which will produce a level of cost called the Acceptable Quality Level (AQL), as shown in Figure 1-4.

The items which are traditionally considered to be the appropriate costs of quality control and of bad quality include:

a. Costs of quality control

- maintaining a quality control system
- maintaining a final inspection system

b. Costs of poor quality

- manufacturing losses
- scrap and rework
- warranty
- repair
- customer defections
- product service

There are basically two things wrong with the traditional static analysis:

1. The costs that are considered are much too narrow.
2. Improved quality is an investment in the future.

We will develop these ideas more deeply in Total Quality Management Chapter 2.

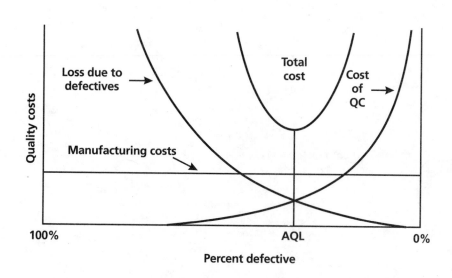

Figure 1-4

Traditional View of the Acceptable Quality Level

1.3 SUMMARY AND PREVIEW OF THE TOTAL QUALITY MANAGEMENT MODULE

In Total Quality Management Chapter 2 we develop the major strategic issues involved in Total Quality Management. Sections 2.2 and 2.7 present a Company Application Scenario illustrating TQM. Section 2.3 discusses TQM's central focus on *customer satisfaction*. Section 2.4 discusses TQM's focus on *continuous improvement*. The Japanese call this *kaizen*. Section 2.5 looks at human resources. Section 2.6 discusses methods for attaining a revolution in TQM, including networking, standards, and awards. Total Quality Management Chapter 3 discusses more traditional statistical quality control issues. In Section 3.1 we give an introduction to statistical production quality. In Sections 3.2 and 3.6 we present a Company Application Scenario for Presto Pistons. Section 3.3 gives a review of statistical tools for those who may need a refresher. Section 3.4 discusses control charts, while Section 3.5 discusses inspection policy.

CHAPTER 2

TQM in Practice

Shoji Shiba, Alan Graham, and David Walden, the authors of A New American TQM—Four Practical Revolutions in Management *(Productivity Press, 1993) have graciously allowed this chapter to be a condensation of their book. They are not responsible for the condensation, nor do they implicitly give approval to other chapters of this textbook. The figures in this chapter have also been reprinted from their book by permission.*

2.1 INTRODUCTION

The fundamental philosophy of TQM is that satisfying the customer is the be-all and end-all of any business enterprise which expects to survive in the long run. To fully satisfy customers means to fulfill their expectations for the product, or their desires and hopes for a product. This, in turn, requires that the customer be fully understood and cared for.

Traditionally, companies have focused on **product-out**, which treats the product itself as the mission of the firm. Product-out suggests that the company makes what it considers to be a good product. Workers and managers often believe that their job is to do what is laid out in the production manual, and nothing more. Often the attitude is that the complaining customers don't even know what they want; e.g., they are using the product in the wrong fashion!

However, TQM focuses on **market-in**, which is centered on feedback from the marketplace. The job is not done well until the customer is completely satisfied. The Japanese have a saying, "The customer is God." Every employee of the firm has "customers who are God." Employees who deal directly with external customers are, of course, in this position. But also internally to the company, each step in a process must serve all subsequent processes. Whoever uses the product of my work is really my customer. In fact, I am likely to have many customers for my work and to be the customer of many others.

TQM cannot be truly effective unless the market-in approach suffuses the entire company and reaches all employees at every level. And, of course, things do not remain the same. Customer needs and desires change, so the company must change with it. Also, both the company and competitors in the search for higher quality will continually be finding better ways to do things. The Japanese call this continuous improvement idea *kaizen*.

These are not small changes in the company culture that we are talking about. They amount to a revolution. TQM cannot succeed unless the CEO and the other top management are on board. TQM cannot succeed unless workers and managers are motivated to work together for long term quality goals, rather than short term financial goals.

Quality is too big an issue to be confined within one company. Companies can learn from each other and cooperate with each other. Suppliers can be required to learn and use TQM techniques. The firm can establish standards to measure itself against the best performers in the industry. This is called **benchmarking**. Major awards such as the Deming, Baldridge, and European Quality awards have inspired many companies to greater things. The Europeans have promulgated a standard called ISO 9000, which provides a very broad type of benchmarking, and encourages uniformity so that products which take several companies to create can achieve high quality in an economic fashion.

2.2 COMPANY APPLICATION SCENARIO—ENGINEERING SOFTWARE SYSTEMS

Engineering Software Systems derives most of its revenue from a product called CADS, for "Computer Aided Design Search." Basically, the user enters a type of problem to be solved, various types of choices which can be made, rules for combining choices, and a method for evaluating a given design. The computer then tries many trial designs, searching for the best ones that can be found, and reports a number of good candidates to the user. The user then makes the final choice. It is also a DSS (Decision Support System) in the sense that the user can reject designs or make changes and let the computer continue to search, and so on.

Thirty years ago, Jack Slade, then an engineer working for Northinghouse, conceived and developed his first program, CADS.1. Because Northinghouse had little interest in developing his software, he quit the company and set up Engineering Software Systems (ESS) with his wife, Marilyn, in their kitchen. He had no competition. Ironically, Northinghouse soon needed his software and became his first major customer, eventually buying eight copies of CADS.1. ESS prospered and soon took over the Slade's whole house, and then the first of several buildings. In the process, the CADS program grew and also became more sophisticated. The firm now has 300 employees, and is marketing CADS.5.3, with Jack Slade as president and CEO. ESS has always been a "family firm" with norms of loyalty, informality, and very hard work. There have always been large bonuses given out when business was good, which was most of the time.

Now, however, there are signs of stress, and Jack Slade is beginning to think that something must be done. The first problem is that a competitor's product, CADPRO, is beginning to take many long-time customers away from CADS. The marketing department has called many of the defectors to try to find out what is wrong, but the feedback has been a little confusing.

Some of the complaints seem to be that the product is *too* automatic and doesn't let the user take control and direct the search very easily. Some of the complaints seem to be more that CADPRO is easier to use and is harder to make mistakes with. Some of the complaints are more about customer service. There are complaints about lost orders, about waiting too long for a promised software disk, and about being shunted around between several troubleshooters when a bug is found.

Jack Slade was impatient with the idea that CADS might be too automatic. "These people just don't understand!" he fumed. "CADS uses the latest form of tabu search; it's miles ahead of CADPRO. Furthermore, the user can always get more control of the search by overriding the nominal systems values! These people just have to learn to use the product properly. I'm going to commission a major rewrite of the product manual to make it even clearer how superior our automatic search method is to that of CADPRO. And while we're at it, let's beef up our explanation of why automatic methods are superior to manual methods. And just to be safe, we'll highlight how to override the system."

And Jack was *truly* puzzled by users who found CADPRO easier to use than CADS. "While we're at it, let's give a lot more examples in the rewrite to teach these guys how better to use our product. There's nothing wrong with this product. We just need better *customers*!!!"

However, Jack took the complaints about customer service very seriously, although he wasn't quite sure what to do about it. ESS had always been an informal family sort of place. When there were customer complaints in the old days, the eight employees would get together and work out a fix. But with 300 employees this just didn't work as well. Jack finally decided to prepare a series of three lectures on high quality customer service. Once this was accomplished, he divided the company into five groups of about 60 employees each and gave the lecture series five times, until everyone had received it. Then he gave short written quiz to everyone, with a $25 incentive for getting a high score.

It took four months to revise the user's manual and to send the revision out to all current users. By about six months after that, it had become evident that neither of the fixes was doing its job. CADS was still losing customers to CADPRO at about the same rate, and the level of complaints and confusion regarding customer service were about the same. Raymond Star, Jack Slade's long time banker and close friend, finally intervened to ask Jack to get outside help to deal with these problems. Reluctantly, Jack agreed and brought in an outside firm, Quality Associates, to try to get things back on the right track. They sent a senior partner, Seth Stag, to assess the situation.

2.3 FOCUS ON THE CUSTOMER

2.3.1 Market-in

The strategic statement "Focus on *market-in* rather than *product-out*!" is pretty difficult to argue with conceptually. Certainly, a company which listens well to the marketplace and bends its efforts to satisfying that marketplace *should* do better than a company which produces what it feels the market should want and then tries to "re-educate" the market. But just how is this to be accomplished? What needs to change in the company, and what is the path to accomplish that change?

One needed change is to the idea of specialization of labor to attain greater efficiency. Under the product-out framework (supported by classical economics), the workers specialize in following efficient standard routines, while managers work on improvement. But market-in recognizes that the force of constantly changing customer needs makes such specialization inefficient. Everyone in the company must do both routine daily work and contribute to improvement. Division of labor is good in a static environment, but it does not allow for reaction fast enough to keep satisfying customers in a dynamic, rapidly moving world. And rapid change is everywhere—in what the customer wants, in technology, staff needs, the political situation, and so on. (This idea is really very similar to Schumpeter's "gale of competition.") A very good way to think of TQM is as "management in the face of rapid change."

Before the 1950s it was felt to be impossible to run a four-minute mile. Then Roger Bannister did it for the first time. Now running a four-minute mile is a prerequisite for any serious runner. The point here is that the requirement for change is not only coming from customers, but also from other companies which are achieving TQM. Like Alice in Wonderland, we must run pretty hard just to stay in one place.

The customer is not really interested in how the company is organized internally. The customer is interested in product quality, cost, and delivery. (These form a generalized idea of quality often called just QCD). These require cross-departmental cooperation. No one department can provide QCD alone. Thus, the organization really needs sort of a matrix organization—one organization for doing daily work, and a cross-functional structure to ensure customer satisfaction. This is needed to enlist all parts of the company in a constant effort to understand both customer and internal problems, and to improve and align with changing times.

Traditional companies are not well-suited to working on total customer satisfaction. They concern themselves with the product rather than the way of making it, with results but not root causes. They spend a great deal of time working out missions, goals, standards, and policies rather than seeing them as part of a process of continuous improvement. They manage their employees rather than involving them in the struggle. TQM must be a broad, democratic movement. It cannot be enforced by a small group of upper management, nor can it succeed without the support of top management. The energy for making TQM happen can only come from getting everyone in the company to participate, and to participate skillfully. It is the manager's job to teach everyone how to do this; how to do *market-in*, and how to satisfy the customer.

2.3.2 Knowing the Customer

If we are to achieve *market-in* rather than *product-out*, it is first of all necessary to understand the customer much more deeply. How can we focus on customer satisfaction without really knowing what the customer wants and doesn't want?

Traditional Methods. The most traditional (and clumsiest) way of trying to do this is simply to guess what the customer wants and make that product. If it sells well, without many complaints, fine. If not, change the product somehow and try to sell it again. There are at least four things wrong with this approach:

   a.   It is extremely wasteful to develop a product which may not be wanted.
   b.   The procedure is too slow to track changing customer needs.
   c.   It can never achieve accurately what the customer wants.
   d.   Dissatisfied customers will not complain (they will vote with their feet).

An improved version of this idea is to develop an early form of the product (called a pilot or a prototype) and pay a number of potential customers to try it and give a critique. (For software products, the tester is often given a free copy of the final software in return.) While this idea is indeed better, it is still subject to the same problems. First, the prototype may require very extensive revision, so that resources will be wasted. Second, the prototype itself tends to define the kinds of solutions that the customer is supposed to think about. Thus, we still may not be able to get close enough to what the customer really wants. Finally, producing and revising prototypes may still be much too slow of a process to keep up with customer tastes. No, we must consult the customer much earlier than this.

Market Research. Another approach (often called *market research*) can be used when the product (or new variation) is still in the conceptual design stage. Here one designs a questionnaire or survey and sends it out to a few hundred potential customers chosen at random. When the questionnaires have been returned, they are tabulated and analyzed statistically. This approach is widely used and gets around many of the difficulties of testing only the finished product. However, there are still a number of problems. First, a large number of questionnaires are never returned. Those that are returned are often not very representative of the customers at large. (In particular, those who do not like the product may simply not return the questionnaire rather than say so.) A second important problem is that the questionnaire provides a framework for thinking and answering the questions provided by the company instead of by the user. Since the user cannot ask questions or respond in other ways, this is a serious limitation. Nevertheless, this kind of market research remains an important way of learning about the consumer.

Customer Visitation. In-depth personal interviews with a small number of companies likely to be your customers is a superior way to get to know your customers intimately. There are seven key points to successful interviews:

   1.   **Clarify the purpose.** Likely purposes for customer visits might be:

      a.   To learn your customer needs
      b.   To learn about competitors
      c.   To demonstrate your customer focus

2. **Set a concrete target.** Set a time deadline for completing all the interviews and choose a number of customers to visit accordingly.

3. **Train for visits.** Teach the interviewers how to ask questions and how to take careful notes. Practice with interviews inside the company. Use verbal, open-ended questions. Ask questions from several points of view to confirm facts. Do not use tape recorders; they are distracting. Write down everything that is said and your reaction.

4. **Respect the customer.** Study background material on the customer before the visit. Prepare the customer about what to expect and what will happen during the visit. Explain how the results will be used and what types of follow-up should be expected.

5. **Continuously improve your procedure.** There is considerable variation in companies and what will work in the interview. Be flexible; be prepared to change and to improve your procedures. After the first visit, analyze your weaknesses for root causes. Then develop ways to improve.

6. **Limit the number of interviews.** Shiba suggests that 10 interviews will get about 70 percent of the customer understanding that is available from these interviews, and that 20 interviews will get about 90 percent.

7. **Apply the fishbowl principle.** Traditional market research is like standing outside a fishbowl and measuring behavior inside the fishbowl. Customer visitation and similar techniques are methods for actually jumping into the fishbowl (the market), swimming around and seeing what is really going on, and then jumping back out again to analyze the situation.

Getting Employee Input. None of these methods needs to be used in isolation. For example, it is quite reasonable to solicit internal employee input as to problems with the customer at the same time customer research is underway. Internal surveys and/or interviews can help identify problems and solutions to problems both in the product itself and in service. Such surveys can help point out changes necessary for quality improvements.

2.3.3 Internal Customer Problems

Internal customers are the people and activities within an organization that are the customers of other people or activities. For example, job shop scheduling is the customer of

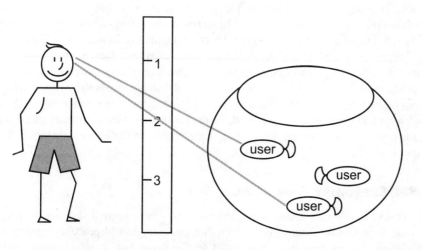

Figure 2-1

Studying the Fishbowl from the Outside

Reprinted from A New American TQM—Four Practical Revolutions in Management *by Shoji Shiba, Alan Graham, and David Walden (Productivity Press, 1993) by permission.*

Figure 2-2

Swimming in the Fishbowl

Reprinted from A New American TQM—Four Practical Revolutions in Management *by Shoji Shiba, Alan Graham, and David Walden (Productivity Press, 1993) by permission.*

MRP; distribution is the customer of manufacturing, which in turn is the customer of design, and so forth.

The needs of customers inside and outside the firm may conflict with each other in many situations. Often the processes of a traditional manufacturing or service firm are designed more to fill the needs of internal customers than of outside customers. One example is a job shop supervisor who may schedule large runs of each product so that the machines do not have to be set up very often for product changes. But very large runs may make it difficult for a customer to get a desired item quickly. In another example, the product designer may wish to have a small number of variations of the product to simplify and standardize the design process. However, consumers are likely to demand a large variety of products suited exactly to their various needs. A balance needs to be struck between the needs of the internal customers and the outside customers. The solution is perhaps to step back a bit and recognize that the needs of the inside group must themselves be analyzed in the context of serving the larger, long-range needs of the outside customer. The customer is God!

2.3.4 Customer Retention

The cost of losing a customer is not only the loss of the current sale but the loss of the income stream of all future sales which that customer would probably have generated. This is equally true in manufacturing and service firms, but we will concentrate here on service. TQM has been most active in manufacturing firms, but quality consciousness is increasing and moving into the service sector. Perhaps 70 to 80 percent of employment in the United States is in the service field. Because so many services are intangible, the inter-action between the service providers and the customer is absolutely essential. Very often this interaction influences customer happiness more than the actual product or service. Face-to-face contact between the customer and the doctor/clerk/teller/bus driver is extremely important.

While manufacturers measure waste in terms of scrap, rework, and returns, service companies measure waste in terms of customer defections. Companies need to learn how to measure defections, estimate their costs, and improve the service process to increase retention in the future.

There is a definite relationship between customer retention and long-term profits. One way to look at this is to estimate the lifetime extra profit of gaining a new customer (or the lifetime cost of losing an existing customer). This is sometimes called the "lifetime retention value." Taco Bell, for a simple example, estimates the lifetime value of a retained customer at $11,000. Similarly, if a customer buys a new $16,000 Saturn every three years, the lifetime value in sales (at 8% discounting) would be about $67,000. Clearly, the dealership should work very hard to keep its customers!

2.4 CONTINUOUS IMPROVEMENT

2.4.1 Overview

Every product (whether a good or a service) is created by a process. For that reason, the TQM philosophy is that by far the best way to improve quality is to improve the methods, procedures, equipment, and personnel used in making the product. Note that when we are centering our attention on the process, we are not concentrating on the results. Good results will come if the process is good. Good results cannot come from a bad process. The process drives the results.

This point of view and way of doing things is very different from that in traditional com-panies. Traditionally the emphasis is on goals: market share, short-term profits, product per-formance, and so on. TQM believes that strong results cannot be sustained for very long by cajoling personnel to have better objectives. The objectives are only important in helping to choose a good methodology and process. That process, properly followed, will automati-cally lead to strong results. We might call this philosophy **management by process**.

Management by process

1. Set a goal.
2. Create a process, including people and organization, to meet the goal.
3. Develop a way to measure your progress.
4. Start the plan and monitor your progress.
5. Analyze where you have problems.
6. Revise goals, process, and input measurements.
7. Repeat.

The important thing here is to continually revise the process as needed to achieve the desired output. Looking at the outputs is important, not for their own sake, but to see how the process is working.

A Definition of Continuous Improvement. Continuous improvement is based on two major ideas:

1. Scientifically-based improvement
2. Repeated small improvements

Scientifically-based improvement means the use of a logical scientific approach and a structure for team or individual effort. A scientific approach means that one systematically considers a variety of possible solutions until the very best one can be found. A formal structure for a team's efforts makes sure that everyone participates, even the shyer team members.

In his book, Shiba discusses a concept called the WV model, which is an abstraction to help understand the procedure of continuous improvement. The WV model conceives problem solving as an alternation between thought (planning, analyzing) and experience (getting information from the real world through surveys, interviews, and data gathering). Using the analogy of Figures 2-1 and 2-2, problem solving is repeatedly jumping in and out of the fishbowl. Figure 2-3 shows this alternation. Visually, the path forms a W and then a V, which is why Shiba calls it the WV model.

The point of this diagram is to alternate back and forth to make a small improvement, and then to repeat to make the next small improvement.

The sequence is:

- Sense the problem.
- Check out the problem with some data.
- Choose an improvement method.
- Check out the method with more data.
- Plan and carry out the solution.
- Check out whether it is working with data.
- If the solution is good, implement it permanently.

This model reminds us not to skip steps. For example, don't skip directly from "customers are complaining" to "fire the marketing VP."

There are three types of improvement we are interested in:

1. Process control
2. Reactive control
3. Proactive control

We will describe each of these three types briefly here. Process control is covered extensively in Total Quality Management Chapter 3. Reactive control is discussed in Section 2.4.2; proactive control is discussed in Section 2.4.3.

Process Control. Suppose that you have a well-defined, effective process for doing a manufacturing (or service) function. You have to keep watching the process to keep correcting it if it gets out of balance. This is usually called **control charting**. However, the authors call the more generic process of controlling it the SDCA cycle:

S	=	Standard— Have a standard process and procedures.
D	=	Do — For example, manufacture some items.
C	=	Check — Do the control charting.
A	=	Act — Fix the process if necessary to return to the standard.

Figure 2-3

Shiba's WV Model for Problem Solving

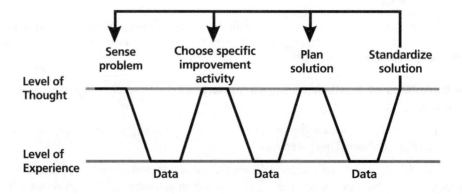

Reactive Improvement. So far we have talked about simply keeping a good process from going astray. But suppose the process has weak points—it needs to be improved. We will talk more about how to tell when a process is weak in Total Quality Management Chapter 3, but there are basically several possibilities:

- The control charts show the process to persistently be out of control.
- The product itself is unsatisfactory in cost and/or quality.
- There is a well-known bottleneck or problem in the process.

In this case, TQM suggests seven steps as a standard methodology for improving weak processes. These are known as the "7 QC" or simply as the "seven steps":

1. Select a specific improvement that is desired.
2. Collect data to understand the exact nature of the problem.
3. Find the root causes of the most common version of the problem.
4. Plan and implement a solution.
5. Check with new data that the solution was effective.
6. Make the new solution permanent and routine.
7. Think about what could have been done better, and zero in on the problem to be tackled next. Repeat.

Note that the seven steps also alternate between thinking and looking at the data. In fact, the last few steps are really just the SDCA cycle for holding on to the improvement.

Proactive Improvement. Reactive improvement tends to focus on a known specific weak point in the process. But many times the need is more vague and strategic. We need to make a proactive improvement, which is inherently much more difficult. In this case, we need to add three more steps before the seven steps:

A. Sense the broader problem.
B. Explore the broader situation.
C. Formulate the broader problem.
   1. Select a specific, desired improvement.
   2. Collect data to understand the exact nature of the problem.
   3. Find the root causes of the most common version of the problem.
   4. Plan and implement a solution.
   5. Check with new data that the solution was effective.
   6. Make the new solution permanent and routine.
   7. Think about what could have been done better, and zero in on the problem to be tackled next. Repeat.

Note that the three added steps require a much more strategic sense of the problem. We will discuss both reactive and proactive improvement in more detail in Sections 2.4.2 and 2.4.3.

2.4.2 Reactive Improvement

The most important and most difficult of the seven steps of reactive improvement is the first one. We now look at the first step in greater detail.

Select a Specific Improvement that Is Desired. Shiba divides this step into four parts:

1. Focus on weakness
2. Problem exploration
3. Selection of theme
4. Statement of theme

Focusing on how to improve our strengths has the unfortunate tendency to cause us to jump to solutions instead of understanding the problem: "What can we do to improve the product finish?" It is more helpful to focus on the facts, on the process, and on causes, rather than solutions. Of course, management must be properly trained not to be upset when weaknesses are presented, but to react positively. This is not always easy.

How can one select which problem to work on out of the many candidates? One important point is to take any known problem and trace forward until it causes another problem, and then trace that forward, and so on, until finally you discover either excessive cost or customer unhappiness. Unless it is ultimately related to one of these, the problem is not worth working on. Once you have done this, trace the problem backward until a root cause can be found which can be remedied. For example, suppose a machine is in poor alignment. Go forward to see that it causes defective product, and thus excessive cost. Then go backward to see that the poor alignment is caused by a worn part, which in turn is caused by infrequent maintenance. This can finally be fixed.

Finally, the problem needs to be stated clearly and cogently. Again, use a weakness orientation to direct the team toward the process and the causes rather than too quickly to solutions. Make the theme customer-oriented. State it as a problem, not a solution. Focus on a single problem, and make every word well-defined.

The 7 QC Tools. There are many types of tools used to perform the seven steps of reactive improvement. Many of the more statistical tools are presented in Total Quality Management Chapter 3. However, there are seven simple tools, called the **7 QC tools**, which TQM emphasizes both because they are simple to use and often very useful.

1. **Check sheet**—A check sheet is a simple form for the collection of data which allows you to check off each occurrence of data, such as weights, sizes, defects, etc. The check sheet is calibrated so that in the process of collecting the data you automatically create a histogram.
2. **Stratification**—Stratification means separating the data into groups to clarify effects. For example, data on defects on a machine might be grouped by separate operators, to see clearly whether one operator produces fewer errors than another.
3. **Pareto chart**—A Pareto chart is a simple bar chart, with the height of each bar representing the importance of a particular problem. The bars are organized in descending order to focus on the most important problems.
4. **Cause-and-effect diagram**—It is easier to solve a problem if the causes and their interrelations are diagrammed. A cause-and-effect diagram shows the main effect as a box to the right, with a horizontal line to the left. Then primary causes are shown branching off, and second-level causes are shown branching off from the primary ones. This is also called a fishbone diagram.
5. **Graphs**—Graphs are devices for visualizing data easily. There are many kinds of graphs, such as bar, line, circle, and so on.
6. **Histogram**—A histogram is basically a graph that shows how data (weights, diameters, etc.) vary. It is usually a bar graph which shows the statistical distribution over equal intervals. We will learn more of the uses of histograms in Total Quality Management Chapter 3.
7. **Scatter diagram**—A scatter diagram is used to support hypotheses on cause-and-effect relationships. For example, a scatter diagram might plot annealing temperature versus final hardness of a shaft.

2.4.3 Proactive Improvement

Reactive improvement is basically myopic—we look around carefully for the next good small improvement, and make it. Proactive improvement is more strategic—the company faces several major directions that could be followed and must decide which one to take.

For the reactive case, we were able to give a rather complete methodology, including the 7 QC steps and the 7 QC tools. But by its very strategic nature, methodologies for proactive improvement are less straightforward. The types of data needed for proactive improvement are basically qualitative; that is, image or language data. Kawakita [1977] has evolved five principles for collecting this type of strategic data.

Kawakita's 5 Principles.

1. **360-degree view.** To create a new product or a new process, you cannot believe your own ideas so strongly that you become insensitive to the customer's needs. You are looking for something new. This contrasts with reactive improvement and process control, where a strong hypothesis is often useful to provide focus.

2. **Stepping-stone approach.** When crossing a stream using stepping stones, you often can succeed only by stepping on one stone, and then opportunistically deciding which to step on next. Similarly, in making a visit to a customer to look for data, leave a flexible schedule: be able to step from one person or place to the next as the opportunity arises during the day. This contrasts with reactive improvement, where perhaps a rigid schedule for customer focus groups may be appropriate.

3. **"By chance."** Recognize opportunities to solve your problem from unexpected situations that may seem unrelated to the problem at hand. By concentrating your attention and sensitivity, you can make the most of the unexpected.

4. **Intuitive capability.** Logic may tell you certain data are unimportant, but if intuition says otherwise, then this is important—human intuition has great capability to find something new.

5. **Qualitative data.** Collect qualitative data, not quantitative data. Collect real cases and personal experiences. The customer may try to generalize, but you must ask for specific personal experience and history. For example, the different types of defects are more important for proactive problems than the number. By contrast, for reactive improvement or simple process control, quantitative data is central.

The Language Processing™ Method (LP) for Proactive Improvement.

The origin of the Language Processing™ Method (LP) is Jiro Kawakita's early work with students doing fieldwork in the 1950s. Methods he developed then for gathering and analyzing data have evolved into the problem-solving approach now called the Language Processing™ Method (LP). We outline the Language Processing™ Method (LP) as adapted for use in the field of quality improvement. Shiba gives more supporting details to these methods.

1. **Agree on a topic.** Begin with careful thought and with team agreement on the appropriate topic to be considered. In many other types of discussions or arguments, an entire meeting may be held without precise agreement on the topic being discussed.

2. **Write and understand the data.** Next, each member of the team writes down several facts they know about the theme (you can use ideas also). Each fact is written on a separate card. Writing the facts makes them explicit so they can be examined by all team members.

3. **Group similar data.** The team then works together to group facts that intuition says are similar to each other. Writing high-quality facts is difficult, although people new to this tool often don't recognize the difficulty. Grouping facts is also difficult, since people new to the tool find it easier to group by logical classification.

4. **Title groups.** The groups of similar facts are then given titles that express the same meaning or images of the group of facts, but at the next higher level of

abstraction. Grouping and titling continue until a hierarchy of no more than five groups exist.

5. **Lay out groups and show relationships among them.** The group hierarchies are then laid out on the page to show clearly the internal structure of the groups and the relationships among the groups.

6. **Vote on the most important low-level issues and draw conclusions.** Once the team has reached a common understanding of the individual facts, their groups and hierarchy, and the relationship among the groups, the team votes on the most important low-level facts. From the important low-level facts a conclusion is drawn. Finally, the team decides what next steps are appropriate.

2.5 HUMAN RESOURCES

2.5.1 Overview

It is critically important that everyone in a company be involved fully in customer satisfaction and continuous improvement activities. TQM is a mass democratic revolution. In today's world it is not enough to depend on only a few select scientific geniuses, financial wizards, or strategic masterminds in a company. Today, absolutely everyone must be motivated and then empowered to improve the way they do their jobs and satisfy their customers (whether external or internal). To help make it possible to help everyone to achieve these goals, companies must change the way they think about and plan work.

All Work Has Two Functions. All companies or departments/units within a company have two different types of basic work—their daily work and their continuous improvement work. The historical method of organizing work within a company produces a division of labor between workers who do the daily work and managers who make improvements in the way daily work is done.

However, this classical organization does not react fast enough for the pace of change in today's world. More than that, it kills human creativity. Few people are satisfied doing the same thing every day according to standard. TQM aims instead to develop human creativity by uniting daily work and improvement work. Daily work is any repeated activity, however long or short the repetition. Examples of daily work include running a machine, typing memos, making coffee, supervising staff, preparing a monthly report, doing a quarterly forecast, and preparing the annual hiring plan. Improvement work is aimed at improving processes for daily work and almost always involves discovering new things. Improvement work itself is more effectively done if a well-structured process is used.

Implementation. Usually people want creative jobs. Nevertheless, when the concept of the dual function of work is introduced, most people view the improvement work as an extra burden for which they have no time. An underlying reason may be a natural human avoidance of change. Since the purpose of TQM is to address the need for rapid change, it is important to put systems in place to facilitate systematic improvement and change and eliminate the "not my job" attitude. In the following sections, we look at various ways to implement the new attitude toward work in the face of this resistance. In particular, we shall discuss the importance of teamwork, involvement of the top leadership, and methods for empowering workers to share in the decision making process.

2.5.2 Teamwork

Teams and teamwork are a fundamental part of the way TQM organizes work. Teamwork is important to quality improvement for several reasons:

- Cross-functional teams are needed to handle greater complexity.
- Individual genius is not sufficient; collective genius must fill this lack.
- Companies must avoid over-specialization and compartmentalization.
- Group learning is more effective for the company than individual learning.
- Groups motivate each other to keep going in the face of difficulty.
- Group learning becomes a group asset as well an individual one.

The most common symptom of teams that don't work is interpersonal conflict. The TQM approach provides methods that minimize conflict in three ways:

1. Providing teams with a clear mission
2. Requiring that plans be based on objective facts
3. Providing a standardized process for analyzing problems and reaching a consensus

Types of Teams. The QC (quality control) circle was invented in Japan to fill the position between the traditional, too-rigid task force team and the traditional, too-flexible informal group. The goal in establishing the QC circle was to establish a work group that continuously works on work-related improvement, by bringing together all the members of a group on a voluntary (or semi-voluntary) basis for individual and mutual development.

TQM has developed three main kinds of teams:

1. Quality circle or quality control (QC) circle
2. Quality improvement team (QI teams, or QITs)
3. Cross-functional team (or cross-company team)

QC circles are at a low level; cross-functional teams are at a reasonably high level; and QI teams are about in the middle. Quality circles and QITs function within one functional area, such as the production floor. Cross-functional or cross-company teams work across functional boundaries. Quality circles are permanent; QITs and cross-functional teams exist only for the length of the task.

QC circles are often made up of individuals who spend most of their time doing work according to standard, for example, workers on a manufacturing line or people doing standard paperwork. The QC circle is a continuing activity that allows the group to work regularly to improve its performance. QC circle activities are mostly concerned with reactive improvement, but sometimes with proactive improvement. QITs are established most often to accomplish a reactive improvement task, although sometimes QITs address proactive tasks. Cross-functional teams are more usually established to accomplish a single proactive improvement, although they could also work on a reactive improvement.

Cross-functional teams allow all functions to meet multiple requirements. Close relationships between different parts of a company yield greater efficiency and faster cycle time. Such teams can coordinate all functions to make market-driven changes.

There are at least three areas of potential difficulty with cross-functional teams:

1. Conflicts among different functional business units

    - Different unit goals
    - Desire of each unit to be independent

2. Conflicts among team members

    - Home unit interests
    - Different experience
    - Personal goals
    - Lack of respect for others on the team
    - Different ranks of people on the team

3. Conflicts between team effort and home unit effort

    - Insufficient time for cross-company efforts
    - Mistrust by home units of teams to take into account real business issues

We may classify ways of dealing with these problems into three groups:

1. Setting up the team
2. Running the team
3. Closing out the team

In terms of setting up the team, it is important to choose a team with sufficient breadth and experience and add one or two junior people as a learning experience. Avoid an over-rigid initial definition of goals. Set aside enough time from regular activities from the start. Make team efforts the first priority, and have a rigid deadline.

In terms of running the team, have travel or social activities to build team loyalty. Avoid divisive debate early in the process. Give TQM training, and direct the focus of the team on the process. Report process rather than results for interim reports. This avoids the tendency of upper management to dictate the solution halfway through.

In terms of closing out the team, the whole team should report the results. The team's findings must be trusted and implemented. Look thoughtfully for ways to improve the process for the next time.

QC Circles. As opposed to cross-functional teams, QC circle members are from within a single functional group, which reduces the potential for conflicts and promotes long-term development of individual and team skill. In Japan, a quality control circle is a small group of about three to ten workers, in whose activities all members participate. If seven employees work together in the same production line, all seven participate in the circle activities; no one is left out. The circle has a two-fold work-related objective: quality control to minimize the quality fluctuation in products and services, and improvement of quality in products and services. In achieving these objectives, the group hopes to work toward the development of the individual worker, which is its main goal.

Two principal features enable the QC circle to reach its goal. First, it applies appropriate process improvement methods, which its members have to learn and apply to the problems they take up. Without this methodology, it would be difficult to improve the quality of a product. Second, QC circles are voluntary in the sense that the workers decide whether they want to set up a circle or not. If they do organize a circle, the choice of problem to focus on is also theirs: they decide on the manner of data gathering, on the planning of countermeasures, and on other matters. In a true QC circle, there is no such thing as an "order from above."

However, someone in management must remain responsible for a team's improvements. Otherwise, the organization could lose control of its activities and adversely affect customer satisfaction. Of course, maintaining control without disempowering a team is a delicate business. Some companies have found it useful for management to suggest the initial problem areas or to review the theme together. Management also may need to review the implementation plan, especially if it affects others. The trick is to maintain awareness of what the team is doing without guiding the team too much, trusting good improvement processes to produce useful results, and then standing behind those results.

Problem solving in the QC circle is a continuous process. Often a group will begin by tackling simple problems, such as cleanliness in their workshop or miscommunication between workers, and move on to more complex ones, especially problems in product quality, productivity, and those that affect multiple groups. This continuity is only possible because the company supports the group. The QC circle also gives workers the opportunity for self-development. Workers learn from each other's strengths; during QC circle conventions, circles share with one another the processes (not the results) they have discovered to be beneficial to their workshops. From a company viewpoint, the most important function of QC circles is to institutionalize the dual function of work for the participants.

QC Circles in the United States Versus Japan. There are now five million participants in QC circles in Japan, and circles in 60 countries. Perhaps one-third of the companies in Japan that have more than 30 employees have QC circles.

The idea that there are cultural factors that make QC circles work better in Japan than in the United States is probably overstated. If one were to consider companies according to national stereotypes, Hitachi would probably be described as being like an American company (frontier spirit), and Florida Power & Light would be like a Japanese company (discipline and structure of improvement activities).

Perhaps the worst mistake that American companies make is expecting immediate competence and enthusiasm in 100 percent of the work force as a quick result from implementing QC circles. This is a mistake that can lead to abandonment of goals and actual failure by default. It would be well to establish realistic expectations regarding responses, enthusiasm, and performance.

The authors suggest seven principles for activating teamwork in QC circles:

1. **Create symbols and norms.** The team needs an identity, which can be supplied by such things as a team name, flags, banners, and logos. Behavioral norms facilitate teamwork.

2. **Understand team members.** Abraham Maslow provides a theoretical framework for understanding needs through his theory of self-actualization, which has four basic elements:

   a. Motives are highly complex.
   b. Lower level needs must be satisfied before higher level needs.
   c. There are always higher level needs to be satisfied.
   d. There are more ways to satisfy higher needs than lower level needs.

3. **Walk, then run.** Teams need early success. Start each team on a problem that is worthwhile but can be solved easily. Choose a problem theme just slightly beyond the team's current knowledge and ability. Provide support for analysis and solution. If there is a big problem to work on, chop it into smaller pieces.

4. **Delegation is only for daily work.** Do not delegate downward—team members must do the work themselves. Neither should you delegate upward—team members are responsible for finding the solution. The job of improvement cannot be delegated. The need to delegate is a symptom that the wrong people are on the team. Everyone is equal within a team. The team members themselves have to gather supplies, take meeting minutes, and participate in problem-solving processes of the team.

5. **Active listening speaks louder than words.** Carl Rogers recognized that a creative problem-solving capacity resides in every individual and developed techniques for releasing that capacity. He advised the following principles of active listening:

   • Listen with empathy, understanding both feeling and content.
   • Clarify by restating, paraphrasing, or summarizing.
   • Question and explore.

   Active listening reduces defensiveness, enhances self-esteem, encourages cooperation, and identifies problems and solutions.

6. **Create an environment for team learning.** Creating an environment conducive to team learning involves attending to three elements: the setup of meetings, the physical arrangement of people at meetings, and the psychological rhythm of meetings.

   The most difficult part of teamwork activities is getting people to reliably come to meetings. It is important to prepare adequately for the meetings.

Schedule them at fixed times well in advance. Do not postpone meetings; this leads to reduced interest and the danger of not meeting again. Take good notes; follow up on absentees. Avoid excessive meetings by good use of bulletin boards, answering machines, and e-mail. Start and finish meetings on time. Always end the meetings with a between-meetings assignment and some socialization at the end.

7. **Structure group and individual work.** Finally, it is important to structure both group work and individual work. In group work, consensus is sought on tasks to be done and the methods of accomplishing the tasks. The tasks are then allocated to individuals or combinations of individuals for execution. Much of the work of the team is actually done as the work of individuals or combinations of individuals.

Creativity in Team Processes. Many people see the group aspects of TQM as a hindrance to creativity. This concern perhaps reflects an unawareness of the differences between creating an original idea and creating an original arrangement of existing ideas, and individual creativity and team creativity.

Creating new arrangements or forms of existing ideas can be very powerful. This is what engineering is all about—the application of scientific ideas. This is what the human resources staff does, and what the sales management staff, the marketing staff, and the manufacturing staff do. Keeping in mind that TQM is a mass movement and companies have but a few geniuses, you see why companies get their best leverage out of teamwork.

2.5.3 Top Leadership

CEO Involvement. The most important aspect of a strategy for implementing TQM is CEO involvement. Successful introductions of TQM in Japan, Europe, and the United States have all started with involvement from the top. The next most important criterion is the absence of strong trade union resistance. But opposition of the workers' organization can be slowly reduced by the efforts of the CEO to build trust and create a role for the unions in the TQM implementation.

Middle- or upper-management may try to introduce TQM without the CEO's involvement, but the long-term success of such an approach depends upon a strong societal quality culture. This approach sometimes works in Japan, but would seem unlikely to succeed in the United States or Europe. It is conceivable for a plant manager or division manager to create an island of TQM if this manager is, in effect, the CEO of his or her operation. In such cases, a manager must control the operation and have no interference from above that negates divisional TQM efforts. However, when the sponsor moves or departs, such TQM islands tend to disappear.

Thus, a company should hesitate before trying to introduce TQM without strong motivation on the part of the CEO. In this situation there is a strong chance of failure, and, once a company fails, success subsequently becomes much more difficult. The initial failure creates a belief within the company that TQM doesn't really work.

The authors have collected Japanese data indicating that if the CEO is involved in QC circle implementation, additional levels of management and workers can be involved in turn. The CEO can bring on board the upper managers and facilitators. If the CEO can make upper managers and facilitators enthusiastic, then middle managers can be convinced. Finally, the middle managers and facilitators bring in workers from the shop or individual contributors.

What Does Top Management Involvement Mean? In unsuccessful cases, the CEO tends to approve the initial TQM decision; in a successful case the CEO makes the decision. In unsuccessful cases, the CEO delegates to quality specialists; in successful cases the CEO initiates planning for implementation. In unsuccessful cases the CEO is passive; in successful cases the CEO participates directly in improvement activities.

What Motivates the CEO to Lead? The first motivator is learning. Most of the CEO's learning comes from outside the company: seminars, pressure from a parent company, communication with other CEOs, and personal experience. Personal experience is particularly influential. The CEO of Xerox visited Fuji Xerox; the CEO of Florida Power & Light visited the Kansai Electric Company.

However, learning alone is not enough to provide the necessary motivation to the CEO. Learning only creates interest in actually doing TQM. The second motivator is fear or crisis: increased costs, reduction of worker motivation, decreased sales or market share, or even bankruptcy. That is not to say that the crisis itself is the motivator. Actual crises are clear to everyone, but by then it may be too late. The CEO's job is to focus on the latent crises that others in the company may not yet see.

2.6 GOALS AND STANDARDS

As we have said many times, TQM is not a process of isolated geniuses creating quality, but of systematic continuous improvement and imitation of successful methods. For this reason, TQM cannot succeed if it is isolated in a single company. It must be done in cooperation with the network of companies, customers, and suppliers. This is called networking. The company must imitate success stories in other companies in the industry, which is called benchmarking. The company can well measure itself by broad industry standards, such as the ISO 9000. It should also strive to be the very best, and to covet major awards for quality, such as the Deming, Baldrige, and European Quality awards. Finally, the company needs to become involved in a broad network of quality among many companies, giving and taking in a joint effort to improve global quality.

Networking. One problem in implementing TQM is that for some types of information and skill, a catch-22 exists that makes internal development of methods difficult, so that societal diffusion becomes all the more important. For example, it is difficult for CEOs to be taught new methods of leadership by those below them in the company hierarchy; therefore, CEOs must get most of their information about TQM from outside their company hierarchy.

At all levels in a corporation, the existence of success stories and managers experienced in TQM makes TQM easier to practice. But how does a company that is just beginning its TQM implementation find success stories on which to model is own activities or experienced managers on whom to model its behavior? Executives should be looking outside their own companies or organizations for knowledge, training, and examples of TQM practice.

Companies need to participate in societal networking of TQM for reasons beyond the simple desire to gain efficiency in their TQM implementations. A company is unlikely to be able to do high-quality work in a low-quality culture. If a company resides in a national or regional environment of poorly-trained workers, customers tolerant of low-quality products, and weak competitors, it is unlikely that the company can find the will and the means for producing high-quality products. In particular, a company cannot stand on quality alone, without quality suppliers.

To summarize, companies need to network for three reasons:

1. To avoid reinventing the wheel of quality
2. To create mutual learning and sharing among companies
3. To create a quality culture in which to do business

Benchmarking. Robert C. Camp of Xerox Corporation gives the following two definitions of benchmarking:

1. Benchmarking is the continuous process of measuring products, services, and practices against the toughest competitors or those companies recognized as industry leaders.
2. Benchmarking is the search for industry best practices that lead to superior performance.

Camp also discusses the following benchmarking paradigm at length:

Planning Phase

1. Identify what is to be benchmarked.
2. Identify comparative companies.
3. Determine data collection methods and collect data.

Analysis Phase

4. Determine the current performance "gap."
5. Project future performance levels.

Integration Phase

6. Communicate benchmark findings and gain acceptance.
7. Establish functional goals.

Action Phase

8. Develop action plans.
9. Implement specific actions and monitor progress.
10. Recalibrate benchmarks.

Return to step 1.

ISO 9000. ISO 9000 is a set of quality standards developed in Europe which have become the de facto standard for doing business in Europe, and which have been widely adopted around the world. ISO 9000 is a set of five worldwide standards which establish a framework for TQM. These are not standards for measuring *products*, but standards for measuring *processes*. This measuring is accomplished basically by internal and external audits of the company. The idea is to make sure that a certified company has a quality system that can ensure that it can meet its published *product* standards. These standards have been fully adopted by the twelve nations of the European Economic Community (EEC).

In 1987, the same year the ISO 9000 standards were announced, the United States adopted a nearly identical system. By 1992 more than 20,000 plants or facilities in Great Britain had adopted the standards and become certified. Another 20,000 had been certified in other EEC countries. Only about 620 U.S. companies had adopted the system. Japan had also adopted the standards, and had mounted a major national effort to meet them. The mechanics and benefits of ISO 9000 are described in more detail by Ross [1995].

Awards for Quality.

Deming Award. Deming popularized quality control in Japan in the 1950s and eventually became a national hero for quality in Japan. Using the royalties from a book based on his lectures, Deming established the Deming prize in Japan. This is a very prestigious award, and has been credited with accelerating Japan's drive toward exceptional quality. No more than one Deming prize is awarded per year.

Baldrige Award. In the United States, congress established the similar Baldrige Award in 1987. The Baldrige Award has had immense impact in the United States, just as the Deming Prize did in Japan. The award has created a national standard for quality, and hundreds of corporations use its criteria as a basic guide for TQM.

European Quality Award. The European Foundation for Quality Management (EFQM) granted the first European quality awards in 1992. There are two types of award. One, more similar to the Deming award, can be won only by a single firm. Another type of award is more like the Baldrige, and is available to any firm with a sufficiently high score on a number of categories.

2.7 COMPANY APPLICATION SCENARIO—REPRISE

Seth Stag spent six weeks interviewing Jack Slade, his top management, the software engineers and programmers, customer support, shipping, accounting and marketing. With Jack Slade's permission, he also conducted extensive interviews with a number of customers, including those who had moved from using CADS to CADPRO, those still using CADS but who had recently voiced complaints, and those still using CADS who had not complained. He stratified his sampling procedure to get a reasonable mix of large and small companies, highly technical engineering and less technical engineering users, and so forth.

As he analyzed his interviews, it soon became obvious to Seth what the real nature of the problem was. The more interviews and data came in, the more he became convinced. He wrote out a rather complete analysis of the difficulties that ESS was facing. The only problem was, he couldn't figure out a good way to present his findings to Jack Slade, since his conclusion was that all the problems stemmed from Jack Slade!! When he voiced his concerns to Sylvia Stalone, another senior partner at Quality Associates, she suggested he make a mock half-hour presentation to Jack Slade in front of the other senior partners, to solicit their advice. This was soon arranged, and Seth gave the report shown in Figure 2-4.

A Mock Report to Jack Slade

Jack Slade, you are a brilliant and unbelievably successful man, a genius of sorts. You had the idea for CADS.1 thirty years ago, when there was no other software product remotely competitive. It was not important whether the product function aligned itself perfectly with what the customer wanted, again because there was no competition. Nor was it important whether the product was extremely easy to use: it was the only show in town!

Times have changed. Your very fantastic growth has spawned competition. CADPRO is a product comparable to yours. You clearly have lost some market share to CADPRO, and are continuing to do so. Since there is now some very effective competition, you can no longer put out a product that you think the customers *should* want. In TQM terms, this is called the *product-out* approach. Instead, you must find what the customers *do* want, and then try to put out a product which gives it to them. In TQM terms, this is called the *market-in* approach.

To be more specific, you have developed a very sophisticated automatic tabu search method. My samples suggest that perhaps 30 percent of your customers appreciate having this method as an option, and maybe 10 percent use it to the exclusion of less automatic methods such as interactive search. But your software requires a fair amount of user effort to override the automatic search! CADPRO's automatic search method is less sophisticated; it is also almost effortless in CADPRO to shift back and forth between methods. In fact, CADPRO users who want only interactive search need hardly be aware that the automatic search mode is available! Mr. Slade, rewriting the manual to try to educate customers to want what you have simply won't work. You need to revamp the product to keep your fancy method, perhaps, but to copy CADPRO's user flexibility in the search method. Similarly, rewriting the product manual to explain how better to use the product isn't much use if CADPRO is truly easier to use.

Figure 2-4

A Mock Report to Jack Slade

Figure 2-4

A Mock Report to Jack
Slade (continued)

I recommend that you tabulate the various complaints about your product, on both the automatic search issue, and the more general issue of user friendliness. Carefully choose ten to twenty companies. Go out and do in-depth interviews with each personally. When you analyze the data, keep *market-in* firmly in mind. Change the product to fit what the customers want, rather than educating the customers to what you want.

Finally, there's the whole question of the quality of your production process: lost orders, late orders, confused customer service, and so forth. These also are symptoms of the way your company was formed, Mr. Slade. You were a bright "hot shot" and you naturally hired other bright hot shots. You developed norms of loyalty, informality, and hard work. Unfortunately, such a culture often leads to an unregimented individualistic style, often called *the wild west*. As you are aware, this culture must gradually be changed if you are to raise the quality of the production process. You have given lectures to all of your staff. Unfortunately, this is not really nearly enough to accomplish much of anything. History shows that in order for anything to change, you yourself must become deeply committed to TQM and study it intensely in other companies. Then there is a whole complex process for phasing in TQM within your company. For starters, I recommend that you read *A New American TQM—Four Practical Revolutions in Management*" by Shiba, Graham, and Walden.

Aftermath. The senior partners listened attentively and sympathetically to Seth Stag's mock presentation to Jack Slade. Then they discussed among themselves how to proceed. Some wanted to tone down the product aspect and only to suggest more training for the production process at ESS. However, Sylvia Stalone pointed out the following facts:

a. Raymond Star had intervened to get outside help for Jack.
b. Jack was familiar with how serious his situation was.

She therefore suggested that Seth Stag invite both Raymond Star and Jack Slade out to dinner at a local restaurant, and present the full story to them as gently as possible.

As it happened, Jack Slade took the presentation fairly well. It had definitely been a good move to invite Raymond Star, who was much more than a banker to Jack. While Jack was still not convinced that the customers could not be trained better, he agreed to the in-depth interviews and to talk to Seth Stag and Raymond Star again after that time. He also agreed to take an exhaustive TQM course for CEOs offered by the Quality Institute in Chicago. While it was too early to be sure, Seth Stag felt comfortable that things were on the right track at last for Engineering Software Systems.

Statistical Production Quality

3.1 INTRODUCTION

The most fundamental point in TQM, which we have stressed repeatedly, is that long-range strategic quality cannot be obtained by inspecting the final product and discarding or reworking those units which do not meet pre-set standards. In the short run, this is a very expensive way of maintaining some standards. In the middle run, since we are paying no attention to the *process* by which we are making units, we have little protection against the process drifting or breaking down. In the longest run, our ignorance of the process prevents us from making repeated small improvements to the process and lowering our costs.

One's ability to move from the old methods of quality by inspection to a full appreciation of continuous improvement using process control depends on answering the following questions:

1. What are the sources of product variability in use?
2. What are the sources of variability in the production process?
3. In what ways does the process vary over time?
4. What is the distinction between a capable process and a controlled process?
5. How can charts be useful for process control?
6. How can charts be useful for process improvement?

Sources of Product Variability. Taguchi suggested that variation of performance of a product in use (he called this **functional variation**) comes from three basic sources:

1. **Environmental noise.** This noise is comprised of external factors that arise from the environment in which the product is being used. Examples include temperature, humidity, dust, voltage fluctuations, vibration, and human error. Note that here the noise is influencing performance as seen in the field.
2. **Aging noise.** Aging noise is internal deterioration of the product due to mechanical wear, weathering, fatigue, and alignment drift.
3. **Production noise.** This is variation in the product from unit to unit when shipped. It is caused by variation in the manufacturing process.

Taguchi applied the concepts of environmental noise, aging noise, and production noise to sources of variability in the manufacturing process as well as to units of product. His methods of statistical experiments for design are aimed primarily at reducing these problems at the design stage.

Sources of Process Variability. Experts in dealing with process variation tend to classify process variation into two types: let us call them Type 1 and Type 2. Type 1 variation is caused by a special problem of one type or another. Examples include a less skilled temporary operator, use of the wrong grade of oil, or a broken cutting tool. Various experts call Type 1 variation **assignable causes**, **local faults**, **special causes**, or **sporadic problems**.

Type 2 variation, on the other hand, is caused by problems with the overall system itself. Examples include poor supervision, poor training, a cramped workstation, or inappropriate methods. Various experts call Type 2 variation **chance causes**, **system faults**, **common causes**, or **chronic problems**.

Process Variability Over Time. Statistical process control methods typically track some measurement that is a summary description of the units being produced at a station (such as weight, diameter, or thickness). Samples are taken at regular points in time, and the mean and the variability of that measurement are charted. If these quantities are stable over time, then only Type 2 or common causes may be assumed to be operating. If they are not stable (for example, if one sample has a very high mean), then Type 1 or assignable causes are assumed present, and an investigation is made to determine the exact nature of the problem.

The kinds of Type 1 problems which may be observed include the following:

1. Mean shifts up and down unpredictably
2. Mean increases (or decreases) permanently at a point
3. Mean increases (or decreases) gradually over time
4. Variability increases gradually over time
5. Variability is erratic over time
6. Mixtures of the above

The type of problem often gives a clue to finding the cause. For example, a gradual increase in the roughness of parts might be due to increasing tool wear.

Economic Control of Manufacturing. When a process is not in a controlled state, the cost of the process is likely to be very high even though adequate product is being shipped to the customers. Shewhart recognized very clearly that the presence of out-of-control behavior in a process is a signal that the process is currently experiencing high costs due to waste and inefficiency. To see this clearly, we next discuss the distinction between process control and process capability.

Since the ideas of process control and process capability both involve comparison of actual variation patterns to pre-established norms, it is easy to understand why the two are often confused. However, the origin and meaning of these two concepts are entirely different. That the process is *capable* means that the characteristics of the product are currently falling within specifications and hence that the customer is currently satisfied. That the process is, in addition, falling within the limits of variation for routine process operation implies that the customer is not only satisfied, but is being satisfied by a cost/effective means of production. Product specifications were set at the engineering design stage. Allowable process variation is being set continually by the observed historical pattern of deviation of the process.

Figure 3-1 compares the issues of product conformance and process control. Figure 3-1(a) shows that the product is currently meeting specifications. Figure 3-1(b) shows the same quality characteristic in the form of control charts for the average quality of a sample and the average variability in a sample. The process variation currently does not seem to fall within the predictable limits defined by common-cause variation. The process is not in control in terms of either its mean or variability.

Since the process is not in control in a statistical sense, although it may be making a product satisfactory to the customer, we are most likely spending much more money to

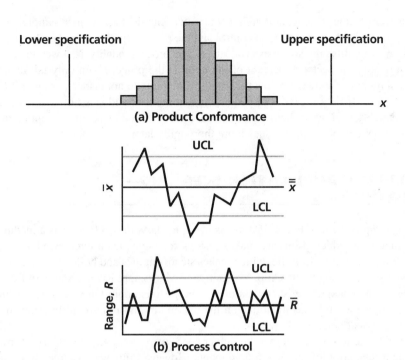

(a) Product Conformance

(b) Process Control

make the product than we would if it were in control. Shewhart's control chart is a tool which helps us to be aware that the process is no longer in a routine state and that continued operation in the current conditions will be wasteful.

Control charts involve taking regular samples, plotting the mean and variability of each sample, and watching for patterns or unusual means or variabilities that indicate the process has changed. There are three basic purposes that such control charts can serve:

1. To serve as a means to help identify sporadic (Type 1) faults in the process, and help suggest corrective actions
2. To serve as a means to help identify chronic (Type 2) faults in the process, and help suggest corrective actions
3. To help provide a tool for making a sound decision directly at the workstation as to whether to take action to adjust the process or leave it alone

Although these may seem similar, in fact they are not. Activities 1 and 2 are strictly off-line activities, which will often be accomplished by quality circles or management intervention. Activity 3 must be done on-line by the operator and can only refer to preliminary screening for sporadic faults. This screening must be sufficient to decide whether additional off-line investigation is warranted. In order for control charting to be useful in pinpointing off-line problems and helping to solve them, it is necessary to understand that we are using a three-step process:

1. Using charting to identify the presence of process faults
2. Using experience and diagnostic methods to find the basic cause of the fault that has thus been identified
3. Developing a good action plan to effectively correct the fault on a permanent basis

To Final Inspect or Not to Final Inspect? Given the realization that final inspection is no substitute for good control of the process for making the product or for continuous improvement of that process, the question still remains: is final "acceptance sampling" of the product before delivery a sound idea? If so, how should this inspection procedure be designed and carried out?

The answer is rather simple, although it contradicts classical acceptance sampling theory. If the process is in good statistical control and the process quality is higher than a certain break-even quality, do not inspect at all. If the process quality is lower than that break-even quality, inspect 100 percent of the item. If the process is in only fair control but quality stays either above or below the break-even point, do not inspect, or inspect 100 percent as before. If the process is in poor statistical control, and it is not clear whether the process quality is above or below break-even, then modified inspection sampling may be appropriate. We explore these issues more thoroughly later in the chapter.

3.2 COMPANY APPLICATION SCENARIO— PRESTO PISTONS

Jack James, the president of Presto Pistons, is in a quandary. Presto Pistons is a medium-sized machine shop which primarily makes pistons for large steam engines. One of his largest customers is Southern Belle, which makes steam engines and boiler assemblies for tourist steamboats which ply the Ohio, Missouri, and Mississippi Rivers. Southern Belle's purchasing agent issued a new specification for the pistons about ten weeks ago, which significantly tightened the specifications on the maximum and minimum diameter to be allowed for any piston accepted.

Jack's first reaction had been that the tighter specs were not really necessary; he tried to negotiate a relaxation of the new requirements. However, this was completely unsuccessful. In fact, Southern Belle became somewhat testy that the attempt was even made. Soon the relationship became somewhat cool. Jack next thought that he could wait them out, that sooner or later they would be forced to accept the existing product. But this did not happen. In fact, Southern Belle pointedly sent him a fax of an internal memo listing possible alternative suppliers. Jack was now beginning to believe that steps should be taken to improve the product. But what, and by whom?

Controlling the Product Versus Controlling the Process. A simplified description of the process for determining a piston diameter is as follows. First a blank casting is made, which is somewhat too large. Then a numerically controlled milling machine with a coarse cutting tool takes off most of the excess material. Next, a numerically controlled milling machine with a fine cutting tool takes off most of the rest of the excess material. A final grinding and polishing step produces the final diameter.

Staff engineers did an initial study which revealed that the problem lay with the coarse milling machine, which seemed to produce variable results, often already below specs. As a temporary solution, management decided to take off a smaller amount of material with the coarse milling machine and do a 100 percent inspection of these partially finished products. The smaller ones already within appropriate specs would then be processed further and finished. The rest would have a brief second pass through the coarse milling machine, followed by a 100 percent inspection, and so on. Just to make sure, there would also be a final 100 percent inspection of pistons meant for Southern Belle, to make sure all product shipped was within their new standards. Final product that was too small would be scrapped. Final product that was too large could be reworked.

This rather ad-hoc process worked pretty well, and there was even some discussion about making it permanent. However the president, Jack James, felt that this solution was much too costly and did not really get at the root cause of the problem. So he commissioned his staff to study the new problem. They determined that the coarse milling machine was of an old technology and could not be retrofitted. They had researched a new milling machine that had a track record for superior accuracy. They wanted approval to buy it.

Jack felt this was premature. In his experience there was a tendency to go run after a new machine to solve a problem rather than learning how to use the existing equipment better. So, as a first step, he commissioned a study of how quality was currently being maintained on the coarse milling machine and how it might be improved. They could always fall back on a new machine.

3.3 REVIEW OF STATISTICAL TOOLS FOR QUALITY MANAGEMENT

3.3.1 The Basics

Summarizing Data. Methods for process control and final inspection all depend on using samples from a manufacturing and/or an engineering process to make inferences about the past, present, or future behavior of the entire process. Thus, a basic knowledge of data structures, probability, statistics, and econometric methods is necessary for understanding this material. While you are assumed to possess some background in these areas, a brief review may be appropriate.

Suppose that an engineer is studying a pilgering machine which extrudes a metal bar into a series of nuclear fuel tubes. The tubes are supposed to weigh 8.5 pounds each; it is desired to check periodically to see if the machine is producing tubes of the right weight.

Once a week, five tubes are selected at random from the latest batch and weighed. Table 3-1 gives samples for 13 weeks, each of which is a record of the weights of five tubes drawn at random for that week. The table also lists the average weight and range for each sample, as well as a grand average, and an average range for the 13-week period.

The average of the observed values of a sample is defined as:

$$\overline{X} = (X_1 + X_2 + \ldots + X_n)/n \qquad (1)$$

In Table 3-1 the weights of nuclear fuel tubes from a pilgering machine are listed five in a row for each weekly sample. The average of the first sample, for example is:

$$\overline{X}_1 = (8.4 + 8.5 + 9.4 + 8.0 + 9.0)/5 = 8.66 \text{ pounds}$$

If we assume that the process is drifting slightly from week to week, then 8.66 pounds is an estimate of the weights being generated by the process in week 1. However, if we feel that the drift of the process is negligible, then 8.66 is an estimate of the weights being generated by the process throughout the 13 weeks. We are also very interested in how variable the weights of the fuel tubes are that are being generated. One important measure is the sample variance, and its square root, the sample standard deviation. The sample variance, denoted by S_x^2 is defined as:

Table 3-1

Fuel Tube Weights (Kilograms)

Sample	X_1	X_2	X_3	X_4	X_5	Mean $\overline{X}$	Range R
1	8.4	8.5	9.4	8.0	9.0	8.66	1.4
2	9.3	8.9	8.6	7.6	8.5	8.58	1.7
3	7.8	7.2	8.6	8.5	7.6	7.94	1.4
4	9.8	9.0	8.4	8.4	8.5	8.82	1.4
5	8.4	9.7	8.5	9.2	8.5	8.86	1.3
6	8.3	7.9	7.4	8.1	8.1	7.96	0.9
7	8.4	8.0	8.7	8.7	8.1	8.38	0.7
8	8.6	8.2	9.0	8.2	9.1	8.62	0.9
9	7.2	8.1	8.6	8.2	8.3	8.08	1.4
10	7.8	8.7	8.5	8.9	9.1	8.60	1.3
11	8.0	7.8	8.6	9.4	8.1	8.38	1.6
12	8.0	7.4	7.9	8.1	8.5	7.98	1.1
13	8.4	9.0	8.3	9.9	9.4	9.00	1.6

$$\overline{X}_{av} = 8.451 \qquad \overline{R} = 1.28$$

$$S_x^2 = [(X_1 - \overline{X})^2 + (X_2 - \overline{X})^2 + \ldots + (X_n - \overline{X})^2] / (n - 1) \qquad (2)$$

Very often we are more interested in the square root of the sample variance because it is expressed in the same units as the data. It is called the sample standard deviation S_x. It is something like an average variation of the data, except that larger deviations get more than their share of the weight. Again for the first sample:

$$S_x^2 = [(8.4 - 8.66)^2 + (8.5 - 8.66)^2 + (9.4 - 8.66)^2 + (8.0 - 8.66)^2 + (9.0 - 8.66)^2]/4$$

$$S_x^2 = 1.173/4 = 0.279$$

$$S_x = [0.279]^{0.5} = 0.53$$

Thus we estimate the variance of the process in week 1 at 0.279, and the standard deviation as 0.53. If we feel that the process is stable over the 13 weeks, then these also estimate the variance and standard deviation of the entire process.

Another important measure of the variability of the process is the range, denoted by R, the difference between the largest and smallest value in the sample:

$$R = X_L - X_S \qquad (3)$$

The range of the first week's sample in the table is $R_1 = 9.4 - 8.0 = 1.4$.

For normal distributions when a sample of size 5 is drawn, the range divided by the constant 2.326 gives another estimate of the standard deviation. In this case $1.4/2.326 = 0.60$, which relates well to our sample standard deviation of 0.53. Since the range gives good estimates of the standard deviation for small samples, and because it is very easy to use, the range is typically used in quality control applications.

Basic Concepts of Probability, Distributions, and the Normal Distribution.

These ideas are briefly presented in Appendices A and G on the normal distribution. We do not give most of them here. However, we discuss the unit normal table, and give an abbreviated table for convenience.

Suppose a normal distribution has mean μ and standard deviation σ; we wish to know the probability that a value will be less than x.

1. Calculate $z = (x - \mu)/\sigma$.
2. Look up the corresponding percentile in Table 3-2.

Example 3-1. The height of Romulans is 75 inches, with a standard deviation of 4 inches. Assuming normality, what is the probability that a Romulan is over 83 inches tall? We have $z = (83 - 75)/4 = 2.00$. We see that 97.7 percent of Romulans are below this height, and so 2.3 percent are over 83 inches tall.

Table 3-2

Unit Normal Table

z Value	Percentile	z Value	Percentile
0.0	.500	1.5	.933
0.1	.540	1.6	.945
0.2	.579	1.7	.955
0.3	.618	1.8	.964
0.4	.655	1.9	.971
0.5	.692	2.0	.977
0.6	.726	2.1	.982
0.7	.758	2.2	.986
0.8	.788	2.3	.989
0.9	.816	2.4	.992
1.0	.841	2.5	.994
1.1	.864	2.6	.995
1.2	.885	2.7	.996
1.3	.903	2.8	.997
1.4	.919	2.9	.998

Example 3-2. What height must a Romulan have to be in the bottom 25th percentile of heights? Now we use the table backwards. We look up 0.250 and interpolate back to find the z. The table goes down to only a cumulative probability of 0.500. However, it is symmetric around 50 percent. So we can look up a z for 75 percent, and then put a minus sign on it. We interpolate to get $z = -0.68$. Now, since $z = (x - \mu)/\sigma$ we have that the desired x is given by:

$$x = \mu + z\sigma = 75 + (-0.68)(4) = 75 - 2.72 = 72.28$$

Thus, the shortest 25 percent of Romulans are under 72.3 inches tall.

3.3.2 Sampling Distributions

Sampling from Stable Populations. We know that taking the average $\overline{X}$ of a sample of size n from a large stable population gives us an estimate of the unknown mean of the population. Suppose now we repeat this process several times; we would find that the $\overline{X}$ values obtained would themselves vary, due to the inherent variability in the sampling process. This variation depends partly on the variability of the parent population, and partly on how large a sample we have drawn.

More specifically, if we draw samples of size n from the parent population and find their means, the results themselves will have a distribution, called the sampling distribution.

Let us first give the mean and variance of the sampling distribution for $\overline{X}$ in terms of the original population. It can be shown (we omit the proof) that sampling is unbiased, that on average sampling gives the right answer, and that is that $E(\overline{X}) = \mu_X$. Next it can be shown (no proof) that the error, as represented by the sampling (not sample) variance, goes down as $(1/n)$ where n is the sample size, that is, that $V(\overline{X}) = V(x)/n = \sigma^2/n$. Thus, as the sample size increases, the sample means $\overline{X}$ tend to cluter around the true mean with ever reduced spread.

This nice relationship holds true for any parent population whatever, so long as the population is stable and has an absolutely constant mean; that is, the process is in perfect statistical control. If there is any drift at all in the mean, these results have to be modified, as discussed below.

Central Limit Theorem. So far we have been able to specify the mean and variance of the sampling distribution of the average of a sample of size n taken from a population in statistical control. What, if anything, can we say about the form of the sampling distribution? Here a powerful theorem (which we will not prove) comes to our aid. The **Central Limit Theorem** states that if we draw repeated samples from the same distribution, then for large sample sizes n, the sampling distribution of $\overline{X}$ will be approximately normal. The approximation gets better and better for larger n. This remarkable result does not depend on how nice the original distribution was, only that we draw from exactly the same distribution, and that we draw independently each time. In practice, convergence is remarkably fast.

3.3.3 Statistical Exercises

Summarizing Data.

1. You are the production manager for a line making flashlight batteries. There are numerous complaints about the quality of your product, in particular the battery life. You decide to set up a sampling procedure to test the batteries produced on each shift. What are the potential advantages and disadvantages of each of the following types of sampling?

   a. Test four batteries taken at the beginning of the shift.

    b. Test four batteries spaced equally through the shift.
    c. Test four batteries picked at random during the shift.
    d. Test every battery.

2. The data in Table 3-3 represent the length in inches of standard pieces of finished lumber produced in a sawmill. Five pieces comprised a sample. A new sample was drawn every two hours over four eight-hour shifts.

    a. Calculate sample means and ranges.
    b. Calculate the grand mean and the average range.
    c. Do you think the mean of the process is stable? Why?
    d. Do you think the variability of the process is stable? Why?

3. For the data in Table 3-3:

    a. Tabulate the number of individual operations at each length.
    b. Prepare a frequency histogram of the data (a bar chart).
    c. Comment on the shape of the distribution.

4. For the data in Table 3-3:

    a. Tabulate the first four individual sample standard deviations.
    b. Tabulate the grand sample standard deviation.

    (*Hint:* Using the histogram from problem 3 can save you a lot of work.)

5. The data in Table 3-4 represents the diameters of shafts that are supposed to have a nominal diameter of 2.070 inches. Samples of size four were drawn from the process once every two hours.

    a. Calculate sample means and ranges.
    b. Calculate the grand mean and the average range.
    c. Do you think the mean of the process is stable? Why?
    d. Do you think the variability of the process is stable? Why?

6. Investigate whether the process in Table 3-4 has a time trend using a regression package such as in Pom-Pom. How do your results square with what you learned from problem 5?

7. A board game uses two dice, one red and one white. The values on each die are: 0, 1, 2, 3, 4, or 5. Both are tossed. Let X_1 be the result for the red die, and X_2 be the result for the white die.

Table 3-3

Length of Standard Lumber
Pieces in Inches

Sample	X_1	X_2	X_3	X_4	X_5
1	116	117	115	116	115
2	122	120	116	119	110
3	116	119	116	113	116
4	117	118	113	120	116
5	111	119	120	117	114
6	121	117	116	117	118
7	118	115	116	115	119
8	116	119	111	118	117
9	116	116	114	115	115
10	117	114	119	116	118
11	120	120	118	117	113
12	122	114	115	119	116
13	113	110	111	114	109
14	114	116	118	116	122
15	120	119	114	121	120
16	121	119	118	119	117

Table 3-4

Diameters of Shafts

Sample	X_1	X_2	X_3	X_4
1	2.068	2.063	2.073	2.070
2	2.092	2.060	2.064	2.068
3	2.081	2.090	2.051	2.079
4	2.074	2.064	2.094	2.076
5	2.064	2.063	2.086	2.098
6	2.071	2.080	2.057	2.084
7	2.087	2.097	2.082	2.072
8	2.065	2.058	2.072	2.086
9	2.085	2.044	2.054	2.091
10	2.073	2.084	2.085	2.073
11	2.068	2.071	2.065	2.065
12	2.073	2.106	2.074	2.083
13	2.107	2.081	2.121	2.073
14	2.092	2.059	2.101	2.089
15	2.090	2.099	2.086	2.075
16	2.107	2.094	2.075	2.087

a. Compute $E(X_1)$ and $Var(X_1)$.
b. Find the probability distribution of the sum $X_1 + X_2$.

   (***Hint:*** There are 36 possible outcomes which can be shown in a 6-by-6 table. Each outcome has probability 1/36. Now simply count those with the same sum.)

8. In problem 7:
   a. Show $E(X_1 + X_2) = E(X_1) + E(X_2)$.
   b. Show $Var(X_1 + X_2) = Var(X_1) + Var(X_2)$.
   c. Using the probability distribution you found for $Y = X_1 + X_2$, evaluate the probability that $2.5 < Y < 6.5$.

The Normal Distribution.

9. In problem 8, approximate the distribution of $X_1 + X_2$ using a normal distribution. How good an approximation does this give for (c)?
10. Assume a process is in good statistical control and that individual measurements follow a normal distribution with mean of 36.43 and standard deviation of 0.75. What percentage of the output is expected to lie within the range 35.5 and 37.2?
11. For a process that makes window panes, the thickness of the glass can be assumed to have a normal distribution with a mean of 0.31 centimeters and a standard deviation of 0.025 centimeters. Below what value will 5 percent of the thicknesses be?
12. Thirty samples of five ball bearings are weighed. The grand mean of the individual items is 250.4 grams. The grand standard deviation of the individual items is 1.36 grams. What do you predict the standard deviation of the sample means should be (approximately)?

3.4 CONTROL CHARTS

3.4.1 Overview

In this section we develop the theory and practice of control charts in some detail. In Section 3.4.2 we discuss control charts for data which vary numerically, such as width, weight, diameter, and so forth. In Section 3.4.3 our attention shifts to control charts for data which have an all-or-nothing characteristic called **attributes**, such as defects or blemishes.

3.4.2 Control Charts for Variable Data

Charting Basics. The basic charts for variable data are the $\overline{X}$ chart (chart of the sample mean versus time) and the R chart (chart of the sample range versus time). We present here all the necessary equations and procedures for these charts.

The first step is proper selection of the samples. It is important to choose samples in such a way as to avoid observations which are contaminated by special problem situations (Type 1 variation). This makes it easier to see Type 1 variation when it occurs between two successive samples.

In classic control charting, one should avoid sampling from different machines, sampling over extended periods of time, and sampling from products with mixed sources. The sample size should be small because sampling is expensive, and we wish the sample to be homogenous.

On the other hand, the sample size should be larger in order to minimize the statistical error in estimating the current process mean and variability. As a reasonable compromise, sample sizes are very often taken at $n = 5$ for historical reasons (easy hand computation). Sample sizes between $n = 3$ and $n = 6$ are most common. Sometimes only samples sizes of $n = 1$ or $n = 2$ are practical. This case will be discussed later. In order to start control charting, a fairly large base of perhaps 20 to 60 samples is desirable, although again only a smaller number may sometimes be practical.

The following mathematical steps define how to set up and maintain $\overline{X}$ and R control charts. Define n as the sample size, k as the number of samples, X_{ij} as the jth measurement of the ith sample, $(X_L)_i$ as the largest value of the ith sample, and $(X_S)_i$ as the smallest value. Let μ_R be the true unknown mean of the ranges, let μ_X be the true unknown process mean, and let σ_X the true unknown process standard deviation.

1. Calculate the average of each sample: $\overline{X}_i = \Sigma X_{ij}/_n$.
2. Calculate the range of each sample: $R_i = (R_L)_i - (R_S)_i$.
3. Calculate the grand average: $\overline{X}_{av} = \Sigma X_i / k$.

(Equivalently, we may also add up all nk sample values and divide by nk.) This is an estimate of the true process mean μ_X and becomes the centerline of the $\overline{X}$ control chart.

4. Calculate the average of the sample ranges $\overline{R} = \Sigma R_i / k$.
5. The true standard deviation of the process is related to the true range of the process by $\sigma_X = \mu_R/d_2$ where d_2 is a constant (for normal distributions) depending on the sample size. An abbreviated table for d_2 is given in Table 3-5.
6. The formulas for the centerline, and upper and lower control limits (UCL and LCL) for the $\overline{X}$ control chart are as follows: (We use plus or minus three standard deviations of the sampling distribution.)

$$\text{CENTERLINE} = \overline{X}_{av}$$
$$\text{UCL} = \overline{X}_{av} + (3\overline{R})/(d_2 n^{0.5})$$
$$\text{LCL} = \overline{X}_{av} - (3\overline{R})/(d_2 n^{0.5})$$

Table 3-5

Variable Control Chart Constants

n	d_2	A_2	D_3	D_4
2	1.128	1.880	0.000	3.267
3	1.693	1.023	0.000	2.575
4	2.059	0.729	0.000	2.282
5	2.326	0.577	0.000	2.115
10	3.078	0.308	0.223	1.777
15	3.472	0.223	0.348	1.652
20	3.735	0.180	0.414	1.586

7. If we define $A_2 = 3/(d_2 n^{0.5})$ as a function of n, then these formulas simplify to:

$$\text{UCL} = \overline{X}_{av} + A_2 \overline{R}$$
$$\text{LCL} = \overline{X}_{av} - A_2 \overline{R} \tag{4}$$

Values for A_2 for differing values of n are also given in Table 3-5.

8. We omit the details for deriving the R control chart, noting only that it is possible to estimate σ_R directly from $\overline{R}$. The centerline is $\overline{R}$, and the limits are plus or minus $3\sigma_R$. Again simplifying the constants, we have:

$$\text{CENTERLINE} = \overline{R}$$
$$\text{UCL} = D_4 \overline{R}$$
$$\text{LCL} = D_3 \overline{R} \tag{5}$$

The constants D_3 and D_4 for differing values of n are also given in Table 3-5.

Out of Control Conditions. $\overline{X}$ and R control charts for variable data graphically depict how many standard deviations each observation (of either sample average or range) lies above or below the base line. If a point is more than 3 standard deviations above or below the mean, we will call it a level-3 point. If it is between 2 and 3 standard deviations either above or below, we will call it a level-2 point. A level-1 point is between 1 and 2 standard deviations from the base line. A level-0 point is less than 1 standard deviation from the base line.

Many users of control charts look only for points lying outside the limits in order to specify that a process is out of control. However, this is only one of several conditions that we should be alert for. There are at least four classes of out-of-control behavior on either $\overline{X}$ or R charts that it is useful to be on the lookout for:

- A high proportion of points near or beyond the control limits
- Sudden shifts in the level
- Trends or cyclic behavior
- Bimodal behavior

For each of these we will discuss briefly shop conditions that could cause this problem, and then give one or more diagnostic tests for the problem.

A High Proportion of Points Near or Beyond the Control Limits. This may be due to poor control in the nature of incoming raw materials or overcontrol of the process. It may also be a secondary symptom of trends or bimodal behavior discussed later.

Test 1: Out of control if a single point is level-3 in $\overline{X}$ or R chart.

Test 2: Out of control if two out of three consecutive points are level-2 or level-3.

Test 3: Out of control if four out of five consecutive points are level-1, level-2 or level-3.

All of these tests look for an unusual number of observations far from the mean. These conditions are illustrated in Figure 3-2.

Sudden Shifts in the Level. This may be caused by changes in the production process, changes in the methods of measurement, a new type of raw material, a trainee worker, or new machines or tooling.

Test 4: Out of control (either $\overline{X}$ or R charts) if eight consecutive points lie strictly above or below the centerline.

This condition is illustrated in Figure 3-3.

Trends or Cyclic Behavior. This condition may be caused by tool wear, a trainee operator, fatigue, maintenance cycles, or accumulation of wastes.

Figure 3-2

Tests 1, 2, and 3.
Observations Far from the
Mean

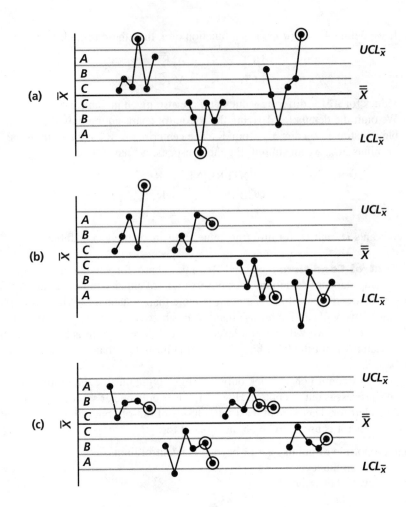

Test 5: Out of control ($\overline{X}$ or R charts) if six successive points show a continuing increase or decrease. This condition is indicated in Figure 3-4.

Bimodal Behavior. Situations in which there are two separated sets of observations, one high and one low, may be caused by more than one process being charted, improper sampling techniques, and possible overcontrol of the process.

Test 6: Out of control if eight successive points have no level-0 points among them.

This is illustrated in Figure 3-5.

Figure 3-3

Test 4. Shifts in the Level

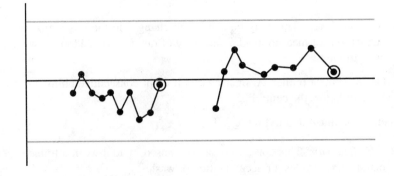

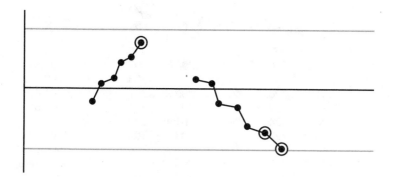

Figure 3-4

Test 5. Upward/Downward Trends

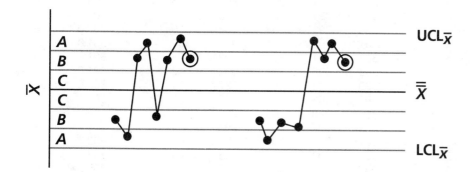

Figure 3-5

Test 6. Bimodal Behavior

Example: Roller Bearings. Data was taken from a process that machines roller bearings for airline baggage carousels. The outside diameter of the bearings were measured following the milling operations. Measurements were taken accurate to 0.0001 inch. Samples were taken from the process every two hours. Each sample consisted of $n = 5$ observations. The purpose of the samples was to form the basis for initial $\overline{X}$ and R charts. The results of the first 30 samples, along with the calculated $\overline{X}$ and R for each sample are shown in Table 3-6. The actual measurements are of the form 5.7300, 5.7297, and so on. Only the last three digits are shown in the table. First we calculate the average of the sample means and the average range, as shown at the bottom of the table. Next we calculate the control limits for the $\overline{X}$ and chart, using the formulas from equation 3-10, and the values of the constants from Table 3-5:

$\overline{X}$ *Chart.*

$$\text{UCL} = \overline{X}_{av} + A_2\overline{R} = 300.24 + (0.577)(8.033) = 300.24 + 4.64 = 304.88$$
$$\text{LCL} = \overline{X}_{av} - A_2\overline{R} \qquad\qquad\qquad\quad = 300.24 - 4.64 = 295.60$$

R Chart.

$$\text{UCL} = D_4\overline{R} = (2.115)(8.033) = 16.99$$
$$\text{LCL} = D_3\overline{R} = (0)(8.033) \quad = 0.00$$

We now proceed to construct the charts. A few simple rules are helpful:

1. Individual values are represented as dots. Sequential dots are connected. (This makes it easier to see patterns in the data.)
2. Plot the R chart directly below the $\overline{X}$ chart, using the same horizontal scale. (This makes it easy to correlate the two results for the same sample.)
3. Use a solid line for the centerlines, and dashed lines for the control limits.
4. Circle points that are out of control. (If a point is out of control for more than one reason, circle it once for each.)

Table 3-6

Roller Bearing Milling
Process Data

Sample	1	2	3	4	5	$\overline{X}$	R
1	300	297	300	301	300	299.6	4
2	299	300	299	294	297	297.8	6
3	301	297	299	297	303	299.4	6
4	301	296	301	306	303	301.4	10
5	300	304	297	296	301	299.6	8
6	300	294	301	301	299	299.0	7
7	297	299	299	303	304	300.4	7
8	303	306	299	306	306	304.0	7
9	297	299	301	296	304	299.4	5
10	307	299	296	297	301	300.0	10
11	296	300	303	299	297	299.0	7
12	294	301	297	303	296	298.2	9
13	300	299	304	300	303	301.2	5
14	299	299	298	304	300	300.0	6
15	301	297	294	306	307	301.0	13
16	301	301	304	298	301	301.0	6
17	303	298	304	302	302	301.8	6
18	300	303	309	287	301	300.0	22
19	301	305	301	300	300	301.4	5
20	300	298	300	299	302	299.8	4
21	298	297	301	296	305	299.4	9
22	301	300	299	300	301	300.2	2
23	305	302	308	305	304	304.8	6
24	297	305	295	297	300	298.8	10
25	296	302	299	300	304	300.2	8
26	304	300	296	296	297	298.6	8
27	303	302	302	302	298	301.4	5
28	303	298	292	317	296	301.2	25
29	295	300	301	296	299	298.2	6
30	297	301	296	303	305	300.4	9

$$\overline{X}_{av} = 300.24 \qquad \overline{R} = 8.033$$

We always analyze the R chart first. This is because if any points are out of control on the range chart, it may affect $\overline{R}$, and thus project misleading information on the $\overline{X}$ chart, as we shall see in this example. Figure 3-6 shows the $\overline{X}$ and R charts determined initially. As we look at the R chart, we see that there are two samples with ranges which exceed the control limit. Therefore we suspect that there are special causes increasing the process variability at these points. We now go back and examine these points, samples 18 and 28, to see if we can find good reasons for these special samples. Our records show that at these points there were power brownouts reducing the voltage to the plant by about 20 percent. The operator states that it is very difficult to completely compensate for this problem, and that the output tends to become quite a bit more variable.

Since we now know the reason that samples 18 and 28 indicated an out-of-control situation, we remove these samples (from both charts), recalculate the centerlines and control limits, and replot the charts. We have $\overline{X}_{av} = 300.21$ and $\overline{R} = 6.929$.

$\overline{X}$ *Chart.*
    UCL $= 300.21 + (0.577)(6.929) = 300.21 + 4.00 = 304.21$
    LCL $=$ $\qquad\qquad\qquad\quad = 300.21 - 4.00 = 296.21$

R *Chart.*
    UCL $= (2.115)(6.929) = 14.65$
    LCL $= (0)(6.929) \qquad = 0.00$

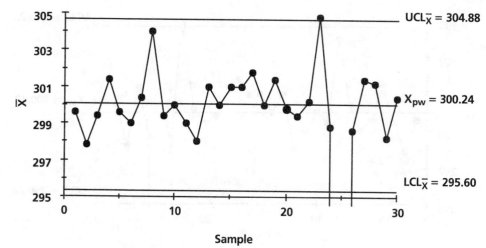

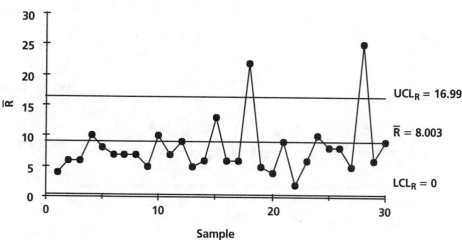

Figure 3-6

Initial $\overline{X}$ and R Charts for the Roller Bearing Example

The revised control charts after deleting 18 and 28 are shown in Figure 3-7.

Again we first examine the R chart. There are now no points outside the control limits, and none of the tests we discussed previously appears to have been violated. Thus the R chart shows the process to be in good statistical control with respect to variability. However, on examining the $\overline{X}$ chart, we see that now sample 23 is above the control limit. The investigation of this point reveals that a relief operator was responsible for the rolling bearing operation for a short time. It seems very likely that this was responsible for the problem. As a result this operator will be given more training before being allowed to staff this station again. When this point is removed, the resulting control charts are both within their proper limits.

Control Charts for Individual Measurements. The point of taking a sample of several points at a certain time is to be able to observe all data affected by the same special causes. Sometimes, however, it is not practical to take samples of size greater than one. For example, some measurements, such as temperature, accounts receivable, or machine downtime will simply not vary very much if at all for points closely spaced in time. Or it may be deemed simply too expensive to take samples larger than one. There are several possible ways to modify the charting procedure for this case. We will discuss the X and R_m charts approach here.

The construction of X and R_m control charts is very similar to the construction of $\overline{X}$ and R charts, except for two things. First, the "average" of the sample is now the single value X itself. Second, we find a range R_m for a given point artificially, by finding the

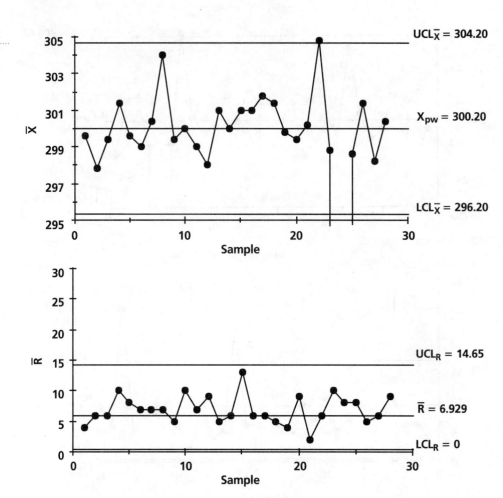

range of the last n values of the observations X. (R_m stands for moving range.) It is customary to choose n very small, typically $n = 2$ or $n = 3$. This is to minimize the chance of including older data that comes from an out-of-control situation.

As an example, suppose $n = 3$ and the ten X_i values are

i	1	2	3	4	5	6	7	8	9	10
X	12	15	17	13	15	19	11	14	11	13
R	—	—	5	4	4	6	8	8	3	3

Note that R_1 and R_2 are not defined; there are not enough previous points. R_3 is the largest of the first three values minus the smallest. That is, $R_3 = 17 - 12$. In the same way, $R_4 = 17 - 13$, and so on.

Construction of the X and R_m Charts.

1. Let there be k measurements X_i. The sample mean $\overline{\overline{X}} = \Sigma X_i / k$ is the center line of the X chart.
2. Use moving ranges R_i = the range of $(X_i, X_{i-1}, \ldots X_{i-n+1})$.
3. The average of the moving ranges, $\overline{R}_m$, is the centerline for the R chart.

$$\overline{R}_m = \Sigma R_i / (k - n + 1)$$

4. The control limits for the R_m chart are:

$$UCL = D_4 \overline{R}_m \qquad\qquad LCL = D_3 \overline{R}_m$$

Here D_4 and D_3 are taken from Table 3-5 for the n associated with the moving range.

5. Estimate the process standard deviation by $\sigma_X = \overline{R}_m/d_2$. ($d_2$ is from Table 3-5 for the n associated with the moving range.)
6. Control limits for the X chart are:

$$\text{UCL} = \overline{X} + 3\sigma_X \qquad \text{LCL} = \overline{X} - 3\sigma_X$$

Example. A chemical plant takes a sample from its continuous process every hour to monitor grams of phosphate per gallon of solution. Samples taken closer together would not show much variability. The moving range method is to be used for control, with $n = 2$. Forty observations are taken, as shown in Table 3-7.

X Chart Limits.

$$3\sigma_X = 3\overline{R}_m/d_2 = (3)(7.692)/(1.128) \quad = 20.46$$
$$\text{UCL} = \overline{X} + 3\sigma_X = 77.90 + 20.46 \quad = 98.36$$
$$\text{CENTERLINE} = \overline{X} \qquad\qquad = 77.90$$
$$\text{LCL} = \overline{X} - 3\sigma_X = 77.90 - 20.46 \quad = 57.44$$

R_m Chart Limits.

$$\text{UCL} = D_4 = (3.267)(7.692) \quad = 25.13$$
$$\text{CENTERLINE} \qquad\qquad = 7.69$$
$$\text{LCL} = D_3 = (0)(7.692) \qquad = 0.00$$

Next the control charts are constructed, as shown in Figure 3-8. This example makes clear the danger of first evaluating the X chart. The X chart taken alone is quite well behaved. There are no points outside the control limits, nor are there long runs above or below the average, or trends, or clumps of points near the control limits.

However, the R_m chart tells quite a different story. From observation 11 to observation 24 there is a long run of points with below-average range, defining out-of-control points (last of eight in a row) for points 18, 19, 20, 21, 22, 23, and 24. Also, point 9 is out of control since it is the last of three points, two of which are almost outside the limits.

Table 3-7

Hourly Data from Chemical Plant (Last 2 Digits)

Sample	X	R_m	Sample	X	R_m
1	79	–	21	75	7
2	72	7	22	79	4
3	71	1	23	81	2
4	88	17	24	80	1
5	65	23	25	72	8
6	73	8	26	73	1
7	84	11	27	88	15
8	64	20	28	86	2
9	84	20	29	76	10
10	75	9	30	79	3
11	79	4	31	76	3
12	81	2	32	81	5
13	84	3	33	85	4
14	83	1	34	74	11
15	77	6	35	59	15
16	82	5	36	66	7
17	77	5	37	89	23
18	82	5	38	73	16
19	83	1	39	82	9
20	82	1	40	77	5

$$\overline{X} = 77.90 \qquad \overline{R}_m = 7.692$$

Figure 3-8

X and R_m Control Charts for
the Chemical Process

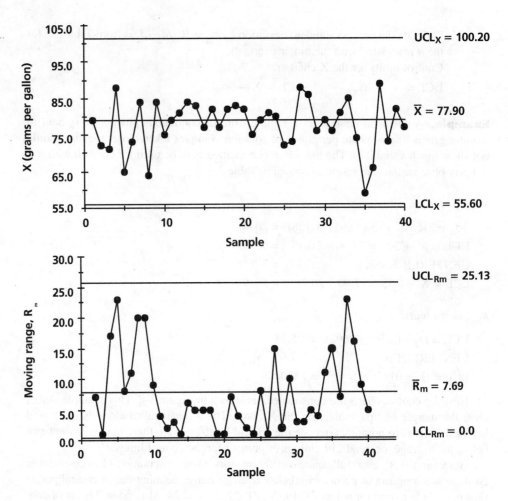

Figure 3-8

X and R_m Control Charts for
the Chemical Process

It would seem the process fluctuated widely for about the first 10 points, then was extremely stable for 24 points, and then began to fluctuate again. These control charts cannot be fixed by the removal of a point or two. Something major is going on with the process that management must deal with.

3.4.3 Control Charts for Attributes

Basics. To this point we have been concerned with quality characteristics that can be measured quantitatively, such as diameter, weight, and so forth. However, some quality characteristics called **flaws** may be simply represented as present or absent. Such situations might include surface flaws on a car fender panel, cracks in an ingot, color variations on a boat's finish, or wrinkles in a sheet of tinned steel. Such defects cause a part to simply be called a defective part. We call such types of evaluations **evaluation by attribute**. Many measurements that could be made quantitatively are still made on a yes/no basis in the interest of economy. (For example, a rod may be determined to be less than a certain diameter simply by seeing whether a piece of wire will go all the way around it.)

First we define some terms:

1. A **defect** is a fault which causes an item not to meet specifications. Each instance for the same item is a separate defect.
2. A **defective** item has one or more defects.
3. The **number of defective items** in a sample of n items is denoted by d.
4. The **fraction defective** is d/n.

Control Chart for Fraction Defective. Consider a large stamping press which produces the fender for an automobile. The process has the following types of defects: scratches, cracks, roughness, and wrinkles. If a fender has at least one of these problems, it is considered to be defective. Recently the company has been on a drive to improve quality and has decided to chart the process. Two hundred fenders were inspected every shift, and the inspection continued initially for 40 shifts. A fraction defective control chart, a p chart, is used to study the process. Table 3-8 shows the fraction defective in each shift's sample of $n = 200$ fenders for 40 consecutive shifts. (The fraction defective has been rounded for ease of exposition.)

The mean fraction defective is 0.0615 .

Now, as usual, we can plot a chart of p for each sample, using .0615 as the centerline. What shall we do for a range, in order to show lower and upper control limits?

Here probability theory comes to our rescue. In a sample of size n, if the probability of any particular fender being defective is p, and if the defective fenders are relatively independent of each other, then the number of defectives in the sample follows a binomial distribution. Thus the mean number of defective fenders d is $E[d] = np$ and the variance is $\text{Var}[d] = np(1 - p)$.

But p is simply given by $p = d/n$, that is we divide by n, which divides the mean by n, and the variance by n^2. Thus the (approximate) mean proportion of defective fenders d is:

$$E[p] = \bar{p}$$
$$\text{Var}[p] = \bar{p}(1 - \bar{p})/n\bar{p}$$

Thus our p chart has limits:

CENTERLINE $= \bar{p}$
UCL $= \bar{p} + 3[\bar{p}(1 - \bar{p})/n]^{0.5}$
LCL $= \bar{p} - 3[\bar{p}(1 - \bar{p})/n]^{0.5}$

For our particular example,

CENTERLINE $= 0.0615$
UCL $= 0.0615 + 3[(.0615)(.9385)/200]^{0.5}$
$= 0.0615 + 0.0510 = 0.1125$
LCL $= 0.0615 - 0.0510 = 0.0105$

We do not need a range chart, since we are essentially determining the range theoretically.

Sample	Fraction Defective	Sample	Fraction Defective
1	0.08	21	0.08
2	0.06	22	0.10
3	0.05	23	0.07
4	0.02	24	0.13
5	0.06	25	0.08
6	0.10	26	0.09
7	0.08	27	0.03
8	0.06	28	0.08
9	0.06	29	0.05
10	0.05	30	0.15
11	0.05	31	0.07
12	0.01	32	0.03
13	0.04	33	0.06
14	0.04	34	0.08
15	0.05	35	0.06
16	0.08	36	0.08
17	0.01	37	0.01
18	0.08	38	0.02
19	0.09	39	0.05
20	0.02	40	0.05

Table 3-8

Fraction Defective Data for Automobile Fenders

$$\bar{p} = 0.0615$$

Figure 3-9 shows the p chart for the fraction defective data of Table 3-8.

Note that the process is not in good control. Two samples, for shifts 24 and 30, have a fraction defective above the upper control limit. Three samples, for shifts 12, 17, and 31 have a fraction defective below the lower control limit. There is also a run of eight shifts below the average from shift 8 to shift 15. Also, the mean percentage of defects for the first 20 shifts is 5.4 percent, while the mean number of defects for the next 20 shifts has risen to 6.8 percent.

After careful discussions with the operator, it was discovered that a new set of procedures for stamping had been put in place in shift 22. These had caused the operator considerable difficulty, and some modifications had to be made. By shift 32 the new procedure was working fairly well, and by the last 10 shifts the defect rate appeared to have returned to typical levels of about 5 percent defects. After further tuning of the new procedures, the defect rate dropped to a new stable position of about 3.5 percent.

Control Chart for Number Defective. Sometimes we may desire to make a control chart by plotting the number of defectives d in the sample instead of the fraction defective p. This just a slight variation on the p chart, in fact a rescaling of centerline, UCL, and LCL by the factor n:

$$
\begin{aligned}
\text{CENTERLINE} &= n\bar{p} \\
\text{UCL} &= n\bar{p} + 3[n\bar{p}(1 - \bar{p})]^{0.5} \\
\text{LCL} &= n\bar{p} - 3[n\bar{p}(1 - \bar{p})]^{0.5}
\end{aligned}
$$

Notice that if $\bar{p}$ is small and we define $\bar{d} = n\bar{p}$, then the control limits are approximately

$$
\begin{aligned}
\text{CENTERLINE} &= \bar{d} \\
\text{UCL} &= \bar{d} + 3\bar{d}^{0.5} \\
\text{LCL} &= \bar{d} - 3\bar{d}^{0.5}
\end{aligned}
$$

Thus the control limits depend only on the average number of defectives in the sample. (Technically we have really used the fact that the binomial distribution may be approximated by the Poisson distribution in this case.)

Control Chart for Number of Defects. Charts for fraction defective or total number defective consider an item to be equally defective whether it has one defect or eight. In many situations we might prefer to count the total number of defects so that an item with many defects counts more.

Suppose that an individual item has m different ways to have a defect, where m is very large. Suppose the probability that any one of these will occur is q, where q is very small.

Figure 3-9

p Chart for the Fraction of Fenders Defective

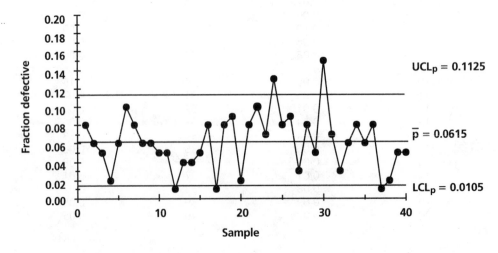

Then the distribution of number of defects on an individual item is binomial with mean mq and variance $mq(1 - q)$ and the distribution of the total number of defects on n individual items in a sample has mean mnq and variance $mnq(1 - q)$. Define the total number of defects in one sample by c, and the average number of defects in all the samples together as $\bar{c}$. Thus $E(c) = mnq$. Now, noting that n is large and $1 - q$ is very close to 1.0, we have approximately $\text{Var}(c) = \bar{c}$ also. Thus we are dealing with a Poisson distribution. Finally, our control limits are given by:

CENTERLINE $= \bar{c}$
UCL $= \bar{c} + 3\bar{c}^{0.5}$
LCL $= \bar{c} - 3\bar{c}^{0.5}$

(Our arguments in this section were not mathematically very precise. A probability text should be consulted if a more rigorous treatment is desired.)

3.4.4 Control Chart Exercises

Control Charts for Variable Data.

1. A quality control engineer uses only the violation of the UCL or the LCL limits of the $\bar{X}$ chart, without the zone rules, trend rules, and so forth. He says that violation of these limits, after all, is what conformance to product specifications is all about. How would you answer him?
2. Chart and discuss Table 3-1 in Section 3.3.1 concerning fuel tube weights.
3. Chart and discuss Table 3-3 in the Exercises for Section 3.3 concerning length of lumber pieces.
4. Chart and discuss Table 3-4 in the Exercises for Section 3.3 concerning the diameters of shafts.
5. Given the table of tinplating thickness shown in Table 3-9 for samples of size $n = 4$:

   a. Calculate the $\bar{X}$s and the Rs for all 10 samples.
   b. Calculate $\bar{X}_{av}$ and $\bar{R}$.
   c. Calculate the control limits.
   d. Chart and interpret.

6. Control charts are to be set up for thickness measurement on a process that makes window glass. The current specification for the thickness of the glass sheets is 0.244 ± 0.002 inches. After collecting 25 rational samples of size $n = 4$ at two-hour intervals, the data were used to determine that the sum of the sample means was 6.091 inches and the sum of the sample ranges was 0.0152 inches. Use this information to determine the centerlines and upper and lower control limits for both the $\bar{X}$ and the R charts.

Table 3-9
....
Tin Plate Coatings (Grams)

Sample	X_1	X_2	X_3	X_4	X_5
1	29.1	30.5	31.0	30.7	31.1
2	29.2	30.3	30.5	29.0	30.1
3	33.0	33.2	32.2	32.8	32.5
4	31.6	30.8	30.6	29.1	30.9
5	30.3	30.8	31.5	32.2	30.4
6	30.5	30.4	29.8	29.6	29.4
7	31.2	30.3	29.0	27.9	29.5
8	26.5	29.4	31.2	28.5	28.4
9	29.0	30.5	30.3	29.2	29.0
10	31.1	31.0	30.4	29.3	30.7

7. The data in Table 3-10 give the averages and ranges for the weights of a premium auto tire in pounds. The sample size is $n = 5$. From the first 20 samples, set up and interpret $\overline{X}$ and R charts. Explain in some detail whether or not the process seems to be in control. If the process does seem to be in control, plot the next 10 samples, and comment on what you find.

8. Data has been collected to construct control charts for monitoring the thickness of a gasket. Thirty samples of size $n = 4$ have been collected. The quality control engineer was transferred to a different division before finishing the charts. You are given her notes and find that all you know is that the UCL for the R chart is 0.0056 centimeters and the UCL for the $\overline{X}$ chart is 0.6902 centimeters. The raw data page cannot be found, but you are aware that the sample size was $n = 6$. Finish setting up the two charts, including centerlines, UCLs, and LCLs.

9. A chemical process has produced the data shown in Table 3-11, which are measures of the sulfur concentration (parts per million). Samples of size $n = 1$ are taken once every two hours.

    a. Graph the data first without the control limits. Comment on what you see.
    b. Compute the sample moving ranges using $n = 2$.
    c. Calculate $\overline{X}$ and $\overline{R}_m$.
    d. Estimate the process standard deviation.
    e. Construct X and R_m charts for these data and plot the data.
    f. Identify all signals that indicate out-of-control situations.

Control Charts for Attributes.

10. Can one ever use attribute data to describe data which are more quantitative? Give an example where this can be done, and explain the advantages and disadvantages of using the attribute approach.

11. A p chart has a centerline of $\overline{p} = 0.09$, UCL = 0.132, and LCL = 0.048. For some time it has been stable around the centerline, except for an occasional point beneath the LCL. The operator has ignored them, feeling that low values are good. The boss says that the process is out of control and must be investigated thoroughly. Comment.

12. A copper tube is made by cold extrusion. This occasionally causes surface cracks, which are the source of most of the defects. It is decided to chart the process to look for improvements. During three consecutive shifts, 30 samples of size $n = 100$ were collected. The results are shown in Table 3-12.

    a. Establish the centerline and control limits for a p chart.

Table 3-10

Sample Means and Ranges
for Premium Tires (Lb.)

Sample	$\overline{X}$	Range	Sample	$\overline{X}$	Range
1	10.402	0.151	16	10.362	0.151
2	10.390	0.185	17	10.380	0.191
3	10.448	0.182	18	10.350	0.083
4	10.432	0.060	19	10.378	0.112
5	10.428	0.088	20	10.384	0.095
6	10.382	0.103	21	10.392	0.067
7	10.358	0.111	22	10.378	0.083
8	10.440	0.194	23	10.362	0.164
9	10.366	0.108	24	10.348	0.190
10	10.368	0.117	25	10.338	0.155
11	10.360	0.115	26	10.366	0.148
12	10.402	0.070	27	10.346	0.191
13	10.332	0.084	28	10.374	0.153
14	10.356	0.175	29	10.339	0.246
15	10.314	0.109	30	10.368	0.140

Table 3-11

Sulfur Concentration in Parts per Million

Sample	X_i	Sample	X_i	Sample	X_i
1	5.9	16	6.2	31	6.6
2	5.9	17	5.7	32	6.4
3	6.0	18	5.9	33	5.8
4	6.1	19	5.7	34	6.3
5	5.9	20	5.8	35	6.0
6	6.1	21	6.7	36	5.7
7	5.9	22	6.1	37	5.8
8	6.0	23	5.8	38	5.8
9	6.0	24	6.2	39	5.7
10	6.0	25	5.3	40	5.7
11	6.2	26	5.4	41	6.4
12	5.9	27	7.0	42	5.5
13	6.6	28	5.7	43	5.9
14	6.1	29	6.6	44	5.7
15	5.9	30	5.8	45	5.7

Table 3-12

Number of Defectives in Copper Tubing

Sample	#	Sample	#	Sample	#
1	3	11	4	21	1
2	6	12	5	22	3
3	2	13	4	23	6
4	5	14	5	24	1
5	2	15	1	25	5
6	4	16	4	26	3
7	4	17	2	27	0
8	4	18	0	28	2
9	2	19	2	29	5
10	3	20	3	30	0

b. Construct the p chart; comment on the control of the process.

c. Sampling continued in the fourth shift with data as follows: 9, 9, 8, 1, 7, 5, 8, 9, 3, 13. Plot the new data on the chart, and comment again on the control of the process.

13. The stamping process which produces automobile fenders produces defects which are primarily scratches. It is decided to keep track of the number of defects on 45 consecutive shifts using a c chart. One hundred fenders are sampled each shift and the total number of defects are tabulated in Table 3-13.

Table 3-13

Number of Defects in 100 Panel Samples

Sample	Defects	Sample	Defects	Sample	Defects
1	2	16	2	31	8
2	11	17	4	32	10
3	3	18	7	33	8
4	8	19	7	34	6
5	5	20	5	35	4
6	11	21	0	36	4
7	4	22	1	37	8
8	7	23	0	38	6
9	4	24	3	39	4
10	8	25	1	40	9
11	7	26	0	41	6
12	8	27	4	42	2
13	3	28	2	43	7
14	2	29	0	44	6
15	9	30	0	45	9

      a. Calculate the centerline and limits for the appropriate c chart.

      b. Construct the c chart.

      c. Comment on what may be happening in this process.

14. A lumber mill that produces high grade finished lumber is concerned that the lumber contains too many knotholes and similar defects. Each sample collected was actually 25 twelve-foot-long 1" x 8" boards. The resulting data is shown in Table 3-14.

      a. Calculate the centerline and control limits for the appropriate c chart.

      b. Plot the c chart and interpret it. Label all out-of-control points and comment on the state of the process.

      c. Assume that corrective action was taken for all problems. Remove the samples affected and reconstruct the c chart.

15. Following the corrective actions taken in problem 14, another 30 samples were collected, and are shown in Table 3-15.

      a. Plot the new data on a continuation of the old graph with the old limits.

      b. If it seems appropriate, construct new control limits for the data, and comment on the process.

Table 3-14

Defects per 25 Twelve-Foot-Long 1" X 8" Boards

Sample	Defects	Sample	Defects	Sample	Defects
1	3	16	0	31	5
2	6	17	7	32	5
3	4	18	4	33	6
4	4	19	7	34	5
5	6	20	12	35	5
6	5	21	7	36	3
7	7	22	6	37	6
8	1	23	7	38	5
9	6	24	8	39	7
10	6	25	8	40	5
11	5	26	10	41	4
12	5	27	3	42	2
13	4	28	1	43	3
14	7	29	4	44	3
15	5	30	2	45	0

Table 3-15

Further Lumber Samples

Sample	Defects	Sample	Defects	Sample	Defects
46	4	56	3	66	4
47	3	57	2	67	2
48	5	58	4	68	5
49	2	59	1	69	6
50	0	60	4	70	4
51	2	61	4	71	3
52	2	62	3	72	1
53	1	63	0	73	4
54	4	64	2	74	3
55	1	65	2	75	1

3.5 INSPECTION POLICY

3.5.1 Introduction

Overview. Raw materials enter a company from a vendor. There are certain specifications the company requires that these materials must meet. What is the best way to make sure this quality requirement is met? Work-in-process moves from one department to another within a company. There are certain specifications that the "customer" department requires that the WIP meet. What is the best way for the "producer" department and or the "customer" department to make sure this quality requirement is met? Finished product moves from the company to a customer. What is the best way for the supplier and/or the customer to assure high quality?

Historically companies have solved this problem by having the producer test a sample of the product just before shipment, and/or the customer test a sample of the product just after receipt. The producer must balance the cost of testing versus the cost of having the lot rejected or of reworking or replacing the bad items. The consumer must balance the cost of testing versus the cost of items failing in use. There are three types of inspection for goods or services that may be employed:

 a. No inspection
 b. 100 percent inspection
 c. Acceptance sampling

If no inspection is done, both producer and consumer are trusting the producer's design and production process sufficiently to assume that testing is not worth the cost. If 100 percent inspection is done, all goods or services are tested, and the defectives are either scrapped and replaced or else reworked. With acceptance sampling, a sample of the goods is tested to determine if the remainder should be accepted, rejected, or subjected to 100 percent inspection.

Classical Acceptance Sampling. Historically the producer's design process and manufacturing process was considered too unreliable to allow shipping or accepting the goods with no inspection. Also, 100 percent inspection was considered too expensive in many or most cases. The cost of inspection may be very high, which makes 100 percent sampling prohibitive. This is especially true if the testing process is destructive; that is, destroys the sample. (For example, when light bulbs are left on until they burn out to test their lifespans. 100 percent sampling is not possible.)

Lot-by-lot acceptance sampling can be used whenever the transfer of goods or services occurs in large batches or lots. There are many variations, all of which are based on taking a sample from the batch, testing it, and noting the number of defects (or defectives). Based on this number, the lot may be accepted, rejected, or subjected to 100 percent testing of the whole lot.

Continuous flow acceptance sampling can be used whenever the goods are created or transferred continuously; for example, a product coming off a conveyer belt. Since there is no lot to be accepted or rejected, all continuous flow sampling plans are based on **clear sampling**. If the number of units between two defective units is larger than a specified number, those units can be accepted and shipped. If not, all units in between must be 100 percent inspected.

A Modern View. Much attention was given to acceptance sampling in textbooks and in many companies in the past. However, acceptance sampling emphasizes finding bad product rather than not producing it in the first place. As we emphasized in Total Quality Management Chapter 2, the whole modern thrust of TQM is to push quality further and further upstream; that is, to continuously improve the production process and to continuously improve the product design, underscoring the TQM slogan "You can't inspect quality in; you have to build it in."

If the production process is not in control, and particularly if we do not know the quality of product currently being produced, then final sampling can, indeed, give us information about the current quality. However, if the process is currently in good statistical control by the use of control charting and other methods, then we will know the overall fraction defective in the process. Under these conditions, we will show that acceptance sampling gives us no information about the rest of the lot. Testing the sample tells us only about the quality of the items in the sample. This implies that we should either test everything or test nothing, depending on how high the known quality of the process is. We now discuss this issue in more detail.

3.5.2 Stable Processes

A **stable manufacturing process** is defined as a process with a known constant proportion of defectives p. Furthermore, the knowledge that any one item is defective does not affect the probability that any other item is defective. That is, the process is random. An important result is that lots from such a process should either be sampled 100 percent or not at all.

Inferiority of Partial Sampling. Let the lot have N items. We draw a sample of size n from the lot (without replacement). Define the $N - n$ items which are not sampled as the remainder. The remainder items are independent, and each has a probability p of being defective. Thus the expected number of defective items for a single member of the remainder is p, and since expectations add, the expected number of defectives in the total remainder is $(N - n)p$.

Now we test the first item in the sample. Whether it is defective or not does not affect whether a given member of the remainder is defective, since we are assuming independence. Thus each member of the remainder still has probability p, and the expected number of defectives in the total remainder is still $(N - n)p$. Thus the first test gave us exactly zero information about the remainder.

Now we test the second item in the sample, and again the expected number of defectives in the remainder is $(N - n)p$. But we may repeat this over and over for every member of the sample. Thus, independent of the actual number of defectives d in the sample of n that we experience, our expectation for the remainder is unchanged. This implies the following theorem:

Theorem for Sampling Stable Processes

> *For a stable process with a process of known percentage defective* p, *items tested give no information about the rest of the lot. If it is worthwhile testing an item, it is only for its own sake. This implies that either there should be no inspection, or 100 percent inspection!*

W. Edward Deming offered an alternative to acceptance sampling for stable processes. We turn to this next.

Deming's kp Rule. Given a stable process and our theorem above that acceptance sampling is not useful for this type of process, we are left with the necessity of determining when no inspection is appropriate, and when 100 percent inspection is appropriate. Let:

p = the known average percentage of defective items in lots being produced
    (remember p is assumed stable and items are independent)

k = the cost to inspect one item

K = the net cost of not inspecting a defective item (total cost less the cost of a
    replacement item)

How do we decide whether to inspect none or all of the items? Inspecting one item costs us k. But in case the item was defective (with probability p) the inspection saves us K (we must make a replacement item but K was net, not gross). Thus, if we inspect an item our expected net opportunity cost is $(k - pK)$.

This opportunity cost will be positive (we shouldn't inspect) precisely if $p <= k/K$.

The Rule. For a stable process with known p, a cost of k to inspect a unit, and a net cost of K for not detecting a defective:

  a. If $k/K > p$ then do no inspection.
  b. If $k/K <= p$ then do 100 percent inspection.

How do we estimate p, k, and K?

The proportion defective p may be known quite accurately from control charts we are keeping on the process. (One sort of control chart we may keep is the proportion defective for occasional small samples. The purpose here would primarily be for process improvement, not final sampling.)

Estimating the cost k of inspecting one item is relatively straightforward. It includes standard cost accounting of the resources necessary to do the testing, both in terms of direct labor and such overhead items as indirect labor, materials, depreciation, and so on. If inspection sometimes damages the item, it would include the repair cost times the probability of occurrence.

Estimating the cost K of allowing a defective item to be shipped is much more difficult. There are the more direct and calculable costs of:

  a. Doing warranty repair
  b. Replacing the item
  c. Rework on the item
  d. Rework on assemblies using the item

There are also very serious costs which are harder to measure:

  a. Cost of recalls
  b. Lawsuits
  c. Lost customer loyalty

Since the full costs for K are very hard to estimate, a reasonable policy is to first estimate $K' < K$, the more objective part of K. If $p > k/K'$ then 100 percent testing is definitely necessary, and the subjective components of K need not be estimated. On the other hand, if $p < k/K'$ then some estimate of the subjective parts of K will be necessary.

Destructive Testing. An interesting question is: What happens if Deming's rule suggests 100 percent testing, but testing is destructive, so that 100 percent testing is not possible? Let c be the gross cost of producing one unit and selling it. Since testing is destructive, it follows that testing costs at least c: that is, $k > c$. But the gross cost of producing one unit includes the eventual cost of it being defective, so that $c > pK$. Thus, we have $k > pK$ or $p < k/K$ so that 0 percent testing is optimal.

For stable processes with destructive testing, do no final inspection.

Example 3-3. A manufacturer of a $50,000 airborne radar buys a critical subassembly from a vendor. The inspection cost to test for defective subassemblies is $15. If a defective unit is assembled into a finished unit, it will be caught in final testing; however, necessary rework will cost $2400. On average the proportion of defective incoming subassemblies is 7 in 1000. The vendor's process is stable. What should be done?

Solution. We should inspect 100 percent because $k/K = 15/2400 = 0.00625 < p = 0.007$. Note that since k/K is close to p, the decision between 0 and 100 percent inspection is rather marginal. The decision in practice may turn on other factors. Note also that we should make every effort at design and process and improvement to reduce p to make 0 percent inspection optimal.

3.5.3 Non-stable Processes

So far we have dealt with *stable* processes: the proportion p is fairly well known and is stable. We define a **chaotic** process, on the other hand, as a process for which p is not very well known. A chaotic process most likely results from a process in poor control, for which p fluctuates wildly and therefore is hard to predict. However, it may also be that the process is stable but has recently been modified, so that the new p is not yet known. We would like to discuss acceptance sampling issues for this case. We will distinguish between **mild chaos**, for which the uncertainty in p is not too large, and **severe chaos**, where the uncertainty is large.

Mildly Chaotic Processes. We distinguish three mildly chaotic process cases.

Mildly Chaotic Principle

a. If p wanders but stays less than k/K, do no sampling.
b. If p wanders but stays more than k/K, do 100 percent sampling.
c. If p wanders above and below but stays close to k/K, do 100 percent sampling.

The proof of this principle is left as a problem. (***Hint on (c)***: If there is little difference in cost between sampling and not sampling, it is perhaps safer to sample in case p estimates are in error.)

Severely Chaotic Processes. Suppose the fraction defective of a vendor's process wanders considerably. The following is a simple but robust rule. (Adapted from a rule attributed to Orsini [1982].)

Inspection Rule for Chaotic Processes

a. If $k/K < 0.001$ do 100 percent sampling.
b. If $k/K > 0.01$ do 0 percent sampling.
c. In between, test items one at a time:

- If there are no defectives after 500, accept the rest.
- If a defect is encountered, test all the rest.

While this rule is just a simple heuristic, there are some common sense elements to it.

First, an unpredictable vendor should not be assumed to have defects fewer than 1 in 1000. Therefore, if sampling costs are that low, sample fully. Second, the vendor probably will not have defects of more than 1 in 100. This would be a poor vendor; some information should have been available to reject the vendor. Finally, for the in-between case, a defect in a sample of 500 certainly would suggest that 100 percent sampling is not costly, since $k/K < 1/100$. On the other hand, if there are no defects after sampling 500, a p of less than 1/500 is suggested, which makes not sampling fairly safe.

3.5.4 Inspection Exercises

1. Prove the mildly chaotic principle given in the text.
2. An automobile manufacturer inspects every incoming new differential from a supplier to make sure it conforms to specifications.

   a. What general information would you need to decide if this inspection policy is a good one?
   b. Try to make your answer in (a) more specific to fit the example of automobiles and tires.

3. The same auto manufacturer learned about Deming's kp rule. He constructed a p chart from past history for percentage of defective differentials. The p chart indi-

cated that the process producing differentials was stable with an average fraction defective of 0.0015. Further study indicates that it costs about $2 to inspect an incoming differential and $112 to replace a defective differential before the car leaves the factory.

 a. What is the optimal inspection policy?
 b. What, if anything, should be done about the incoming differential supplier's process?

4. Suppose a production process is basically stable, except that the proportion of defectives is decreasing slowly over time, due to learning. How could you estimate the current p to use Deming's rule, other than to draw a new sample and test it?

3.6 COMPANY APPLICATION SCENARIO—REPRISE

3.6.1 Diagnosing the Problem

The team commissioned by the president to investigate quality control at the coarse milling machine looked at sampling records produced before the new overly expensive method to improve tolerances. The operator took samples of three pistons every hour, measured their diameters, and averaged them. These were then plotted on a graph, using the desired diameter as a base line. If the diameter seemed to be running high, the operator made a fine tuning adjustment to bring it down somewhat. If it seemed to be running low, the operator adjusted to bring it up somewhat. This was strictly on an intuitive basis, with no range charting or control limits.

Data from three representative shifts about three months prior is shown in Table 3-16. James Flynn, one of the members of the team, was familiar with the construction and use of $\overline{X}$ and R charts. Using this data, he proceeded to determine the centerlines and the

Table 3-16

Piston Diameters (Excess Over 4 Inches)

Sample	X_1	X_2	X_3	$\overline{X}$	R
1	0.5448	0.5428	0.5451	0.5442	0.0023
2	0.5464	0.5427	0.5429	0.5440	0.0037
3	0.5447	0.5423	0.5443	0.5438	0.0024
4	0.5450	0.5441	0.5443	0.5445	0.0009
5	0.5450	0.5447	0.5429	0.5442	0.0021
6	0.5432	0.5442	0.5425	0.5433	0.0017
7	0.5429	0.5448	0.5431	0.5436	0.0019
8	0.5445	0.5437	0.5427	0.5436	0.0018
9	0.5471	0.5463	0.5462	0.5465	0.0009
10	0.5461	0.5465	0.5472	0.5466	0.0011
11	0.5450	0.5471	0.5456	0.5459	0.0021
12	0.5452	0.5468	0.5459	0.5460	0.0016
13	0.5442	0.5423	0.5448	0.5438	0.0025
14	0.5445	0.5455	0.5456	0.5452	0.0011
15	0.5457	0.5447	0.5451	0.5452	0.0010
16	0.5447	0.5457	0.5464	0.5456	0.0017
17	0.5472	0.5459	0.5457	0.5463	0.0015
18	0.5452	0.5477	0.5472	0.5467	0.0025
19	0.5451	0.5471	0.5449	0.5457	0.0022
20	0.5476	0.5466	0.5459	0.5467	0.0017
21	0.5434	0.5441	0.5451	0.5442	0.0017
22	0.5433	0.5428	0.5453	0.5438	0.0025
23	0.5443	0.5425	0.5438	0.5435	0.0018
24	0.5437	0.5446	0.5440	0.5441	0.0009

upper and lower control limits for the $\overline{X}$ and R control charts. These calculations are provided below. The centerlines are given by $\overline{X}_{av} = \sum \overline{X}_i/24 = 0.5449$ inches; $\overline{R} = \sum R_i/24 = 0.0018$ inch.

The control limits for the $\overline{X}$ charts are:

$$UCL = \overline{X}_{av} + A_2\overline{R} = 0.5449 + (1.023)(0.0018) = 0.5467 \text{ inch}$$
$$LCL = \overline{X}_{av} - A_2\overline{R} = 0.5449 - (1.023)(0.0018) = 0.5431 \text{ inch}$$

The control limits for the R charts are:

$$UCL = D_4\overline{R} = (2.575)(0.0018) = 0.0046 \text{ inch}$$
$$LCL = D_3\overline{R} = (0)(0.0018) = 0.0 \text{ inch}$$

Remember that the values for A_2, D_3, and D_4 were given in Table 3-5.

Figure 3-10 shows the resulting $\overline{X}$ and R charts for the coarse milling machine. Remember that the R chart must show good statistical control before the $\overline{X}$ can be meaningfully interpreted. After a careful inspection, the R chart does not show any out-of-control conditions; the range seems to be in good statistical control. However, inspection of the $\overline{X}$ chart gives a very different picture. Sample values 18 and 20 violate Test 1 by being level-3 points (outside the control limits). Sample values 7, 8, 9, 10, 11, 18, 19, and

Figure 3-10

$\overline{X}$ and R Charts for the Coarse Milling Machine

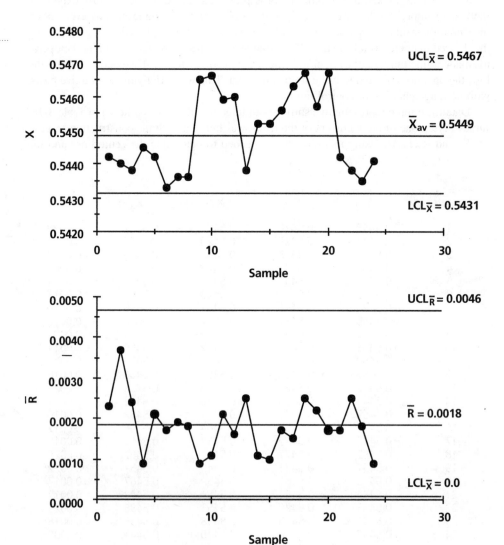

20 violate Test 2 by having two out of three points that consecutively are at least level-2 (groups that are nearly outside the control limits). Most of the sample values violate Test 3 by having four out of five consecutive points that are not level-0. Points 1 to 8 consecutively are below the mean, violating Test 4. Intuitively the chart seems to show that the mean of the process is sporadically shifting up and down.

3.6.2 Overcontrol of the Coarse Milling Machine

As we have seen, the statistical signals are very clear. What is causing the mean of the process to shift up and down in this fashion? Fortunately, the operators had been required to keep a log of their actions during the sampling period. The log showed that an adjustment had been made to decrease the diameter slightly just before sample 1, to increase it about sample 7, to decrease it again about sample 11, to increase it at sample 16, and to decrease it again at sample 20. It would appear that the operators had been overcompensating, and overcontrolling the process.

The operators were overadjusting the process because they could not distinguish between the natural random forces of a process in statistical control, and sporadic problems needing correction. Typically, they were making unnecessary corrections to random variations, and thus producing sporadic problems of their own. The consequences of this mistake are very serious. Each time an adjustment is made that should not be made, a new source of variation in the process is introduced. Thus the attempt to increase quality actually leads to a decrease in quality. Furthermore, each time the operators stopped to make these unnecessary corrections, productivity suffered.

The special team reported their findings to Jack James with several recommendations:

1. Postpone any decision to consider a new machine.
2. Train operators and supervisors in the concepts and methodology of statistical quality control.
3. Provide incentives for using the new methods by rewarding operators and supervisors showing the most improvement.

3.6.3 Aftermath

Six months after the new training and procedures had been instituted, the quality of the original process had improved to meet Southern Belle's requirements. The special costly procedures to meet the specs were no longer required and the proposal for a new machine was shelved permanently.

BIBLIOGRAPHY

Total Quality Management

Aguayo, R. (1990). *Dr. Deming: The American Who Taught the Japanese about Quality*. New York, NY: Lyle Stuart.

Akao, Y. (1990). *Quality Function Deployment: Integrating Customer Requirements into Product Design*. Cambridge, MA: Productivity Press.

American Society for Quality Control (1988). *'88 Gallup Survey: Consumers' Perceptions Concerning the Quality of American Products and Services*. Milwaukee, WI: ASQC.

American Society for Quality Control (1989). *Quality: Executive Priority or Afterthought?* Milwaukee, WI: ASQC.

Amsden, D., H. Butler and R. Amsden (1991). *SPC Simplified for Services*. White Plains, NY: Quality Resources.

Asaku, T. and K. Ozeki (1990). *Handbook of Quality Tools: The Japanese Approach*. Cambridge, MA: Productivity Press.

Brown, M. C. (1992). *Baldrige Award Winning Quality: How to Interpret the Malcolm Baldrige Award Criteria*. White Plains, NY: Quality Resources/Milwaukee, WI: ASQC Quality Press.

Business Week (1991). "The Quality Imperative," Special issue devoted to quality. New York, NY: McGraw-Hill.

Crosby, P .B. (1979). *Quality Is Free*. New York, NY: McGraw-Hill.

Crosby, P. B. (1989). *Let's Talk Quality*. New York NY: McGraw-Hill.

Deming, W. E. (1975). "The Logic of Evaluation," *Handbook of Evaluation Research*. Eds. E. L. Struening and M. Guttentag, Beverly Hills, CA: Sage Publications, 1, 53–68.

Deming, W. E. (1982). *Quality, Productivity and Competitive Position*. Cambridge, MA: Massachusetts Institute of Technology, Center for Advanced Engineering Study.

Deming, W. E. (1993). *The New Economics for Industry, Government, Education*. Cambridge, MA: MIT Center for Advanced Engineering Study.

Eureka, W. and N. Ryan (1988). *The Customer Driven Company: Managerial Perspectives on QFD*. Dearborn, MI: SAI Press.

Feigenbaum, A. V. (1983). *Total Quality Control*. New York, NY: McGraw-Hill.

Feigenbaum, A. (1991). "Quality: An International Imperative," *Journal for Quality and Participation*, 16.

Florida Power and Light. *FPL's Total Quality Management*. Miami, FL.

Ford Motor Company (1990). "Ford Worldwide Quality System Standard Q-101," Dearborn, MI: Corporate Quality Office.

Garvin, D. A. (1988). *Managing Quality*. New York, NY: The Free Press.

Garvin, D. A. (1991). "How the Baldrige Award Works," *Harvard Business Review*, 80–93.

Gitlow, H. and S. Gitlow (1994). *Total Quality Management in Action*. Englewood Cliffs, NJ: Prentice-Hall.

Griffin, A. and Hauser, J. (1991). "The Voice of the Customer," *MIT Marketing Center Working Paper No. 91-2*, Cambridge, MA: Massachusetts Institute of Technology.

Hillkirk, J. (1992). "Europe Upstages Quest for Baldrige Award," *USA Today*.

Imai, M. (1986). *KAIZEN—The Keys to Japan's Competitive Success*. New York, NY: Random House.

Ishikawa, K. (1990). *Introduction to Quality Control*. Tokyo, Japan: 3A Corporation.

Juran, J. M., and F. M. Gryna, Jr. (1980). *Quality Planning and Analysis*, (2nd edition). New York, NY: McGraw-Hill.

Kane, E. J. (1986). "IBM's Quality Focus on the Business Process," *Quality Progress*, 26–23.

Kawakita, J. (1977). *A Scientific Exploration of Intellect*. Tokyo, Japan: Kodansha, 49–70.

Kawakita, J. (1991). *The Original KJ Method*. Tokyo, Japan: Kawakita Research Institute.

Kearns, D. T. and D. A. Nadler (1992). *Prophets in the Dark: How Xerox Reinvented Itself and Beat Back the Japanese*. New York, NY: Harper Collins.

Lawler, E. E. and S. A. Mohrman (1985). "Quality Circles after the Fad," *Harvard Business Review* 63, 65–71.

Logothetis, N. and H. P. Wynn (1989). *Quality through Design*. Oxford, UK: Clarendon Press.

Melan, E. H. (1985). "Process Management in Service and Administrative Operations," *Quality Progress*, 52–59.

Miller, J. G., et al. (1992). *Benchmarking Global Manufacturing*. Homewood, IL: Business One Irwin.

Neave, H. (1990). *The Deming Dimension*. Knoxville, TN: SPC Press.

Nemoto, M. (1987). *Total Quality Control for Management*. Englewood Cliffs, NJ: Prentice-Hall.

Pierce, R. J. (1991). *Leadership, Perspective, and Restructuring for Total Quality*. Milwaukee, WI: ASQC Quality Press.

Robinson, A. Ed., (1991). *Continuous Improvement in Operations: A Systematic Approach to Waste Reduction*. Productivity Press, Cambridge, MA.

Ross, J. (1995). *Total Quality Management: Text, Cases and Readings* (2nd Edition). Delray Beach, FL: St. Lucie Press.

Scherkenbach, W. W. (1991). *Deming's Road To Continual Improvement*. Knoxville, TN: SPC Press.

Scholtes, P. (1988). *The Deming User's Manual—Parts 1 and 2*. Madison, WI: Joiner Associates.

Shewhart, W. A. (1931). *Economic Control of the Quality of Manufactured Products*. Princeton, NJ: D. Van Nostrand, Inc. Reprinted by the American Society for Quality Control, Milwaukee, WI.

Shiba, S. (1988). "How I Have Observed Quality Management in European Countries," *Proceedings of the 6th EOQC European Seminar on Education and Training*.

Shiba, S., A. Graham and D. Walden (1993). *A New American TQM—Four Practical Revolutions in Management*. Portland, OR: Productivity Press.

Taylor, F. W. (1911). *Principles of Scientific Management*. New York, NY: Harper & Brothers.

Thurow, L. (1992). *Head to Head*. New York, NY: William Morrow.

Walton, Mary (1990). *Deming Management at Work*. New York, NY: Putnam.

Statistical Production Quality

Belaire, P. M., and Deacon, R. J. (1987). "The Strategic Approach to Quality Improvement Using Design of Experiments Concepts," *Symposium on Quality: Design, Planning, and Control, ASME Winter Annual Meeting*, PED 27, 147–157.

Box, G. E. P., W. G. Hunter and J. S. Hunter (1978). *Statistics for Experimenters*. New York, N.Y.: John Wiley.

Chan, L. K., S. W. Cheng and F. A. Spiring (1988). "A New Measure of Process Capability: C_{pm}," *Journal of Quality Technology*, 20, 162–175.

Clausing, D. P. (1988). "Taguchi Methods Integrated into the Improved Total Development," *Proc. IEEE International Conference on Communications*, Philadelphia, PA, 826–832.

"*Continuing Process Control and Process Improvement*," (1987). Dearborn, MI: Corporate Quality Office, Ford Motor Company.

Corbett, J., M. Dooner, J. Meleka and C. Pym (1991). *Design for Manufacture: Strategies, Principles and Techniques*. Reading, MA: Addison-Wesley.

Deacon, R. J. (1983). "Reduction in Visual Defects in an Injection Molding Process," *Society of Plastics Engineers, National Technical Conference Proceedings*, 97.

Deacon, R. J. and P. M. Belaire (1988). "Quality Improvement: Design of Experiments Methodology," *IMPRO 88 Conference Proceedings*, Chicago, IL: Juran Institute.

Dehnad, K. (1989). *Quality Control, Robust Design, and the Taguchi Method*. Pacific Grove, CA: Wadsworth & Brooks/Cole, Advanced Book and Software.

Deming, W. E. (1950). *Some Theory of Sampling*. New York, NY: John Wiley.

Deming, W. E. (1953). "On the Distinction between Enumerative and Analytic Surveys," *Journal of the American Statistical Association* 48, 244–255.

Deming, W. E. (1986). "Principles of Professional Statistical Practice." *Encyclopedia of Statistical Sciences 7*. Edited by Kotz-Johnson. New York, NY: John Wiley.

Dessouky, M. I., S. G. Kapoor and R. E. DeVor (1987). "A Methodology for Integrated Quality Systems," *J. of Eng. for Ind., Trans. ASME*, 109, 241–247.

DeVor, R., T. Chang and J. Sutherland (1992). *Statistical Quality: Design and Control*. New York, NY: Macmillan.

Duncan, A. J. (1986). *Quality Control and Industrial Statistics* (5th Edition). Homewood, IL: Richard D. Irwin.

Ford Motor Company (1984). *Continuing Process Control and Process Capability Improvement*.

Gitlow, H. and P. Hertz (1983). "Product Defects and Productivity." *Harvard Business Review*, 131–141.

Gitlow, H., A. Oppenheim and R. Oppenheim (1995). *Quality Management: Tools and Methods for Improvement* (2nd Edition). Burr Ridge, IL: Richard D. Irwin.

Grant, E. L. and R. S. Leavenworth (1988). *Statistical Quality Control*. (6th Edition) New York, NY: McGraw-Hill.

Hunter, J. S. (1985). "Statistical Design Applied to Product Design," *Journal of Quality Technology*, 17:4, 210–221.

Jessup, P. T. (1985). "Process Capability, The Value of Improved Performance," *Proc. IEEE International Communications Conference*, ICC85.

Jiang, B. C., J. T. Black, D. W. H. Chen and J. N. Hool (1991). "Taguchi-Based Methodology for Determining/Optimizing Robust Process Capability," *IIE Transactions*, 23, 169–184.

Kackar, R. N. (1985). "Off-Line Quality Control, Parameter Design, and the Taguchi Method," *Journal of Quality Technology* 17, 176–209.

Kackar, R. (1986). "Taguchi's Quality Philosophy: Analysis and Commentary," *Quality Progress*, 21–29.

Kane, V. E. (1989). *Defect Prevention: Use of Simple Statistical Tools*. Milwaukee, WI: Marcel Dekker.

Keats, J. B., and N. F. Hubele, eds. (1989). *Statistical Process Control in Automated Manufacturing*. New York, NY: Marcel Dekker.

Krismann, C. (1990). *Quality Control: An Annotated Bibliography Through 1988*. White Plains, NY: Quality Resources.

Kume, Hitoshi (1985). *Statistical Methods for Quality Improvement*. Tokyo, Japan: AOTS Press.

Mendenhall, W., L. Ott and R. Schaeffer (1993). *Elementary Survey Sampling*. Belmont, CA: Duxbury.

Moen, R. D., T. W. Nolan and L. P. Provost (1989). *Improving Quality Through Planned Experimentation*. New York, NY: McGraw-Hill.

Montgomery, D. C. (1990). *Introduction to Statistical Quality Control*. New York, NY: John Wiley.

Orsini, J. (1982). "Simple Rule to Reduce Total Cost of Inspection and Correction of Product in State of Chaos," Ph.D. Dissertation, Graduate School of Business Administration, New York University.

Papadakis, G. P. (1985). "The Deming Inspection Criteria for Choosing Zero or 100 Percent Inspection," *Journal of Quality Technology*, 17:3, 121–127.

Phadke, M. S. (1989). *Quality Engineering Using Product Design*. Englewood Cliffs, NJ: Prentice-Hall.

Pugh, S. (1991). *Tool Design: Integrated Methods for Successful Product Engineering*. Reading, MA: Addison-Wesley.

Ryan, T. P. (1989). *Statistical Methods for Quality Improvement*. New York, NY: John Wiley.

Sadsworth, H. M., ed. (1988). *Taguchi Methods (Special Issue of Quality and Reliability Engineering)*, Chichester, UK: Wiley-Interscience.

Shewhart, W. A. (1939). Statistical Method from the Viewpoint of Quality Control. Ed. W. E. Deming. Washington, D.C.: The Graduate School, Department of Agriculture.

Sullivan, L. P. (1985). "Reducing Variability: A New Approach to Quality," *Quality Progress* 17:7, 15–21.

Taguchi, G., A. E. Elsayed and T. Hsiang (1989). *Quality Engineering in Production Systems*. New York, NY: McGraw-Hill.

Taguchi, G. and Y. Wu (1979). *Introduction to Off-Line Quality Control*. Meieki Nakamura-Ku Magaya, Japan: Central Japan Quality Control Association.

Wheeler, D. J. (1992). *Understanding Statistical Process Control* (2nd Edition). Knoxville, TN: Statistical Process Controls, Inc.

Woodall, W. H. (1987). "Conflicts Between Deming's Philosophy and the Economic Design of Control Charts," *Frontiers in Statistical Quality Control 3*, Eds. H. J. Lenz, G. B. Wetherill and P. T. Wilrich, Heidelberg, Germany: Physica-Verlag, 242–248.

Appendices 7

A Brief Review of the Normal Distribution

PROBABILITY DISTRIBUTIONS

An ordinary function at a point takes on a single value, i.e., $f(2) = 3$. However, a random variable can take on any one of many values, probabilistically. If there are only isolated and distinct values that can be taken on, where each value is assigned a probability (which all add to 1.0) then we speak of a discrete random variable with a probability function. (Discrete because only isolated values can happen; random variable because the variable can take on any one of many values, and a probability function assigns probabilities to them.)

For example, if we toss a fair coin three times and count the number of heads, we get a random variable and associated probability function:

x (heads)	0	1	2	3
f(x) (probability)	0.125	0.375	0.375	0.125

The cumulative distribution function simply adds up the probability of getting less than or equal to x:

x	0	1	2	3
F(x)	0.125	0.500	0.875	1.000

PROBABILITY DENSITY FUNCTIONS

If a random variable X is continuous, the probability that X achieves a particular value will be 0. But it still makes sense to talk about the probability that $1.5 <= x <= 2.0$, for example. Instead of having a probability function, we now will have a probability density function $f(x)$. $P(1.5 <= x <= 2.0)$ will now be represented by the area under the $f(x)$ curve between 1.5 and 2.0. The cumulative distribution function (CDF), the probability that any actual value t is less than x, denoted $F(x)$, will be represented by the area under the $f(x)$ curve between minus infinity and x.

As an example, suppose a random variable X has a probability density function (pdf) of $f(x) = 0.5x$ for $0 <= X <= 2$. This pdf is shown in Figure A-1. The value of the cumulative distribution function for $X = 0.5$ is $F(0.5) = 0.25$. This could be shown by calculus, but in this simple case we can find the area under the curve in Figure A-1 by a simple knowledge of triangles. Then $P(0.5 <= X <= 1.0) = F(1.0) - F(0.5) = (1/4) - (1/16) = 0.1875$. This illustrates the fact that we can get any information we want about the distribution using the CDF, which we will utilize when we look at the normal distribution later.

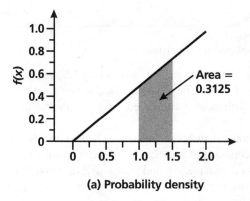

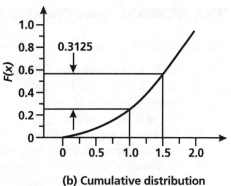

(a) Probability density (b) Cumulative distribution

Figure A-1

Example of a Continuous
Probability Density Function

EXPECTED VALUE

The idea of the expected value (or average value) of a random variable X, denoted $E(X)$, is very important; it is the most important single summary of a distribution. In particular, if we want to approximate a random variable by a single number, for example, we would most likely use the expected value.

The expected value of a probability function is obtained simply by multiplying each value for x by its probability and adding up (we are literally forming a weighted average of the x's); that is,

$$E(x) = \Sigma x f(x), \text{ and similarly, } E(x^2) = \Sigma x^2 f(x)$$

A common notation for $E(x)$ is μ_X. For our example where we tossed a coin three times, and counted the heads:

x (heads)	0	1	2	3
f(x) (prob.)	0.125	0.375	0.375	0.125
xf(x)	0	0.375	0.750	0.375

$$\mu_X = E(x) = 0 + 0.375 + 0.750 + 0.375 = 1.5$$

Indeed, if someone asked us for a very short answer for the number of heads, we might summarize by saying 1.5.

For a continuous distribution, we would also multiply x by $f(x)$ everywhere, and find the area under the curve. (We omit the calculus here since it is not really needed to understand the concept.)

We can also obtain the expectation for any function of x, say $g(x)$ by simply multiplying $g(x)$ by $f(x)$ and adding up over all x. A very important expectation is the average squared deviation from the mean, called the variance:

$$Var(X) = \sigma^2_X = \Sigma(x - \mu_X)^2 f(x)$$

An equivalent formula which is much easier for calculations is:

$$Var(X) = E(x^2) - [E(x)]^2$$

In our same coin tossing example, we have

x (heads)	0	1	2	3
f(x) (prob.)	0.125	0.375	0.375	0.125
x²f(x)	0	0.375	1.5000	1.125

Thus $Var(X) = \sigma^2_X = [0 + 0.375 + 1.5 + 1.125] - (1.5)^2 = 3.0 - 2.25 = 0.75$.
The standard deviation is $\sigma_X = (0.75)^{0.5} = 0.866$.

THE NORMAL DISTRIBUTION

The normal distribution has a number of convenient properties:

a. There is just one normal distribution for a given mean μ and standard deviation σ.

b. A single table called the unit normal deviate table can be used to construct any desired percentile of any normal distribution. A simplified version of this table is shown in Appendix G.

c. For a positive z, read the corresponding distribution percentile in the table. For a negative z read 1.0 minus the percentile given for the corresponding positive z.

d. In general, given a normal distribution with mean μ and standard deviation σ, and desiring the value of distribution with percentile P look up the corresponding z. Then the value W is given by: $W = \mu + z\sigma$. As an example, suppose we know the distribution is normal with mean 160 and standard deviation 40; we desire the 90th percentile of the distribution. The z corresponding to 0.90 is about 1.3, so approximately $W = 160 + (1.3)(40) = 212$.

e. If X and Y are normal random variables with means $E(X)$ and $E(Y)$, variances $V(X)$ and $V(Y)$ and covariance $\mathrm{Cov}(X,Y)$, then the random variable which is their sum $X + Y$ is also normally distributed with mean

$$E(X) + E(Y)$$

and variance

$$V(X) + V(Y) + 2\mathrm{Cov}(X,Y)$$

f. In particular, if X and Y are uncorrelated then their means and variances simply add.

Linear Regression with Many Variables

BEST LINEAR FIT

In general, if there are m causal variables, then we could write the regression equation as

$$P_{t,k} = \hat{P}_t + \sum_{i=1,m} \hat{B}_{i,t} X_{i,t,k}$$

Just as before, we use $\hat{P}$ and $\hat{B}_{i,t}$ as the values of the coefficients which minimize squared errors for a particular set of data. (To simplify notation in the following development, we eliminate the time subscript t if it causes no confusion.) Just as before, we use $P_k = \hat{P} + \sum_{i=1,m} \hat{B}_{i,k} X_{i,k}$ as the prediction for observation k.

As before, we may apply the method of least squares to find the linear prediction which fits the data best:

$$\text{Minimize } \sum_{k=0,n-1}(P_k - Y_k)^2$$

The normal equations are exactly analogous to the one variable case:

Normal Equations

$$\overline{Y} = \hat{P} + \sum_{i=1,m} \overline{X}_i \hat{B}_i$$
$$(\overline{X}_1\,\overline{Y}) = \overline{X}_1 \hat{P} + \sum_{i=1,m} \overline{X}_1 \overline{X}_i \hat{B}_i$$
$$(\overline{X}_2\,\overline{Y}) = \overline{X}_2 \hat{P} + \sum_{i=1,m} \overline{X}_2 \overline{X}_i \hat{B}_i$$
$$\ldots$$
$$(\overline{X}_m\,\overline{Y}) = \overline{X}_m \hat{P} + \sum_{i=1,m} \overline{X}_m \overline{X}_z \hat{B}_i$$

The job of solving three simultaneous equations is laborious, and four or more is way out of hand. Fortunately, the regression software complementing this book does this kind of work easily.

COEFFICIENT OF MULTIPLE DETERMINATION

We have already seen that the coefficient of determination for the simple two-variable case is defined as the explained variability as a percentage of the total variability. The coefficient of multiple determination (often also called R^2) is defined in exactly the same way as

$$R^2 = SSR/SST$$

where SSR = sum of squares explained by the regression

$$= \sum(P_k - \overline{Y})^2$$

and SST = original sum of squares with no variables

$$= \Sigma(Y_k - \overline{Y})^2$$

Again, regression packages perform all these computations automatically.

REGRESSION WITH NO CONSTANT TERM

The principle is the same as for one variable. Use the standard multi-variate equations, except treat the average of each single variable as if it were zero.

SIGNIFICANCE OF VARIABLES/REGRESSION

Since there are many factors involved in creating sales that we do not understand very well, the past sales that we are fitting with regression may be considered to be values of a random variable. Thus, if we took a different sample of n observations to use for fitting the regression, we would obtain a somewhat different equation with a different constant and different coefficients. That is to say, we might consider the regression equation itself to be a random "variable." It is thus quite possible for a regression to have a good R^2 or percentage improvement in the fit, but that this result is only due to random variation. It is also possible that any single variable, such as housing starts, appears very useful, but that result is only due to random variation.

This possibility is especially likely if the number of variables in the regression is almost as large as the number of data points. For example, suppose a regression has four variables (counting the independent variable) and four data points. Counting the constant, we must fit four constants to four data points. But this is just solving four equations in four unknowns. We can always get a perfect fit, regardless of the data! To be sure the regression is meaningful, then, one requirement is that the number of observations be considerably greater than the number of variables being fit.

Define

SST = original sum of squares $\qquad = \Sigma(Y_k - \overline{Y})^2$
SSR = sum of squares explained by the regression $= \Sigma(P_k - \overline{Y})^2$
SSE = remaining error
$\quad$ = SST – SSR $\qquad\qquad\qquad\qquad = \Sigma(Y_k - P_k)^2$
m $\quad$ = number of variables in regression
$\quad$ = total constants to fit
n $\quad$ = number of observations

Next we need an intuitive idea of **degrees of freedom**. Degrees of freedom represents the amount of information available from a data set. The n data points start with n degrees of freedom. Each time a parameter is estimated it "uses up" one degree of freedom. Estimation of the mean $\overline{Y}$ uses up one degree of freedom, so forecasting based simply on the average has $(n-1)$ degrees of freedom. Similarly, forecasting based on the regression uses up m degrees of freedom, leaving $(n-m)$ degrees of freedom. In doing the regression we start with $(n-1)$ degrees of freedom and end with $(n-m)$, so the regression uses $(m-1)$ degrees of freedom.

One very conservative way to try to say whether the fitted regression could have happened "at random" is to perform a statistical test with a null hypothesis that the R^2 is really 0 and only appears larger. We explain how to do this without proof. You are referred to a text on statistics or econometrics, such as the one by R. Pindyck and D. Rubinfeld [1991] referred to in the Forecasting Module, for justification.

First we calculate the following expression for the regression:

$$F = [SSR/(m - 1)]/[SSE/(n - m)]$$

Here the expression in the numerator had $(m - 1)$ degrees of freedom, that in the denominator had $(n - m)$. This is called the F ratio for the regression. For the example in Chapter 2 of the Forecasting Module for Table 2-5, the F ratio would be given by

$$F = [1016.2/1] / [25.3/2] = 80.3$$

The numerator has 1 degree of freedom and the denominator has 2 degrees of freedom. By referencing an F-table in a statistics book, you could verify that the F ratio with these degrees of freedom would have to be larger than 18.51 to conclude the regression is not simply random at the 5 percent confidence level, so here we pass the test. There are similar tests involving **t-statistics** to check whether or not it is safe to assume that a given single variable improves the fit rather than being a random occurrence.

In any event, these conservative statistical tests were originally developed for scientists who needed to be almost sure that their model was correct. A businessman usually is satisfied to know that using the model will be helpful more often than not.

Special Types of Regression Variables

There are a lot of special types of variables which find extensive application in business. We discuss some of them briefly here.

TREND VARIABLES

If demand appears to be increasing or decreasing over time, then the time of the observation itself is often a very important variable. The way time is scaled is not important, as long as the scaling does not distort linearity. For example, observations at the beginning of 1990, 1991, 1992, and 1993 could be scaled with $t = 0, 1, 2$, and 3, or $t = 10, 15, 20$, and 25, or simply $t = 1990, 1991, 1992$, and 1993. The first would have the advantage that trend corrections would be figured from 1990 as the base value. We shall use the coefficient of the time variable to be T_t to be consistent with usage in smoothing models presented in Chapter 3 of the Forecasting Module.

A point is that more complicated models do not always predict more accurately than simpler ones; in fact, their predictions often predict are much worse. The problem is that there is a tendency to confuse the fact that because the complicated model forecasts the *past* better (that is, fits the data better) that it must forecast the *future* better. If this seems reasonable, review Section 1.1 of the Forecasting Module.

In particular, there is no reason for an *apparent* trend in the data to be a *real* trend. For that matter, the trend often changes over time, which the regression ignores. To give some idea of the nature of this problem, consider a comparison of a regression model with only a constant term (forecast = average of data) against a second model with a trend factor for the following data for the last seven periods: 5, 15, 10, 25, 30, 25, 40.

Suppose that we are interested in forecasting at the end of period 0 for the demand in period 9. The seven-period average of the data is 21.4. Thus the forecasting model (at period 0) with no trend term would predict $P_{0,9} = 21.4$.

The linear trend model $P_{0,k} = P_0 + T_0 k$ has a (rough) least squares fit of $P_{0,k} = 34 + 5k$ and would predict $P_{0,9} = 79$, which is much higher.

Now suppose the real situation is that shown in Figure C-1. In this case models without trend correction will give superior results.

DUMMY VARIABLES

In many cases in forecasting, we wish to incorporate (into the forecast) causal variables which are logical either/or variables rather than quantitative. For example, Crawly

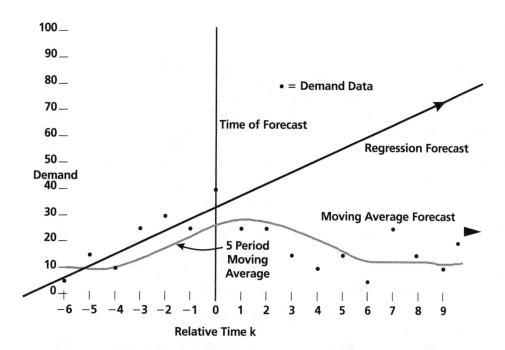

Figure C-1

More Complicated
Procedures Are Not Always
Better

Caterpillars' management knew that sales were different in years for which sales were limited by their capacity, and years when it was not. Rather than discard the data for which sales was constrained, they might include two dummy variables X_1 and X_2 such that

$X_1 = 1$ if capacity limited; 0 otherwise
$X_2 = 0$ if capacity limited; 1 otherwise

If they also included the variable $X_3 =$ (disposable income), then the regression equation would become

$$P_k = \hat{B}_1 X_{1,k} + \hat{B}_2 X_{2,k} + \hat{B}_3 X_{3,k}$$

We don't want or need the constant term here, for the following reason. During capacity limitation we really have the equation

$$P_k = \hat{B}_1 + \hat{B}_3 X_{3,k}$$

while otherwise we have the equation

$$P_k = \hat{B}_2 + \hat{B}_3 X_{3,k}$$

Thus in either situation we really have an implicit constant term. If we put in another one as well, the coefficients would not be well determined. We could always add any amount D to the constant appearing in both equations, for example, and then subtract that same D from both $\hat{B}_1$ and $\hat{B}_2$ to get an alternate equation with the same fit.

Actually there are many situations (such as for seasonal factors) for which we would like a main variable to represent the average effect of the dummy variables, with the dummy coefficients representing changes from this average. That is, in our example, we would want to know average sales over all the years, and then how much the constrained years do worse than this and how much the unconstrained do better.

For this purpose we start with the regression constrained through zero

$$P_k = \hat{B}_1 X_{1,k} + \hat{B}_2 X_{2,k} + \hat{B}_3 X_{3,k}$$

We also calculate that a fraction m_1 of the data points have $X_{1,k} = 1$, and a fraction $m_2 = 1 - m_1$ have $X_{2,k} = 1$. Thus the weighted average of the value of $\hat{B}_1 X_1 + \hat{B}_2 X_2$ is $m_1 \hat{B}_1 + m_2 \hat{B}_2 = A$. Then the equivalent regression equation we want is

$$P_k = A + (\hat{B}_1 - A)X_{1,k} + (\hat{B}_2 - A)X_{2,k} + (\hat{B}_3)X_{3,k}$$

Similar "tricks" work just as well if there are two or more groups of dummy variables, each of which have frequencies which add up to 100 percent. However, those tricks are a bit more complicated; we do not go into them here.

There is an alternative method of setting up dummy variables which is very common, although somewhat less convenient. We simply remove one of the variables in each set of dummy variables. When any of the other variables is 1, things are as before. However if they are all 0, the omitted variable is understood to be 1. In our previous example

$$P_k = \hat{P} + \hat{B}_2 X_{2,k} + \hat{B}_3 X_{3,k}$$

When capacity is limited, only the implicit variable is on and we have the equation

$$P_k = \hat{P} + \hat{B}_3 X_{3,k}$$

When capacity is not limited, we have the equation

$$P_k = (\hat{P} + \hat{B}_2 X_{2,k}) + \hat{B}_3 X_{3,k}$$

The trouble with this particular formulation is that it is a little messier to correct the coefficients so that they are deviations from the overall average.

Dummy variables can also be used to represent other qualitative variables such as seasonal factors, week of the month, day of the week, sex, marital status, education, occupation, and social status. An interesting situation arises when two sets of dummy factors are not independent of each other. In such cases it is sometimes necessary to put in combination dummy variables. We will not try to discuss this issue here.

SEASONAL VARIABLES

Perhaps the most commonly used dummy variables in forecasting are *seasonal* variables. The sales of many items follow a pattern which repeats each year. Sales of air conditioners are high in the summer, low in the winter. Children's clothing sales are high in late summer, with secondary peaks at Christmas and at Easter. Most seasonal patterns are either monthly or quarterly; a trend correction term is also often added to recognize the longer term pattern of change.

A typical quarterly model with no other variables might be

$$P_k = A_k + q_1 X_{1,k} + q_2 X_{2,k} + q_3 X_{3,k} + q_4 X_{4,k}$$

where each of the X's is a dummy variable with value 1 in the quarter indicated by its first subscript. After regressing through the origin, we would have

$$P_k = A^* + \sum q_i^* X_{i,k}$$

Define $\hat{P} = \sum q_i^*$ and $\hat{B} = q_i^* - A^*$.
Then the final regression after adjustment is

$$P_k = \hat{P} + Tt_k + \hat{B}_1 X_{1,k} + \hat{B}_2 X_{2,k} + \hat{B}_3 X_{3,k} + \hat{B}_4 X_{4,k}$$

In this equation, P_k now represents demand in an average season (deseasonalized) for time t of zero, T represents the estimated trend per year, t_k is the year for observation k, and the $\hat{B}_i$ represent additive seasonal factors, adjusted to be represented as deviations from an average season. (They therefore now add to 0.)

LAGGED VARIABLES

In some situations it might be reasonable that changes in the variable to be forecast can best be explained not by current changes in the causal variables, but by changes in the independent variables one or more periods ago. Consider our example of microwave oven sales as explained by housing starts, and suppose that a period in the problem represents six months.

The reason we expect housing starts to be related to oven sales is that builders usually incorporate ovens into new houses directly. However, the ovens do not need to be bought when the houses are started, but somewhat later. Thus it might be reasonable to suggest that the level of oven sales in *this* period is related to housing starts *L periods* ago. If we decide to investigate $L = 2$, for example, we would make paired observations of sales in period t and housing starts in period $(t - 2)$. The model is something like

$$P_{tk} = \hat{P}_t + \hat{B}_t X_{t,L-2}$$

If, in fact, this is a better hypothesis than a lag of 0, a higher R^2 will probably result.

What if a fractional lag is appropriate? What if, for example, the real lag is about 0.6 periods? In this case we may pair Y_t with both X_t and X_{t-1}:

$$P_{tk} = \hat{P}_t + \hat{B}_1 X_{t,k} + \hat{B}_2 X_{t,k-1}$$

If the regression gives a significant weight to both the 0-lag and the 1-lag terms, there is some evidence that a fractional lag was appropriate.

Estimating Seasonal Factors

In this appendix, we discuss a number of ways of estimating seasonal factors.

JUDGMENTAL METHODS

Judgmental methods have great advantages in being able to correct for such circumstances as cooler summers, a late Easter, and similarity or complementarity with other items. The primary disadvantage is that experts are inefficient for large amounts of data manipulation.

MANUAL METHODS (WITH TREND)

Manual methods are basically simple approximations to regression, and thus are somewhat less accurate, but easy to deal with and modify intuitively. Let N be the number of cycles in the data, with m periods in each, giving mN data points:

1. For the first m-period seasonal cycle, and the last m-period seasonal cycle, compute the average demand.
2. Estimate m-period-seasonal cycle trend as
   (final m-period average – initial m period average)$/(N-1)$.
3. Estimate overall trend per period as
   (m-period-seasonal cycle trend)$/m$.
4. Considering the mN data points as a time series, and numbering the first period as 1, make the following deseasonalized estimate for each period:
   Deseasonalized demand in t = (grand average) – ($mN/2 - t$))trend.
5. Compute all apparent seasonal factors as before, based on the individual deseasonalized estimates, rather than the average for the year.
6. Average apparent seasonal factors over the same period in all years.
7. Factors may require slight correction to add to 0 for additive factors, or to m for multiplicative factors.

WINTERS' METHOD

Winters' [1960] (see Forecasting Module) method is basically a trend-corrected exponential smoothing model, with additional equations to smooth the (multiplicative) seasonal factors at the same time. It thus needs three smoothing constants instead of two, which he calls α, β, and γ. Winters' model has the advantage that seasonal factors are updated each period along with trend and average at relatively low cost and data requirements. It has the typical disadvantage of a one-product model, that the fairly new data on which one seasonal factor can be based is small, and hence, if the demand is noisy, little reliance may be placed on the seasonal factors generated.

The model basically assumes that as demand increases due to the trend, the seasonal pattern increases proportionately, as shown in Figure D-1. (ΔF_t is shorthand for $(F_t - F_{t-1})$).

$$F_t = (F_{t-1} + T_{t-1}) + \alpha[(D_t/a_{t-m}) - (F_{t-1} + T_{t-1})] \tag{1a}$$

$$T_t = T_{t-1} + \beta(\Delta F_t - T_{t-1}) \tag{1b}$$

$$a_t = a_{t-m} + \gamma[(D_t/F_t) - a_{t-m}] \tag{1c}$$

$$P_t = a_t F_t \tag{1d}$$

$$P_{t,k} = a_{t+k-m}(F_t + kT_t) \tag{1e}$$

Note that, as usual, we deseasonalize demand (D_t/a_{t-m}) in (1a) first, solve the deseasonalized model, and then reseasonalize it in the predictive equations (1d) and (1e). The first two equations (1a) and (1b) are exactly a variant of the trend corrected system.

However, we now add an equation for smoothing seasonal factors (1c). One estimate of the seasonal factor for time t is our estimate from one year ago, a_{t-m}. A different estimate is given by the current apparent seasonal factor D_t/F_t. Then equation (1d) says the derandomized estimate of current demand P_t is given by the deseasonalized estimate, F_t, times the appropriate seasonal factor a_t. Equation (1e), on the other hand, says that the forecast $P_{t,k}$ looking k periods into the future is just the deseasonalized estimate ($F_t + kT_t$) times the appropriate future seasonal factor, which would be a_{t+k} except that this updated seasonal factor won't be available for k more periods. Thus we use a_{t+k-m} as the next best alternative.

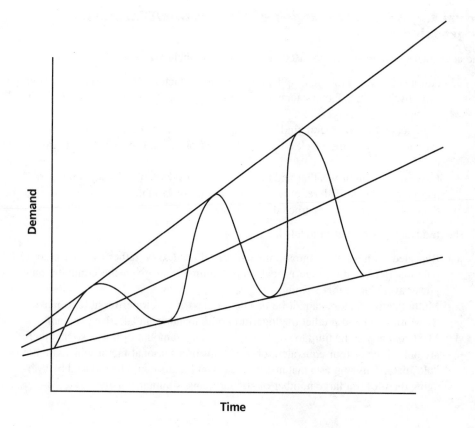

Figure D-1

Seasonal Series with Increasing Trend and Multiplicative Seasonal Factors

Demand

Time

REGRESSION/DISCOUNTED REGRESSION

Overview

Running a regression on at least two years of past data with dummy variables for seasonal factors on a product at time t produces a mean, a trend, and seasonal factors, all of which may be updated next period simply by rerunning the regression. If the trend is suppressed, this produces results very similar to but better than the first stationary manual seasonal factor model above. If the trend is not suppressed, this produces results very similar to but much better than the second trend manual seasonal factor model. (Trend is fitted by least squares, rather than crudely as the average increase between the first and last season.)

By adding a discount factor $(1 - \alpha)$ and adjusting the weights to add to 1.0, we are doing a full trend corrected additive seasonal factor model, which is optimal under the regression assumptions if the trend is not suppressed, and a stationary additive seasonal factor model if the trend is suppressed.

Brief Method Description

With regression or discounted regression, besides the current estimate F_t and the trend estimate T_t, we estimate (if, for example, we are using monthly periods) twelve seasonal coefficients $a_1, a_2, \ldots a_{12}$ from 12 dummy variables $X_1, X_2, \ldots X_{12}$.

At this point you may wish to review the use of dummy variables in Appendix C. The salient points are:

1. Temporarily suppress the regression constant.
2. Subtract a constant from the resulting dummy coefficients sufficient to make the revised coefficients add to 0.
3. Add the same constant to the suppressed regression constant, which gives P_t.

Advantages/Disadvantages of Regression/Discounted Regression

The advantages of regression and discounted regression include:

1. Automatic estimation, and updating of seasonal factors, from period to period. This gives additive factors many of the advantages of multiplicative factors, without their disadvantages.
2. Easy adaptation to several kinds of seasonal factors. For example, one might both estimate a day of the week effect and a week of the year effect if the period is daily.
3. Easy adjustment of weather and holiday variations, by simply readjusting period numbers in the procedure, or adding other dummy variables.
4. Seasonal factors are constructed to add to zero.

The disadvantages of these models include:

1. Repeated running of a regression each period used to be rather expensive computationally, but this issue is really now unimportant given the computational power available at this writing.
2. Multiplicative factors cannot be handled, unless it is felt permissible to make a transformation and predict the logarithm of demand as an additive problem.
3. Most cogently, a medium to small item has a large amount of noise, so that there are only three or four equivalent observations of a seasonal factor which are not "old" data. This suggests that noise in seasonal factors could be reduced by averaging them over a large number of similar items, simultaneously.

Forecasting Multiple Product Models

It is perhaps worthwhile to repeat here the basic analogy between smoothing models, which average out noise over past data for the given product, and multiple product models, which also average out noise by averaging over similar products. In exponential smoothing (or moving averages) we have a tension between wanting to average in older and older data to further reduce the noise and wanting to avoid using data which is "old" and no longer representative of the current situation. In multiple product models we have a tension between wanting to average over larger and larger groups of products to further reduce the noise, and wanting to avoid using products with very different seasonal patterns or trends.

The art of grouping "similar" products is very difficult, and is perhaps best done judgmentally.

LOGARITHMIC REGRESSION MODEL

Suppose that there are G products in a group, numbered $1, \ldots, g, \ldots, G$, all assumed to have the same multiplicative seasonal factors and all assumed to have the same multiplicative (we have not used this before) trend. That is, our model might be:

$$P_{t,g,k} = (F_t)(T_t)^k(A_{t+k})(p_g) \tag{1}$$

Here $P_{t,g,k}$ represents the forecast to be made for product g at time t for k periods into the future. F_t is the de-seasonalized estimate of sales over the entire product group (aggregated by dollar value). T_t represents the rate of growth (e.g., 1.015) for the entire product group per period, so that the trend for k periods would be $(T_t)^k$. A_{t+k} is the multiplicative seasonal factor for the entire group for period $t + k$ as estimated in period t. (The trend and seasonal factors are also assumed to hold for each individual item, which is only an approximation.) Finally, p_g is the fraction of total sales expected to be realized by product g as seen at time t. (In the next period the logarithmic regression will be rerun, and all these estimates will be updated.)

Now (2) cannot be run directly by regression, which applies only to additive models. However, if we assume the error term is also multiplicative, we can simply take logarithms of everything and produce a linear model (we write F'_t to mean $\log(F_t)$ and so forth to save space):

$$P'_{t,g,k} = F'_t + kT'_t + A'_{t+k} + p'_g \tag{2}$$

Using regression, we need one variable for the constant F'_t, one for the linear trend T'_t, m dummy variables for the additive seasonal factors A'_{t+k}, which need to be adjusted to add to zero, and G dummy variables for the additive product share p'_g, which also need to be adjusted to add to zero.

This regression has TG data points, where T is the number of periods in the regression data history, and G the number of products. It needs to estimate only $2 + m + G$ coefficients, while if each were run individually it would have T data points and estimate $2 + m$ coefficients. For $G = 100$ and $T = 48$ and $m = 12$, this represents a vast savings in computational effort. If the products truly fit this model fairly well, it also will involve a much better forecast for the individual products.

HIERARCHICAL MODELS

The simplest possible hierarchical model has been historically widely used by such companies as Sears and Montgomery Ward in forecasting major catalogue sales (in the heyday of major catalogues). It groups items only for the purpose of estimating a common multiplicative seasonal pattern, but otherwise forecasts each SKU (stock keeping unit, or individual item) separately. For, say, the autumn six-month catalogue, items are naturally grouped into similar "lines" of perhaps 100 or 200 items, assumed to have roughly the same seasonal pattern. Sales in each line are totaled week by week, and each total is divided by the average line sales per week, generating an apparent seasonal pattern. These seasonal patterns are saved over four or five years. Since back-to-school times, weather, and other factors vary from year to year, the forecaster chooses which pattern is likely to be most representative for the coming season. This pattern is selected, and any final judgmental adjustments are made. The resulting pattern becomes the multiplicative seasonal pattern for each item of the line, each of which is then forecast individually.

This traditional hierarchical forecasting method might be called decentralized-hierarchical, because only seasonal pattern estimation is centralized. It is appropriate if items in the line have very different trends, or random walk to noise ratios (small volume items often have a smaller random walk to noise ratio.)

R. G. Brown [1962] (see the Forecasting Module) introduced what might be called the centralized-hierarchical model:

$$F_t = (F_{t-1} + T_{t-1}) + \alpha[(D_t - a_{t-m}) - (F_{t-1} + T_{t-1})] \tag{3a}$$

$$T_t = T_{t-1} + \beta[(\Delta D_t - \Delta a_{t-m}) - T_{t-1}] \tag{3b}$$

$$a_t = a_{t-m} + \gamma[(D_t - F_t) - a_{t-m}] \tag{3c}$$

$$P_t = F_t \tag{3d}$$

$$P_{tk} = F_t + kT_t + a_{t-k-m} \tag{3e}$$

$$q_{tj} = q_{t-1,j} + \delta[D_{tj}/D_t - q_{t-1,j}] \tag{3f}$$

$$P_{tjk} = q_{tj}P_{tk} \tag{3g}$$

Equations (3a) to (3e) represent a standard of Winters type forecasting procedure for the aggregate sales of the full line of products, say in dollars. Equation (3a) smooths normalized aggregate sales. Equation (3b) smooths the aggregate trend. Equation (3c) smooths the aggregate additive seasonal factors. Equations (3d) and (3e) predict aggregate sales for k periods into the future. Equations (3f) and (3g) disaggregate the forecasts to give forecasts for individual products. Equation (3f) smooths the estimate of the item's fraction of total product line sale. Equation (3g) estimates product forecasts by this percentage of the line forecast.

Estimating Forecast Errors

OVERVIEW

In the forecasting module, we talked primarily about various methods for forecasting average or *expected* demand in any single future period $(t + k)$ given that the last demand we have currently experienced is for period t. We called this estimate $P_{t,k}$. Actually, for planning and control purposes the individual period forecasts are often but steps along the way to a slightly different objective. We are often very interested in the *distribution* of total demand over a *group of periods* immediately to come called the **forecast interval**.

For example, in planning inventories the purpose of forecasting demand is to know how much to protect against a high demand which might occur before the *next* order can arrive. The past is sunk; we need not plan for it, except to cover any unfilled orders. The next order can be expected to take care of its own problems when it arrives. We must plan exactly for the interval that is in between; here we are under the gun.

FOUNDATIONS

Continuing the inventory example, suppose the **lead time** (time between placing an order and its arrival) is a known w periods, and the order cycle (number of periods planned between successive orders) is c periods. Define $I = w + c$ as the number of periods in the forecast interval. Then if we are deciding how much to order at time t, we will be interested in the total distribution of total demand over the interval I from $(t + 1)$ to $(t + I)$.

This distribution is really very complicated and difficult to obtain in full. Actually, all we really need is an appropriate "high" value, perhaps the 95th percentile, or something like that. However, this high estimate may change depending on just how costly it is to stock out. Our usual compromise in practice is to settle for trying to forecast the mean demand on the interval I, call it P_I, and the standard deviation of demand, call it S_I, and to assume an approximately normal distribution of demand. Normal approximations to real forecast distributions are typically quite good from about the 10th percentile to the 90th percentile, fair from the 2nd percentile to the 98 percentile, and poor further out in the tails. (There are just too many real world situations which our models cannot capture which occasionally cause very bad forecasts and give us "fat tails".)

Since we are typically interested in the 90th to the 95th percentile as our "high" estimate of demand, the normal approximation is not bad. Our high estimate H_I is then

$$H_I = P_I + zS_I \qquad (1)$$

where z is the standardized normal deviate for the percentile desired. In practice, when the tails are very fat, a somewhat larger z can be used. For example, for the 95th percentile a z of perhaps 2.5 might be used in practice rather than the value of about 1.7 given in the normal deviate table. The inventory control manager might make this correction based on judgment arising from past experience. Or she might simulate the effect of using different z values on past demand history in a full blown inventory simulation. The latter possibility cannot be discussed in detail here.

Then our problem reduces to finding the expected interval demand, P_I, and the expected standard deviation over the interval, S_I. Finding the mean total forecast for the interval knowing the individual forecasts is easy:

$$P_I = \sum_{k=1,I} P_{t,k} \tag{2}$$

It is important to note that simply adding individual expected demands to get total expected demands is *exactly* right and does not depend on knowing that the individual demand forecasts are uncorrelated. This is fortunate since, as we will discuss below, these forecasts will typically be positively correlated. (The fact that correlation does not matter in taking a sum of averages follows directly from the statistical fact that the expectation of a sum of random variables is equal to the sum of the expectations always, without any qualifications.)

Estimating the standard deviation of the forecast, S_I, is a more difficult matter. We will discuss three major approaches:

   a. Extrapolating from one-period errors
   b. Smoothing past interval errors
   c. Extrapolating from the interval forecast

EXTRAPOLATING FROM ONE-PERIOD ERRORS

In order to extrapolate from one-period errors to interval errors, we first must track the size of one-period errors. Each period we calculate our forecast error for this period, namely this demand compared with the forecast from last period:

$$E_t = D_t - P_{t-1,1} \tag{3}$$

We cannot smooth this error directly, since negative errors will cancel each other out; we are interested in the average *size* of errors more than their sign. Thus we focus on the absolute value of the error, $|E_t|$, which we call the absolute deviation or AD, and the smoothed value of the AD, which is called the MAD for mean absolute deviation. We then may smooth the AD to estimate a current value of the MAD:

$$(MAD)_t = (MAD)_{t-1} + \psi(|E_t| - (MAD)_{t-1}) \tag{4}$$

The normal distribution has the nice property that its MAD is 80 percent of the standard deviation, so our estimate for the current standard deviation of forecast, S_t, is given by:

$$S_t = 1.25(MAD)_t \tag{5}$$

Now let us think first about the stationary case. In this case our forecast of errors for the very near future, say period $t + k$, might simply be:

$$S_{t,k} = S_t \tag{6}$$

Now we have estimated standard errors $S_{t,k}$ for each period in the forecast interval as all equal S_t, and therefore estimate variances $V_{t,k}$ all as $|S_t|^2$. If these I demands were completely uncorrelated, then the variance of the sum of these demands V_I is just the sum of the variances:

$$V_I = \sum_{k=1,I} V_{t,k} = I|S_t|^2 \qquad (7)$$

However, the forecasts will almost always be positively correlated. In the extreme, if the period demands were *perfectly correlated* then:

$$V_I = I^2|S_t|^2 \qquad (8)$$

These represent the two extremes possible for positively correlated demands; the truth will be somewhere in between. Hence we may conclude:

$$I^{0.5}S_t <= S_I <= IS_t \qquad (9)$$

Thus, for an interval of five periods in a stationary problem, we estimate the standard deviation as between 2.2 and 5.0 times that for one period.

Early authors often assumed that demands were independent in each period and hence that the square root rule was appropriate. In the first place, demands are usually somewhat positively correlated. More seriously than that, we do not *know* the individual demand means, but have only estimated them. In particular, $P_{t,k}$ are all being estimated by our estimate P_t. If P_t currently (without our knowledge!) is larger than the true mean, all $P_{t,k}$ will tend to be larger than their true means; if P_t is smaller, all $P_{t,k}$ will tend to be smaller. This introduces a rather high positive correlation to the forecasts.

In his early forecasting work, Brown suggested the following procedure to correct for the positive correlation. For a large group of similar items, estimate S_I and S_t for each item based on a simulation of historical data. Define $Y = \log(S_I/S_t)$ and $X = \log(I)$ (natural logarithms). Then fit the regression, forced through the origin:

$$Y = \omega X \qquad (10)$$

Taking anti-logs of both sides, we obtain finally:

$$S_I = I^\omega S_t \qquad (11)$$

Here one would hope that the value of ω lies between 0.5 and 1.0 and represent a good compromise for the group of items being tested, since this same value is to be used for all.

There are a number of things wrong with Brown's procedure, however. First, for small volume items, the forecast error tends to be dominated by the noise and so an ω of 0.5 is more appropriate. But for large volume items, the error tends to be dominated by the lead or lag in forecasting P_t, and hence an ω closer to 1.0 is more appropriate. While this might be dealt with by segregating the items into volume classes, this complicates the analysis, and reduces the sample size, increasing noise.

Second, some major sources of error are being ignored. The leadtime I is not really fixed, but often varies considerably, which introduces additional error. Also, as we have said, the random walk in the mean increases errors as we go into the future.

Third, trying to correct this procedure for trends and seasonal factors gets extremely complicated. We do not go into this here, except to say that most such attempts are quite unsatisfactory.

Finally, having separate estimates for P_t and S_t in the computer can cause practical problems. The inventory manager often needs to manually readjust P_t to take into account major changes in sales level due to a drastically lowered price, improved product, special promotion, or obsolescence due to a new competitor. The effect may be to double or triple P_t or to cut it nearly to zero. The manager also needs at that point to readjust S_t for the item upward or downward, but typically has no idea how to do it. In practice S_t is usually just left untouched, which causes S_I to be drastically underestimated (overestimated), causing drastic under-ordering (over-ordering) of replacement inventories, leading to excessive stockouts (inventories).

All of these reasons lead us to consider alternative procedures.

SMOOTHING PAST INTERVAL ERRORS

In the second procedure, at each time t we record $(P_I)_t$, our interval forecast at time t. Then when the associated order actually comes in, we record the actual leadtime I', and the actual demand over the actual forecast interval $(D'_I)_t$. This produces an actual absolute forecast error for the interval:

$$|(E'_I)_t| = |(D'_I)_t - (P_I)_t|$$ (12)

Direct smoothing of past interval errors gets around some of the problems of the period error method. There is no need to estimate an extrapolation parameter ω separately for many small groups of items. Errors in the lead time estimates and greater errors in further periods are incorporated directly.

On the other hand, there is still no obvious method for incorporating seasonality and/or trend. Also there is no automatic correction of S_t when P_t is changed in a major way. We turn to a third method which has the potential to solve these problems.

EXTRAPOLATING FROM THE INTERVAL FORECAST

In the third procedure one would fit S_I directly as a function of P_I, again for a particular group of items. If such a function could be found and were reasonably accurate, then a great many problems discussed previously would be solved.

Let us develop intuitively what such a function might look like. If there were no random walk in the demand mean, so that the mean forecasts $P_{t,k}$ were essentially known, no errors would be introduced through forecasting, and the only error would be due to the noise of individual customers deciding whether or not to buy in a given period. If customers then came in independently and individually, and bought one item at a time, it is well known that demand would be Poisson in distribution. For this simple case, the mean is equal to the variance, so that:

$$S_I = A(P_I)^{0.5}$$ (13)

(A may be larger than 1.0 if customers tend to buy several items at once.) On the other hand, if there were little noise, but a great deal of forecasting problems due to random walks and so forth, we have noticed in practice that such difficulties are often directly proportional to the demand level, that is:

$$S_I = BP_I$$ (14)

If it is assumed that these two error components are relatively independent of each other, we can add the two variances, and take the square root to get the composite formula:

$$S_I = [AP_I + (BP_I)^2]^{0.5}$$ (15)

The author has fit such a formula with a great deal of success for several groups of items at a large mail order house where each group had items with widely varying demands. Previous attempts to fit an $I^\omega S_t$ type formula failed badly, since the value estimated for ω depended heavily on whether demands in a subgroup were large or small.

To get historical pairs of P_I, S_I to analyze, one goes through a procedure much like that in procedure two. That is, for each time t, first make the forecast $(P_I)_t$, then wait and find the actual time the order came in, giving a true interval I', and then find the actual demand $(D_{I'})_t$. Forming the forecast errors, taking absolute values and averaging them yields good estimates of S_I.

Standard regression methods will not work for estimating equation (15) since it is not a linear expression. Taking logarithms does not result in a linear expression either. However, plotting the (P_I, S_I) pairs on logarithmic paper gave very interesting results. The data did form a nice function giving errors from knowing the forecast. For small demand products the slope was about 0.5, while for large demand products it was about 1.0, as we had hoped. We saw a practical method for estimating A and B. We divided the items into three classes; small-volume, mid-volume and large volume. For the small volume items, we found A by fitting (13), treating this piece of the function as approximately linear. For the large volume items, we found B by fitting (14), again by assuming the piece approximately linear. We then inserted these estimates into (15) and checked the fit of the resulting formula by calculating its mean square error.

In this pilot study, this all worked very well. A typical formula for one particular group was $S_I = [0.95P_I + (0.25P_I)^2]^{0.5}$ indicating that for small volume items errors were indeed Poisson, while for large volume items the standard deviation was about 25 percent of the forecast. For items which are not typically bought one at a time, units should be measured in terms of an average purchase amount before applying the Poisson assumption.

Table of the Normal Distribution

Normal Probability Distribution and Unit Normal Loss Function				
Standardized Variate	Probabilities		Unit Normal Loss	
z	F(z)	1–F(z)	L(z)	L(-z)
.00	.5000	.5000	.3989	.3989
.01	.5040	.4960	.3940	.4040
.02	.5080	.4920	.3890	.4090
.03	.5120	.4880	.3841	.4141
.04	.5160	.4840	.3793	.4193
.05	.5200	.4800	.3744	.4244
.06	.5239	.4761	.3697	.4297
.07	.5279	.4721	.3649	.4349
.08	.5319	.4681	.3602	.4402
.09	.5359	.4641	.3556	.4456
.10	.5398	.4602	.3509	.4509
.11	.5438	.4562	.3464	.4564
.12	.5478	.4522	.3418	.4618
.13	.5517	.4483	.3373	.4673
.14	.5557	.4443	.3328	.4728
.15	.5596	.4404	.3284	.4784
.16	.5636	.4364	.3240	.4840
.17	.5685	.4325	.3197	.4897
.18	.5714	.4286	.3154	.4954
.19	.5753	.4247	.3111	.5011
.20	.5793	.4207	.3069	.5069
.21	.5832	.4168	.3027	.5127
.22	.5871	.4129	.3027	.5186
.23	.5910	.4090	.2944	.5244
.24	.5948	.4052	.2904	.5304
.25	.5987	.4013	.2863	.5363
.26	.6026	.3974	.2824	.5424
.27	.6064	.3936	.2784	.5484
.28	.6103	.3897	.2745	.5545
.29	.6141	.3859	.2706	.5606
.30	.6179	.3821	.2668	.5668
.31	.6217	.3783	.2630	.5730
.32	.6255	.3745	.2592	.5792
.33	.6293	.3707	.2555	.5855
.34	.6331	.3669	.2518	.5918
.35	.6368	.3632	.2481	.5981
.36	.6406	.3594	.2445	.6045
.37	.6443	.3557	.2409	.6109
.38	.6480	.3520	.2374	.6174
.39	.6517	.3483	.2339	.6239

Normal Probability Distribution and Unit Normal Loss Function				
Standardized Variate	Probabilities		Unit Normal Loss	
z	F(z)	1–F(z)	L(z)	L(-z)
.40	.6554	.3446	.2304	.6304
.41	.6591	.3409	.2270	.6370
.42	.6628	.3372	.2236	.6436
.43	.6664	.3336	.2203	.6503
.44	.6700	.3300	.2169	.6569
.45	.6736	.3264	.2137	.6637
.46	.6772	.3228	.2104	.6704
.47	.6808	.3192	.2072	.6772
.48	.6844	.3156	.2040	.6840
.49	.6879	.3121	.2009	.6909
.50	.6825	.3085	.1978	.6978
.51	.6950	.3050	.1947	.7047
.52	.6985	.3015	.1917	.7117
.53	.7019	.2981	.1887	.7187
.54	.7054	.2946	.1857	.7287
.55	.7088	.2912	.1828	.7328
.56	.7123	.2877	.1799	.7399
.57	.7157	.2843	.1771	.7471
.58	.7190	.2810	.1742	.7542
.59	.7224	.2776	.1714	.7614
.60	.7257	.2743	.1687	.7687
.61	.7291	.2709	.1659	.7759
.62	.7324	.2676	.1633	.7833
.63	.7357	.2643	.1606	.7906
.64	.7389	.2611	.1580	.7980
.65	.7422	.2578	.1554	.8054
.66	.7454	.2546	.1528	.8128
.67	.7486	.2514	.1503	.8203
.68	.7517	.2483	.1478	.8278
.69	.7549	.2451	.1453	.8353
.70	.7580	.2420	.1429	.8429
.71	.7611	.2389	.1405	.8505
.72	.7642	.2358	.1381	.8581
.73	.7673	.2327	.1358	.8658
.74	.7703	.2297	.1334	.8734
.75	.7733	.2267	.1312	.8812
.76	.7764	.2236	.1289	.8889
.77	.7793	.2207	.1267	.8967
.78	.7823	.2177	.1245	.9045
.79	.7852	.2148	.1223	.9123
.80	.7881	.2119	.1202	.9202
.81	.7910	.2090	.1181	.9281
.82	.7939	.2061	.1160	.9360
.83	.7967	.2033	.1140	.9440
.84	.7996	.2004	.1120	.9520
.85	.8023	.1977	.1100	.9600
.86	.8051	.1949	.1080	.9680
.87	.8078	.1922	.1061	.9761
.88	.8106	.1894	.1042	.9842
.89	.8133	.1867	.1023	.9923
.90	.8159	.1841	.1004	1.0004
.91	.8186	.1814	.0986	1.0086
.92	.8212	.1788	.0968	1.0168
.93	.8238	.1762	.0955	1.0250
.94	.8264	.1736	.0953	1.0330
.95	.8289	.1711	.0916	1.0416
.96	.8315	.1685	.0899	1.0499

Normal Probability Distribution and Unit Normal Loss Function				
Standardized Variate	Probabilities		Unit Normal Loss	
z	F(z)	1–F(z)	L(z)	L(-z)
.97	.8340	.1660	.0882	1.0582
.98	.8365	.1635	.0865	1.0665
.99	.8389	.1611	.0849	1.0749
1.00	.8413	.1587	.0833	1.0833
1.01	.8438	.1562	.0817	1.0917
1.02	.8461	.1539	.0802	1.1002
1.03	.8485	.1515	.0787	1.1087
1.04	.8508	.1492	.0772	1.1172
1.05	.8531	.1469	.0757	1.1257
1.06	.8554	.1446	.0742	1.1342
1.07	.8577	.1423	.0728	1.1428
1.08	.8599	.1401	.0714	1.1514
1.09	.8621	.1379	.0700	1.1600
1.10	.8643	.1357	.0686	1.1686
1.11	.8665	.1335	.0673	1.1773
1.12	.8686	.1314	.0659	1.1859
1.13	.8708	.1292	.0646	1.1946
1.14	.8729	.1271	.0634	1.2034
1.15	.8749	.1251	.0621	1.2121
1.16	.8770	.1230	.0609	1.2209
1.17	.8790	.1210	.0596	1.2296
1.18	.8810	.1190	.0584	1.2384
1.19	.8830	.1170	.0573	1.2473
1.20	.8849	.1151	.0561	1.2561
1.21	.8869	.1131	.0550	1.2650
1.22	.8888	.1112	.0538	1.2738
1.23	.8907	.1093	.0527	1.2827
1.24	.8925	.1075	.0517	1.2917
1.25	.8943	.1057	.0506	1.3006
1.26	.8962	.1038	.0495	1.3095
1.27	.8980	.1020	.0485	1.3185
1.28	.8997	.1003	.0475	1.3275
1.29	.9015	.0985	.0465	1.3365
1.30	.9032	.0968	.0455	1.3455
1.31	.9049	.0951	.0446	1.3446
1.32	.9066	.0934	.0436	1.3636
1.33	.9082	.0918	.0427	1.3727
1.34	.9099	.0901	.0418	1.3818
1.35	.9115	.0885	.0409	1.3909
1.36	.9131	.0869	.0400	1.4000
1.37	.9147	.0853	.0392	1.4092
1.38	.9162	.0838	.0383	1.4183
1.39	.9177	.0823	.0375	1.4275
1.40	.9192	.0808	.0367	1.4367
1.41	.9207	.0793	.0359	1.4459
1.42	.9222	.0778	.0351	1.4551
1.43	.9236	.0764	.0343	1.4643
1.44	.9251	.0749	.0336	1.4736
1.45	.9265	.0735	.0328	1.4828
1.46	.9279	.0721	.0321	1.4921
1.47	.9292	.0708	.0314	1.5014
1.48	.9306	.0694	.0307	1.5107
1.49	.9319	.0681	.0300	1.5200
1.50	.9332	.0668	.0293	1.5293
1.51	.9345	.0655	.0286	1.5386
1.52	.9357	.0643	.0280	1.5480
1.53	.9370	.0630	.0274	1.5574
1.54	.9382	.0618	.0267	1.5667

Normal Probability Distribution and Unit Normal Loss Function

Standardized Variate	Probabilities		Unit Normal Loss	
z	F(z)	1–F(z)	L(z)	L(-z)
1.55	.9394	.0606	.0261	1.5761
1.56	.9406	.0594	.0255	1.5855
1.57	.9418	.0582	.0249	1.5949
1.58	.9429	.0571	.0244	1.6044
1.59	.9441	.0559	.0238	1.6138
1.60	.9460	.0540	.0232	1.6232
1.61	.9463	.0537	.0227	1.6327
1.62	.9474	.0526	.0222	1.6422
1.63	.9484	.0516	.0216	1.6516
1.64	.9495	.0505	.0211	1.6611
1.65	.9505	.0495	.0206	1.6706
1.66	.9515	.0485	.0201	1.6801
1.67	.9525	.0475	.0197	1.6897
1.68	.9535	.0465	.0192	1.6992
1.69	.9545	.0455	.0187	1.7087
1.70	.9554	.0446	.0183	1.7183
1.71	.9564	.0436	.0178	1.7278
1.72	.9573	.0427	.0174	1.7374
1.73	.9582	.0418	.0170	1.7470
1.74	.9591	.0409	.0166	1.7566
1.75	.9599	.0401	.0162	1.7662
1.76	.9608	.0392	.0158	1.7558
1.77	.9616	.0384	.0154	1.7854
1.78	.9625	.0375	.0150	1.7950
1.79	.9633	.0367	.0146	1.8046
1.80	.9641	.0359	.0143	1.8143
1.81	.9649	.0351	.0139	1.8239
1.82	.9656	.0344	.0136	1.8436
1.83	.9664	.0336	.0132	1.8432
1.84	.9671	.0329	.0129	1.8529
1.85	.9678	.0322	.0126	1.8626
1.86	.9685	.0314	.0123	1.8723
1.87	.9693	.0307	.0119	1.8819
1.88	.9699	.0301	.0116	1.8916
1.89	.9706	.0294	.0113	1.9013
1.90	.9713	.0287	.0111	1.9111
1.91	.9719	.0281	.0108	1.9208
1.92	.9726	.0274	.0105	1.9305
1.93	.9732	.0268	.0102	1.9402
1.94	.9738	.0262	.0100	1.9500
1.95	.9744	.0256	.0097	1.9597
1.96	.9750	.0250	.0094	1.9694
1.97	.9756	.0244	.0092	1.9792
1.98	.9761	.0239	.0090	1.9890
1.99	.9767	.0233	.0087	1.9987
2.00	.9772	.0228	.0085	2.0085
2.01	.9778	.0222	.0083	2.0183
2.02	.9783	.0217	.0080	2.0280
2.03	.9788	.0212	.0078	2.0378
2.04	.9793	.0207	.0076	2.0476
2.05	.9798	.0202	.0074	2.0574
2.06	.9803	.0197	.0072	2.0672
2.07	.9808	.0192	.0072	2.0770
2.08	.9812	.0188	.0068	2.0868
2.09	.9817	.0183	.0066	2.0966
2.10	.9821	.0179	.0065	2.1065
2.11	.9826	.0174	.0063	2.1163
2.12	.9830	.0170	.0061	2.1261

Normal Probability Distribution and Unit Normal Loss Function				
Standardized Variate	Probabilities		Unit Normal Loss	
z	F(z)	1–F(z)	L(z)	L(-z)
2.13	.9834	.0166	.0060	2.1360
2.14	.9838	.0162	.0058	2.1458
2.15	.9842	.0158	.0056	2.1556
2.16	.9846	.0154	.0055	2.1655
2.17	.9850	.0150	.0053	2.1753
2.18	.9854	.0146	.0052	2.1852
2.19	.9857	.0143	.0050	2.1950
2.20	.9861	.0139	.0049	2.2049
2.21	.9864	.0136	.0048	2.2148
2.22	.9868	.0132	.0046	2.2246
2.23	.9871	.0129	.0045	2.2345
2.24	.9875	.0125	.0044	2.2444
2.25	.9878	.0122	.0042	2.2542
2.26	.9881	.0119	.0041	2.2641
2.27	.9884	.0116	.0040	2.2740
2.28	.9887	.0113	.0039	2.2839
2.29	.9890	.0110	.0038	2.2938
2.30	.9893	.0107	.0037	2.3037
2.31	.9896	.0104	.0036	2.3136
2.32	.9898	.0102	.0035	2.3235
2.33	.9901	.0099	.0034	2.3334
2.34	.9904	.0096	.0033	2.3433
2.35	.9906	.0094	.0032	2.3532
2.36	.9909	.0091	.0031	2.3631
2.37	.9911	.0089	.0030	2.3730
2.38	.9913	.0087	.0029	2.3829
2.39	.9916	.0084	.0028	2.3928
2.40	.9918	.0082	.0027	2.4027
2.41	.9920	.0080	.0026	2.4126
2.42	.9922	.0078	.0026	2.4226
2.43	.9925	.0075	.0025	2.4325
2.44	.9927	.0073	.0024	2.4424
2.45	.9929	.0071	.0023	2.4523
2.46	.9931	.0069	.0023	2.4623
2.47	.9932	.0068	.0022	2.4722
2.48	.9934	.0066	.0021	2.4821
2.49	.9936	.0064	.0021	2.4921
2.50	.9938	.0062	.0020	2.5020
2.51	.9940	.0060	.0019	2.5119
2.52	.9941	.0059	.0019	2.5219
2.53	.9943	.0057	.0018	2.5318
2.54	.9945	.0055	.0018	2.5418
2.55	.9946	.0054	.0017	2.5517
2.56	.9948	.0052	.0017	2.5617
2.57	.9949	.0051	.0016	2.5716
2.58	.9951	.0049	.0016	2.5816
2.59	.9952	.0048	.0015	2.5915
2.60	.9953	.0047	.0015	2.6015
2.61	.9955	.0045	.0014	2.6114
2.62	.9956	.0044	.0014	2.6214
2.63	.9957	.0043	.0013	2.6313
2.64	.9959	.0041	.0013	2.6413
2.65	.9960	.0040	.0012	2.6512
2.66	.9961	.0039	.0012	2.6612
2.67	.9962	.0038	.0012	2.6712
2.68	.9963	.0037	.0011	2.6811
2.69	.9964	.0036	.0011	2.6911
2.70	.9965	.0035	.0011	2.7011

Normal Probability Distribution and Unit Normal Loss Function

Standardized Variate	Probabilities		Unit Normal Loss	
z	F(z)	1–F(z)	L(z)	L(-z)
2.71	.9966	.0034	.0010	2.7110
2.72	.9967	.0033	.0010	2.7210
2.73	.9968	.0032	.0010	2.7310
2.74	.9969	.0031	.0009	2.7409
2.75	.9970	.0030	.0009	2.7509
2.76	.9971	.0029	.0009	2.7609
2.77	.9972	.0028	.0008	2.7708
2.78	.9973	.0027	.0008	2.7808
2.79	.9974	.0026	.0008	2.7908
2.80	.9974	.0026	.0008	2.8008
2.81	.9975	.0025	.0007	2.8107
2.82	.9976	.0024	.0007	2.8207
2.83	.9977	.0023	.0007	2.8307
2.84	.9977	.0023	.0007	2.8407
2.85	.9978	.0022	.0006	2.8506
2.86	.9979	.0021	.0006	2.8606
2.87	.9979	.0021	.0006	2.8706
2.88	.9980	.0020	.0006	2.8806
2.89	.9981	.0019	.0006	2.8906
2.90	.9981	.0019	.0005	2.9005
2.91	.9982	.0018	.0005	2.9105
2.92	.9982	.0018	.0005	2.9205
2.93	.9983	.0017	.0005	2.9305
2.94	.9984	.0016	.0005	2.9405
2.95	.9984	.0016	.0005	2.9505
2.96	.9985	.0015	.0004	2.9604
2.97	.9985	.0015	.0004	2.9704
2.98	.9986	.0014	.0004	2.9804
2.99	.9986	.0014	.0004	2.9904
3.00	.9986	.0014	.0004	3.0004

Table of Random Numbers

14129	77073	85739	75168	68865	38058	23074	23710	39539	78120
59470	02961	21174	88079	94705	75397	14199	26567	65049	46722
39183	96260	12844	76833	62011	25762	69081	19410	33744	99365
47970	70849	40524	98356	55036	09238	67952	55804	64730	96618
77124	23193	61760	07404	93432	49526	68647	28348	75240	73293
20393	40184	89129	26897	25676	12063	13046	52946	91558	24167
97992	03430	17520	34098	57613	35494	36520	71523	64663	56510
07028	52081	26235	06210	90028	99059	73365	52892	33517	48230
61595	72142	26188	20812	84791	95480	18267	01143	16039	55086
67565	75927	73987	69710	03384	94259	17762	73487	86915	75655
67543	97209	25890	19073	51797	79720	01202	86033	81881	17074
13588	86559	53200	32943	63088	76773	59439	18566	27254	69452
17640	54475	89817	57752	07562	45600	46019	49993	22985	47291
09950	17899	34988	19185	34979	57317	68188	92658	45425	61380
89636	49918	82684	54044	99800	15974	06110	45986	96692	62066
39223	30361	50520	23751	01383	20323	94899	29259	53014	27413
25344	41706	28151	61299	75143	13373	88870	89490	40134	52147
58188	01137	17839	12021	64878	43315	86230	30863	07076	16720
29522	42338	90510	88429	40225	85360	94779	64171	81532	86569
03987	33682	27155	92087	46733	18847	46702	21257	92740	34616
82310	33854	67934	61771	37146	09131	34292	32059	76567	37686
12022	27093	41747	25692	67800	88160	76162	11680	12772	39977
63742	09612	97786	25211	80480	82935	20981	53887	57911	33970
47551	62470	59444	35343	42454	87977	68667	77542	14700	53314
90820	46474	75492	64974	66638	28086	07629	23793	98013	25164
48280	48172	87262	86779	83409	92630	87434	04955	56074	79214
67265	92698	85478	91976	86012	40031	99590	15781	83057	60030
80326	39067	78567	01702	21290	68581	87516	15830	96482	39638
45579	98397	43868	39337	47875	37173	60105	42251	03810	76799
74041	58169	83090	88673	34267	92610	26840	37483	06935	20689
13026	60410	55242	71155	16949	59500	29571	26084	37850	05283
70797	30042	82013	53771	92555	14230	91513	07594	76772	31336
21034	99470	80362	36048	63738	63082	55678	83996	96450	82813
82430	28158	94530	03239	13372	81365	33189	33845	30740	75300
09610	62455	17057	39454	25915	63626	36906	23351	14360	81945

32359	33131	20580	02721	29967	78893	17798	71056	61021	34990
59432	37989	93968	14094	83377	79698	78790	51535	04375	49865
51050	46970	10318	03604	71999	62074	88037	50651	69840	67313
61947	83718	75963	54698	45166	21550	61635	96798	03383	62082
12059	65174	30699	49925	59090	36051	38725	55822	25317	13653
57546	67538	82970	52096	49342	95139	02199	42152	34480	87188
34023	96668	30358	60293	66032	52650	27220	40725	30595	02057
29038	19092	20200	43966	74631	16586	45588	72738	81682	64779
77328	49254	70091	96992	44365	55630	05133	53021	35022	74388
54695	95628	22372	11950	65424	40094	73366	33948	76940	95333
42127	63313	53260	19372	46970	09049	60060	85189	07135	46909
82940	60016	08546	90428	68948	98005	19828	32190	99721	43557
03325	26032	88385	48690	77454	63737	63129	01890	75111	55406
19884	70333	51560	88060	84292	54255	38890	74278	89448	53097
04031	16071	63500	45428	43144	18910	03137	80605	89452	33330
28066	82980	57752	21683	02510	68424	92287	52862	69306	74340
61067	23985	33567	06077	64074	79410	80629	64725	05248	14499
39536	67928	61511	62679	94227	74762	55145	66589	84406	48700
83639	33817	19558	37482	53490	75592	04841	27612	93036	29560
79936	03629	30082	96298	70254	71269	34999	86000	50618	42117
42740	80545	21094	27046	11534	05341	96193	51516	68523	15202
53340	80627	82646	92746	07667	23138	26775	58657	16861	48664
21719	94699	40752	16324	31254	79107	32259	17061	69513	35430
52653	27715	20748	91842	48600	78066	71844	55411	39956	29536
05731	96635	21331	67855	16675	48338	75714	64086	64292	15429
10600	03920	71904	98622	47738	93223	63630	29624	71445	23157
23047	19175	95279	12753	13541	17764	86780	18355	10233	88496
46623	12519	45551	92826	93850	76481	66083	88560	57369	03385
26076	40180	46890	16070	05296	42108	46825	95726	76211	54312
90026	24390	08080	50329	36692	38215	44014	77337	50210	95227
44441	30052	87151	54211	72980	35464	96634	66584	60973	51431
35651	80244	28214	77143	94152	57355	07394	75736	33996	25060
68042	10382	40366	05720	58041	92035	85236	95536	23877	40234
37016	64490	42362	55785	82248	05839	66314	64084	60468	47992
81800	25220	44230	53222	77642	20734	32497	50266	28183	99938
54985	42384	88024	04398	24379	22043	01100	57486	99607	25799
14490	25682	61776	99234	21637	91151	29730	78560	97023	37674
27726	80782	58869	47945	66428	88529	37344	15232	01327	67243
57842	65495	56072	93831	35440	93172	94328	98781	82116	09427
88049	20139	27466	28054	89015	71150	50058	11856	70132	18560
23298	10771	75896	74782	72233	76750	35614	02423	43958	55035
90694	30976	89487	72737	32092	85770	59080	83665	52329	30288
95039	61350	88580	20040	24264	91376	02090	69611	45468	43456
54783	32056	19062	57764	31717	90070	52397	42428	03528	61014
83868	84594	39998	13606	65584	72547	30027	96773	57910	32691
50444	81765	03749	76199	70579	16536	16495	60322	59986	92182
75558	61558	77634	22744	83089	60488	72779	36574	79417	40472
98680	80661	93710	97890	38791	37823	79052	65355	04549	55660
81264	46911	91087	88266	71204	66869	31570	50711	65620	29217
82821	86180	58170	91617	09643	44373	65302	50732	25820	74173

83895	39727	92500	27473	60071	39528	26974	76068	72657	01641
74221	41003	27819	83538	26022	34594	66255	96620	01088	14100
83150	67236	33640	49169	60997	09439	71616	70370	13973	10232
68329	12993	45788	28361	04089	17510	19285	38530	94099	50631
39216	82238	62395	81625	46863	49034	57764	05571	27540	78591
34815	47686	30645	93904	26921	28565	18790	40481	34713	45384
28127	71077	27244	12813	95398	44393	55717	17380	57939	35133
79667	34152	21495	57526	05515	56396	37344	40110	38175	36891
10690	75781	43935	04265	19617	78496	27389	21734	48510	60248
19639	82110	32036	14802	79755	83762	13182	75890	08330	42942
12669	27767	73430	48922	12013	28236	49812	93639	48161	44632
69571	12617	20683	11066	85843	40339	11625	40135	49522	76391
18832	94496	97353	64663	99623	73497	53010	85616	29143	61072
41768	06057	69859	25906	15288	67681	53936	44850	91170	72226
78563	38290	04014	68281	12850	18088	69183	31923	18281	48498
58244	89701	80435	18633	88663	96638	54963	28897	24270	28630
23835	08797	89382	86332	66046	24049	94494	12621	39780	80098
75221	21077	77346	88240	43719	38437	92570	39441	51951	58642
07046	22590	67933	09379	51262	58312	64526	31983	72078	12790
20501	72430	27464	94514	34566	86628	87815	66546	50848	56280
12414	68261	98148	18665	43661	51430	40849	08387	15071	28368
42892	11530	70930	31942	43415	32792	98906	89342	45849	74094
74841	69140	19083	27242	20184	69061	10788	77553	07173	47697
74002	21150	64653	26270	56830	93811	02654	34749	97518	12984
85535	97965	02010	32070	90193	95823	99266	72054	41380	36977
03591	76818	37576	43456	46956	52898	32399	49467	13070	25317
42950	11752	03657	79771	39066	32508	93780	25186	24924	94873
65891	37032	59490	11272	32423	11297	70047	83727	01013	30432
46160	76924	58559	43951	83955	39530	08127	59200	44163	23900
39781	46278	21827	53210	29465	54333	28668	08763	82058	41414
87819	38764	48080	15783	41915	81486	97853	90395	72053	14877
60633	49739	31150	34839	81610	29041	08823	20392	49276	64025
86082	30679	93410	06446	11184	16221	90927	17678	76127	42239
45113	21365	14438	23136	96151	33939	88241	71548	49037	60698
77210	58450	45550	62543	64133	86227	93753	36083	74392	74411
28052	04302	38110	57473	43522	22181	08630	95386	77994	91995
74161	96845	50307	93761	53678	54849	12416	26655	36470	94652
12069	63291	38611	33969	69443	16358	63088	56746	65844	18425
16346	98097	44873	01297	30851	42500	25642	59591	07680	34654
29868	49724	65635	20020	19623	37173	04589	90817	48940	78733
43561	13743	27694	89407	76235	10710	96936	87500	95361	02190
18892	79964	38238	73187	76628	42270	44259	74028	89272	34835
24116	28724	36501	13457	43367	58543	98993	80224	16067	37920
07937	25225	13165	42114	10009	80432	82054	81970	04277	87034
79094	73047	23554	74445	14191	31369	50857	52268	87400	90076
17532	14223	65333	21747	37592	55633	49924	16847	84299	01985
87262	52815	41470	51036	67687	42707	67657	27398	67677	95350
71482	48775	81779	88692	08038	55660	67978	54680	44347	52729
04647	78513	44092	14013	60754	80022	22695	98744	78322	77446
21374	30877	67172	42420	51753	91217	12460	28717	58834	71590

94567	91960	97637	41289	21458	91391	02171	26873	73722	74907
84339	37310	62186	77657	52172	03016	96964	32199	31290	15128
71130	91121	06201	45673	54845	63729	90850	30671	27520	63088
92185	04143	74233	67035	86199	62142	65624	91050	71050	42263
55598	73888	48120	15320	61410	75577	75243	89490	01041	88178
53288	27378	21364	58203	84713	75094	99279	23330	61075	04353
43706	58912	25850	66240	68236	40056	51544	58849	32317	13325
27745	05482	87328	83309	62730	47320	33025	10292	96624	47544
87849	20490	28131	07833	71490	29674	52892	97811	99423	78156
14392	97164	90895	79534	68340	49316	88088	80397	58499	28775
89231	33823	46091	20028	93285	85290	05358	97012	57084	69869
49886	90838	65644	23592	45690	79084	14426	56630	56370	42747
04474	35150	53015	44157	49300	37746	78184	94355	95348	71830
21439	19336	05406	78199	87047	39747	47192	11474	30420	62657
63792	92428	18248	85481	30272	41576	45368	13471	93040	37052
91131	88273	13381	50996	02917	30336	74350	96693	63582	92791
14028	89989	52910	28197	94636	21760	60820	68336	73223	43642
33071	15782	03344	66037	35281	47731	18269	68961	17014	33585
00470	24373	03206	63311	75042	32557	44883	90553	71225	69568
82930	85490	68088	48041	24632	02674	28762	90361	31869	59541
45302	13700	22585	29267	96325	28814	08416	43899	16220	50096
10300	11666	78114	01816	88379	46632	88606	36646	52360	09811
95354	19215	44773	63941	65039	50611	44087	40131	24076	59480
04260	17059	87600	36860	48571	13037	03287	68928	98491	89942
60761	79083	84569	70404	20160	18982	92683	66759	31700	70225
53691	23063	51817	59127	07306	69273	78542	17226	78234	88285
98420	54658	64271	94537	74142	45086	38369	27072	73157	24298
61557	52372	38178	05710	97030	82241	68950	77483	11799	25620
17683	09006	11000	15213	96043	52047	79274	92739	09557	17161
91798	44201	19786	51617	17490	95771	28710	19938	68968	81299
97529	83093	06775	47145	85007	86580	65367	69465	01713	94239
91760	82664	80944	29051	96748	21412	33111	11170	18772	75423
19096	69639	99456	55895	55160	75841	73215	07448	25600	60029
67670	35597	36326	83330	17564	40673	88033	47796	91179	04718
75084	19831	28450	85736	92399	65773	92700	26464	18552	99639
34145	08760	60618	44036	65735	20331	23702	29350	52352	34145
88712	47397	11574	00092	69650	13278	27395	49014	83592	12384
76718	10391	32911	54891	06780	40599	60490	85334	91267	65323
57444	30447	84088	33732	81736	59777	05510	85225	92087	58456
25861	28728	92161	13429	27708	34564	27968	10757	19487	38477

Financial Tables

Table I-1 Future Value

Future Value of $1

$F = P(1 + r)^n$

r = interest rate; n = number of periods until valuation; P = $1

Periods = n	2%	4%	6%	8%	10%	12%	15%	20%	25%
1	1.02000	1.04000	1.06000	1.08000	1.10000	1.12000	1.15000	1.20000	1.25000
2	1.04040	1.08160	1.12360	1.16640	1.21000	1.25440	1.32250	1.44000	1.56250
3	1.06121	1.12486	1.19102	1.25971	1.33100	1.40493	1.52088	1.72800	1.95313
4	1.08243	1.16986	1.26248	1.36049	1.46410	1.57352	1.74901	2.07360	2.44141
5	1.10408	1.21665	1.33823	1.46933	1.61051	1.76234	2.01136	2.48832	3.05176
6	1.12616	1.26532	1.41852	1.58687	1.77156	1.97382	2.31306	2.98598	3.81470
7	1.14869	1.31593	1.50363	1.71382	1.94872	2.21068	2.66002	3.58318	4.76837
8	1.17166	1.36857	1.59385	1.85093	2.14359	2.47596	3.05902	4.29982	5.96046
9	1.19509	1.42331	1.68948	1.99900	2.35795	2.77308	3.51788	5.15978	7.45058
10	1.21899	1.48024	1.79085	2.15892	2.59374	3.10585	4.04556	6.19174	9.31323
11	1.24337	1.53945	1.89830	2.33164	2.85312	3.47855	4.65239	7.43008	11.64153
12	1.26824	1.60103	2.01220	2.51817	3.13843	3.89598	5.35025	8.91610	14.55192
13	1.29361	1.66507	2.13293	2.71962	3.45227	4.36349	6.15279	10.69932	18.18989
14	1.31948	1.73168	2.26090	2.93719	3.79750	4.88711	7.07571	12.83918	22.73737
15	1.34587	1.80094	2.39656	3.17217	4.17725	5.47357	8.13706	15.40702	28.42171
16	1.37279	1.87298	2.54035	3.42594	4.59497	6.13039	9.35762	18.48843	35.52714
17	1.40024	1.94790	2.69277	3.70002	5.05447	6.86604	10.76126	22.18611	44.40892
18	1.42825	2.02582	2.85434	3.99602	5.55992	7.68997	12.37545	26.62333	55.51115
19	1.45681	2.10685	3.02560	4.31570	6.11591	8.61276	14.23177	31.94800	69.38894
20	1.48595	2.19112	3.20714	4.66096	6.72750	9.64629	16.36654	38.33760	86.73617
22	1.54598	2.36992	3.60354	5.43654	8.14027	12.10031	21.64475	55.20614	135.5253
24	1.60844	2.56330	4.04893	6.34118	9.84973	15.17863	28.62518	79.49685	211.7582
26	1.67342	2.77247	4.54938	7.39635	11.91818	19.04007	37.85680	114.4755	330.8722
28	1.74102	2.99870	5.11169	8.62711	14.42099	23.88387	50.06561	164.8447	516.9879
30	1.81136	3.24340	5.74349	10.06266	17.44940	29.95992	66.21177	237.3763	807.7936
32	1.88454	3.50806	6.45339	11.73708	21.11378	37.58173	87.56507	341.8219	1262.177
34	1.96068	3.79432	7.25103	13.69013	25.54767	47.14252	115.80480	492.2235	1972.152
36	2.03989	4.10393	8.14725	15.96817	30.91268	59.13557	153.15185	708.8019	3081.488
38	2.12230	4.43881	9.15425	18.62528	37.40434	74.17966	202.54332	1020.675	4814.825
40	2.20804	4.80102	10.28572	21.72452	45.25926	93.05097	267.86355	1469.772	7523.167

Table I-2 Present Value

Present Value of $1

$P = F(1 + r)^{-n}$

r = discount rate; n = number of periods until payment; F = $1

Periods = n	2%	4%	6%	8%	10%	12%	15%	20%	25%
1	.98039	.96154	.94340	.92593	.90909	.89286	.86957	.83333	.80000
2	.96117	.92456	.89000	.85734	.82645	.79719	.75614	.69444	.64000
3	.94232	.88900	.83962	.79383	.75131	.71178	.65752	.57870	.51200
4	.92385	.85480	.79209	.73503	.68301	.63552	.57175	.48225	.40960
5	.90573	.82193	.74726	.68058	.62092	.56743	.49718	.40188	.32768
6	.88797	.79031	.70496	.63017	.56447	.50663	.43233	.33490	.26214
7	.87056	.75992	.66506	.58349	.51316	.45235	.37594	.27908	.20972
8	.85349	.73069	.62741	.54027	.46651	.40388	.32690	.23257	.16777
9	.83676	.70259	.59190	.50025	.42410	.36061	.28426	.19381	.13422
10	.82035	.67556	.55839	.46319	.38554	.32197	.24718	.16151	.10737
11	.80426	.64958	.52679	.42888	.35049	.28748	.21494	.13459	.08590
12	.78849	.62460	.49697	.39711	.31863	.25668	.18691	.11216	.06872
13	.77303	.60057	.46884	.36770	.28966	.22917	.16253	.09346	.05498
14	.75788	.57748	.44230	.34046	.26333	.20462	.14133	.07789	.04398
15	.74301	.55526	.41727	.31524	.23939	.18270	.12289	.06491	.03518
16	.72845	.53391	.39365	.29189	.21763	.16312	.10686	.05409	.02815
17	.71416	.51337	.37136	.27027	.19784	.14564	.09293	.04507	.02252
18	.70016	.49363	.35034	.25025	.17986	.13004	.08081	.03756	.01801
19	.68643	.47464	.33051	.23171	.16351	.11611	.07027	.03130	.01441
20	.67297	.45639	.31180	.21455	.14864	.10367	.06110	.02608	.01153
22	.64684	.42196	.27751	.18394	.12285	.08264	.04620	.01811	.00738
24	.62172	.39012	.24698	.15770	.10153	.06588	.03493	.01258	.00472
26	.59758	.36069	.21981	.13520	.08391	.05252	.02642	.00874	.00302
28	.57437	.33348	.19563	.11591	.06934	.04187	.01997	.00607	.00193
30	.55207	.30832	.17411	.09938	.05731	.03338	.01510	.00421	.00124
32	.53063	.28506	.15496	.08520	.04736	.02661	.01142	.00293	.00079
34	.51003	.26355	.13791	.07305	.03914	.02121	.00864	.00203	.00051
36	.49022	.24367	.12274	.06262	.03235	.01691	.00653	.00141	.00032
38	.47119	.22529	.01924	.05369	.02673	.01348	.00494	.00098	.00021
40	.45289	.20829	.09722	.04603	.02209	.01075	.00373	.00068	.00013

Table I-3 Future Value of Annuity

Future Value of Annuity of $1 in Arrears

$$F = P \left[\frac{(1+r)^n - 1}{r} \right]$$

r = interest rate; n = number of payments

No. of Payments = n	2%	4%	6%	8%	10%	12%	15%	20%	25%
1	1.00000	1.00000	1.00000	1.00000	1.00000	1.00000	1.00000	1.00000	1.00000
2	2.02000	2.04000	2.06000	2.08000	2.10000	2.12000	2.15000	2.20000	2.25000
3	3.06040	3.12160	3.18360	3.24640	3.31000	3.37440	3.47250	3.64000	3.81250
4	4.12161	4.24646	4.37462	4.50611	4.64100	4.77933	4.99338	5.36800	5.76563
5	5.20404	5.41632	5.63709	5.86660	6.10510	6.35285	6.74238	7.44160	8.20703
6	6.30812	6.63298	6.97532	7.33593	7.71561	8.11519	8.75374	9.92992	11.25879
7	7.43428	7.89829	8.39384	8.92280	9.48717	10.08901	11.06680	12.91590	15.07349
8	8.58297	9.21423	9.89747	10.63663	11.43589	12.29969	13.72682	16.49908	19.84186
9	9.75463	10.58280	11.49132	12.48756	13.57948	14.77566	16.78584	20.79890	25.80232
10	10.94972	12.00611	13.18079	14.48656	15.93742	17.54874	20.30372	25.95868	33.25290
11	12.16872	13.48635	14.97164	16.64549	18.53117	20.65458	24.34928	32.15042	42.56613
12	13.41209	15.02581	16.86994	18.97713	21.38428	24.13313	29.00167	39.58050	54.20766
13	14.68033	16.62684	18.88214	21.49530	24.52271	28.02911	34.35192	48.49660	68.75958
14	15.97394	18.29191	21.01507	24.21492	27.97498	32.39260	40.50471	59.19592	86.94947
15	17.29342	20.02359	23.27597	27.15211	31.72248	37.27971	47.58041	72.03511	109.6868
16	18.63929	21.82453	25.67253	30.32428	35.94973	42.75328	55.71747	87.44213	138.1085
17	20.01207	23.69751	28.21288	33.75023	40.54470	48.88367	65.07509	105.9306	173.6357
18	21.41231	25.64541	30.90565	37.45024	45.59917	55.74971	75.83636	128.1167	218.0446
19	22.84056	27.67123	33.75999	41.44626	51.15909	63.43968	88.21181	154.7400	273.5558
20	24.29737	29.77808	36.78559	45.76196	57.27500	72.05244	102.4435	186.6880	342.9447
22	27.29898	34.24797	43.39229	55.45676	72.40275	92.50258	137.6316	271.0307	538.1011
24	30.42186	39.08260	50.81558	66.76476	88.49733	118.1552	184.1678	392.4842	843.0329
26	33.67091	44.31174	59.15638	79.95442	109.1818	150.3339	245.7119	567.3773	1319.489
28	37.05121	49.96758	68.52811	95.33883	134.2099	190.6989	327.1040	819.2233	2063.952
30	40.56808	56.08494	79.05819	113.2832	164.4940	241.3327	434.7451	1181.881	3227.174
32	44.22703	62.70147	90.88978	134.2135	201.1378	304.8477	577.1004	1704.109	5044.710
34	48.03380	69.85791	104.1838	158.6267	245.4767	384.5210	765.3653	2456.118	7884.609
36	51.99437	77.59831	119.1209	187.1022	299.1268	484.4631	1014.3456	3539.009	12321.95
38	56.11494	85.97034	135.9042	220.3159	364.0434	609.8305	1343.6221	5098.373	19255.30
40	60.40918	95.02552	154.7620	259.0565	442.5926	767.0914	1779.0903	7343.858	30088.66

Table I-4 Present Value of Annuity

Present Value of Annuity of $1 in Arrears

$$P = F\left[\frac{(1+r)^n - 1}{r}\right]^{-1}$$

r = discount rate; n = number of payments

No. of Payments = n	2%	4%	6%	8%	10%	12%	15%	20%	25%
1	.98039	.96154	.94340	.92593	.90909	.89286	.86957	.83333	.80000
2	1.94156	1.88609	1.83339	1.78326	1.73554	1.69005	1.62571	1.52778	1.44000
3	2.88388	2.77509	2.67301	2.57710	2.48685	2.40183	2.28323	2.10648	1.95200
4	3.80773	3.62990	3.46511	3.31213	3.16987	3.03735	2.85498	2.58873	2.36160
5	4.71346	4.45182	4.21236	3.99271	3.79079	3.60478	3.35216	2.99016	2.68928
6	5.60143	5.24212	4.91732	4.62288	4.35526	4.11141	3.78448	3.32551	2.95142
7	6.47199	6.00205	5.58238	5.20637	4.86842	4.56376	4.16042	3.60459	3.16114
8	7.32548	6.73274	6.20979	5.74664	5.33493	4.96764	4.48732	3.83716	3.32891
9	8.16224	7.43533	6.80169	6.24689	5.75902	5.32825	4.77158	4.03097	3.46313
10	8.98259	8.11090	7.36009	6.71008	6.14457	5.65022	5.01877	4.19247	3.57050
11	9.78685	8.76048	7.88687	7.13896	6.49506	5.93770	5.23371	4.32706	3.65640
12	10.57534	9.38507	8.38384	7.53608	6.81369	6.19437	5.42062	4.43922	3.72512
13	11.34837	9.98565	8.85268	7.90378	7.10336	6.42355	5.58315	4.53268	3.78010
14	12.10625	10.56312	9.29498	8.24424	7.36669	6.62817	5.72448	4.61057	3.82408
15	12.84926	11.11839	9.71225	8.55948	7.60608	6.81086	5.84737	4.67547	3.85926
16	13.57771	11.65230	10.10590	8.85137	7.82371	6.97399	5.95423	4.72956	3.88741
17	14.29187	12.16567	10.47726	9.12164	8.02155	7.11963	6.04716	4.77463	3.90993
18	14.99203	12.65930	10.82760	9.37189	8.20141	7.24967	6.12797	4.81219	3.92794
19	15.67846	13.13394	11.15812	9.60360	8.36492	7.36578	6.19823	4.84350	3.94235
20	16.35143	13.59033	11.46992	9.81815	8.51356	7.46944	6.25933	4.86958	3.95388
22	17.65805	14.45112	12.04158	10.20074	8.77154	7.64465	6.35866	4.90943	3.97049
24	18.91393	15.24696	12.55036	10.52876	8.98474	7.78432	6.43377	4.93710	3.98111
26	20.12104	15.98277	13.00317	10.80998	9.16095	7.89566	6.49056	4.95632	3.98791
28	21.28127	16.66306	13.40616	11.05108	9.30657	7.98442	6.53351	4.96967	3.99226
30	22.39646	17.29203	13.76483	11.25778	9.42691	8.05518	6.56598	4.97894	3.99505
32	23.46833	17.87355	14.08404	11.43500	9.52638	8.11159	6.59053	4.98537	3.99683
34	24.49859	18.41120	14.36814	11.58693	9.60857	8.15656	6.60910	4.98984	3.99797
36	25.48884	18.90828	14.62099	11.71719	9.67651	8.19241	6.62314	4.99295	3.99870
38	26.44064	19.36786	14.84602	11.82887	9.73265	8.22099	6.63375	4.99510	3.99917
40	27.35548	19.79277	15.04630	11.92461	9.77905	8.24378	6.64178	4.99660	3.99947

Classic Static Flow Shop Results

OVERVIEW

Since the flow shop is a special case of the job shop, we did not give it special separate treatment in the Scheduling Module. However, there are a number of classic results for the special case of a static flow shop with makespan objective. Job i has processing times p_{i1}, $p_{i2}, \ldots, p_{im}$ on each machine, with arrival time $a_i = 0$; the objective is to minimize the completion time of the full set of jobs (makespan). Under these conditions permutation schedules, that is schedules which preserve the order in which jobs are processed on each machine, are attractive. They are somewhat easier to analyze than general schedules. They are optimal for the case $m = 2$ and $m = 3$, and appear to be close to optimal otherwise for larger m.

What kinds of real world problems satisfy these assumptions fairly well—flow shop, static, makespan? While there are not many pure flow shops in practice, there is a large class of extended flow shops which may be analyzed as flow shops by certain tricks. Also there are certain types of projects with resource constraints which can be analyzed as static flow shops with makespan objective. First, we discuss these issues in a little more detail. In following sections we present Johnson's Algorithm for the two-machine case, and the CDS heuristic for the m machine case.

EXTENDED FLOW SHOPS

There are a number of important variations on flow shops, which might be called "skip flow shops," "reentrant flow shops," "compound flow shops," or "finite queue" flow shops. These are illustrated in Figure J-1.

In skip shops (for example, flexible manufacturing cells) some jobs will skip some machines. (When this does not change the travel time for the job, this may be treated as giving the job zero process time and top priority at the affected machines.)

In reentrant shops (for example, annealing furnaces, where the jobs are tempered several times) some machines may be visited more than once by the same job. This is messy to model formally, but relatively easy to deal with in many heuristic approaches.

In a compound flow shop, each machine in the flow line may be replaced by a group of parallel machines, a batch machine, or a continuous flow process. Compound flow shops are extremely common: for example, food processing plants, beer plants, paper and pulp mills, and pilgering shops. Adding another parallel machine at a bottleneck is often an easier way to increase capacity than scrapping the old machine to bring in a larger one. Compound flow shops are not always recognized due to their complexity (the basic flow

Figure J-1

Types of Extended Flow
Shops

(a) Skip Flow Shop

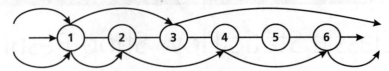

(b) Re-entrant Flow Shop

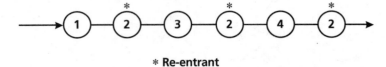

* **Re-entrant**

(c) Compound Flow Shop

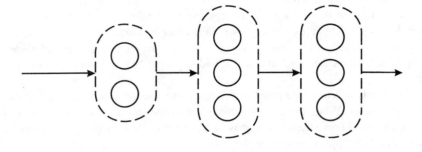

(d) Finite Queue Flow Shops

shop organization may not be very recognizable on the floor). Compound flow shops will become much more common in the future as flexible manufacturing cells allow complex processes to take on the characteristics of parallel machines. It is often possible to approximate each group of machines as an aggregate machine, and solve by standard flow shop algorithms and heuristics.

To show an important application of the static flow shop problem with makespan objective, consider a project with m resources, and n subprojects (see the Project Management Module). The subprojects all use the same resources in the same sequence, and are independent. Such a resource constrained project can be accurately solved by the methods developed here.

THE 2-MACHINE PROBLEM

Proposition 1. Permutation schedules are optimal for:

a. Two-machine static flow shops, for any regular objective,
b. Three-machine static flow shops for the makespan objective.

Intuition

To see (a), if i immediately precedes j on machine 1, but comes after j on machine 2, we could interchange i and j on machine 1, and hurt no completion time.

Proving (b) would similarly involve showing that the first two machines can have the same sequence. But by reversing time in the problem, (possible only for makespan) the last two machines can have the same sequence.

The most famous flow shop result is probably that of Johnson [1954] (Scheduling Module).

Proposition 2 (Johnson's Rule). For the two-machine flow shop makespan problem, with machines first available at times t_1 and t_2 and all jobs available at time zero:

a. Schedule the subgroup of jobs that are shorter on the first machine than on the second by SPT (shortest processing time first), using the first machine's processing time.
b. Then schedule the remainder of the jobs by LPT (reverse SPT), using the second machine's processing time.

Intuition

The intuitive idea behind Johnson's algorithm is that the second machine starts out starved for work. Therefore, if we process short jobs on the first machine first, we will more quickly get some work to the second machine. Notice that the idea that the second machine is starved arises from the static assumption that there were no half finished jobs initially waiting on machine 2, which does not necessarily (or even usually) hold in a dynamic shop.

Two other heuristics which utilize the same ideas but allow starting with a more typical dynamic shop include:

- **Ratio heuristic:** Schedule the job next with smallest (current) ratio p_{j1}/p_{j2}.
- **Palmer heuristic:** Schedule the job next with smallest (current) difference $(p_{j1} - p_{j2})$.

While these heuristics are not always optimal for the exact Johnson assumptions, they are quite accurate and robust for a number of more complicated situations when Johnson's Rule fails, due to its static nature.

Example J-1. Yogi Yorivich is the head of passports and customs at the South Estonian airport. A group of eight important American congressmen are impatient to get to the banquet, and a bus is waiting. Unfortunately, passports and customs takes a long time. Yogi consults a medium, who tells him the times in the table below for each congressman. How should Yogi prioritize the congressmen to minimize the time until they can all board the bus?

Congressman	1	2	3	4	5	6	7	8
			Time in Tenths of Hours					
Passport	5	3	2	6	5	4	8	6
Customs	2	5	2	5	6	7	3	2

Solution. We put the jobs shortest on passport in SPT order, and those shortest in customs in LPT order. The X marks just divide jobs into SPT and LPT.

					Optimal Solution				
Congressman	**2**	**6**	**5**		**4**	**7**	**1**	**3**	**8**
Passport	3	4	5		6	8	5	2	6
Customs	5	7	6		5	3	2	2	2
Finish Passports	3	7	12		18	26	31	33	39
Finish Customs	8	15	21		26	29	33	35	41

So the poor congressmen must wait 4.1 hours for dinner. (This is based on actual experience landing in Siberia from the United States!) It is easy to see that this is, indeed, the optimal solution. Certainly the makespan must be always at least the total time on the first machine plus the shortest possible job on the second machine. (Why?) This would be $39 + 2 = 41$.

In the exercises, you will be asked to show that the ratio heuristic would give a differing sequence but obtain the same optimal solution of 41, while the Palmer heuristic gives an answer of 42.

The *m*-Machine Problem

The *m*-machine problem cannot be solved exactly; we must try to develop heuristics. In order to trust a heuristic, it is useful to have a good idea of what makespan the best possible solution could obtain, that is, a lower bound. We first present a lower bound for the *m*-machine makespan problem, and then the CDS heuristic.

Proposition 3. For the *m*-machine static flow shop problem, a lower bound on the optimal solution can be obtained as follows:

1. Let P be the longest sum of processing times for any job.
2. Let S_i be the shortest processing time on either the first or last machine for any other job.
3. Then $L = P + \Sigma S_i$ is a lower bound to possible makespans.

There are several good classic heuristics which extend the two-machine results to the static *m*-machine makespan problem. These include heuristics developed by (see the bibliography in the Scheduling Module) Palmer [1965], Gupta [1972], and Campbell Dudek and Smith (CDS) [1970]. The CDS heuristic is perhaps the best of these for the static case, although it also requires more computation. It generates a number of solutions, and picks the best one. Since it is based on Johnson's Rule, it does not generalize well to the dynamic case.

CDS Heuristic. Solve for $m - 1$ different schedules, with $i = 1, m - 1$ for iteration i set

$$P_{j1} = \Sigma_{k=1,i} P_{jk} \text{ and } P_{j2} = \Sigma_{k=1,j} P_{j,m-k+1}$$

(That is, P_{j1} is the sum of times for job j on the first i machines, and P_{j2} is the sum for the last i machines.) Solve the resulting two-machine Johnson's problem for that i, obtaining the ith feasible makespan M_i. The final solution is to take $M = \min \{M_1, M_2, \ldots, M_m\}$.

Basically, the CDS heuristic aggregates the first i machines into one machine and the last i machines into a second machine, and ignores any machines in the middle which may not be included, and treats the resulting problem as a two machine problem. Since the proper aggregation is not clear, try differing I, and select the best of the m candidate solutions.

Example J-2. Five good friends are first in line at a buffet dinner party. There are three stops: (1) Salads, (2) Main Course, and (3) Desserts. They are all time and motion experts and have worked out estimates of the times each will be likely to spend at each station. They wish to order themselves in the line so that the five of them will be finished as early as possible, since they are hungry and plan to sit together.

Person	1	2	3	4	5
Salad	6	8	5	1	2
Main Course	6	5	9	1	8
Dessert	5	9	3	4	6

How should they line up to get out quickest?

Solution. First we find a good lower bound. We have:

$$P = \max \{6 + 6 + 5, 8 + 5 + 9, 5 + 9 + 3, 1 + 1 + 4, 2 + 8 + 6\} = 22$$

with person 2's time the longest.

$$S = \min (6, 5) + \min (5, 3) + \min (1, 4) + \min (2, 6) = 11$$

The lower bound $= L = P + S = 22 + 11 = 33$.

CDS's heuristic for $m = 3$ and $i = 1$ reduces to doing Johnson's Rule *on just the first and third machines*. This yields a schedule 4-5-2-1-3 and a makespan of $M = 35$. For $i = 2$ we add the times on the first and second machines to make an aggregate first machine, and add the times on the second and third machines to make an aggregate second machine, and use Johnson's Rule. This yields a schedule 4-5-2-3-1 with a makespan of $M = 36$. The heuristic then chooses the better of these solutions, and thus reports its solution as 4-5-2-1-3 and a makespan of $M = 35$.

We leave it to the exercises to show that:

1. The CDS solution can be improved by trial and error (basically neighborhood search) to $M = 34$.
2. Trial and error can further verify that there is no feasible solution for $M = 33$, so that the optimal solution is known to be obtainable by CDS followed by a brief neighborhood search.

CLASSIC FLOW SHOP EXERCISES

1. Sequential crew systems are commonly found in the construction of aircraft and ships. Two or more crews follow one another in a fixed sequence to complete a particular task on a unit being processed. Crews perform their assigned work in a fixed sequence with respect to each other, and units are processed by each crew in the same order that the first crew did. Show how a permutation sequence flow shop model can be used to describe these systems. What would it mean if permutation schedules were *not* used?

2. Give two new examples for each of the following types of extended flow shops:

   a. Skip shops
   b. Reentrant flow shops
   c. Compound flow shops
   d. Finite queue flow shops
   e. Zero (internal) queue flow shops

3. Consider a static flow shop with five jobs and three machines, with processing times as shown:

	Job				
Machine	1	2	3	4	5
M1	7	6	9	3	8
M2	10	9	5	3	8
M3	7	3	6	9	13

Suppose these jobs are to be run in the same permutation sequence on every machine, namely 2-1-4-3-5.

a. Calculate the resulting makespan.
b. Calculate the weighted flow of the same schedule, if all weights equal 1.0.

4. Show that if Yogi Yorivich (Example J-1) had employed the Palmer heuristic he would have obtained a third solution which is 1.0 larger than the optimal solution.

5. A manufacturer of copper necklaces has five jobs to schedule for a leading customer. Each necklace in a job requires a stamping operation followed by a stringing/finishing operation. Stringing/finishing cannot begin for a job until all items in the job have been stamped. The table shows the setup for stamping for each job, as well as the times for each necklace for each of the two operations. Find a schedule which completes all items as soon as possible.

Operation Time per Item

Job	Number in Lot	Stamp	Finish	Setup
1	24	2	7	98
2	24	2	6	238
3	96	1	2	62
4	48	4	2	60
5	36	3	7	75

6. Find the makespan generated by the CDS heuristic for the following static problem:

Job	1	2	3	4
M1	4	3	1	3
M2	3	7	2	5
M3	8	2	4	3

7. Find a solution to Example J-2 with a makespan of 34.

8. Prove that no solution can have a makespan smaller than 34, so that your solution in problem 7 is, in fact, optimal.